VLSI

silicon compilation
and the art
of automatic microchip design

RONALD F. AYRES

California Institute of Technology
Information Sciences Institute

Prentice-Hall, Inc., Englewood Cliffs, New Jersey 07632

Library of Congress Cataloging in Publication Data

Ayres, Ronald F.
    VLSI: silicon compilation and the art of automatic
microchip design.

    Bibliography: p.
    Includes index.
    1. Integrated circuits—Very large scale integration
—Design and construction.   I. Title.   II. Title: V.L.S.I.
TK7874.A97 1983   621.381'73   82-23177
ISBN 0-13-942680-9

Editorial/production supervision and
    interior design: *Mary Carnis*
Cover design: *Diane Saxe*
Manufacturing buyer: *Gordon Osbourne*

Dedicated to

Giorgio Ingargiola and programs without roses, Judy and cats, Dick Suchter,
Dave Plumer, JNG, DQP, WLL, the "KL", memory location 80 on the IBM/360 Mod 44,
computer memory references both legal and "illegal",
and all the op-codes that will ever be "reserved to DEC."

Printed in the United States of America

10 9 8 7 6 5 4 3 2 1

ISBN 0-13-942680-9

Prentice-Hall International, Inc., *London*
Prentice-Hall of Australia Pty. Limited, *Sydney*
Editora Prentice-Hall do Brasil, Ltda., *Rio de Janeiro*
Prentice-Hall Canada Inc., *Toronto*
Prentice-Hall of India Private Limited, *New Delhi*
Prentice-Hall of Japan, Inc., *Tokyo*
Prentice-Hall of Southeast Asia Pte. Ltd., *Singapore*
Whitehall Books Limited, *Wellington, New Zealand*

Contents

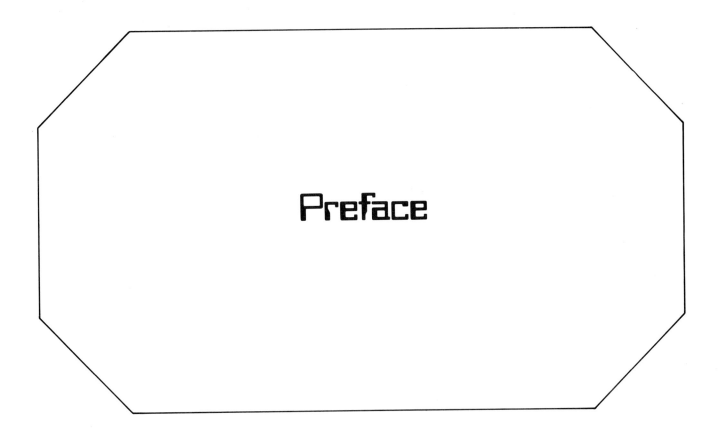

Preface

This text provides an introduction to the emerging field of silicon compilation and the art of automatic chip design generation, perhaps the most exciting area in VLSI chip design today and for some time to come.

This text is intended to give the reader a foundation in techniques and concepts with which to create, understand, and explore silicon compilation. The text can serve as a university textbook for the majority of a one-year graduate course in VLSI computer-aided design, as a handbook for designers of computer-aided design systems, and as a case study of a large software application.

Silicon compilation helps resolve today's acknowledged "hardware crisis": the great difficulty encountered in the generation of new, custom integrated circuit microchips. This difficulty has become a "crisis" only because the physical technology readily exists to produce wide varieties of very powerful and highly desired computational engines. However, the greatest bottleneck involves the translation from the human intent, a behavioral description of what the new chip is supposed to do, into the chip "layout," a complete geometric representation from which these marvelous physical technologies can readily produce reliable, working chips.

Any step toward the resolution of this hardware design crisis brings with it two very important results. First, it brings a vast reduction in cost, and hence an increase in the availability of products that make everybody's life more pleasant. It widens profoundly the applicability of these micro-chip technologies to facilitate even greater and previously unimagined benefits to all of us. Second, it widens the scientific view of information processing and the very character of information itself, by removing some of the barriers that have provided artificial divisions in our ways of thinking, for example, the great division between hardware and software. It brings us closer to a unified feeling for information and its evolution.

The relative costs between the chip design process and the subsequent chip fabrication dramatically expose the design bottleneck. The design process produces a chip layout and the fabrication process turns this layout into real chips. The design process can cost, for state-of-the-art designs, a few million dollars, and a year or more elapsed time from the initial characterization of the chip (usually a short document specifying the intended behavior for the chip) until a working design emerges. Once the design is completed (at which time it is a year behind the state of the art), the fabrication process even for small-volume prototypes can cost well under $10,000 and take under a month.

How is it that we have become accustomed to such immense design costs? The product of this process, a layout, is a picture consisting of about a million individual shapes, all of which together must satisfy the constraints or "syntax" imposed by the fabrication process. A single error in this maze of details often renders the entire chip inoperative. Not only must this giant set of shapes satisfy the silicon "syntax," but it also must make the appropriate statement in this silicon language so that the chip will perform as intended. In addition, the design must satisfy electrical constraints simply because the whole technology is based on properties of electrical phenomena.

This text exposes "silicon compilation," the art of automatic layout design generation, as a substantial solution to our hardware crisis. We who created silicon compilation and introduced the term into computer science use the term "silicon compiler" to denote totally automatic translations from behavioral specifications to correct chip layouts, just as the term "compiler" in software implies totally automatic translation from high-level languages into machine languages. Human interaction is entirely optional, and is limited so to affect in no way the behavioral correctness of the resulting layout.

Working silicon compilers have produced chip layouts in under one hour, from behavioral specifications developed in under one week. These chips range from complete microprocessors to special-purpose, application-dependent microprocessors. These silicon compilers are only the first such tools—design aids that implement the entire design process automatically from behavioral specifications to correct layouts. They exploit silicon's native potentials without adopting the restrictions, inefficiencies, and ways of thinking inherent with older technologies, like the PC-board place-and-route paradigm adopted in "gate array" and "polycell" technologies.

A variety of semiautomatic techniques have emerged from industry and academia which have tended toward isolated and/or partial solutions to limited, well-defined problems. Even complete solutions to subproblems, developed without considering the overall compilation problem, very often render few, none, or negative improvements for the overall chip, particularly when loose ends are left to manual, error-prone intervention. This text, in contrast, emphasizes the overall problem and detailed solutions, sometimes even by using less-than-optimal solutions to subproblems, again, to show a great flexibility and potential.

It is surprising perhaps that the effort required to provide complete automation is actually considerably less than solving in a practical way a majority of subproblems independently, mainly because the compiler writer has complete control over the entire automation. This of course facilitates more efficient solutions whose overall effect surpasses concentrated optimized local solutions.

The possibility of such complex uniformities also makes possible physical technologies as yet unimagined, geared particularly toward use with silicon compilation; the great degree of complexity supported by compilers facilitates new technologies which might otherwise be out of reach to manual design. (We have seen recently that technology has adapted to software compilers with the emergence of Pascal and LISP machines.)

The field of silicon compilation bridges the fields of electrical engineering and software engineering. We find today in the domain of chip design the same kinds of problems and attitudes that existed one or two decades ago in the software domain. In both cases, chip and software designers have been faced with a rapidly growing base technology, which has changed and is changing the relative costs of alternative ways of doing business. The bottleneck ceases to be the limitations of the base technology, but becomes instead the human limitations of formulating the design (layout or program).

Software compiler engineers have been and are faced with the question of how to make most effective use of the growing capacity of memory and speed. When software compilers came to be, people began reluctantly to use them amid fears of losing efficiency and control. Nonetheless, today these fears have nearly vanished, and large software designers now ask not whether to use a compiler at all, but instead which compiler (language) to use. Now, with the capacity of silicon chips continuing to grow very rapidly, chip designers are faced with the same problem of how best to map human skills into this generous silicon terrain.

We explore one silicon compiler in detail to provide continuity among the various techniques and concepts shown. This silicon compiler, RELAY (REcursive Logic ArraYs), was chosen because it is general purpose and illustrates many of the techniques and concepts that apply to all kinds of silicon compilers. RELAY involves the capture of behavior specified in terms of synchronous logic, its translation into an optimized disjunctive form, its simulation and translation into clocked PLA layout structures, its placement and routing, and its electrical or performance modeling.

RELAY is also especially well suited to illustrate the wide and subtle variations and optimizations afforded by the redistribution or reorganization of logic over the chip area. The latter effect clearly exposes the novel flexibility and use of silicon compilers, which renders them indispensible for all high-level design phases, including floor planning—those phases where the majority of major headaches tend to focus in practice because their resolutions are expensive.

The most valuable information derived from these efforts has been a collection of techniques and new ways of thinking which facilitate the creation of these and other silicon compilers. These techniques and concepts form the bulk of this text.

In fact, these very techniques are applicable not only to silicon chips, but also to technologies, some yet to be invented, which derive their function from specifications rendered in terms of two (or three) dimensional layouts (pictures).

We do not cover in detail layout techniques which tend to be dependent on individual fabricators and physical technologies. We also do not cover the underlying physics of microchips in general. Other texts cover these areas and provide the rigorous bases for our abstractions. We resort, for example, to electrical properties only when they must be taken into consideration. We focus instead on the software techniques used to generate layouts of any kind, and to generate complete layouts of a more particular character.

We include a multitude of related programming examples; this is essential in order to enhance confidence and a "can do" attitude, and to show all the essential details that must be considered inevitably in any programming relationship with the computer. We have chosen for this purpose the programming language ICL (Integrated Circuit Language) which was developed especially for exploration into VLSI. ICL is appropriate for use in this kind of text, primarily because many programming details (for many applications) are handled implicitly by ICL. ICL does not burden us with most of those programming details having nothing to do with VLSI (e.g., pointers, memory management, and various other awkwardnesses). In fact, ICL serves well as a clear formal notation, useful in the way that mathematical notations are useful in math texts.

ICL notations are explained as they become parts of examples, so the reader can make very practical use of the examples, at least in their understanding. In fact, all the programming examples have been extracted from this text and run on the computer to verify their correctness and to generate many of the illustrations. ICL is a complete working language which has been used exclusively in the formulation and implementation of two complete silicon compilers, RELAY and BRISTLE BLOCKS, and has been also used to service chip designers nationwide in providing exceptionally economical chip fabrication from layouts.

The seasoned programmer may wonder if the simplicity of expression afforded by this language carries with it a significant loss of efficiency. Surprisingly, empirical evidence to date shows the opposite to be true, perhaps due in large part to the very direct communication afforded by its human orientation.

Acknowledgments

This book was made possible in large part by a wide variety of people engaged in many disciplines, both in the academic and industrial worlds.

For the courageous long-term and persistent presentation of fundamental principles relevant to this subject matter, special thanks go to Dr. Frederick B. Thompson for emphasizing the flexibility of computational linguistics, to Dr. Per Brinch-Hansen for exposing the importance and pleasure of particularly clear program specification, to Dr. Carver A. Mead for discovering a very straightforward and practical view of VLSI systems, to Dr. Tom Apostol for illustrating the ease and practicality of applying abstract mathematical techniques to the widest variety of problems, and to Dr. Herbert Benjamin for lending a boldly realistic view to the very nature of information itself.

More specific to this subject matter, the author is particularly grateful to David Johannsen, Carver Mead, John Wawrzynek, and Charle Rupp for participating in the growth of this field. David Johannsen in particular embraced silicon compilation the very same day the author introduced this subject to an audience at Caltech. He has since expanded and applied many of the early concepts directly to datapath chip architectures, which had previously been proposed and manually implemented by Mead and Johannsen. Carver Mead contributed, among other things, encouragement, excitement and effective generalizations, so as to expand participation in this new field. John Wawrzynek singlehandedly lashed together two early silicon compilers, RELAY and BRISTLE BLOCKS, so as to render chip layouts that utilize some of the best abilities of each compiler. Charle Rupp pursued the field by attempting to generate layouts from pieces as small as individual transistors. These and other points of view together have given rise to this very fertile field.

Also instrumental in developing the field were many fruitful discussions with Ivan Sutherland, Jonathan Allen, George Mager, Walter Klein, Chuck Seitz, George Lewicki, Ricky Mosteller, Telle Whitney, Juda Afek, Danny Cohen, Bernard Goodwin, John Newkirk, Bob Matthews, Ed Cheng, and Paul Tyner.

Of course, the importance of a working environment cannot be overemphasized. The spirit and scientific resources of the California Institute of Technology, together with the industrial participation afforded by the Silicon Structures Project, has provided perhaps the most fertile of possible environments for this and other kinds of scientific and industrial progress.

The guests from industry provided a secure sense of what people really do under the stress of trying to get a chip out the door under a tight schedule, exposing the kinds of computer tools embraced most fervently and the chronic bottlenecks experienced in that endeavor. The academic spirit provided a timeless security entirely unencumbered by hurried short-term business goals. Ivan Sutherland personally exemplified the best of these two worlds simultaneously, providing truly down-to-earth information and resources while maintaining the best of scientific integrity by providing an extraordinarily open mind to ideas from all disciplines.

Another very important working environment is the USC/Information Sciences Institute, providing among other things superb computing resources and very direct introductions to the VLSI activities occurring nationwide within the research community funded by the Advanced Research Projects Agency. It is remarkable and encouraging that major industrial-grade services can be developed quickly and maintained securely within such a delightful and free environment.

The author is indebted to Larry Seiler and Alan Paeth for providing a PLA layout generation program and for providing the character fonts used in the illustrations, all in their independent effort to produce a key debouncing chip for a VLSI design course. Another person, whose name cannot be mentioned for obvious reasons, "magically" provided an abundance of computing time on one critical occasion. Also instrumental have been the superb computers and software provided commercially by Digital Equipment Corporation.

The dedication and illumination provided by the people at Prentice-Hall, the anonymous reviewers of the manuscript, John Wawrzynek, Bernard Goodwin, and George Lewicki have made it possible to accommodate the varied audiences whose distinct fields of interest are necessarily brought together in a text of this kind.

Special thanks go to Dr. Herbert Benjamin for encouraging the conception of this book, and to my brother and sister Gary and Denise, and my parents Anita and Marx, for providing the greatest support, dedication, and challenge over nearly an infinite number of years.

Introduction

The explosive progress occurring in integrated circuit fabrication has resulted in a doubling of circuit density about every two years. Increased circuit densities attract circuits of increased complexity. This progress makes possible today's single-chip microprocessors and large memories. This progress also brings great increases in the sheer complexity involved in the design process. This text introduces compilation as a means of dealing with this increased complexity, a means long standing in the software domain, where enormous complexity first emerged as a serious problem.

The creation of an integrated circuit proceeds in five basic steps. The creators begin by drawing up a functional specification. They then formalize that specification and perform simulations to build their confidence in its correctness. The major task follows as they translate the desired behavior into a two-dimensional language of silicon where implementation appears as very complex sets of intricately overlapping shapes. They send these sets of shapes, together called a layout, to a silicon foundry and receive a large number of chips in return. The creation is completed as they test and package each chip.

The major cost arises in the translation from the formal functional specification into a two-dimensional layout. Typically, a human translator creates pieces of layout with either paper and pencil or computerized graphical editors. Extreme care must be taken in this process, much greater than the care required for software development because the turnaround time and the cost for a run (chip fabrication) is very expensive. The tedium involved in manual layout makes this process very error prone. Even a computerized graphical editor admits anything the designer draws and thus ignores the inherent syntax or constraints imposed by the two-dimensional language of silicon.

To verify adherence to silicon constraints, software has been developed which checks layouts prior to their fabrication on silicon. Some programs look at layouts and flag certain kinds of geometric violations. Other programs try to recreate the schematic representation directly from the layout. These techniques provide for early error detection and thus cut down on the number of silicon fabrications required to debug a layout.

However, such programs cannot catch all kinds of errors. Somebody still has to produce the layout in the first place.

This hardware development technique contrasts current software development techniques. On the one hand, programmers have compilers that translate high-level specifications into machine language. On the other hand, layout designers have decompilers, programs that read the silicon language and try to reconstruct higher-level descriptions.

Decompilers are difficult to create because they must accept all possible expressions in the silicon language, including all tricks of the trade. All design rule checkers, for example, either do not flag all errors, or actually flag many perfectly correct situations as though they were errors.

A compiler, on the other hand, is much easier to create; it has only to accept a well-defined formal language. The only requirement of such a formal language is that it capture the domain of digital behavior.

The layout generated by a working silicon compiler is guaranteed to be correct with respect to both the functional specification and the constraints of the silicon language. Thus, the compiler users (e.g., layout planners) are freed to concentrate on more productive tasks. They can try various architectures and quickly weigh the trade-offs among various layouts and timing proposals. They can detect bottlenecks and choose to lay these out manually. In analogy, software designers hand-code those routines that consume much of the computer resources.

Even though the layout generated by a silicon compiler may consume more area than a layout generated manually, there are two factors that encourage the use of silicon compilers. First, in tomorrow's technology, we may ultimately have 100 times the density available today. This means effectively 100 times today's area and perhaps 100 times today's speed. Software compilers gained acceptance when available memory and speed rendered unprofitable the human effort required for machine language coding. The same applies to the silicon design effort.

Second, in today's technology, one can buy a full microprocessor on a chip; however, the external logic required to employ such a chip in a system can require many more chips than the microprocessor chip, particularly if the external logic is implemented in commercially available SSI or MSI chips. The minimal design time associated with a silicon compiler makes profitable the creation of a single chip to implement the external logic. Implementing many SSI or MSI chips in one custom chip reduces the cost of PC-board manufacturing, a particularly attractive cost reduction for high-volume operations.

ANATOMY OF A SILICON COMPILER

There are two focal points of concern in a silicon compiler. These are readily apparent to users of such a compiler:

1 The *source language*: the language in which the user specifies the desired function, or behavior, to be performed by the new integrated circuit chip.

2 The *target language*: the capabilities of silicon, utilized in a very complex two-dimensional color picture called a layout.

The quality or usefulness of a silicon compiler is measured by:

1 The ease of behavior specification afforded by the source language

2 The efficiency in use of silicon area and the operating speed of the finished chip

The first of these two considerations is perhaps more important and overlooked more. Since the birth of integrated circuit technologies, designers have had direct access to the target language, and have been most concerned with efficient use of the silicon resource.

However, the ultimate value of an integrated circuit chip is measured by how well it solves a particular problem, usually within a larger system. Even the most efficient chip loses substantial value if it performs a service that mismatches the need within the system. The most efficient chip is utilized inefficiently as the system designer has to remold the system and introduce new chips around the given chip, so to accept the services provided by the given chip.

Thus, integrated circuit chips designed with tunnel vision focused only on silicon efficiency serve merely to pass the buck, or inefficiency, off into the overall system within which it ultimately resides.

In contrast, a chip designed with the particular application foremost in mind can afford some silicon inefficiencies if its role within an overall system matches the system's needs very closely. The design of such functionally optimal chips occurs primarily not in the domain of silicon, but in the domain of possible behaviors or functions. The "source language" of a silicon compiler covers precisely this high-level domain.

Perhaps the most innovative progress in the field of silicon compilation revolves around the design of the source language. While there exist many languages capable of representing behavior, for example, nearly all software programming languages, a source language for silicon compilation must:

1 Provide for direct specification of behaviors that are supported most profitably in the native silicon (e.g., parallelism)

2 Simultaneously provide an overall integrity so that the language persists in being a language of behavior, as opposed to merely a language of layout geometry

The overriding importance of the source language is clearly evident today in the software domain. For some time now people have based decisions concerning the choice of a software compiler on the source language supported by the compiler, as opposed to the efficiency of the code it ultimately produces in the target (machine) language. Concern about the efficient use of inanimate resources takes a backseat to human convenience when the entire effort is considered realistically as a whole.

COMPARING SOFTWARE AND SILICON CONSTRAINTS

Software and hardware revolve around the same basic concern: The software designer lays out a one-dimensoinal array of memory, whereas the integrated circuit designer lays out a two-dimensional area of silicon. In each case, various constraints must be satisfied to obtain a working product. In addition, both efforts involve lots of modification.

There are some fundamental differences between the constraints of software and hardware. For example, GOTOs in software implementations cost only the memory required for the GOTO instruction itself. The distance between the location of the instruction and the target address plays no role in either execution time or memory consumption. In contrast, a silicon GOTO requires area for the "wire" connecting the two locations. A longer wire consumes more area and more execution time. Furthermore, a wire in silicon has to avoid obstacles in order to avoid unwanted short circuits. A software GOTO has no obstacles; it does not have to dodge a certain set of words in memory.

Another difference between software and silicon concerns the different layers required in silicon. A signal in silicon may be represented on any one of several layers.

At some point, a signal has to change layers in transit and this requires a complex of three or more shapes to make the transition. In contrast, a software assignment statement generally requires no such transition; all locations in memory are on the same layer. Software does include a few exceptions to this rule, for example, the distinctions between the general-purpose and floating registers on the IBM 360; the A, B, and X registers of the CDC 6600; and in the more abstract domain of datatypes, the distinction between INTEGER and REAL. However, software compilers conveniently hide these troublesome distinctions by providing implicit translations. A silicon compiler hides layer distinctions by automatically introducing the appropriate shapes to implement the transitions.

THE ROLE OF ORGANIZATION

To make layout generation practical by any means, the functional specification must be partitioned into a conceptual organization, or hierarchy. Each level in the hierarchy performs a function sufficiently simple to allow confident implementation. Each level contains deeper levels plus a glue which somehow integrates the deeper levels to form the present level. In software, hierarchical organization is implemented by nested routines. The glue in a routine is all the code excluding subroutine calls. The glue in hierarchical logic is a set of equations that relate the inputs and outputs of the deeper levels. The glue in silicon is an additional layout that integrates the layouts obtained from the deeper levels.

The two-dimensional geometry of silicon places increased significance on hierarchical organization. As layouts emerge from deeper layers, the glue required to integrate these layouts becomes excessive if the layouts cannot be packed together efficiently or if a large amount of area is consumed for routing signals among the cells. A change in hierarchical organization can change the shapes of layouts emerging from deeper levels. It can also modify the distances between cells and thus potentially reduce the area required for signal routing.

The impact of hierarchy in two-dimensoinal silicon often forces hierarchical reorganizations. Reorganization of the hierarchy is especially costly when people create layouts by hand because it destroys some cells already laid out and introduces new cells that have yet to be laid out.

ANATOMY OF THIS TEXT

This text partitioned into three major parts. The first two parts act as the legs on which the third part stands.

The first part deals with integrated circuit layouts, the target language for silicon compilers. The second parts deals with logical behavior, a source language for silicon compilers. The third part provides a marriage between the first two parts, presenting a variety of complete translations from the source behavior to the target layout.

The first chapter introduces the capabilities of the silicon medium, the NMOS technology in particular. It presents basic layout forms and the constraints required to maintain both geometric and electrical integrity. The primary focus of this chapter, however, is to familiarize the reader with the specification of layout embedded within the richness of a programming language. We call such layout specification ''parameterized'' layout specification.

The choice to embed layout specification within a programming language is based on the following benefits:

1   The payout afforded by parameterized layout specification is immense; a minimal amount of careful specification gives rise to a large variety of useful and individual layouts, each with a great degree of confidence.

2   Any silicon compiler, a computer program, must produce layout, a representation in the target language. The production of this layout therefore rests as part of the silicon compiler program specification itself.

The second chapter in this part completes the first chapter's introduction of layout synthesis by presenting an implementation. It introduces techniques of layout representation and analysis. This chapter introduces the bulk of the concepts involved with programming, and the corresponding notations particular to this programming language.

The second part of the text deals with the logical behavior, or functional specification. Truly functional behavior is a phenomenon that is independent of the medium of implementation. We therefore establish a language of behavior which exists independently of integrated circuit layouts. We explore in detail the integrity of this language in its own right, and ultimately provide a formalization of this language again embedded in our programming language.

The second chapter in this part provides a translation from the behavior language into a representation presented in Part 1 which acts directly as a parameter for immediate layout synthesis. At this point, the benefits of embedding both layout specification and behavior specification within one and the same programming language become most clearly evident.

The third chapter in this part augments the behavior language substantially, primarily for human convenience. It introduces the ability to specify logical behavior in an organized manner, therefore maintaining a large degree of confidence even for the specifications of large systems. This chapter includes many examples.

The third part provides various formalisms and general techniques for effective and practical translations from the behavior source language to the layout target language. The majority of techniques introduced apply equally well independent of the particular source language and the particular target language (e.g., NMOS). The key concepts include a representation chosen for intermediate computations, and the mathematical properties (axioms or conventions) maintained and assumed about these intermediate data. The variety of techniques presented differ primarily in the mathematical properties assigned to the intermediate data. Each ultimately renders layouts of distinct character and application. (These techniques render ''gate array'' and ''polycell'' methods as very limited, special cases.)

The first chapter in this part introduces a representation which encompasses both the geometric and behavioral domains. It also discusses the role that conventions (axioms) play in silicon compilation. It presents completely a general translation from the organized behavior language into layout of one particular character. It also sketches a different set of techniques which comprise a ''silicon assembler.''

The second chapter in this part exposes perhaps the most fundamental advantages offered by silicon compilation over manual design techniques. It presents particularly convenient, simple, and high-level means for logic reorganization. Although these reorganizations are provided by simple programs operating in the logical, nonlayout domain, such reorganization profoundly affects the resulting layouts, both in area and electrical performance.

It is here, where we apply algorithms to generate new behavioral specifications, that the power of silicon compilation offers solutions to the high-level problems which in practice cause substantial compromise in chip quality due to intolerably large redesign costs. The key flexibility provided is the automatic and error-free implementation of changes that affect the layout globally and in great detail, although the specification of such changes now requires only one line of obvious text. The key notion here, which applies to all forms of silicon compilation, is the straightforward manipulation of intermediate data in domains other than that of layout.

The third chapter in this part deals with another set of mathematical conventions which renders more efficient layouts in general. Its primary benefit is the reduction in communications costs obtained by reducing the area consumed by ''wires.''

The final chapter introduces an electrical model that can be maintained, or ''grown,'' automatically during layout synthesis. This model ultimately provides an estimate of the chip's operating speed. This tool is useful because designers often need to take performance into account while choosing among different implementations. We see, by example, how logic reorganization affects not only the layout, but also its electrical performance.

Part 1

INTEGRATED
CIRCUIT
LAYOUT

1

Integrated Circuit Layouts and Their Creation

The ultimate goal of any design system for producing integrated circuits is the production of a layout. The layout is a multicolored picture which not only represents a desired function but also acts directly in the fabrication of a working integrated circuit.

The layout is the focal hinge between the integrated circuit designer and the integrated circuit fabricator. The integrated circuit fabricator takes a designer's layout and produces a working chip without even looking at the layout. All human operations involved in transforming a layout into an integrated circuit work independently of the particular layout.

The designer, however, must be concerned with "design rules" given by the fabricator. The fabricator's published design rules tell the designer the limitations of the fabrication process. Limitations must exist for any real-world fabricator. It must be known to the designer, for example, that wires carrying distinct signals must not touch, and in fact the wires must be separated by a finite distance. The fabricator cannot say that any separation greater than zero is sufficient; the physics of quantum mechanics makes discrete the possible physical distances, so a real-world distance greater than zero is also greater than a small nonzero number.

Physics places ultimate limitations, but the fabricator introduces much coarser limitations due to the variety of physical processes used to transform a layout into a working integrated circuit.

CONSTRAINTS ON LAYOUTS OTHER THAN DESIGN RULES Certainly integrated circuits can be built which perform functions different from those performed by other integrated circuits. The function intended by the designer to be performed by the integrated circuit imposes logical constraints. Just as any set of bits can be called a program and be loaded into the computer's main memory, the set of bits must obey some constraints so that it causes the computer to perform an intended function. Constraints on programs represented by sets of bits require, for example, that all instructions represented by the set are instructions known to the computer.

9

Logical constraints include a variety of requirements. Distinct signals, for example, must remain insulated from one another. Subsystems within an integrated circuit impose logical constraints; for example, a signal's inverse as opposed to the raw signal itself may be required as an input. Perhaps the subsystem also requires that two of its inputs never represent a logical 1 at the same time. Logical constraints are common also in software, where for example a matrix multiplication routine might impose constraints on the dimensions of the two input matrices.

Besides logical and physical constraints, electrical constraints enter the picture. Wires must be wide enough to transmit the maximum amount of current that will ever flow through them. Voltages or currents that are used to represent logical ones and zeros must in fact hold sufficiently close to one extreme or the other to remain unambiguous. Subsystems in an integrated circuit must have sufficient patience to allow for delays imposed by the transmission of information through wires and by functional units which impose further delays.

THINKING ABOUT LAYOUTS

Since a layout is a picture, we can imagine that the layout is made up of a large set of individual polygons. Each polygon represents not just the outline of the polygon, but the entire area enclosed by the polygon. Each polygonal area also has a color. Therefore, we can think of a layout as a conglomeration of individual atoms, where each atom is a colored polygon.

Circuit designers, however, rarely think in terms of pure polygons. Although a layout can certainly be described as a set of polygons, or atoms, the designer generally thinks in terms of molecules, tiny but functional units made up of small sets of polygons.

Molecules represent functions such as the inverter, the amplifier, an individual wire or set of connected wires, or the input or output pad. The conglomeration of atoms into molecules represents the gathering of shapes made out of polygons into what software people might call "machine instructions." That is, the functional molecules represent a rendition of a machine language in terms of which we can design larger functions.

We now embark on an exploration of one very useful means by which to specify or create layouts.

1.1 LAYOUT SPECIFICATION WITH TEXT

One way to create a layout is to specify that layout in a language which admits convenient specification of geometric items and their combinations. There are many languages suitable for layout specification. All have in common notations for specifying two-dimensional points.

1.1.1 Point Specification

We will adopt a very concise notation for point specification. A point consists of two numbers called the x and y coordinates, which represent respectively a horizontal and a vertical distance from one unique chosen point called the origin. The pair of numbers zero and zero therefore represent the origin itself. We will package two numbers into a single point by writing first the x-coordinate, then a # sign, and then the y-coordinate:

x-coordinate # y-coordinate

Thus,

0#0   represents the origin, and

5#1   represents the point that is 5 units to the right
              of the origin and 1 unit above the origin (Figure 1.1)

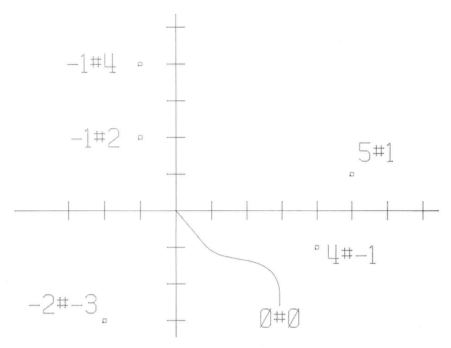

FIGURE 1.1 Coordinate system.

The # sign takes two numbers and produces a point. We allow each number to be an arbitrary REAL, or floating-point number, so that points with fractional distances become expressible. We can represent all the constraints and capabilities of this notation by writing what might be called a rule of grammar:

REAL # REAL $\rightarrow$ POINT

This rule suggests that either REAL may be specified in fact by an arbitrary REAL expression. This rule of grammar admits rich expressions like

5+2 # 7*3

The + operator with which we are all familiar has its own rule:

REAL + REAL $\rightarrow$ REAL

Similarly, * has the rule

REAL * REAL $\rightarrow$ REAL.

We will admit the use of variables as found in programming languages and mathematics. With this capability, the expression

A # B

represents

the point 3#7 if A=3 and B=7, or
the point −2#1.5 if A=−2 and B=1.5

For consistency, of course, we must assume that A and B are variables representing REALs. One obvious advantage to our admission of variables is the ability to specify concisely whole sets of points. For example, the set of points

A # A*A   FOR A FROM 0 TO 1 BY .1

represents the 11 points

0#0, .1#.01, .2#.04, .3#.09, ..., 1#1

which happen to trace out a piece of a parabola (Figure 1.2). Although a parabola is an unlikely piece of a layout, this simple example introduces the great expressibility admitted by the inclusion of program variables.

It is the introduction of program variables that makes silicon compilation possible at all. We will see not only variables of type REAL, but also variables of type POINT, and variables of type LAYOUT, and variables of useful types that we have yet to define. By embedding layout specification in a programming language, we can define functions (procedures) which take in and produce values of all kinds of types and therefore define algorithmically all concepts involved with producing many classes of layouts.

1.1.2 Layout Specification

The simplest layout is a single polygon residing on a layer. Throughout the majority of this text, layers will be represented by colors, for viewing convenience.

A very common polygon is a rectangle having horizontal and vertical edges. We will refer to such a special polygon as a box. Because boxes are so common, we provide two operations, one which creates a single polygon and the other which creates a single box:

1   { POINT$_1$; POINT$_2$; ... ; POINT$_k$ }   \PAINTED   COLOR

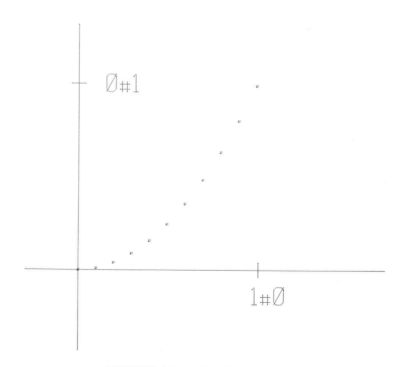

FIGURE 1.2   Points in a parabola.

represents a layout consisting of the one polygon whose vertices reside at POINT_1, $\text{POINT}_2, \ldots, \text{POINT}_k$ and whose area resides on layer COLOR.

> **2** POINT_1 \TO POINT_2 \PAINTED COLOR

represents a box on the specified COLOR. The box is the smallest rectangle containing both POINTs where the edges of the rectangle are vertical or horizontal.

We maintain throughout this text the convention that operators, or verbs, are denoted by a name preceded by a backslash (\). This notation will help us distinguish verbs from nouns. By using names to denote operations, we have at our disposal many operators, each represented by a suggestive name. We will, of course, also use the standard notations for arithmetic expressions.

Figure 1.3 shows the graphical representation of both

> 1#1 \TO 2#2   \PAINTED GREEN,   and
> { 1#1 ; 2#2 ; 3#1 }   \PAINTED RED.

1.1.3 Our Simple View of Layers

We use the following color codes for the five NMOS layers:

> BLUE   =   metal
> RED   =   polysilicon
> GREEN   =   diffusion
> BLACK   =   contact cut
> YELLOW =   implant

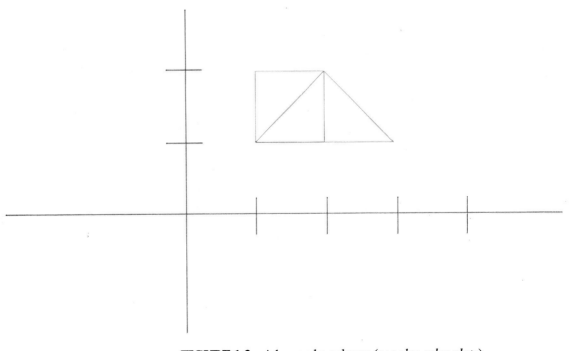

FIGURE 1.3 A box and a polygon (*see also color plate*).

Although we will avoid the discussion of the physics of each layer, it is perfectly practical to think in terms of these pretty colors, whose roles in NMOS can be understood simply. It is in fact this physics independence which allows our understanding of layouts to be so simple as to admit their straightforward, though complex, generation. We are indebted to Carver Mead and Lynn Conway [1980] for the original courage to explore layouts with such effective simplicity.

In analogy, the physical workings of a computer can remain unknown to the machine language programmer, yet the programmer can be very effective knowing only the machine instructions. Each instruction available to the programmer is understood simply in terms of an abstract model which mentions nothing about the implementation of those instructions. In fact, it is the abstract view that encourages the programmer to produce and debug very complex and useful programs.

1.1.4　Complex Layouts

A practical layout consists of much more than a single polygon or box. All we need to add is the ability to form sets of polygons and boxes. We provide two notations for specifying the superpositions of existing layouts:

1　LAYOUT$_1$　\UNION　LAYOUT$_2$

2　{　LAYOUT$_1$　;　LAYOUT$_2$　;　...　;　LAYOUT$_k$　}

The first notation represents a single layout formed from the two given layouts, LAYOUT$_1$ and LAYOUT$_2$. The second notation represents the superposition of an arbitrary number of given layouts. In fact, both notations are interchangeable:

LAYOUT$_1$　\UNION　LAYOUT$_2$　　　　　　is equivalent to

{　LAYOUT$_1$　;　LAYOUT$_2$　}

and

{　LAYOUT$_1$　;　LAYOUT$_2$　;　LAYOUT$_3$　;　LAYOUT$_4$　}　　　is equivalent to

LAYOUT$_1$　\UNION　LAYOUT$_2$　\UNION　LAYOUT$_3$　\UNION　LAYOUT$_4$

Example. Figure 1.4 shows among other things the geometry represented by

A　{　0#0　\TO　2#10　\PAINTED　GREEN　;
　　　　5#0　\TO　7#10　\PAINTED　GREEN　}

B　{　0#0　\TO　2#10　\PAINTED　RED　;
　　　　4#0　\TO　6#10　\PAINTED　RED　}

C　{　0#0　\TO　3#10　\PAINTED　BLUE　;
　　　　6#0　\TO　9#10　\PAINTED　BLUE　}

In fact, we can be more concise by writing instead

A　{　0#0　\TO　2#10　;
　　　　5#0　\TO　7#10　}　　　\PAINTED　GREEN

B　{　0#0　\TO　2#10　;
　　　　4#0　\TO　6#10　}　　　\PAINTED　RED

C　{　0#0　\TO　3#10　;
　　　　6#0　\TO　9#10　}　　　\PAINTED　BLUE.

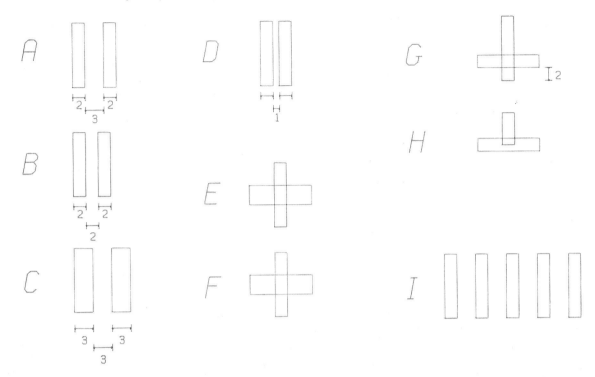

FIGURE 1.4 Design rules (*see also color plate*).

1.1.5 Layout Variables and Displacements

Besides the creation of individual polygons and boxes, and their superpositions, we need almost immediately for our convenience two more abilities to facilitate layout specification. First, there is a great deal of repetition in layout specification. In the example just given, part A specifies two boxes. In fact, it was the designer's intent to place two copies of the same box simply displaced relative to each other by 5 horizontally. The designer would rather specify:

THE_BOX   is   0#0   \TO   2#10   \PAINTED   GREEN
Give the result   {   THE_BOX   ;   THE_BOX   moved to the right by 5   }

The two new abilities required for this expression are

1   The ability to package an arbitrary layout into an indivisible whole and give this whole a unique name, and the ability to refer to a packaged layout simply by its name

2   The ability to make two references to the same layout appear not as two indistinguishable copies lying exactly on top of one another, but as two copies displaced relative to one another

We augment our layout specification language to meet the first new ability by introducing layout variables. We declare to the world that we want a new layout variable, named THE_BOX, by writing

VAR   THE_BOX   =   LAYOUT;

This notation looks something like Pascal's declaration of variables. The word VAR indicates that we wish to declare new variables. An arbitrary list of names follows, the names of our new variables, and finally the "=LAYOUT;" indicates that these variables will represent layouts. Now that we have our new variable, THE_BOX, we can assign it a layout by writing

      THE_BOX   :=   0#0 \TO 2#10   \PAINTED GREEN;

This whole scenario is applicable to more familiar datatypes such as REAL numbers, for example,

      VAR   TWO_PI = REAL;
      TWO_PI:= 3.141592*2;

The REAL variable TWO_PI is now declared and assigned a very popular value.

    Besides packaging layouts into variables, we wish to take an existing layout and move it as a whole. We augment our language once more to allow the new construction

      LAYOUT \AT POINT   →   LAYOUT

which says that expressions of the form

      LAYOUT \AT POINT

are in fact themselves valid layouts. Such an expression represents a layout derived by displacing the given LAYOUT horizontally and vertically by the two coordinates of the POINT, respectively. Thus,

      THE_BOX   \AT   5#0

represents a copy of THE_BOX which lives 5 units to the right of the original THE_BOX. Figure 1.4A may now be specified by

      { THE_BOX ; THE_BOX \AT 5#0 }

For completeness, we can use the \AT operator on complex layouts even if the complex layout is not simply a variable; for example, Figure 1.4A is also specified by

      { 0#0 \TO 2#10   \PAINTED GREEN ;
         0#0 \TO 2#10   \PAINTED GREEN \AT 5#0 }

1.2 A LOOK AT THE NMOS MEDIUM

The NMOS medium attaches electrical and logical properties to our layouts. The functional meaning of layout is therefore represented ultimately in the silicon. People construct layouts with this semantic mapping in mind. This semantic mapping may produce undefined results unless the layout adheres to some simple constraints, called design rules.

    With the layout operations presented thus far, we may create arbitrary pictures, even layouts that have no meaning, in silicon. We now look at the detailed constraints imposed on layouts by the silicon. The constraints lend character to any legal layout we might produce.

1.2.1 Units and Simple Design Rules

Let us choose a unit of distance upon which we can base our discussion. Our units will not be micrometers (a common modern unit), but instead a scalable entity called a lambda. [As of 1981, many fabricators routinely produce integrated circuits where the lambda is 2.5 micrometers. Some will fabricate circuits at lambda equals 2, 1.5, or 1 micrometer or smaller.] Since the fabrication art changes toward smaller and smaller sizes as time passes, we will ignore this continuous scaling by working only in terms of lambda. When we are ready to send our layout to a fabricator, we scale the entire layout by some number that maps lambdas into real-world micrometers.

1.2.2 The Primary Colors and Their Interactions

Of all the layers available in NMOS, only three of them attract the majority of our attention. These primary layers, or colors, are red, blue, and green, which by coincidence are also the three primary colors of color television. Unlike color television, colors in NMOS do not mix to form brand new colors. However, shapes in distinct layers do have very specific interactions when the shapes intersect.

Blue is a very simple layer; it interacts with neither red nor green. This means that we can send a signal on blue and have it cross over a distinct signal traveling on red or green without conflict at the intersection. Our freeway systems, with their overpasses and underpasses, afford this same harmony.

Red and green, on the other hand, do interact at their intersections. Whereas red and blue, or green and blue, operate independently, red and green form a conflict at their intersections. Red is dominant. Red always gets the intersection unconditionally. In addition, green gets a private copy of the intersection on one condition dependent on the value of the signal riding on the red:

> **1** RED carries a one   => green gets through the intersection
> **2** RED carries a zero   => green loses the intersection
>   and hence is broken

An intersection between red and green is a transistor. Red is the gate, or controller, and green is subject to conditional connectedness determined solely by the red.

The transistor is all that ties properties of the electrical world to the properties of the logical or functional world. While the red does definitely affect logically the behavior of the green, the red and green are nonetheless electrically distinct. Signals do not leak from red to green or from green to red. There is never an electrical connection between the red and green at this kind of intersection. There is only a logical or functional connection. The green does not know what turns it on (creates connectedness) or turns it off (breaks connectedness). The red is entirely oblivious to the green. The transistor relates two circuits logically, but the two circuits remain distinctly two circuits electrically, not one fused circuit.

This logical and nonelectrical relationship provides for the coexistence of thousands or millions of electrically distinct circuits. The electrical characteristics of each circuit can be analyzed independently of all other circuits. Thank goodness. The troubles encountered in analyzing the electrical properties of a single circuit grow out of control with even modest growth of the circuit. Meanwhile, the interactions between distinct circuits may be understood simply in terms of logical interactions.

1.2.3 Minimum Sizes and Minimum Separations

Figure 1.4A, B, and C shows pairs of objects of matching colors, together with their minimum allowable dimensions. A green or a red region must be at least 2 lambda wide and a blue region must be at least 3 lambda wide. Any smaller regions border on being nonexistent. So to be sure that the red, green, or blue regions continue to exist through all the fuss that the fabricator must go through, these minimum dimensions must be respected. (Refer to Mead and Conway [1980].)

Figure 1.4A, B, and C also shows the inverse, if you will, of the minimum size constraint. Regions that will represent distinct signals must be separated from one another by a minimum distance. Green pairs must be separated by at least 3, red by 2, and blue by 3. A violation of minimum separation yields an ambiguous result: Do the regions touch or not? Remember that the fabrication process introduces uncertainties, so you must be able to see your layout clearly even if you blur your vision.

These design contraints, a concession to the real world, impose lower bounds on the sizes of layout we may produce. Layouts may not be scaled down arbitrarily. Keep this in mind when we construct for example an inverter, and we wonder why it has to appear so large. We always wish to make things as small as possible because the smaller things are, the more we can place on a single chip and hence the more powerful the chip becomes.

Figure 1.4D shows the minimum separation between a red and a green region which are meant not to interact, 1 lambda. Figure 1.4E and F shows that blue interacts with neither of the other colors and therefore each of the two pairs of colors may cross without constraint.

Figure 1.4G shows that a legal transistor, the intersection between green and red, must include a little overlap on red's part. Figure 1.4H shows an invalid transistor; the red region does not entirely block the green region. What happens then? The effectiveness of red's blocking power is compromised. Even if red carries a zero and therefore blocks the red-green intersection, the green does not become entirely blocked because the signal on green can squeeze around the red blockage. In fact, even if the red crosses the green completely but goes no further to provide an overlap, the uncertainties imposed by the fabricator can possibly shorten the red and hence leave the green only partially blocked. Once again, a valid overlap allows us to blur our vision and still see the green completely crossed.

1.2.4 The Tiny Role of Design Rules on Silicon Compilation

These design rules affect a program which produces layouts only in that they tell us how to place regions relative to one another. As far as silicon compilations are concerned, these design rules are arbitrary and are accepted without question. For example, Figure 1.4I shows us the tightest packing we can achieve legally for routing five independent signals from top to bottom. Figure 1.4I may be specified with the following text, making reference to our predefined green box, called simply THE_BOX:

```
{  THE_BOX  ;        THE_BOX  \AT  5#0  ;        THE_BOX  \AT  10#0  ;
   THE_BOX  \AT  15#0  ;        THE_BOX  \AT  20#0      }
```

The minimum separation constraint requires that the boxes appear displaced from one another by 5 units (2 units for the width and 3 more units for the separation). These design rules appear even more clearly in the following, geometrically equivalent text:

```
VAR      X  =  REAL;
{COLLECT    THE_BOX  \AT  X#0    FOR  X  FROM  0  BY  2+3  TO  20;}
```

This expression forms the same set of boxes, but the separation for all five boxes is specified only once, in the "BY 2+3" clause of the FOR quantifier. Textual or algorithmic specification like this facilitates a concise and sparse specification for the incorporation of design constraints.

The ability to embed design rule constraints concisely in the textual specification provides for much greater confidence in the legality of the resulting layout compared to a specification given graphically, where the boxes are placed one at a time, each time requiring the designer to look carefully at the paper or screen to be convinced that each separation, specified independently, obeys the design rules.

This example is a very simple case of concise design rule incorporation. It turns out that adherence to design rules can be programmed securely into a silicon compiler with very little effort. In practice, design rule dimensions appear very rarely within the program text for a silicon compiler. These dimensions appear in relatively few routines. The design rule constraints are reflected, however, in an entire layout because all pieces pass through these few routines.

A silicon compiler generally never looks at the layouts it produces during execution. It constructs legal layouts at each stage in its execution, and hence never needs to check itself. We can call this "correctness by construction." In fact, we can make the inductive assertion that all generated layouts are legal, and prove the correctness of the entire compiler by providing small proofs for the following situations. Any routine that takes in one or more layouts and produces a new layout requires a proof that

1   Assuming that the given layouts are legal,

2   The resulting layout is legal.

In practice, such proofs are easy because each layout-producing routine actually augments layouts given to it in only minor ways. It is the ultimate composition of these routines during execution that builds very complex layouts.

1.2.5 More Abilities in the Domain of Silicon

We have considered the three primary colors of NMOS. These three layers are all electrically disconnected. Only the red and green layers interact at all. We do have means to connect electrically any pair of layers explicitly with the use of a "contact cut." A contact cut is a small region of black. Here and only here do we consider the black layer. We will take as given the following three layouts, which fuse each possible pair of layers. The very abbreviated names that follow denote, respectively, "Green Contact Blue," "Red Contact Blue," and "Red Contact Green":

```
VAR      GCB,  RCB,  RCG  =  LAYOUT;

GCB:=  {   -(1#1)  \TO  1#1  \PAINTED  BLACK  ;
           -(2#2)  \TO  2#2  \PAINTED  BLUE   ;
           -(2#2)  \TO  2#2  \PAINTED  GREEN      };
RCB:=  {   -(1#1)  \TO  1#1  \PAINTED  BLACK  ;
           -(2#2)  \TO  2#2  \PAINTED  BLUE   ;
           -(2#2)  \TO  2#2  \PAINTED  RED       };
RCG:=  {   -(3#2)  \TO  0#2  \PAINTED  RED   ;
           -(1#2)  \TO  3#2  \PAINTED  GREEN   ;
           -(3#2)  \TO  3#2  \PAINTED  BLUE   ;
           -(2#1)  \TO  2#1  \PAINTED  BLACK      }  ;
```

See Figure 1.5A. Figure 1.5B shows examples of layer changes. Here are the four layouts in text form:

```
1  {  0#0  \TO  5#4   \PAINTED  BLUE   ;
      GCB  \AT  7#2  ;
      9#1  \TO  14#3  \PAINTED  GREEN   }
2  {  0#0  \TO  5#4   \PAINTED  BLUE   ;
      RCB  \AT  7#2  ;
      6#0  \TO  8#-5  \PAINTED  RED    }
```

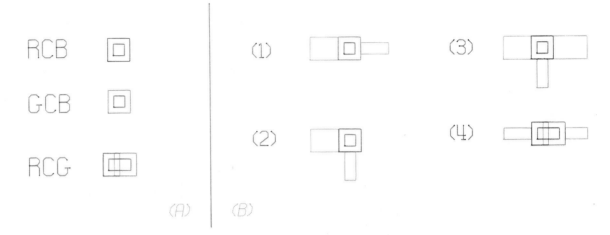

FIGURE 1.5 Electrical connection between layers (*see also color plate*).

```
3 {   0#0   \TO   15#4      \PAINTED   BLUE   ;
      RCB   \AT   7#2   ;
      6#0   \TO   8#-5     \PAINTED   RED   }
4 {   0#0   \TO   5#2       \PAINTED   RED   ;
      RCG   \AT   8#1   ;
      11#0   \TO   15#2      \PAINTED   GREEN      }
```

Notice how in each of these four examples we reference the variables GCB, RCB, and RCG together with a displacement (\AT) for each. Even though each list specifies only three items, the layout represented by each list nonetheless includes five or six individual boxes. We see here the beginnings of concise notations that can represent arbitrarily complex layouts.

1.2.6 More Concise Notations and Programming Languages

As we proceed to make more complex layouts, we will be specifying many colored boxes. Any time we find that we are writing too many characters to express simple things, it is time for us to define new concise notations so that we may move forward more easily. This marvelous and essential freedom of notation is afforded by programming languages through the use of function definitions. Let us dream up a notation so that we can express the first part of Figure 1.5B as

```
{   0#0   \BB   5#4   ;
    GCB   \AT   7#2   ;
    9#1   \GB   14#3   }
```

Rather than saying, for example,

```
POINT   \TO   POINT      \PAINTED   BLUE
```

we say instead

```
POINT   \BB   POINT
```

The new operator BB reads as ''Blue Box.'' We will introduce GB for ''Green Box,'' RB for ''Red Box,'' and similar notations for boxes of other colors. We can define the BB operator to our system simply by defining BB, as in

DEFINE   BB(U:POINT   V:POINT   ) = LAYOUT:
                             U   \TO   V   \PAINTED   BLUE

ENDDEFN

BB is a function that takes in two points, named U and V, and produces a layout, namely

   U \TO V   \PAINTED   BLUE

We define the operator RB by writing

DEFINE   RB(U,V:POINT)=   LAYOUT:
                             U \TO   V \PAINTED   RED
ENDDEFN

The specification of the parameters U and V in the function RB is equivalent to the longer but more illustrative form used in BB. We define the other colored boxes by

DEFINE   GB(U,V:POINT)=LAYOUT: U   \TO   V   \PAINTED   GREEN   ENDDEFN
DEFINE   KB(U,V:POINT)=LAYOUT: U   \TO   V   \PAINTED   BLACK   ENDDEFN
DEFINE   YB(U,V:POINT)=LAYOUT: U   \TO   V   \PAINTED   YELLOW   ENDDEFN

(KB stands for ''Black Box'' and YB stands for ''Yellow Box.'' We will consider yellow boxes soon.) We can now write the text for Figure 1.5B, part 3, concisely as

   {   0#0   \BB   15#4   ;   RCB   \AT   7#2   ;   6#0   \RB   8#-5   }

1.3 BASIC BUILDING BLOCKS: A SILICON MACHINE LANGUAGE

All the tiny layouts that we have constructed so far provide no easily recognized logical functions. We have not shown yet how to invert a signal, or how to perform even the simple logical AND function. We embark on that now.

We are in effect defining for ourselves a silicon ''machine language.'' That is, we will define some very useful layouts which have easily understood logical meanings. These discrete layouts will be the building blocks from which we will construct entire systems. These building blocks are analogous to the machine instructions which a software compiler uses to form entire programs.

At this point we will not describe how these pieces fit together, nor how one would describe in some high-level language a functional system to implement. We present each functional unit as a given.

There is a lot of flexibility in defining a silicon machine language. We choose a simple set of instructions now, and in Chapter 6 we will augment this set to include higher-level instructions, each of which can be implemented more efficiently as a single tailor-made layout than as a union of our lower-level instructions.

For now we will look at the layouts for an inverter, for wires, and for a generalized inverter called a NOR gate. These building blocks provide for the implementation of arbitrary boolean functions. The NOR function together with NOT gives us the familiar AND and OR functions:

AND(x,y) =   NOR(NOT(x), NOT(y))
OR(x,y) =   NOT(NOR(x,   y))

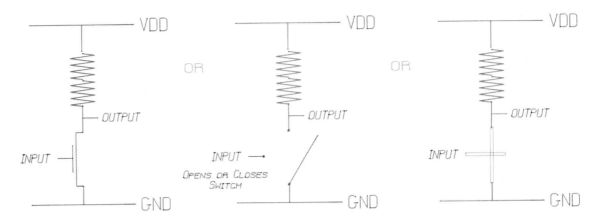

FIGURE 1.6   Inverter schematic.

1.3.1   The Inverter

The inverter is a remarkable device in NMOS. It certainly produces an output which is the logical inverse of its input. However, inverters are also used to provide for electrical amplification, an operation required very often to make sure that electrical signals remain unambiguously a logical 1 or 0. Inverters are used also to provide for dynamic, or short-term, memories.

Figure 1.6 shows a schematic for an inverter in terms of a resistor and a transistor. The output appears between the resistor and the transistor. The resistor, like a spring, loves to pull the output upward to the voltage VDD, a logical 1. The transistor on the bottom either makes or breaks the connection between the output and GND, depending on the transistor's gate (input).

The inverter's input affects the output as follows. If the input is a zero, the connection between the output and GND is broken. Thus, the output, now connected only to VDD, rises to nearly match the voltage VDD itself, a logical 1. Half of the function is now understood; a 0 input yields a 1 output. On the other hand, if the input is a 1, a connection between the output and GND is created and thus the output falls to zero; the output is directly connected to GND. The poor resistor atop has much less pulling power than the direct connection to GND. Hence, a 1 input yields a 0 output, and the inverter appears to work completely. Figure 1.7 illustrates the inverter's operation in a way that is easy to remember. However, the stretching of the resistor is symbolic only, that stretch-

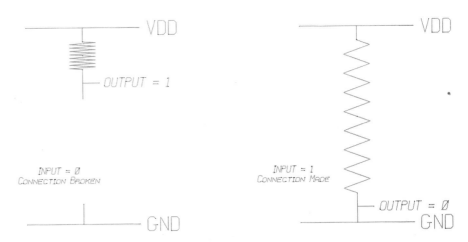

FIGURE 1.7   Inverter's operation.

ing applies in the domain of voltages, but strictly speaking it applies not at all in the domain of the schematic or layout. The resistor in the schematic or layout does not change shape at all geometrically.

1.3.2 Electrical Characteristics of an Inverter

Our description of an inverter thus far is a simplification of a more accurate description which takes into account actual voltages. Voltages represent all our 0s and 1s in NMOS. However, since a voltage is an analog quantity, varying anywhere between VDD (1) and GND (0), we must assure ourselves that we produce only voltages that are close to either VDD and GND and not halfway between VDD and GND.

Consider the following reality. The bottom transistor, which can pull the output to GND, in fact does not make an absolute connection to GND. That connection has a tiny but nonzero resistance, which represents almost an absolute connection. As long as the resistance of the top resistor is sufficiently large (Figure 1.8A), the tiny resistance of the transistor linking the output to ground appears relatively to be a very near zero resistance, or absolute connection. We might ask why not make the pull-up resistor have infinite or nearly infinite resistance, so that the tiny resistance of the pull-down connection can be ignored forever?

We have to consider the other side of the coin. If the input is zero, the transistor almost breaks the connection between the output node and GND. In fact, it appears to break the connection only by imposing a very large resistance between the output node and GND (Figure 1.8B). If we were to make the pull-up resistance as large as the very large resistance of the turned-off transistor, the output would reside not at VDD or GND, but halfway between, a very ambiguous result. So we must make the pull-up resistance smaller than the turned-off transistor's resistance.

We can satisfy both opposing constraints on the pull-up resistor by making:

1 The *turned-on* transistor's resistance at least four times *smaller* than the pull-up resistance

2 The *turned-off* transistor's resistance at least four times *greater* than the pull-up resistance

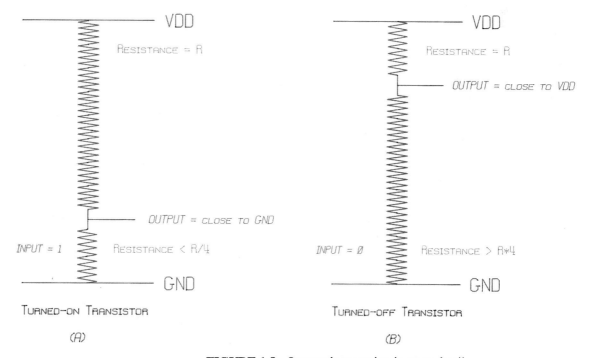

FIGURE 1.8 Inverter's operation in more detail.

With these constraints, the turned-on transistor yields an output of at most .2∗VDD (a close 0), and a turned-off transistor yields an output of at least .8∗VDD (a close 1). The approximate outputs are certainly within tolerance.

We still have a great latitude in defining the pull-up resistance under these constraints because the difference between the resistances of a turned-off and a turned-on transistor easily exceeds the required factor of 16. There is one more consideration, that of speed, which favors making the pull-up resistance as small as possible under these constraints.

We want all our inverters to react as quickly as possible so that the entire chip as a whole can operate as quickly as possible. Consider how a 0 output becomes a 1 output, as the result of changing the input from a 1 to a 0. When the input changes to a zero, the connection between the output and GND breaks immediately. The output at that instant is initially a 0, or in electrical terms, the output contains no charge and reads as zero volts. The resistor pulls the output up to a 1 precisely by letting charge flow from the top VDD source, through the resistor, into the output node (Figure 1.9A). When the output node is filled with charge, the output node represents an unambiguous logical 1. The rate at which the precious charge can flow through the resistor to the output node is very small if the resistor has a very large resistance (Figure 1.9B).

Thus, a high resistance in the pull-up resistor slows the flow of charge from VDD to the output node. It seems we could combat this slowness by assuming that the output node requires only very little charge to fill it, That is, assume that the output node has only a tiny electrical capacitance. Then, even if the charge arrives slowly, we need not wait long because only a small amount of charge would be required. However, at the very minimum, the output node has a substantial capacitance due to the capacitance contributed by the bottom transistor itself, whether the transistor is on or off. This contribution is a fact in NMOS whether we like it or not. Furthermore, everything that we will ultimately attach to the output node will contribute even more capacitance (Figure 1.9C).

What do we do to obtain the fastest possible inverter? First, we avoid loading down the output node with giant capacitances. Second, we minimize the pull-up resistance under the constraint that the pull-up resistance must be some well-defined factor greater than the pull-down resistance of the turned-on transistor.

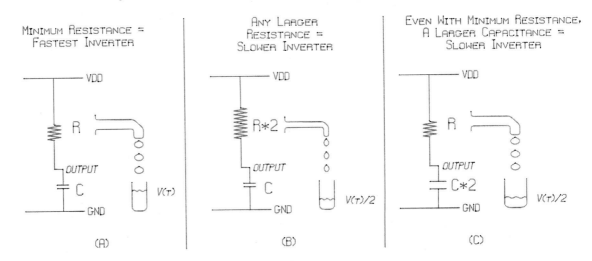

THE "WATER LEVEL" IN EACH TUB (CAPACITOR) REPRESENTS THE VOLTAGE AT THE OUTPUT NODE AS A FUNCTION OF TIME.

SLOWNESS = RESISTANCE ∗ CAPACITANCE

FIGURE 1.9 Resistance and capacitance affect time.

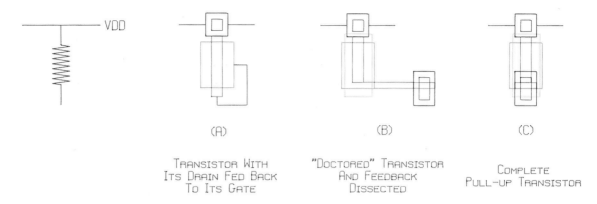

(A)   (B)   (C)

TRANSISTOR WITH   "DOCTORED" TRANSISTOR
ITS DRAIN FED BACK   AND FEEDBACK   COMPLETE
  TO ITS GATE   DISSECTED   PULL-UP TRANSISTOR

FIGURE 1.10   Pull-up resistor (*see also color plate*).

1.3.3   Inverter Layout

We have seen the simple layout for a transistor, a simple red-green intersection. Given the layout for a resistor, we would be all set to generate quickly the layout for an entire inverter.

A resistor inhibits the flow of electricity typically by imposing many small obstacles. However, it would take a great deal of area on the silicon to impose a uniform but substantial continuum of obstacles. Instead of imposing obstacles to obtain the effect of a resistor, a very clever idea has been introduced which facilitates a very area-efficient implementation.

The resistor is implemented by a transistor with its gate fed directly from its source (Figure 1.10A). Let us consider hypothetically the stability of the two logical states of the inverter's output. If the output somehow is a 0 now, the pull-up resistor finds its gate tied to that 0. This in effect breaks the connection between VDD and the output of the inverter. Thus, in this case the output feels no force toward VDD and remains calmly at 0. On the other hand, if the output is somehow a 1 now, the pull-up resistor finds its gate tied to that 1, and the output appears to be connected directly to VDD. Hence, an output equal to 1 has a strong tendency to remain a 1.

We get into trouble only when we consider how the output changes from a 0 to a 1, with this pseudoresistor. For example, if the output is presently a 0, the output has no reason whatsoever to rise to a 1 even when we break the connection between the output and GND by feeding the inverter with a 1. We find ourselves in a dilemma, much like the dilemma in automobiles where we know that the car will run and continue running if only we can get it started. We must get the output above 0 initially so that the gate of the pull-up transistor begins to make some form of connection with VDD. Once the gate opens up a little, charge will flow through the pull-up transistor to the output and to the pull-up transistor's gate, thus opening the gate even more. This chain reaction, which we must start somehow, will pull the output up to a 1.

We get the flow started from VDD to the output by doctoring the pull-up transistor. By placing a yellow box over the transistor, we in effect place a permanent doorstop at the gate. This doorstop keeps the gate from closing all the way regardless of the voltage at the gate. In this way, the pull-up reaction is always primed to proceed.

Figure 1.10B shows a pull-up transistor (resistor) dissected into its two parts, the yellowish transistor itself and the electrical connection between the gate and the source. Figure 1.10C shows a compact layout for a complete pull-up. It appears odd perhaps that the pull-up transistor is so long and thin, certainly when compared with the transistors we have considered thus far. The length of a transistor affects the resistance of that transistor, as shown in Figure 1.11. As we have seen, we want to have careful control over resistances so that we can maintain legal resistance ratios in order to produce unambiguous voltages.

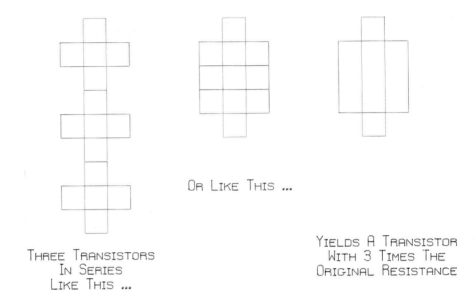

THREE TRANSISTORS
IN SERIES
LIKE THIS ...

OR LIKE THIS ...

YIELDS A TRANSISTOR
WITH 3 TIMES THE
ORIGINAL RESISTANCE

THE LENGTH OF A TRANSISTOR
AFFECTS THE TRANSISTOR'S RESISTANCE

FIGURE 1.11

Following is the text that defines the pull-up layout. We present it as a function that takes in two parameters and produces a layout. There are two reasons for this parameterized form of layout. First, it is easier to describe the geometric points in terms of the two Y-values, BOTTOM and TOP (Figure 1.12) because all interesting points lie close to these two Y-values. Second, the parameterized layout represents not just one layout, but a whole class of layouts which implement pull-ups of arbitrary resistances.

```
DEFINE    PULL_UP(TOP,BOTTOM:REAL)=   LAYOUT:
    {    GCB  \AT  0#TOP  ;
         -1.#TOP-2  \GB  1#BOTTOM+3;
         -2.5#BOTTOM+.5  \YB  2.5#TOP-1.5;
         -3.#BOTTOM+2  \RB  3#TOP-3;
         RCG  \ROT  -90  \AT  0#BOTTOM+2    }          ENDDEFN
```

Figure 1.12 shows PULL_UP(0,−13) and PULL_UP(0,−13−8). Figure 1.12A has a resistance four times that of our minimum-size transistor, and the pull-up in part B has a resistance eight times that size.

It is possible, of course, to call PULL_UP passing values which will yield an illegal pull-up. For example, PULL_UP might be called erroneously with the parameter BOTTOM actually greater than the parameter TOP. In fact, not only must BOTTOM be less than TOP for a legal pull-up, but BOTTOM also must be at least 7 units below TOP so that the red box is at least 2 units tall. Remember that the design rules require any red shape to be at least 2 units wide. Even though a debugged silicon compiler that calls PULL_UP will never give illegal values to PULL_UP, it would be nice to be sure, nonetheless, that all PULL_UPs are legal. That is, if there are bugs in the silicon compiler, we want to know about that as soon as possible. By placing checks in the PULL_UP function, we can be sure that all pull-ups are legal if the PULL_UP function

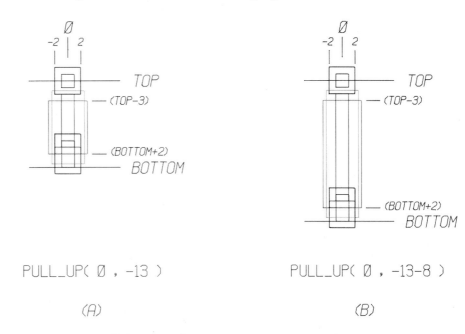

FIGURE 1.12 Examples of pull-up transistors.

never complains about illegal parameters. We impose parameter checking in PULL_UP by redefining PULL_UP as follows:

DEFINE   PULL_UP(TOP,BOTTOM:REAL)=   LAYOUT:
            DO   IF TOP <   BOTTOM+7   THEN   HELP;   FI
            GIVE   the pull-up text shown earlier
ENDDEFN

We have augmented our language at this point. Where we previously introduced the PULL_UP function with this general format:

    DEFINE   PULL_UP(TOP,BOTTOM:REAL)=   LAYOUT:
                value
    ENDDEFN

we now insert the checking action by writing instead:

    DEFINE   PULL_UP(TOP,BOTTOM:REAL)=   LAYOUT:
                DO   action
                GIVE   value
    ENDDEFN

In fact, we can and will take the liberty to use the

    DO   action   GIVE   value

clause in place of any value.
    In addition, we can use the IF form

    IF   value   THEN   action   ELSE   action   FI

to represent an action.

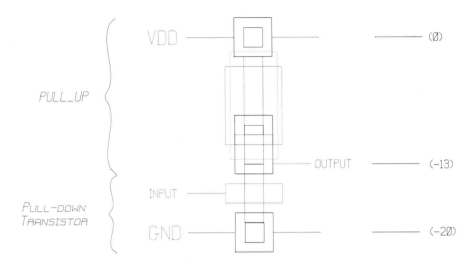

FIGURE 1.13

Now we can define a standard inverter (Figure 1.13) by

```
VAR        INVERTER  =  LAYOUT  ;
INVERTER:=  {     PULL_UP(0,−13);
                  −1#-13  \GB  1#-19;
                  −3#-15  \RB  3#-17;
                  GCB  \AT  0#-20     };
```

The call to PULL_UP in this case yields no error message because the parameters 0 and −13 do not violate the condition expressed in the PULL_UP function.

1.3.4   A Variation on the Inverter: The NAND Gate

We can very simply augment the inverter now to perform some multiple input logical functions. Consider Figure 1.14A. It looks like an inverter but it contains two inputs instead of one input. Its function is understood easily by considering under what conditions a pull-down action occurs. With the inverter, the pull-down occurs when the input is 1. With the two-input inverter, the pull-down occurs only when both inputs are 1. If either input (or both inputs) are zero, the connection between the output and GND is broken. Thus the two-input inverter pulls down on the logical AND of the two inputs. We call the two-input inverter a NAND (Not AND) gate because the output of the inverter is always the inverse of the pull-down condition. (A pull-down condition of TRUE yields a 0 output, and vice versa.)

However, by placing two pull-down transistors in series as we have in the NAND gate, the effective pull-down resistance doubles (Figure 1.11). This means that we must double the pull-up resistance in order to maintain the 4-to-1 resistor ratio (Figure 1.14b). We can maintain the 4-to-1 ratio another way. Figure 1.14C shows a NAND gate where each of the pull-down resistances is cut in half. Each resistance is cut in half effectively by doubling the width of the green, thus giving room for twice as much flow across the red gate. Figure 1.14D shows a legal five-input NAND gate. Each pull-down transistor is five times as wide as it is tall.

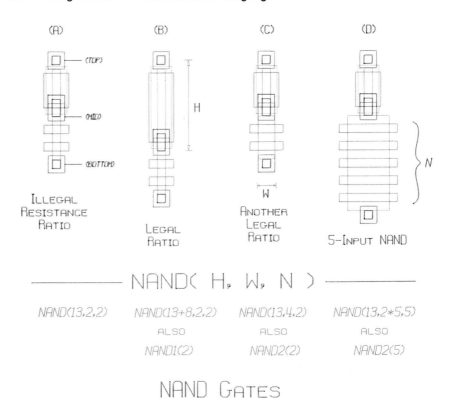

FIGURE 1.14   NAND gates.

We specify a very flexible n-input NAND gate textually as follows. First, we will make use of local variables, that is, variables which are to exist privately within the NAND text and which interfere with no other variables. We declare local variables the same way that we have been declaring variables all along, with the VAR statement. However, to make these variables local, we enclose the VAR declarations together with the local text within a BEGIN...END construct; that is, a value which uses local variables may be expressed by

```
BEGIN     declarations
          value
END
```

The NAND function is defined by

```
DEFINE    NAND(H,W:REAL      N:INT)  =   LAYOUT  :
    BEGIN             VAR     TOP,MID,BOTTOM,Y=REAL;      AN_INPUT=LAYOUT;
         DO           TOP:=   0;
                      MID:=   TOP   −  H;
                      BOTTOM:=  MID  −  3  −  N*4;
                      AN_INPUT:=    −W/2  −2  #  −1      \RB      W/2  +  2  #  1;
         GIVE         PULL_UP(TOP,MID)       \UNION
                      {  −W/2#MID      \GB      W/2#BOTTOM   ;
                         GCB  \AT  0#BOTTOM           }      \UNION
                      {COLLECT     AN_INPUT  \AT  0#Y
                            FOR  Y  FROM  MID−3  BY  −4;  &&  REPEAT  N;}
         END          ENDDEFN
```

The value of NAND is expressed with our "DO action GIVE value" format. The action in this case defines three pivotal reference positions, TOP, MID, and BOTTOM, and also a layout called AN_INPUT. TOP is set to zero, MID is set to be H units below TOP, and BOTTOM is set to be not only the mandatory 3 units below MID, but also an additional 4 units for each input. The action section concludes by defining the layout called AN_INPUT, which is a red box extending to the left and right by not only W/2 (enough to span the vertical green box leading to GND), but by an additional 2 units to satisfy the design rule, which requires red to extend beyond green by 2 units.

The NAND function's value itself is represented by a \UNION of three parts. The first part is the PULL_UP itself, tailor-made to the positions TOP and MID. The second part of the union contains both the green box, which connects the bottom of the pull-up to GND, and the blue-to-green contact at the bottom, which will be used to tap into a GND coming in on blue. The third part of the union is a computed list of red boxes, one for each input. Each red box is described by the text following the word COLLECT the text

        AN_INPUT   \AT   0#Y

The "\AT 0#Y" moves the box so that it resides at the value in Y. We get the N distinct input red boxes by varying Y for each element in the list of red boxes. We vary Y and determine the number of red boxes by the quantifier which follows the word COLLECT and the red box value, the

        FOR   Y   FROM   MID-3   BY   -4;   &&   REPEAT   N;

The first part of this quantifier says that Y starts at MID-3 and then for each subsequent iteration, drops down by 4 units. This first part is itself a valid quantifier, but it never terminates. [We could make it terminate by writing

        FOR   Y   FROM   MID−3   BY   −4   TO   some value;

but we would have to figure out that "some value," that is, the final value that we wish Y to represent. That value in this case is MID−3 − 4*(N−1). But rather than twisting our minds and increasing the probability of an error on our part, we will resort to the original composition of two quantifiers.] The second part of our original complex quantifier is

        REPEAT   N;

and this quantifier simply specifies a number of iterations; in our case, we want exactly one iteration per input. We form our complete desired quantifier by forcing both the FOR and the REPEAT quantifiers to iterate in unison. The operator && has been used precisely to do this. Our complex quantifier formed with the && terminates as soon as either quantifier terminates. Since the first quantifier, the FOR, never terminates, the termination will always be dictated by the REPEAT quantifier.

Now that we have the very flexible NAND function, we are again faced with the possibility that NAND can be called with parameters that will produce illegal NAND gates. We should place checks within the function NAND just as we have done within the function PULL_UP. That will be left to the reader.

We can also define a new NAND function which takes in only the parameter N, the number of inputs, and which computes correctly the two other parameters H and W. Here are two possible renditions for such a convenient NAND function:

DEFINE   NAND1(N:INT) = LAYOUT: NAND(13+8*(N−1), 2, N)   ENDDEFN
DEFINE   NAND2(N:INT) = LAYOUT: NAND(13, 2*N, N)   ENDDEFN

Figure 1.14B shows NAND1(2) and Figure 1.14C shows NAND2(2). Both forms are legal. NAND1 maintains the required 4-to-1 ratio by lengthening the pull-up 8 units per additional input. That is, where each additional input increases the pull-down resistance by 2 units in length, NAND1 compensates by increasing the pull-up resistance by 8 units in length. NAND2, on the other hand, leaves the pull-up resistance constant and instead maintains a constant pull-down resistance by reducing the resistance of each input transistor by a factor equal to the number of inputs. That is, NAND2 cuts each pull-down transistor's resistance by widening the green portion by 2 units per input. Notice that NAND1(1) and NAND2(1) produce identical layouts (see how they call NAND), and in fact this layout is precisely our standard inverter. We will compare these two versions of NAND gates after we consider the NOR function.

1.3.5 Another Variation on the Inverter: The NOR Gate

The NAND gate is formed by placing the pull-down transistors in series. The NOR gate, in contrast, is formed by placing the pull-down transistors in parallel. Figure 1.15A shows a two-input NOR gate. This represents the NOR function (Not OR) because the pull-down condition is the OR of the inputs. That is, if either input (or both) is a 1, the connection between the output and GND is made.

Unlike the NAND gate, the NOR gate imposes no new restrictions on resistances. The total pull-down resistance is certainly no more than the resistance of a single pull-down transistor, because the resistances appear in parallel. In fact, we might wonder why we could not now halve the pull-up resistor and save area in the pull-up. That would work nicely only if both pull-down transistors are turned on. However, we still want the pull-down to work even if only one of the pull-down transistors is turned on. In the worst case, we can imagine that only one of the inputs to the NOR gate is 1, and hence we must leave the pull-up resistance as is.

We can generate an n-input NOR gate by starting simply with an inverter and then by appending one pull-down transistor in parallel for each additional input. The NOR layout is generated by the function

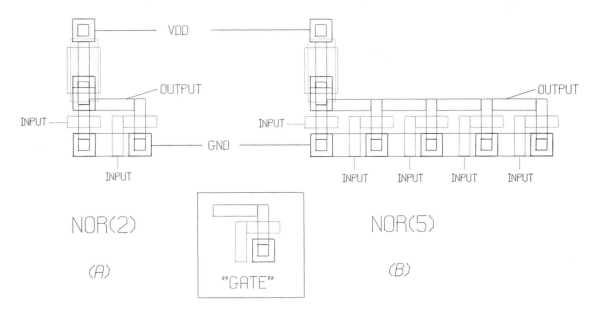

FIGURE 1.15 NOR gates (*see also color plate*).

```
DEFINE      NOR(N:INT)=   LAYOUT:
            BEGIN     VAR  GATE=LAYOUT;       TOP,MID,BOTTOM,X=REAL;
            DO        TOP:=   0;
                      MID:=   TOP−13;
                      BOTTOM:=   MID−7;
                      GATE:=  {          1#MID−1   \GB   9#MID+1;
                                         9#MID+1   \GB   11#BOTTOM+1;
                                         GCB  \AT   10#BOTTOM;
                                         5#BOTTOM−2   \RB   7#MID−2;
                                         7#MID−2   \RB   13#MID−4     }  ;
            GIVE      INVERTER   \UNION
                      {COLLECT   GATE  \AT  X#0
                                       FOR  X  FROM  0  BY  10;  && REPEAT  N−1;}
                      \UNION   (−2#BOTTOM−2  \BB  2+10*(N−1)#BOTTOM+2)
            END       ENDDEFN
```

The action part of the NOR function defines the local variables TOP, MID, and BOT-TOM very much as we did in the NAND function. However, this time these variables are constant. Their definition serves as a convenience for the subsequent specification. With the NOR gate, the number of inputs manifests itself only by enlarging the layout horizontally. The action part of the NOR function defines a new local variable of type LAY-OUT called GATE. GATE represents precisely the appendage required for one additional NOR input.

The value portion of the NOR function forms the union of our standard INVERT-ER and a list of GATE appendages, and then one more item. The list of GATE append-ages,

```
{COLLECT    GATE  \AT  X#0    FOR  X  FROM  0  BY  10;  && REPEAT  N−1;}
```

represents an array of the GATE layout where each gate is displaced by X. X starts at 0 and increments by 10. This list contains n − 1 GATEs, where n is the number of inputs. The value portion of the NOR function includes one other item in the union, a single blue box that ties the GND terminals on all the GATEs.

1.3.6   The NAND Gate versus the NOR Gate

As we proceed to implement complex logic arbitrarily in terms of NAND and/or NOR gates, we have a great deal of flexibility in our choice of gates. We have already seen how to implement arbitrary logic by using NOR gates exclusively. A similar analysis shows that we could alternatively use NAND gates exclusively. In fact, if we use NAND gates, we have provided two different classes of NAND gates, the tall kind produced by NAND1 and the short, fat kind produced by NAND2. The following table compares the two NANDs and the NOR in terms of area, pull-up resistance, capacitance, and slowness. The variable n represents the number of inputs.

	Area	*Pull-up Resistance* (R)	*Capacitance* (C)	*Slowness* (R*C)
NAND1	n	n	n	n*n
NAND2	n*n	1	n*n	n*n
NOR	n	1	n	n

Considering area, NAND1 grows taller by n, NAND2 grows both taller and wider by n, and NOR grows wider by n. In terms of pull-up resistance, only NAND1 grows by n. Capacitance is proportional to the area of all green-red intersections. Both NAND1 and

NOR increase pull-down transistor area by n, and hence contribute capacitance linear in n. NAND2, on the other hand, increases transistor area by n in both dimensions, thus contributing n∗n capacitance.

The slowness of each of these devices is determined by multiplying its pull-up resistance by its capacitance. Figure 1.9 shows why the voltage on the output node increases at a rate that is inversely proportional to each of the pull-up resistance and the capacitance. That is, if we double the pull-up resistance, charge flows twice as slowly, and if we independently double the capacitance, the output node requires twice as much charge to produce the same voltage. Thus, the slowness of the pull-up process is R∗C, where R is the pull-up resistance and C is the capacitance associated with the output node.

Why do we consider only the pull-up time in determining the speed at which a device can change state? What about the pull-down time? That is, it takes time to pull the output node down from a 1 to a 0. We can ignore pull-down time in our analysis because with all these devices the pull-down process always proceeds about four times faster than does the pull-up process. This factor of 4 is derived simply from our choice of resistor ratios. That is, we analyze the pull-down time in the same way that we analyze the pull-up time. The pull-down process drains charge from the output node by sucking it from the output node, through the pull-down transistors, down to GND. Since the pull-up and pull-down processes either give or take charge from the same capacitance of the output node, the two processes differ in speed due only to their differences in resistances. The pull-down process works four times as quickly as the pull-up process simply because the pull-down resistance is four times smaller than the pull-up resistance.

Our comparison chart clearly exposes the NOR gate as champion in speed. The NOR gate is also unsurpassed in area efficiency in general. For very small n though, NAND2 appears to win the area contest. However, there is a tendency to use large n if possible because the percentage of area dedicated to the pull-up resistor in the NOR gate decreases as n increases. A larger n provides effectively a device with a slightly higher density of input gates. With NOR as champion, we now consider an even more efficient layout for the NOR gate.

1.3.7 From the Champion NOR Gate to the Programmable Logic Array

Let us consider another layout for a NOR device. Figure 1.16 shows a four-input NOR gate laid out quite differently from what we have seen thus far. Even though the layout appears predominantly vertical like our old NAND gate and not horizontal like our old NOR gate, this is nonetheless a NOR gate. We have cleverly slipped in a 90-degree rotation for the pull-down section. The output node now runs vertically and not horizontally, and GND now runs horizontally and not vertically, at least near the input gates. Also, GND and output have switched colors. GND runs horizontally in green and the output node runs vertically in blue. (If the vertical output were to run in green, it would cross all the red inputs in series and actually form a NAND gate.) The bottom of the layout is no longer GND, but rather the output node itself.

This new layout also has a pairwise nature to it. Between the red inputs, we see in green an alternating sequence of output and GND. The GND is in green, and the output pops up from blue into green, all ready to kiss the green GND. Each GND and output are connected by a small piece of green which crosses one red input. This gives each red input the ability to make or break a connection between the output and GND, independently.

What advantages has this new layout over the old layout? First, the inputs are closer together, having an average separation of only seven as opposed to our old input separation of ten. Second, each input may be fed from the left- or the right-hand side. In

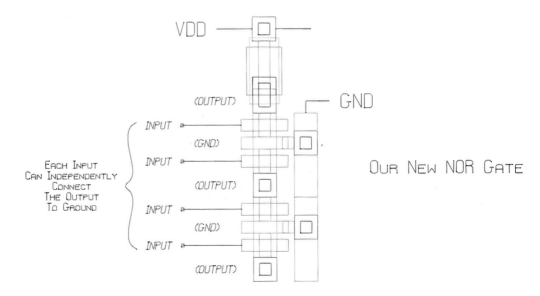

FIGURE 1.16   Another NOR gate (*see also color plate*).

fact, an input can enter the NOR gate and pass right through it (with perhaps a tiny jog to dodge the green-to-blue contact on the right) and go on to another destination. The inputs of our old NOR gate cannot escape upon entry; they are surrounded by green.

We form this new NOR gate out of three pieces, as shown in Figure 1.17, specified as follows:

```
VAR       PULL_UP,  GND_UNIT,  PULL_DOWN_UNIT  =  LAYOUT;

PULL_UP:=   PULL_UP(0,−13);          "a minimum size pull-up"
GND_UNIT:=  {    −2#0  \BB   2#−14;
                 GCB  \AT   0#−5;
                 −(4#6)  \GB  −(2#4)     };
DEFINE    PULL_DOWN_UNIT(LEFT,RIGHT:REAL)   =   LAYOUT:
    {    −2#0  \BB   2#−10;
         GCB  \AT   0#−12;
         LEFT#−3  \RB   RIGHT#−1;
         LEFT#−6  \GB   RIGHT#−4;
         LEFT#−9  \RB   RIGHT#−7     }          ENDDEFN
PULL_DOWN_UNIT:=   PULL_DOWN_UNIT(−4,4);
```

This program text not only sets the three new layout variables to their respective layouts, but it also defines a function called PULL_DOWN_UNIT in terms of which we define the layout variable by the same name. (There is no ambiguity in using the same name for both a variable and a function.) It might seem verbose to define a function that will be used only once, but in fact that function was used more than once, precisely to determine by trial and error appropriate values for the parameters LEFT and RIGHT. If you will notice, the parameterless PULL_DOWN_UNIT layout variable has LEFT and RIGHT extending beyond the minimum distances dictated by design rules alone. These values were chosen to fit well for our subsequent and more general incorporation of NOR gates.

Also note that we have not yet provided the small green links in the PULL_DOWN_UNIT between the horizontal GND wire and the two extreme ends of the blue vertical output wire. We will later introduce these green links, which will complete the pull-down transistors.

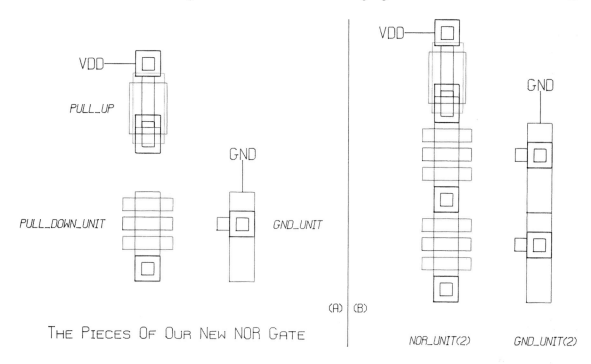

THE PIECES OF OUR NEW NOR GATE

FIGURE 1.17

Figure 1.17B shows the results of the two following functions. Rather than finishing the NOR gate as a whole right now, we leave it dissected into two primary and independently useful pieces:

```
DEFINE    NOR_UNIT(N:INT)  =  LAYOUT:
      BEGIN        VAR  Y=REAL;
           PULL_UP  \AT  0#14     \UNION
           {COLLECT  PULL_DOWN_UNIT  \AT  0#Y
                    FOR  Y  FROM  0  BY  −14;  &&  REPEAT  N;}
      END          ENDDEFN

DEFINE    GND_UNIT(N:INT)  =  LAYOUT:
      BEGIN        VAR  Y=REAL;
           {COLLECT  GND_UNIT  \AT  0#Y
                    FOR  Y  FROM  0  BY  −14;  &&  REPEAT  N;}
      END          ENDDEFN
```

Figure 1.18 shows three entire NOR gates sharing the same GND supply:

```
{  NOR_UNIT(2);    NOR_UNIT(2)  \AT  8#0;    NOR_UNIT(2)  \AT  16#0;
   GND_UNIT(2)  \AT  16+7#0  }
```

Each of the three NOR gates is still missing the green links that cross each red input to form the pull-down transistors. We are almost ready to put them in. Note also that the three NOR gates share exactly the same red inputs. If we were to put in all the green links to complete all the pull-down transistors, each of the three NOR gates would function identically. To get three NOR gates performing different functions from one another, we will place the green links to form pull-down transistors not everywhere, but at a subset of all the possible places. In other words, each vertical NOR gate will compute the NOR of a different subset of inputs.

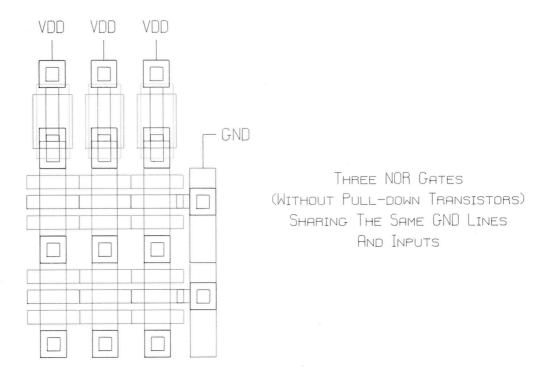

FIGURE 1.18

1.4 EFFICIENCY IN LAYOUTS FORMED LIKE CRYSTALS

What if we do leave out some of the pull-down transistors as suggested above? A NOR gate with four red wires passing through but which nonetheless uses only two or three of the red wires as active inputs is clearly wasting area. Why not shorten that NOR gate to a height of two or three instead of the oversized four?

Consider Figure 1.19. Figure 1.19A shows a three-input-NOR gate layout with green links placed not everywhere but only at such positions so that the three NOR gates labeled A, B, and C perform the logical NOR functions shown textually in the figure. Figure 1.19B shows a symbolic abstraction of the same. Figure 1.19C shows symbolically an attempt to shrink each NOR gate so that each NOR gate by itself is as small as possible. Figure 1.19D shows the layout required to implement that shrinking.

What do we see? Our optimization of each NOR gate, performed in isolation, yields not an improvement in the overall layout, but a degradation in overall area efficiency. We now encounter perhaps the most pervasive and least intuitive property of two-dimensional layout.

Many people make an implicit assumption that reflects perhaps a software background. That is, given a large program to implement, we break it up into smaller pieces or subroutines (like our individual NOR gates) and then go about implementing each subroutine in isolation. Our conception of the large program now consists of the small pieces and also an overall structure in which these pieces fit. Given the fixed structure, we go and implement each small piece in isolation. We always try to optimize each small piece because we know that an improvement in any piece yields an improvement in the overall large program. With a fixed overall structure, we can optimize each piece arbitrarily in isolation and always achieve an overall improvement.

This "optimization in isolation" generally does not apply in two-dimensional layouts. Although each NOR gate has been optimized in isolation, Figure 1.19D shows that we have suffered an overall degradation.

Why do the optimizations of software and layout differ so dramatically? The

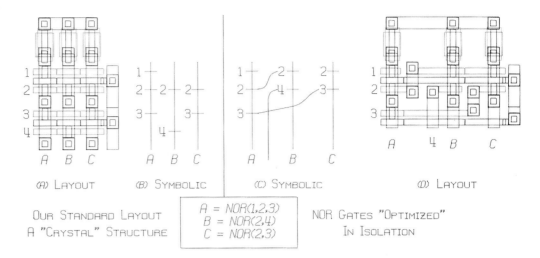

FIGURE 1.19 Local optimization doesn't always win.

difference centers around the requirement to move information. In software, information and control is transferred by a MOVE or a GOTO instruction. In each case, the memory (area) required for the instruction is very small and constant. Both the memory and execution time are independent of the distance between the source and destination locations.

In the world of two-dimensional layout, however, the area required to implement the movement of data is not a small constant; rather, it depends at least linearly on the distance between the source and destination locations. The wire on which information travels takes space for both its internal area and the separation required between itself and all other layout. Look at the area taken by the new vertical wires introduced in Figure 1.19D. Look also at the enlarged separations between the vertical NOR gates. These separations accommodate the new wires and their required separations.

The area taken by the new wires in Figure 1.19D is actually only a small part of the area loss. What really costs is the unused area, or the decrease in layout density. This unused area arises necessarily because the only way we could make use of it would be to contort each NOR gate so that the NOR gates appear to seep into the unused space. However, a contorted NOR gate will consume more area than its original form, and will also have a larger perimeter. The larger perimeter then contributes to the area required by the necessary separations.

It is the crystal structure of our NOR gates in Figure 1.19A that enables them to fit together so tightly. Crystal structures implement very tight packings. Crystal structures by definition impose a high degree of regularity or conformity on their atoms. As we found in figure 1.19, we save area by conforming to a very regular structure. This area saving is so dramatic that even if we waste some of the possible computation provided by the structure (e.g., by leaving out some transistors), we still win over a tailor-made but irregular structure, as shown in Figure 1.19D.

1.4.1 A Case for Wires

In both software and two-dimensional layout, the movement of information consumes a large part of the resources. The resources required for active computation, the interaction of data from distinct sources, are less in comparison. Consider the following FORTRAN statement:

$$A \ = \ B \ + \ C \ * \ D$$

It appears to specify exactly one data transfer, the "=." In fact, it really requires the following data transfers when actually implemented at the level of many microcode languages:

1	Multiplier's INPUT#1	:=	C
2	Multiplier's INPUT#2	:=	D
	MULTIPLY		
3	TEMPORARY	:=	Multiplier's RESULT
4	Adder's INPUT#1	:=	B
5	Adder's INPUT#2	:=	TEMPORARY
	ADD		
6	A	:=	Adder's RESULT

This microcode does not even reflect the additional data transfers required to set the main memory's address register, which initiates the actions to fetch the FORTRAN variables B, C, and D. At least three-fourths of this microcode specifies only data transfers. What a waste? As the old saying goes, you've got to be in the right place at the right time.

As we acknowledge the large role of data movement in all kinds of computation, we still might ask why data movement appears to be of less concern in software. The miracle of random access memory (RAM) reduces dramatically the costs of all data transfers. You can get from here to there almost instantly and independently of distance. (The true miracle of random access memory began to be exploited consistently only recently with the emergence of "list" processing, where, believe it or not, most of the data stored in memory are in fact merely the addresses of other memory locations.)

However, a RAM can handle at most one data transfer at a time. For a RAM to handle several data transfers, we spread the transfers out over time, handling them one at a time. Thus, the cost of multiple transfers with a RAM manifests itself in the dimension of time. In contrast, a layout pays for communication in area, but all the communications can occur simultaneously.

Wires implement communication in layout. Since communication plays so large a role in computation, it is the placement of wires that dominates our consideration in forming layouts. Those wasted slots in our NOR gates where we had originally planned to put transistors are in fact not wasted at all. Those nontransistor slots now perform the noble job of hosting wires. It is interesting to note that even when we optimized each NOR gate in isolation, there is still in Figure 1.19D an unused transistor slot at the intersection of the third input and the output labeled B.

1.4.2　Multiple Crystals

We will see shortly that a single giant crystal structure does not always win big. Sometimes it is most efficient to break a large computation into several separate crystal structures which then communicate over irregular wires. Each structure can often be implemented by a very tight crystal of atoms which are very specific to that part. Forcing upon ourselves a single giant crystal implementation might require that the atoms of this integrated crystal be so general-purpose in nature that each atom might be much larger than the sum of the sizes of the different atoms used in the divided implementation.

1.4.3　The Heart of the Programmable Logic Array: The Programmable NOR Plane

Now that we have a tight layout for multiple NOR gates which share the same inputs (Figure 1.18), let us finish it off by adding in the little green patches which will complete some of the pull-down transistors. Thus far we have the NOR array less the pull-down transistors. Rather than putting in all possible pull-down transistors, which would render all NOR gates equivalent, let us specify which transistors to add with a convenient list of boolean values, TRUEs and FALSEs.

We start by considering the introduction of the pull-down transistors in a single NOR gate. We can specify which transistors to add by a list of boolean values, which we will call the logic of a NOR column. The following text introduces a new datatype which can represent a list of booleans:

TYPE   NOR_COLUMN_LOGIC   =   { BOOLEAN } ;

Examples of NOR_COLUMN_LOGIC include

{TRUE;FALSE;FALSE;TRUE}
{FALSE;FALSE;TRUE;TRUE;TRUE}

The "TYPE" statement given above is somewhat analogous to FORTRAN's DIMEN-SION statement (or Pascal's ARRAY). Both declare objects that consist merely of a repetition of other objects. Our declaration, unlike FORTRAN's, does not specify an upper bound to the length of such a list of boolean values. Our objects of type NOR_COLUMN_LOGIC can have different and arbitrary lengths.

The TYPE declaration is different from our more familiar VAR declaration, which declares new variables of a specific type. This TYPE declaration, in contrast, declares no variables; rather, it defines a brand new datatype. We could now, for example, declare new variables of type NOR_COLUMN_LOGIC by using our VAR declaration:

VAR   X,Y = NOR_COLUMN_LOGIC;

This declaration renders X and Y to be variables of type NOR_COLUMN_LOGIC.

Let us now define a new version of our NOR_UNIT function. This new version will take as its parameter not an INTeger, which represents merely the number of inputs, but instead, a list of booleans that specifies which pull-down transistors to include. We can deduce the total number of inputs just by computing the length of the list.

Before we present the new NOR_UNIT function, it will be helpful to understand a notation for referring to the elements in any list, such as our list of booleans called NOR_COLUMN_LOGIC. We introduce a new and extremely useful kind of quantifier designed especially to walk through lists. The quantifier

FOR   variable $E   list ;

which reads "FOR variable an-element-of list," causes one iteration for each element in the specified list. The quantifier sets the specified variable to represent each element in the list. For example, the quantifier

FOR   X $E   {TRUE;FALSE;FALSE;TRUE};

causes four iterations and sets X to the sequence of values: TRUE,FALSE,FALSE, and TRUE.

Besides introducing this "list" quantifier, let us introduce a new way to use any quantifier. Mathematics has a concise notation for expressing summations using the Greek capital letter sigma. The sigma notation specifies conveniently three things:

1 The fact that we are taking a sum, and not, for example, a product
2 The set of values for a variable to take on
3 An expression which uses that variable

The sigma notation as a whole represents the sum of the value of an expression which is evaluated repeatedly as a variable takes on values over a set of values.

Our language includes a similar notation, which is expressed via the following syntax:

Operator   Expression   Quantifier

The operator specifies how we combine the values of the expression, where the expression is reevaluated for each iteration caused by the quantifier. For example, the notation

+   I   FOR I FROM 1 TO 10;

represents the number 55, that is, the sum of I where I takes on the integer values between 1 and 10. Similarly,

+   I∗I   FOR I FROM 1 TO 5;

represents the sum of I∗I as I runs from 1 to 5, or in this case simply the number 55. The expression

+   1   FOR I FROM 1 TO 15;

represents the sum of 1 as I runs from 1 to 15, or more simply, this expression counts the number of iterations caused by the quantifier. Similarly, if LIST is of type NOR_COLUMN_LOGIC, a list of boolean values, and if B is of type BOOLEAN, then

+   1   FOR B $E   LIST;

represents the length of LIST; that is, it sums up 1s, one 1 per iteration.

We can define our new NOR_UNIT function, which takes in a NOR_COLUMN_LOGIC, by writing:

```
DEFINE     NOR_UNIT(X:NOR_COLUMN_LOGIC)=  LAYOUT:
           BEGIN   VAR   N=INT;  B=BOOLEAN;  LINK=LAYOUT;  Y=REAL;
           DO      N:=     +    1     FOR  B  $E  X;  ;
                   LINK:=   −(1#4)  \GB  1#0;
           GIVE    NOR_UNIT(  (N+1)/2  )              \UNION
                   {COLLECT    LINK    \AT    0#Y
                            FOR  Y  which takes on the appropriate values
                                    so that we place a LINK only at the
                                    desired positions   }
           END     ENDDEFN
```

The action part of this function does two things. It first sets the variable N to the length of the given list of booleans, X. It then defines a little layout, LINK, which is precisely the green patch that will complete a single pull-down transistor. The value portion of this function specifies the union of two things. The first part of the union specifies our old NOR_UNIT constructed with enough pieces to accommodate at least N inputs. We call NOR_UNIT with the parameter (N+1)/2 because the NOR_UNIT provides twice as many inputs as the parameter specifies. (Remember that NOR_UNIT generates pairs of inputs and not individual inputs.) We use (N+1)/2 and not simply N/2 because in case N is odd, we would prefer to have one extra input as opposed to having one too few inputs. The second part of the union forms the collection of green patches, that is, a collection of LINKs placed somehow at the appropriate positions to finish the chosen pull-down transistors.

What values should Y take on in order to place the LINKs at the correct positions? First let us imagine that we want to place the LINKs at all N inputs. We can easily specify half of the placements with the quantifier

FOR   Y   FROM   0   BY   −14;

which will cause a LINK to be placed over the top input of each input pair. (This quantifier by itself will never terminate; that is, it will place an infinite number of LINKs growing downward to infinity, but we will ignore that temporarily.) However, to fill in all the positions, we want to place LINKs not only at the value Y, but also at the value Y-6. If instead of specifying the list of LINKs by using

{COLLECT   LINK   \AT   0#Y   some quantifier}

we were to specify

{COLLECT   LINK   \AT   0#Y+W   some quantifier}

we could then imagine including all the LINKs merely by setting the new variable W to the two values 0 and −6 for each iteration of the "FOR Y..." quantifier. We can make W take on the two values 0 and −6 by writing

FOR   W   FROM   0   BY   −6   TO   −6;

Finally, we can make W take on these two values now for each iteration of Y by writing the grand quantifier

FOR   Y   FROM   0   BY   -14;   !!   FOR   W   FROM   0   BY   −6   TO   −6;

Do you remember how we have already combined two quantifiers using the "&&" notation? The old "&&" notation causes quantifiers to iterate in unison. We have now introduced a new quantifier combination using the symbol "!!." "!!," unlike "&&," causes the two quantifiers to act so that the second quantifier appears to be nested within the first quantifier. We can think of the "!!" operator as forming the Cartesian product of the two given quantifiers. Figure 1.20A shows the Y-quantifier acting alone and part B shows the W-quantifier acting alone. Part C shows our newly nested quantifier acting as a whole, and it looks at the value Y+W caused by each iteration. We can see now that Y+W takes on the values of all positions where we can place a LINK to form a legal pull-down transistor.

Now if we take our quantifier composed so far, and make it step in unison with the quantifier,

FOR   B $E   X;

which sets B to each boolean in X, we get not only the position Y+W for each iteration, but in addition we get the value B for that iteration (Figure 1.20C and D). We already know how to make two quantifiers step in unison, we use the "&&" operator, as in

our position quantifier   &&   FOR   B $E   X;

or more precisely,

(FOR   Y   FROM   0   BY   -14;   !!   FOR   W   FROM   0   TO   −6   BY   −6;)
                                                         &&   FOR   B $E   X;

We now have a very complex quantifier (containing three distinct quantifiers) which gives us for each iteration both a position (Y+W) and a boolean (B) which tells us

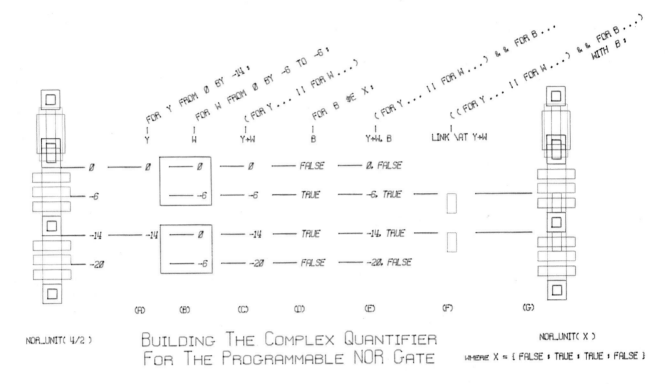

BUILDING THE COMPLEX QUANTIFIER
FOR THE PROGRAMMABLE NOR GATE

FIGURE 1.20

whether or not we want a LINK placed at that position (Figure 1.20E) Does the complex quantifier terminate? Even though the Y-quantifier never terminates, this entire complex quantifier terminates because everything steps in unison to the B-quantifier, and of course the B-quantifier terminates when it reaches the end of the list X.

If we were to use this complex quantifier as is, the value Y+W would still take on all possible transistor positions. Sure the complex quantifier also gives us the variable B, but thus far we have made no use of that variable. What we want to do is simply filter out some of the iterations: namely, those iterations that produce B=FALSE. If we were to ignore all those iterations that have B=FALSE, we would then have only those iterations that set Y+W to the positions where we do want to include the pull-down LINKs.

We can take any quantifier and filter out some of its iterations by writing

the quantifer   WITH   condition   ;

This new notation is itself a quantifier. It acts just like the original quantifier except that it skips those iterations for which the condition yields FALSE. For example, the quantifier

FOR   I   FROM -13 TO   24 ;   WITH   I$*$I $<$ 100   ;

produces iterations for integer I between -13 and 24, where it is true the I$*$I is less than 100.

We filter out from our complex quantifier those iterations that find B=FALSE by writing

our complex quantifier   WITH   B ;

This represents our complex quantifier which will now lose those iterations for which B is FALSE. Figure 1.20F shows the set of LINKs produced with our filtered complex quantifier, that is,

```
(          (FOR  Y  FROM  0  BY  −14;     !!     FOR  W  FROM  0  TO  −6  BY  −6;)
    &&  FOR  B  $E  X;          )
                                                WITH  B  ;
```

We can now specify the new NOR_UNIT function, which takes in a list of booleans by

```
DEFINE    NOR_UNIT(X:NOR_COLUMN_LOGIC)  =  LAYOUT:
    BEGIN    VAR  N=INT;  B=BOOLEAN;  LINK=LAYOUT;  Y,W=REAL;
    DO       N:=  +   1     FOR  B  $E  X;  ;
             LINK:=  −(1#4)  \GB  1#0;
    GIVE     NOR_UNIT(  (N+1)/2  )   \UNION
             {COLLECT    LINK  \AT  0#Y+W
                (   (FOR  Y  FROM  0  BY  −14;  !!  FOR  W  FROM  0  TO  −6  BY  −6;)
                         &&     FOR  B  $E  X;  )          WITH  B;  }
    END      ENDDEFN
```

Figure 1.20G shows the result of NOR_UNIT({FALSE;TRUE;TRUE;FALSE}).

Our new NOR_UNIT function lets us conveniently specify a NOR gate which uses only a specified subset of inputs. Referring to figure 1.21A, we can specify each of the three NOR gates with (from left to right)

1 NOR_UNIT({TRUE;TRUE;TRUE;FALSE})

2 NOR_UNIT({FALSE;TRUE;FALSE;TRUE})

3 NOR_UNIT({FALSE;TRUE;TRUE;FALSE})

We can form the entire layout shown in Figure 1.21C by defining a function that takes in the specification for a set of NOR gates, not just one NOR gate as we have done so far.

How do we specify a set of NOR gates? We have seen that we can specify a single NOR gate very concisely with a single list of booleans, called a NOR_COLUMN_LOGIC, which specifies a subset of inputs. To specify a set of NOR gates,

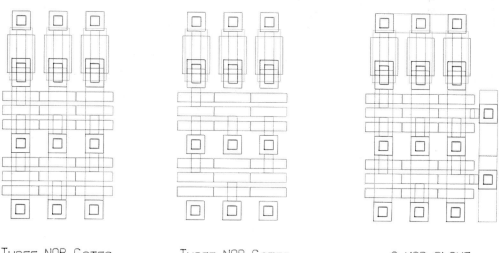

THREE NOR GATES　　　THREE NOR GATES WITH SOME BLUE REMOVED TO SEE THE TRANSISTORS BETTER　　　A NOR_PLANE

(A)　　　　(B)　　　　(C)

FIGURE 1.21

we can convey the information by means of a set of NOR_COLUMN_LOGICs, each of which serves as the input to NOR_UNIT. We introduce this concept of a set of NOR_COLUMN_LOGICs by declaring a new datatype. Let us call this new datatype NOR_PLANE_LOGIC, and define it by

$$\text{TYPE} \quad \text{NOR\_PLANE\_LOGIC} \quad = \quad \{ \quad \text{NOR\_COLUMN\_LOGIC} \quad \} \quad ;$$

A NOR_PLANE_LOGIC is simply a list of NOR_COLUMN_LOGICs, one for each desired NOR gate.

Before we show the function for many NOR gates, let us consider two small computations which we will need to include. Suppose that we have the following variable declarations:

$$\text{VAR} \quad \begin{array}{lll} \text{ALL} & = & \text{NOR\_PLANE\_LOGIC}; \\ \text{ONE} & = & \text{NOR\_COLUMN\_LOGIC}; \\ \text{B} & = & \text{BOOLEAN}; \end{array}$$

That is, ALL represents a whole set of NOR-gate specifications, and ONE represents the specification for just a single NOR gate. How many NOR gates are specified by ALL? We find that out by summing 1 for each element of the list ALL, that is,

$$+ \quad 1 \quad \text{FOR} \quad \text{ONE} \quad \$E \quad \text{ALL};$$

Even though we can imagine that ALL, a NOR_PLANE_LOGIC, is a list of lists, this expression counts up one for each list in the list of lists without even looking at the elements of each ONE list.

We wish also to know how tall each NOR gate is. If ONE is one of the NOR gates represented in ALL, then

$$+ \quad 1 \quad \text{FOR} \quad \text{B} \quad \$E \quad \text{ONE};$$

tells us how many inputs are required for the NOR gate represented by ONE. We will assume that each NOR gate is of equal height, or in other words, that each NOR_COLUMN_LOGIC list in NOR_PLANE_LOGIC has the same length. With this assumption, we can determine the number of inputs represented by each NOR gate simply by counting the number of inputs represented by the first NOR gate. If the variable ONE happens to be set to the first NOR_COLUMN_LOGIC in ALL, the expression given above tells us the number of inputs for the first NOR gate. We can set ONE to the first NOR_COLUMN_LOGIC in ALL by writing

$$\text{ONE} \quad := \quad \text{ALL}[1];$$

The notation "ALL[1]" represents the first element of the list ALL. (This notation is similar to Pascal's array indexing operator.) Where ALL is a NOR_PLANE_LOGIC, a list of NOR_COLUMN_LOGICs, ALL[1] is a single NOR_COLUMN_LOGIC. We can compute the number of input wires belonging to the first NOR gate by replacing the variable ONE with the expression "ALL[1]," as in

$$+ \quad 1 \quad \text{FOR} \quad \text{B} \quad \$E \quad \text{ALL}[1];$$

The function for generating a complete set of NOR gates, which we call NOR_PLANE, is now shown:

```
DEFINE     NOR_PLANE(  ALL:  NOR_PLANE_LOGIC  )  =  LAYOUT:
           BEGIN     VAR  ONE=  NOR_COLUMN_LOGIC;     B=  BOOLEAN;
                     X=  REAL;     WIDTH,HEIGHT=  INT;
           DO        WIDTH:=  +  1  FOR  ONE  $E  ALL;  ;
                     HEIGHT:=  +  1  FOR  B  $E  ALL[1];  ;
           GIVE      {COLLECT       NOR_UNIT(ONE)  \AT  X#0
                           FOR  ONE  $E  ALL;  &&  FOR  X  FROM  0  BY  8;  }
                     \UNION
                     {  GND_UNIT(  (HEIGHT+1)/2  )  \AT  8*(WIDTH−1)+7  #  0  ;
                        −(2#2)  \BB  8*(WIDTH−1)+2  #  2    \AT  0#14    }
           END       ENDDEFN
```

The action portion defines the variables WIDTH and HEIGHT. WIDTH represents the number of NOR gates, and HEIGHT represents the number of input wires in the first NOR gate. The value portion produces the union of two things. The first part represents the entire collection of NOR gates (Figure 1.21A). Each NOR gate is displaced horizontally by X, where X starts at 0 and increments by 8. The quantifier in this first part,

> FOR   ONE $E ALL;   &&   FOR X FROM 0 BY 8;

not only defines the variable X for each iteration, but also defines the variable ONE. Since these two quantifiers step in unison (the "&&"), as X moves to the right by 8, the variable ONE takes on successive NOR_COLUMN_LOGICs in the list ALL. Thus, each iteration defines ONE to be the particular NOR_COLUMN_LOGIC for the corresponding NOR gate. Each NOR gate in the collection is formed tailor-made to implement the logic represented in the variable ONE for each iteration.

The second part of the union includes both the GND_UNIT placed to the far right and also a blue box at the top which connects the tops of the NOR gates together to form a unified VDD region. Figure 1.21C shows a result of our function NOR_PLANE, namely

> NOR_PLANE({   {TRUE;TRUE;TRUE;FALSE}   ;
>   {FALSE;TRUE;FALSE;TRUE}   ;
>   {FALSE;TRUE;TRUE;FALSE}   }   )

Notice how each NOR_COLUMN_LOGIC has the same length, 4.

How can we verify inside the function NOR_PLANE that the input is indeed valid, that is, that the NOR_COLUMN_LOGICs in ALL all have the same length? We might write

> IF   for each NOR_COLUMN_LOGIC in ALL   there is one whose length is not the value HEIGHT,   THEN   HELP

We can express this more formally in our language by writing

> IF   FOR ONE $E ALL;   THERE_IS   length(ONE) not equal to HEIGHT
> THEN   HELP;   FI

or completely formally by

IF FOR ONE $E ALL;   THERE_IS (+ 1 FOR B $E ONE;) <> HEIGHT
THEN   HELP;   FI

We can insert this checking action into the NOR_PLANE function just after the statement that defines the variable HEIGHT. (HELP interrupts program execution so that the user is informed of an exceptional situation.)

EXERCISES

Section 1.3.7

1. Put a check in NAND(H, W, N) to assure legal resistances.

2. Parameterize the NAND function so to accept another REAL parameter, denoting separation between inputs.

2

Representation and Analysis
of Layouts and Other Information

We have seen so far how to create layouts simply by producing a convenient textual specification. In our domain of concern, however, providing for the specification of layout is only half the job. The user went to the trouble to specify a layout in our system only because the user expects our system to provide some sorts of services.

In particular, our services must certainly take into account the particular layout specified by the user. Any services that are blind to the user's specification would not require the specification in the first place. To provide any service dependent on the specification requires that we have a means to examine the layout specified by the user.

2.1 THE THREE R'S OF COMPUTING

All of computing can be understood in terms of reading, writing, and representation. Reading and writing are actions, or verbs. Representation is a noun. The reader reads what the writer wrote by examining the production of the writer, a representation of information in memory.

Let us call writing "synthesis" and reading "analysis" to accentuate the richness of these two fundamental operations. Where writing might imply merely the transference of a mental image of text to a paper-and-ink representation of text, synthesis encompasses the entire formulation of the text.

Similarly, where reading might imply merely the transference of text from a paper-and-ink representation to a mental image of the literal text, analysis encompasses the entire digestion of the text.

These two classes of operation, synthesis and analysis, are conceptually distinct, although during program execution they can interact in the most intimate ways. However, any moment of program execution can be tagged unambiguously as being either analysis or synthesis.

So far in dealing with layouts we have seen only synthesis. We have introduced layout-creation operators such as

Point	\TO	Point	\PAINTED	Layer	→	Layout
Layout	\UNION	Layout			→	Layout
Layout	\AT	Point			→	Layout

These operations create new layouts.

We have as yet no operators that perform analysis. For example, suppose that we create two layouts, L1 and L2, as follows:

```
VAR      L1,  L2  =  LAYOUT;
L1:=     0#0  \TO     1#1    \PAINTED      BLUE;
L2:=     L1   \UNION    (L1     \AT      10#0);
```

Now we wish perhaps to hand L1 over to the plotter so that we can have a picture of L1. The plotter must have access to the fact that L1 is a box painted blue. The plotter (and many other useful programs) needs to peer into a layout and see what it is made of. How does the plotter know that it has something blue to plot? We have no operation like

```
L1      \IS_OF_WHAT_COLOR          →      Blue
```

which can extract the color specified previously with the synthesis operator \PAINTED. Similarly, as yet we have no way at all to distinguish between L1 and L2. We might like to know, for example, that L1 is a single item, whereas L2 is a UNION of two layouts.

2.1.1   The Role of Representation

We need to choose a middle ground, or representation, which sits between layout synthesis and analysis. The middle ground will faithfully represent the relevant information expressed in the synthesis and will serve simultaneously as a convenient medium from which to read and understand the layout.

2.1.2   What Is a Good Representation?

Why do we need a middle ground at all? Why couldn't we simply use the actual text of the specification itself as the middle ground? Consider a program that must perform analysis, such as the plotting program. It could be written to read the text and find, for example, each \UNION operator, and know to plot the layout that appears to the left of the \UNION and then to plot the layout that appears to the right of the \UNION.

However, there are many disadvantages with using the actual text as the memory representation. For example, such a text analyzer would have to know not only what \UNION means and what \TO and \PAINTED means, but would also have to know all about our convenient abbreviations such as \BB (blue box). Not only that, but upon encountering our NAND functions, the text analyzer would have to understand not only our few layout operators, but also the entire programming language. It would have to understand such constructions as

```
{   COLLECT    layout    Quantifier  }
```

and assignment statements (the ''':='''), the DO...GIVE... construction, and the IF-THEN-ELSE construction. Not only would the text analyzer have to recognize them, it would have also to simulate or execute them. Clearly such a text analyzer poses a hard programming task, and what is worse, such a text analyzer will run slowly on the computer because not only will it perform the intended analysis of layout per se, but it will also waste most of its time dealing with irrelevant data such as text characters and linguistic parsing.

A good middle ground, or representation, is a distillation of the relevant information expressed in the specification. A good representation for a layout contains only information relevant to knowing the layout and not information relevant to remembering how the layout was specified. A vast majority of what we can know by looking at the specification itself is irrelevant to the intended layout. Irrelevant information includes such things as:

1 The names of variables (e.g., WIDTH, GATE, NOR_COLUMN_LOGIC, etc.).

2 The fact that we wrote

$$0\#0 \quad \backslash BB \quad 2\#2$$

instead of

$$0\#0 \quad \backslash TO \quad 2\#2 \quad \backslash PAINTED \quad BLUE$$

which happen to represent exactly the same layout

3 The fact that we wrote

$$NAND2(5)$$

instead of

$$NAND(\, 13, 10, 5 \,)$$

4 The fact that the layout came perhaps from a silicon compiler and not, say, from a graphics editor, or whatever.

Most of the information contained in the specification is best omitted from the representation.

2.1.3 The Expression of Synthesis Is Decoupled from Representation

By introducing a distilled representation which resides conceptually between synthesis and analysis, we gain an extremely important flexibility. Because the representation discards irrelevant information delivered in the specification, the representation can in fact be the result of many different kinds of specification. For example, the two very distinct specifications

1 $0\#0 \quad \backslash TO \quad 1\#1 \quad \backslash PAINTED \quad BLUE$
2 $0\#0 \quad \backslash BB \quad 1\#1$

produce entirely identical representations. (From the start we have wanted these two specifications to produce the same thing.)

Distilled representations produced from the different sources can be interchanged arbitrarily because differences between the kinds of specification are entirely absent from the representation. This decoupling of representation from specification frees the language of specification so that we can augment that language arbitrarily.

We must have this flexibility to accommodate the user; we could not have our flexible NAND functions unless we have augmented the layout specification language to include programming facilities. In the meantime, all those programs that read the representation need know only the simple distilled representation, not the varied conveniences and techniques of specification.

2.1.4   A Proposed Representation for Layout

A distilled representation for things of type LAYOUT might read something like the following:

> A LAYOUT is either
> 1   A BOX
> 2   A POLYGON
> 3   Another LAYOUT painted some COLOR
> 4   A union of other LAYOUTs, or
> 5   Another LAYOUT displaced by a POINT

If we were to agree on a representation such as this, we can imagine how our synthesis operators introduced earlier might produce such a representation. Let us declare some variables of type LAYOUT,

> VAR   L1,   L2,   L3,   L4,   L5   =   LAYOUT;

and now specify

> L1   :=   0#0   \TO   1#1;.

L1 will be a LAYOUT in state 1, just a box. If we go on to specify

> L3   :=   L1   \PAINTED   BLUE;

then L3 will be in state 3, where "the other LAYOUT" is L1 and where the "COLOR" is BLUE. Similarly, we can imagine that

> L4   :=   L1   \UNION   L3;
> (or   L4   :=   {   L1   ;   L3   };   )

leaves L4 in state 4, where the "other LAYOUTs" are L1 and L3. Finally,

> L5   :=   L4   \AT   5#0;

leaves L5 in state 5, where the "other LAYOUT" is L4 and the "POINT" is 5#0.

2.1.5   Differences between Layout Specification
and Representation

What are the differences between our synthesis operators and this proposed representation? Consider the layout expression (for a box)

> 0#0   \TO   2*3+A   #   6-B

This LAYOUT happens to reside in state 1.

The representation buys us two things. First, we can determine very quickly from the representation that this layout is a box merely by examining the state of the representation. This ability is virtually absent from the specification; the text of this specification does not even mention the term "box" or "state 1." Continuing with the representation, which we know now resides in state 1, we can examine the (sub)representation for the box referenced in state 1, and thereby have access to the two opposing corners that define the box.

If we assume that the variables A and B contained 0 and 1, respectively, at the time of this specification, then the referenced box has as its opposing corners the points 0#0 and 6#5. The second nice thing about the representation is that the representation has no memory of the fact that the corners were specified as algebraic expressions. Everything in the representation is reduced to simplified constants.

Thus, where our textual specification may express variable quantities, our representation remembers only constants. Layout designers may specify once a large class of layouts by using variables within a function (e.g., the NAND functions presented earlier). However, that one specification gives rise not to one variable representation, but to many constant representations. Each call to the specification produces exactly one representation.

A layout that will appear on silicon is by nature absolutely constant. Thus, the essence of a layout is accurately represented in terms of constants. We have introduced variables only for our convenience in specification. Any program that will examine a layout need consider only constants.

2.1.6   Example of Examining the Representation

Examination of a represented layout is particularly easy. Besides the fact that all data are constant, all the essential forms of layout are represented explicitly. A program that examines a layout first determines in which state the layout resides. We will introduce shortly a simple and convenient notation for doing so. The program has a distinct part corresponding to each of the five possible states.

For example, part of a program that plots a layout might look as follows:

DEFINE   PLOT(L:LAYOUT):

IF L is in state #1 (box)	THEN	plot the single box
IF L is in state #2 (poly)	THEN	plot the single polygon
IF L is in state #4 (union)	THEN	for each layout in the union, go PLOT it

This is not a complete plotting program, but it does illustrate how such a program is divided into pieces, each of which handles independently one of the five possible states.

Parts 1 and 2 look easy. Each has a single concrete object, a box or a polygon, respectively, and each of these can be plotted in its own right without any knowledge of layouts. In contrast, part 4 considers not a box or a polygon, but something just as concrete, a list of LAYOUTs. Part 4 fulfills its job by plotting each layout in the list one at a time. That is, our intended meaning of ''union,'' namely the superposition of layouts, is realized clearly in the plotting program. Part 4 simply plots each layout one at a time by calling PLOT to do it. We know that this will work because PLOT plots any layout, even if it came from a list, and even if the directive to PLOT it came from within the function PLOT itself.

2.2   DATATYPES: THE HEART OF REPRESENTATION

2.2.1   A Clarification of Representation: Datatypes and Instances

Let us introduce a more precise nomenclature about representations. We have already used the term ''representation'' in two very different contexts. We have been developing a single ''representation'' for all possible layouts, so that we may write programs like PLOT, which accept as input any layout whatsoever. On the other hand, we have implied that different layouts are distinguishable only because they have different "representations." A box has, for example, a representation residing in state 1, whereas a polygon has a different representation, a representation residing in state 2.

Let us use the term "datatype" LAYOUT to denote the class of all possible layouts. In contrast, we will use the term "instance of a datatype," or simply "instance," to denote data particular to a given layout.

The datatype (or simply "type") LAYOUT encompasses all that can be known about all layouts in general. Knowledge about this datatype makes no assumptions about any particular layout. In our efforts to create programs that examine layouts, we will be concerned only with the datatype LAYOUT and not with a particular instance of the type layout because we wish our programs to work with all possible layouts.

Where an instance of LAYOUT is the computer's way of knowing a particular layout, the datatype LAYOUT is our way of knowing about all layouts.

2.2.2   Five Major Classes of Datatypes

Most if not all useful datatypes in the computer are formed conceptually by any one of five means. First, some datatypes are so common to all applications that a programming language will introduce these types as givens. Beyond these given types, some languages allow the programmer to define new types which are particularly useful to the particular application. For example, we will define the type LAYOUT because it is relevant to our application, whereas another program, such as a text editor, has no use for such a type. Programming languages support the definition of new types by providing ways to construct new types from old ones.

There are basically four ways to form a new datatype in terms of other datatypes:

0   (The type is built into the programming language.)

1   The new type is a repetition, or set, of another type.

2   The new type is a conglomeration of unrelated types.

3   The new type is any one of a set of unrelated types.

4   The new type is a process, which takes in parameters of certain types, and which yields an output of a certain type.

5   The new type is a "disk resident" version of another type.

At first the differences among these three kinds of construction might seem hazy. In fact, these distinctions are necessary because of the very nature of computing. This will become clearer as we examine each construction below.

No matter what the datatype is, we must know exactly two things about it:

1   How to create new instances of the datatype

2   How to examine an existing instance

Be sure to look for the answers to these questions for each datatype we introduce. These are the only two questions that need be asked about a datatype.

The fact that these are the only two questions relevant to representation characterizes very strictly the very fine role that is played by representation. Representation is a language's way of referring to the computer's memory. Memories provide exactly two services, reading and writing. The first statement above corresponds to writing and the second statement corresponds to reading.

2.2.2.1 Basic types. Our language comes with the following types built in.

 1 INTeger   to represent whole numbers
 2 REAL   to represent fractional numbers
 3 BOOLean   to represent conditions (i.e., TRUE and FALSE)
 4 TEXT   to represent text
 5 POINT   to represent two-dimensional points.

How do we create instances of each type? The first two types are created and examined as they are in FORTRAN or in almost any other language. Instances of the third type, BOOL, are created by any of

TRUE		$\rightarrow$	BOOL
FALSE		$\rightarrow$	BOOL
BOOL & BOOL		$\rightarrow$	BOOL (i.e., logical AND)
BOOL ! BOOL		$\rightarrow$	BOOL (i.e., logical OR)
- BOOL		$\rightarrow$	BOOL (i.e., logical NOT)

Instances of BOOL are examined in constructions that we have already seen, including

　　IF　bool　THEN　something　ELSE　something　FI

Instances of the fourth type, TEXT, are created by enclosing a piece of text between single quotes, that is,

　　' anything '　　$\rightarrow$　TEXT　(e.g., 'Bonjours mes amis!')

TEXT may be examined with the compare operators

　　TEXT = TEXT　$\rightarrow$　BOOL　(i.e., the texts are identical)
　　TEXT <> TEXT　$\rightarrow$　BOOL　(i.e., not equal)

TEXT has also a built-in function WRITE so that

　　WRITE(text);

types the text on the terminal.
　　We have seen already how to create a POINT, that is,

　　REAL # REAL　　$\rightarrow$　POINT

We examine a point by

　　POINT . x　$\rightarrow$　REAL　(x-coordinate)
　　POINT . y　$\rightarrow$　REAL　(y-coordinate)

For example,

　　(3#4) . x　is　3
　　(3#4) . y　is　4

We have operators that combine points to form new points. These operators are basically copies of those defined on REALs, and each such operator proceeds coordinate-wise. For example, "+" is defined between two POINTs and it produces a new point whose x-coordinate is the sum of the x-coordinates of the two given points, and similarly for the y-coordinates. The point operators are

POINT + POINT	$\rightarrow$	POINT	[e.g.,	(3#4) + (1#2)	is 4#6]
POINT − POINT	$\rightarrow$	POINT	[e.g.,	(3#4) − (1#2)	is 2#2]
− POINT	$\rightarrow$	POINT	[e.g.,	− (3#4)	is −3#−4]
POINT * REAL	$\rightarrow$	POINT	[e.g.,	(3#4)*2	is 6#8]
REAL * POINT	$\rightarrow$	POINT	[e.g.,	2*(3#4)	is 6#8]

We have also the following slightly less obvious operators.

POINT \MAX POINT	$\rightarrow$	POINT	[e.g.,	(3#4) \MAX (6#2) is 6#4]
POINT \MIN POINT	$\rightarrow$	POINT	[e.g.,	(3#4) \MIN (6#2) is 3#2]
POINT = POINT	$\rightarrow$	BOOL	(i.e.,	the points are equal)
POINT <> POINT	$\rightarrow$	BOOL	(i.e.,	the points are not equal)
POINT < POINT	$\rightarrow$	BOOL	(i.e.,	the first point lies to the left and below the second point)
POINT > POINT	$\rightarrow$	BOOL	(i.e.,	the first point lies to the right and above the second point)
POINT >= POINT	$\rightarrow$	BOOL	(i.e.,	> or =)
POINT =< POINT	$\rightarrow$	BOOL	(i.e.,	> or =)

The last six operators allow us to compare pairs of points. The "<" ordering is a partial ordering. It is possible that two points are entirely unrelated; that is, it can be true that

P1 = P2	is	FALSE	and
P1 < P2	is	FALSE	and
P1 > P2	is	FALSE	

Each compare operator yields TRUE only if the condition is true for both coordinates. For example,

1#6 < 3#7	is	TRUE	because	$1 < 3$ and $6 < 7$ simultaneously,

but

1#7 < 3#6	is	FALSE	because	$7 < 6$ is false
1#7 > 3#6	is	FALSE	because	$1 > 3$ is false
1#7 = 3#6	is	FALSE		

The \MIN and \MAX operators on POINTs are consistent with this interpretation of "<." Because "<" is a partial ordering, it is possible that

A \MIN B   is neither A itself nor B itself

The \MIN of two points is derived by taking the MIN coordinate-wise. It is always true that

A \MIN B	=<	A	and B
A \MAX B	>=	A	and B

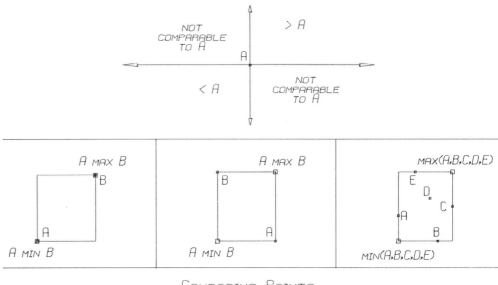

FIGURE 2.1 A point algebra.

Figure 2.1 shows A \MIN B and A \MAX B for various pairs of points. In fact, the smallest box that contains two points A and B is defined by

A \MIN B is the lower-left corner

A \MAX B is the upper-right corner

2.2.2.2 Declaring new datatypes. Now that we have a small set of given types, how do we go about creating new types that will be especially useful for our applications? Our language includes a means for creating new datatypes; we use the "TYPE" statement, which has the following format:

TYPE name-of-new-datatype = a-type-expression ;

The "name-of-new-datatype" is any name we choose for our new datatype. The "a-type-expression" is the particular definition for our new type. This type-expression can take on several forms, as we will soon see. Let us start with the simplest example.

We need a datatype COLOR so that we can subsequently represent such things as RED, BLUE, and GREEN. The type declaration

TYPE COLOR = TEXT ;

declares a type whose name is COLOR and which is represented by a TEXT. This declaration renders the two names COLOR and TEXT absolutely interchangeable in the domain of datatypes. We are saying that any COLOR will be represented by a piece of text.

2.2.2.3 More about COLOR. Let us declare five variables of type COLOR:

VAR RED, GREEN, BLUE, YELLOW, BLACK = COLOR ;

and assign values to these variables:

```
RED:=       'RED'        ;
GREEN:=     'GREEN'      ;
BLUE:=      'BLUE'       ;
YELLOW:=    'YELLOW'     ;
BLACK:=     'BLACK'      ;
```

These assignments are legal because each variable is of type COLOR, which is the same as TEXT, and the right-hand side of each assignment is a new instance of TEXT.

Now we can use simply the names RED, GREEN, BLUE, YELLOW, and BLACK to denote colors and we do not have to write the quotes. Also, if we forget altogether that COLOR is TEXT, then from now on we can believe that there are only these five colors.

A misspelling (e.g., REB) will not pass as a color, whereas if we were accustomed to specifying colors with text, the color 'REB' would not be caught as an error in specification. (Of course, if we do honestly want a color by the name of REB, we could go out of our natural way and specify 'REB', with the quotes.)

2.2.3   Datatype Construction 1: Strings, Arrays, or Lists

Beyond our basic datatypes, we can construct new datatypes of all sorts. Let us now consider one of four possible type constructors, which we will call "string of."

A string represents an arbitrary repetition of another type. The declaration

```
TYPE    POLYGON  =  {  POINT  }  ;
```

declares a brand new datatype whose name is POLYGON and which is represented by an arbitrary repetition of POINTs. We have chosen to represent a polygon simply by a list of its vertices.

We have already seen two other examples of this string construction, namely

```
TYPE    NOR_COLUMN_LOGIC  =    {  BOOL  }    ;
TYPE    NOR_PLANE_LOGIC   =    {  NOR_COLUMN_LOGIC  }    ;
```

in our effort to characterize the programmable NOR gate. In all these cases, the name appearing to the left of the equals sign is a new type which represents a repetition of the type named between the braces (curly brackets). (The name between the braces can itself denote a string, as in the last example. A NOR_PLANE_LOGIC is therefore a string of strings, or a two-dimensional array of BOOLs.)

The notion of repetition comes under different names in different languages. FORTRAN programmers use the word DIMENSION, and Pascal programmers use the word ARRAY to declare repetitions of data. Whereas both FORTRAN and Pascal require as part of the specification the actual length or size of the array, our notation omits any specification of length. For example, an instance of our declared type POLYGON may contain 3 points, 5 points, or 1000 points. Different instances of POLYGON may have different lengths.

(The specification of length has been required historically not to aid the programmer, but to aid the compiler. It has been thought that fixed-size arrays are easier to implement in a computer's memory. In fact, the specification of a fixed length has plagued programmers throughout history.)

Let us declare one other datatype, a string of LAYOUTs:

```
TYPE    LAYOUTS   =    {  LAYOUT  }    ;
```

This declaration makes reference to the type LAYOUT, which we have not yet formally declared. The declaration of type LAYOUT will come soon.

We will use the terms "string," "array," "list," and "set" interchangeably. Whereas mathematically, a "set" imposes no order on its elements, our strings do impose an order, but that order can be disregarded if we so wish.

We must now answer the two questions that must be asked of any datatype. How do we create new instances of type POLYGON, and how do we examine an existing instance of POLYGON? In fact, since our language freely admits the declaration of all kinds of strings, we really want to know in general how to create and examine strings of any type.

2.2.3.1 *Creating instances of strings.*

We specify a new string by writing the elements of the string separated by semicolons, and finally enclosing the whole thing within a pair of braces. We have already adopted this notation for specifying polygons and lists of layouts, and more, that is,

{ point ; point ; … ; point }	→ POLYGON
{ layout ; layout ; … ; layout }	→ LAYOUTS
{ boolean ; boolean ; … ; boolean }	→ NOR_COLUMN_LOGIC
{ nor_column_logic ; … ; nor_column_logic }	→ NOR_PLANE_LOGIC

(The "…" is not part of the literal specification.) For example,

{ 0#0 ; 3#5 ; 7#2 ; 4#1 }	is a POLYGON
{ L1 ; L2 \AT 3#0 ; L3 }	is a LAYOUTS
{ TRUE ; FALSE ; TRUE ; TRUE }	is a NOR_COLUMN_LOGIC
{ { TRUE ; FALSE } ; { TRUE ; TRUE } }	is a NOR_PLANE_LOGIC

A note about lists of layouts: It may seem odd, in light of Section 1.1.4, that here a string of layouts is of type LAYOUTS (plural) and not of type LAYOUT (singular). Previously we have assumed that any list of layouts can be interpreted as an instance of type LAYOUT (singular). This is not really so odd. Surely our list of layouts is of type LAYOUTS, but it will happen also to be of type LAYOUT, as soon as we actually define the LAYOUT type itself. The fact that a LAYOUTS may be viewed as a single LAYOUT is not a property of strings, but rather a property of the way that we will define the type LAYOUT.

There is another way to create a string. Our examples just given each produces a string whose length is known just by looking at the specification itself. We can produce a string not only by writing

{ element ; element ; … ; element }   but also by writing

{ COLLECT   element   Quantifier }.

The latter specification produces a string whose length is determined by the quantifier. For example,

{COLLECT   X#X*2   FOR X FROM 1 TO 5; }
  (point)   (quantifier   )

is equivalent to { 1#2 ; 2#4 ; 3#6 ; 4#8 ; 5#10 }. We have already seen examples of this COLLECT notation when we formed LAYOUTS in our NAND and NOR functions.

Still there are more ways to create strings, but these ways construct strings from existing strings, not just from the elements themselves:

element	<$	string	→	string	(i.e.,	left append)
string	$>	element	→	string	(i.e.,	right append)
string	$$	string	→	string	(i.e.,	concatenation)

The first two operators form a new string by appending one more element onto the left or right of an existing string. The third operator forms a new string from two existing strings by including first the elements of the first string, followed by the elements of the second string.

For example, if we first write

```
VAR    X  =  POLYGON  ;
X  :=    {  10#10  ;  20#20  ;  30#30  }  ;
```

then

0#0 <$ X	is	{ 0#0 ; 10#10 ; 20#20 ; 30#30 }
X $> 40#40	is	{ 10#10 ; 20#20 ; 30#30 ; 40#40 }
X $$ X	is	{ 10#10;20#20;30#30;10#10;20#20;30#30 }

Finally, we have one more operator which reverses the order within a string:

```
REVERSE  (    string    )        →    string
```

2.2.3.2 *Examining instances of a string.*

The most useful way of examining a string is by generating a loop that sets a variable to each element in the string, one at a time. The linguistic name for loop generator is "quantifier." We have already seen the quantifier that examines a string, namely,

```
FOR   variable  $E   string      ;        →    Quantifier
```

If we write

```
VAR    P  =  POINT;    X  =  POLYGON;
X  :=    {  10#10  ;  20#20  ;  30#30  };
```

then the quantifier

```
FOR    P    $E    X    ;
```

causes three iterations, setting P to the values 10#10, 20#20, and 30#30.

For example, suppose that somebody gives us a string of points, X, and asks for that same string back except where each point in the string has been moved to the right by 100 units. We would specify this new string with

```
{  COLLECT    P  +  100#0    FOR  P  $E  X  ;  }
```

This expression combines synthesis and analysis. The quantifier performs analysis; it actually examines the string X in order to set P to each point in X. On the other hand, the general form

```
{  COLLECT    point  quantifier  }
```

synthesizes a new string, as we have already seen.

To understand most easily the string expression just given, note that the following expression is the identity on X:

{   COLLECT   P   FOR   P $E   X ; }

The quantifier sets P to each element of X and the COLLECT puts the elements back together into a copy of the string X. With this identity in mind, any time we wish to transform an existing string into a new string, by applying a function f to each element, we write

{   COLLECT   f(P)   FOR   P $E   X ; }

This time, unlike our identity just given, the new string has as its elements not P, but f(P).

There are two other ways of examining a string. One is called indexing and the other is called tail extraction:

string [integer]   →   element   (i.e., indexing)
string [integer -]   →   string   (i.e., tail extraction)

For example,

X[3]   is the third element in string X

X[3-]   is a substring of X, all of X from the third element on

Thus,

{   10#10   ;   20#20 ; 30#30 ; 40#40 }   [3]   is 30#30
{   10#10   ;   20#20 ; 30#30 ; 40#40 }   [3 -]   is { 30#30 ; 40#40 }

The languages FORTRAN and Pascal provide indexing as the only means of examining an array.

2.2.4   Datatype Construction 2: Records or Cartesian Products

A string is an arbitrary repetition of a single datatype. A record is, in contrast, a small conglomeration of possibly unrelated types.

For example, a single entry in a telephone book contains three things, a NAME, and ADDRESS, and a TELEPHONE_NUMBER. Each of these three things is different from the other two. A NAME denotes only a person or company. An ADDRESS denotes only a geographical location that can be found on a map. Finally, a TELEPHONE_NUMBER denotes a code understood only by the telephone machinery.

In most contexts, these three types of information are not at all interchangeable. For example, the notion of sex applies only to the first type, the notion of zip code applies only to the second type, and the notion of area code applies only to the third type. That is, where an operator like

ADDRESS \ZIP_CODE   →   INTeger

is sensible,

TELEPHONE_NUMBER \ZIP_CODE   →   INTeger

is not well defined when considering the entire world, which may use the same telephone number in different countries.

2.2.4.1 Strings and records are fundamentally different. It would be inappropriate to represent an entry in a telephone book as a string of three things. Strings are very tightly characterized by the property that a string's elements are entirely interchangeable. This must be true of strings because of the ways we allow access to a string.

The indexing expression

string [N]

where N is an integer variable, denotes any element in the string as far as the surrounding program text can assume. Sometimes N will be 3, other times N may be 24, for example. The surrounding program text knows only that this indexing expression yields some element of the string. Thus, all elements in the string must be interchangeable; that is, all elements in a string must have the same type. For example, if

string[1] and string[3]

were to have different types, then the variable expression

string[N]

would have no well-defined datatype. Any expression that would be a member of no datatype is an expression about which we know nothing; we do not even know how to begin examining it.

If we want a string where the type of each element may differ, we can combine the set of possible types we wish to admit into a single "uncertain" type (construction 3 to come shortly). We construct our string so that each element does have the same type, the same "uncertain" type. Thus, the expression

string[N]

yields an element whose type is "uncertain," but that uncertain element can be examined subsequently to resolve the uncertainty that comes with that particular element alone.

2.2.4.2 Declaring a record datatype. We declare a new record datatype by writing a sequence of components, enclosed within brackets:

[selector : type   selector : type   ...   selector : type]

Each component is a pair: a name for that component and a datatype which will serve as that component's representation. (Each component includes a name so that we will have a simple way to refer quickly to that component without regard for the others). For example, the record type

```
[  NAME:         datatype for a person's name
   ADDRESS:      datatype for a geographical location
   NUMBER:       datatype for a telephone number      ]
```

can serve well as an entry in the telephone book. We might declare a new type called TELEPHONE_ENTRY with

```
TYPE   TELEPHONE_ENTRY  =   [  NAME:      PERSON_NAME
                               ADDRESS:   WORLD_LOCATION
                               NUMBER:    TELEPHONE_NUMBER    ] ;
```

This says that the new type TELEPHONE_ENTRY has three components, named NAME, ADDRESS, and NUMBER. Each component is represented respectively by the types PERSON_NAME, WORLD_LOCATION, and TELEPHONE_NUMBER.

We can view a record type as the Cartesian product of its component types. That is, an instance of TELEPHONE_ENTRY is a member of the set defined by the Cartesian product

all   PERSON_NAMEs   X   all   WORLD_LOCATIONs   X   all   TELEPHONE_NUMBERs

2.2.4.3   The telephone book. We can go on to define the datatype of which an entire telphone book is an instance, namely

TYPE   TELEPHONE_BOOK   =   {   TELEPHONE_ENTRY   }   ;

A telephone book thus consists of an arbitrary number of TELEPHONE_ENTRYs. The elements of this string are clearly interchangeable; we may impose freely any order we wish, including alphabetical order by the NAME field.

2.2.4.4   The BOX. Another example of a record datatype is the type BOX, defined by

TYPE   BOX   =   [LOW: POINT   HIGH: POINT   ]   ;

A BOX thus has two components, named LOW and HIGH, each of which is a POINT. We will by agreement assume that the LOW field represents the lower-left corner of the box, and that the HIGH field represents the upper-right corner (Figure 2.2).

2.2.4.5   Creating instances of records. We specify a new box directly in its representation by writing

[LOW: some point   HIGH: some point   ]

For example,

[LOW: 0#0   HIGH: 1#1   ]

is a BOX whose lower-left corner is 0#0 and whose upper-right corner is 1#1.

FIGURE 2.2

This notation is so similar to that of declaring the datatype BOX, we point out that

[LOW: a datatype   HIGH: a datatype   ]   is a datatype, whereas
[LOW: an instance   HIGH: an instance]   is an instance of that
                                                       datatype

In general, if a record type was declared by

[selector$_1$: type$_1$ ...   selector$_k$: type$_k$]

then an instance of that record type is created by

[selector$_1$: an instance of type$_1$ ...   selector$_k$: an instance of type$_k$]

2.2.4.6 *Examining instances of records.* If B is a BOX, then

B   .   LOW   is its lower-left corner
B   .   HIGH   is its upper-right corner

In general, if R is a record, then

R   .   selector$_k$

digs into the record and yields the data associated with the component named "selector$_k$." Thus, if we write

```
VAR       B  =  BOX  ;
B   :=    [  LOW:  0#0    HIGH:  1#1  ]  ;
```

then

B   .   LOW   is 0#0
B   .   HIGH   is 1#1

Suppose that we have a box B. We can create a new box which is a copy of B but which resides to the right of the original by 100 units. This new box is created by writing

[LOW: B.LOW + 100#0   HIGH: B.HIGH + 100#0]

We are creating a new box whose LOW is B.LOW displaced to the right by 100 units, and whose HIGH is B.HIGH displaced to the right by 100 units. Here again we see an intimate mixture of analysis and synthesis. The expressions B.LOW and B.HIGH denote analysis, whereas the rest of the record expression denotes synthesis.

2.2.5 More about BOXes and POLYGONs and the Role of Representation

We now have formal representations for the fundamental elements of layouts: boxes and polygons. These objects are as yet colorless; we will color them when we introduce formally the type LAYOUT.

With our declaration of the type POLYGON, we have supplied implicitly the notation used throughout this text for specifying polygons: that a polygon may be specified in terms of its vertices with the string notation

{ point ; point ;   ...   ; point }

That is, all along we have been specifying polygons directly in terms of their representation.

Boxes, in contrast, have been specified only with the notation

> point   \TO   point

We have not specified boxes directly in terms of the BOX datatype. We could have specified each box directly in terms of its representation by writing

> [LOW: point   HIGH: point]   instead of
> point   \TO   point

Or could we? We could if the \TO operator were defined as in

DEFINE   TO(A,B:POINT)= BOX: [LOW: A   HIGH: B]   ENDDEFN

This definition of \TO assumes always that the first point (A) is the lower-left corner and that the second point (B) is always the upper-right corner. However, this interpretation of the \TO operator is not quite the same as advertised before. The \TO operator has been advertised as producing the smallest box containing the two given points. Therefore,

> 0#0   \TO   1#1
> 1#1   \TO   0#0

should be equivalent, and they should also be equivalent to

> 0#1   \TO   1#0

Each should produce the box whose lower-left corner is 0#0 and whose upper-right corner is 1#1, or in other words, the box

> [LOW: 0#0   HIGH: 1#1]

Referring to Figure 2.1, the smallest box containing two points A and B is always the box whose

> lower-left corner is   A \MIN B   and whose
> upper-right corner is   A \MAX B

Thus, the appropriate definition for \TO is

DEFINE   TO(A,B:POINT)= BOX:
                          [LOW: A \MIN B   HIGH: A \MAX B]   ENDDEFN

We have and will define representations that mirror closely our synthesis operators. However, we will impose a greater degree of standardization on the representation compared to that of the synthesis operators. That is, where the order of the two points specified with the \TO operator is entirely unrestricted, the corresponding representation always has the lower-left corner in the LOW field and the upper-right corner in the HIGH field.

The increased standardization of representation eases the jobs of all programs that examine the representation. For example, had we chosen to declare BOX as

TYPE   BOX =   [ONE_POINT: POINT   OTHER_POINT: POINT] ;

and assume that the two POINTs need not necessarily be the two primary corners, then a program which examines this new kind of box would have to write

B.ONE_POINT   \MIN   B.OTHER_POINT   instead of
B.LOW

to know the lower-left corner.

In fact, our declaration of type BOX should include a comment defining the very particular meanings of its fields:

TYPE   BOX   =   [LOW:POINT   HIGH:POINT   ]   ;   " LOW   =<   HIGH   always "

This condition "LOW =< HIGH" means that LOW is always below and to the left of HIGH. Thus, when a programmer wants to deal with boxes, the programmer will look at the type definition for BOX and see right away that, by convention, LOW is less than HIGH. A condition associated with a datatype always implies two things:

1 The condition is true of any existing BOX.

2 Any BOXes that you create had better satisfy this condition.

The first statement is a gift to the examiner of any BOX. The second statement is in contrast an imposition to creators of BOXes. However, we can ignore this imposition entirely if we always use the \TO notation to create boxes because the \TO operator goes to the trouble of satisfying the imposition.

We will now define some very useful operations upon BOXes. BOXes are of interest in their own right, independent of their role as shapes in a layout.

Notice how we will take advantage of our assumption about the LOW and HIGH fields in BOXes.

2.2.6 Roles of the Minimum Bounding Box (MBB) of a Layout

One major role BOXes play, besides being a part of a layout, is that a box serves as a marvelously simple estimation of the size and location of a layout, or any picture. The minimum bounding box (MBB) of a layout (or any picture) is the smallest box that encloses the entire picture. Figure 2.3 shows the MBB of a layout.

Of what use is the MBB of a layout? There are several. Let us first consider the job of plotting a layout onto a sheet of paper or video screen. It is most convenient for the user if the user can freely create layouts of any size and location. One layout might be small enough to fit in a box 10 units on a side, whereas another layout might be so large as to require a box 10,000 units on a side. Nonetheless, the user generally likes to see the whole layout and to see it as large as the paper or screen admits. Thus, our plotting program will provide a useful service if it enlarges or shrinks the layout just so that it will occupy the whole screen or paper.

A plotting program can determine simply from the given layout's MBB alone the appropriate scaling factor (and displacement) that will render an image of the layout to fill the paper. The portion of the plotting program that determines the appropriate scaling can be written with no knowledge of layouts—with knowledge only of boxes. That program takes in two boxes, the MBB of the layout and the box defining the size and coordinate system of the paper, and computes a transformation that maps the interior of the first box into the interior of the second box. Thus, this scaling feature of plotting can be used verbatim for plotting pictures in general, even nonlayouts such as illustrations with text and with colors other than those found in layouts.

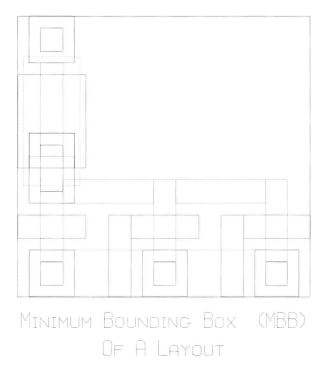

MINIMUM BOUNDING BOX (MBB)
OF A LAYOUT

FIGURE 2.3

MBBs have another use. We may wish for some reason or other to search through a layout to find, say, a polygon or box that encompasses a given point. For example, a person might point to a polygon within a layout shown on the screen. To know which item the user has in mind, we wish to examine the layout and determine which polygon within the layout surrounds the user's point of interest. All the user tells us by pointing is a single point on the screen.

We can go and examine the entire layout, looking at each polygon and box until we find the one containing the point of interest. On the other hand, we might be wasting a lot of time. For example, if the user's point of interest does not lie within the layout's MBB, we can deduce immediately that the point lies within no part of the layout whatsoever. The user has pointed entirely outside the layout in this case.

Even if the user is pointing within the layout's MBB, we may still be able to avoid searching the entire layout. Suppose that the layout appearing on the screen was formed originally as a union of, say, five sublayouts (Figure 2.4). We can always find the polygon of interest by searching in each of the five sublayouts. However, if we know the MBB of each of the sublayouts, we can ignore completely those sublayouts whose particular MBBs do not contain the point of interest. That is, where the entire layout appearing on the screen has a large MBB, each sublayout may have a smaller MBB. Some of the sublayouts may have MBBs which do not contain the point of interest even though the MBB for the entire layout does. We will come back to this idea in Section 2.7 when we explore layout editing by means of interactive graphics.

2.2.7 The MBB of Polygons and Sets of Boxes

Let us now define some useful operations on boxes. We will define the operators

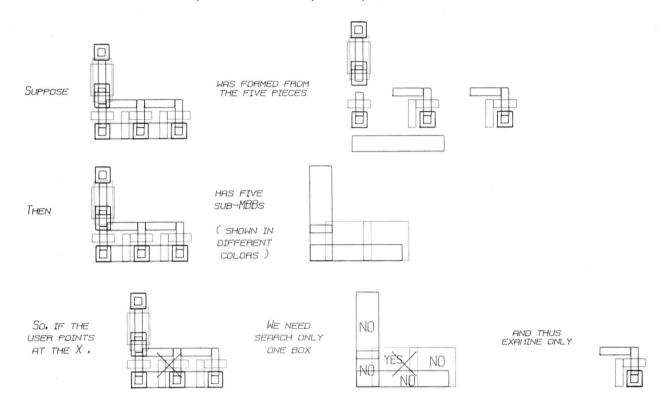

SUPPOSE   WAS FORMED FROM
               THE FIVE PIECES

THEN   HAS FIVE
               SUB-MBBs

               (SHOWN IN
               DIFFERENT
               COLORS)

SO, IF THE   WE NEED   NO   AND THUS
USER POINTS   SEARCH ONLY   EXAMINE ONLY
AT THE X ,   ONE BOX   NO YES NO
                                      NO

MBBs At Sublayouts Can Serve To
Focus Searches Through The Geometry

FIGURE 2.4

POINT \IN BOX	→	BOOL	(i.e.,	is POINT inside BOX ?)
BOX \TOUCHES BOX	→	BOOL	(i.e.,	do the BOXes touch ?)
BOX \MAX BOX	→	BOX	(i.e.,	the smallest BOX containing both BOXes)
BOX \AT POINT	→	BOX	(i.e.,	a displaced BOX)
POLYGON \MBB	→	BOX	(i.e.,	the MBB of a POLYGON)
BOX \PERIMETER	→	POLYGON	(i.e.,	turn a BOX into an equivalent POLYGON)

2.2.7.1 *POINT \IN BOX → BOOL*. How do we know if a given point lies inside a given box? Consider our compare operator "<" on points. A point P is inside a box B if and only if both of the following are true:

> P lies to the right and above the lower-left corner (i.e.,   B.LOW =< P)
> P lies to the left and below the upper-right corner (i.e.,   P =< B.HIGH)

Thus, the definition

> DEFINE   IN(P:POINT   B:BOX) = BOOL:
>   (B.LOW =< P)   &   (P =< B.HIGH)   ENDDEFN

defines insidedness. (The "&" operator represents the logical AND of the two conditions.)

The one-dimensional analogy of a box is a linear interval defined by the set of all numbers lying between the low and high ends of the interval. The "insidedness" condition for an interval reads just as our "insidedness" for a box:

$$low \quad =< \quad i \quad \& \quad i \quad =< \quad high$$

2.2.7.2 *BOX \ TOUCHES BOX → BOOL.*

How do we know if two given boxes touch one another? Two boxes touch if they have a nonempty intersection. The intersection is nonempty if it contains a point P such that P lies inside both boxes.

A point P is inside both box A and box B if

$$A.LOW \quad =< \quad P \quad \& \quad P \quad =< \quad A.HIGH \qquad (\text{inside of A}) \qquad \&$$
$$B.LOW \quad =< \quad P \quad \& \quad P \quad =< \quad B.HIGH \qquad (\text{inside of B})$$

Let us rewrite these four conditions in a different order:

$$A.LOW \quad =< \quad P \quad \& \quad B.LOW \quad =< \quad P \quad \&$$
$$P \quad =< \quad A.HIGH \quad \& \quad P \quad =< \quad B.HIGH$$

Looking at the first line alone, we can say that

$$A.LOW \quad =< \quad P \; \& \; B.LOW \quad =< \quad P \qquad \text{implies} \qquad A.LOW \; \backslash MAX \; B.LOW \quad =< \quad P$$

and also vice versa

$$A.LOW \; \backslash MAX \; B.LOW \quad =< \quad P \qquad \text{implies} \qquad A.LOW \quad =< \quad P \; \& \; B.LOW \quad =< \quad P$$

That is, the first line is equivalent to

$$A.LOW \quad \backslash MAX \quad B.LOW \quad =< \quad P$$

and similarly the second line is equivalent to

$$P \quad =< \quad A.HIGH \quad \backslash MIN \quad B.HIGH$$

Thus, the entire condition that a given point P lies in the intersection is

$$(\; A.LOW \quad \backslash MAX \quad B.LOW \quad =< \quad P \;) \quad \&$$
$$(\; P \quad =< \quad A.HIGH \quad \backslash MIN \quad B.HIGH \;)$$

Boxes A and B touch precisely if such a point P exists. How do we know if such a P exists? Do we try all possible points P? No, we need not try all infinitely possible points. Note the following:

If P exists such that

$$(A.LOW \quad \backslash MAX \quad B.LOW \quad =< \quad P) \quad \&$$
$$(P \quad =< \quad A.HIGH \quad \backslash MIN \quad B.HIGH)$$

then we can conclude that

$$A.LOW \; \backslash MAX \; B.LOW \quad =< \quad P \quad =< \quad A.HIGH \; \backslash MIN \; B.HIGH$$

or more simply that

$$A.LOW \; \backslash MAX \; B.LOW \quad =< \quad A.HIGH \; \backslash MIN \; B.HIGH$$

Thus, if P exists in both boxes, we deduce that

$$A.LOW \; \backslash MAX \; B.LOW \quad =< \quad A.HIGH \; \backslash MIN \; B.HIGH$$

Similarly, if this latest condition is true, then

$$P \;=\; A.LOW \;\backslash MAX\; B.LOW \qquad or \qquad P \;=\; A.HIGH \;\backslash MIN\; B.HIGH$$

is a point that satisfies the condition.

Thus, the existence of such a P is entirely equivalent to the condition

$$A.LOW \;\backslash MAX\; B.LOW \quad =< \quad A.HIGH \;\backslash MIN\; B.HIGH$$

which very happily contains no references to P. We now define \TOUCHES by writing

DEFINE   TOUCHES(A,B:BOX) = BOOL:
   (A.LOW \MAX B.LOW) =< (A.HIGH \MIN B.HIGH)   ENDDEFN

2.2.7.3 BOX \MAX BOX → BOX. Consider now how to determine the smallest box that will contain two given boxes A and B. A single box has the nice property that if two points P and Q reside inside the box, so do the points

$$P \;\backslash MIN\; Q \qquad and \qquad P \;\backslash MAX\; Q$$

That is,

$$
\begin{aligned}
&B.LOW \;=<\; P \quad\&\quad P \;=<\; B.HIGH \qquad (P \; in \; B)\\
&B.LOW \;=<\; Q \quad\&\quad Q \;=<\; B.HIGH \qquad (Q \; in \; B)
\end{aligned}
$$

implies (by reordering these four compares) that

$$
\begin{aligned}
&B.LOW \;=<\; P \quad\&\quad B.LOW \;=<\; Q \quad\&\\
&P \;=<\; B.HIGH \quad\&\quad Q \;=<\; B.HIGH
\end{aligned}
$$

which further implies (treating each line independently) that

$$
\begin{aligned}
&B.LOW \;=<\; P \,\backslash MIN\, Q \quad (and \quad B.LOW \;=<\; P \,\backslash MAX\, Q \qquad trivially)\\
&P \,\backslash MAX\, Q \;=<\; B.HIGH \;(and \quad P \,\backslash MIN\, Q \;=<\; B.HIGH \qquad trivially)
\end{aligned}
$$

This assures us then that P \MAX Q and P \MIN Q are in B if P and Q are in B. Thus, the smallest box containing the two boxes A and B, which must certainly contain the four corners of A and B,

$$A.LOW, \qquad A.HIGH, \qquad B.LOW, \quad and \; B.HIGH$$

also contains at least the two points

$$A.LOW \;\backslash MIN\; B.LOW \qquad and \qquad A.HIGH \;\backslash MAX\; B.HIGH$$

The smallest box enclosing the boxes A and B must contain at least the box

$$[LOW: \; A.LOW \;\backslash MIN\; B.LOW \qquad HIGH: \; A.HIGH \;\backslash MAX\; B.HIGH \;\;]$$

It is easy to show also that this box contains both A and B. Now we can define the operator \MAX on boxes with

DEFINE   MAX(A,B:BOX)= BOX:
   [LOW: A.LOW \MIN B.LOW   HIGH: A.HIGH \MAX B.HIGH]   ENDDEFN

2.2.7.4 BOX \AT POINT → BOX. Another operation on boxes we would like is an \AT operator that moves a box by a point, in just the same way that our abstract \AT operator has been moving layouts. We move a box simply by moving its corners:

```
DEFINE    AT(B:BOX    P:POINT)=  BOX:
          [LOW:  B.LOW  +  P     HIGH:  B.HIGH  +  P  ]          ENDDEFN
```

You may wish to apply a mathematical analysis as we have above to prove that for any point Q:

the condition   Q \IN B   is equivalent to   Q+P \IN (B \AT P)

2.2.7.5 *A box's perimeter and a polygon's MBB*. Let us finally define two more operators

```
POLYGON    \MBB          →       BOX
BOX        \PERIMETER    →       POLYGON
```

The first operator yields the MBB of a polygon (i.e., the smallest box containing all the vertices). The second operator turns a BOX into an equivalent PCLYGON.

The MBB of a polygon will be of fundamental importance to our layout MBB function. The PERIMETER of a box will be useful for plotting boxes because the plotter knows only how to plot polygons.

Consider first the perimeter operator. We turn a box into a polygon simply by listing the four corners of the box as vertices of a polygon. That is, we wish to write something like

```
DEFINE    PERIMETER(B:BOX)=  POLYGON:
          {  corner1  ;  corner2  ;  corner3  ;  corner4  }          ENDDEFN
```

The body of this function must be a string of points because this function produces a polygon (not a box). This list of points is

```
{  B.LOW  ;  B.LOW.X  #  B.HIGH.Y  ;  B.HIGH  ;  B.HIGH.X  #  B.LOW.Y  }
```

which traces out the four corners lower left, upper left, upper right, and lower right.

Another way to write this function is

```
DEFINE    PERIMETER(B:BOX)=  POLYGON:
    BEGIN    VAR  L,  H  =  POINT  ;
        DO        [LOW:L    HIGH:H]  :=    B  ;
        GIVE      {  L  ;    L.X#H.Y    ;    H    ;    H.X#L.Y  }
    END                                                               ENDDEFN
```

This rendition of PERIMETER yields exactly the same results. The "action" part of this function, the text following the "DO,"

```
[LOW:L  HIGH:H]  :=  B  ;
```

sets L and H to the LOW and HIGH fields of B. This is equivalent to the two separate assignment statements

```
L  :=  B.LOW  ;
H  :=  B.HIGH  ;
```

Having L and H handy makes the expression of the polygonal perimeter clearer.

Now consider the MBB function on polygons. How do we compute the MBB of a polygon? We compute the smallest box containing all the vertices of the polygon. Suppose for simplicity that the polygon consists of just two vertices P and Q; that is, the given polygon is

{ P ; Q }

We know that the smallest box that contains these two points is

P   \TO   Q   or
[LOW: P \MIN Q   HIGH: P \MAX Q]

What about a polygon containing three points? The smallest box that contains the points P, Q, and R is

[LOW: P \MIN Q \MIN R   HIGH: P \MAX Q \MAX R]

As shown in Figure 2.1, a polygon

{ P_1 ; P_2 ;   ...   ; P_k }

has the MBB

[LOW: P_1 \MIN P_2 \MIN ... \MIN P_k
 HIGH: P_1 \MAX P_2 \MAX ... \MAX P_k]

That is, we can define MBB with

DEFINE   MBB(X:POLYGON)= BOX:
                [LOW: the \MIN of all points in X
                 HIGH: the \MAX of all points in X   ]   ENDDEFN

We write this formally with

DEFINE   MBB(X:POLYGON)= BOX: BEGIN   VAR   P= POINT;
       [LOW: \MIN   P   FOR P $E X;
        HIGH: \MAX   P   FOR P $E X;   ]   END   ENDDEFN

We have written the "cumulative operation"

\MIN P FOR P $E X;

to denote

P_1 \MIN P_2 \MIN ... \MIN P_k where X is   { P_1 ; P_2 ; ... ; P_k }

This "cumulative operation" is another example of our linguistic construction

Operator   Expression   Quantifier

where in this case the operator is \MIN, the expression is P, and the quantifier is "FOR P $E X;." We have already seen this construction in Section 1.4.3.

Let us look at one more example of a cumulative operation. We already know how to find the \MAX of two boxes. Suppose that somebody declares the type BOXES,

TYPE   BOXES   =   {   BOX   }   ;

and asks us to define a function that finds the MBB of an entire set of BOXES. We can define the operator

BOXES   \MBB   →   BOX

by writing

DEFINE   MBB(X:BOXES)=   BOX: BEGIN   VAR   B=BOX;
    \MAX   B   FOR   B $E   X;   END   ENDDEFN

The expression

\MAX   B   FOR   B $E   X;

is equivalent to writing

B_1 \MAX B_2 \MAX   ...   \MAX B_k where X is   { B_1 ; B_2 ;   ...   ; B_k }

2.2.8   Nested Type Expressions: An Example for Multipen Plotters

Let us look at an aspect of plotting which differs for different plotting devices. Many plotters can produce multicolored pictures. Such plotters generally have not one pen, but a set of different-colored pens. We specify to the plotter that we want subsequent figures to come out in a particular color by telling the plotter to change pens before we instruct it to draw the figures.

The plotter has no way of knowing which pens are which colors. The plotter knows only that it has several garages from which to borrow a pen. Each little garage has a specific number. We tell the plotter to change pens merely by specifying a garage number.

Let us assume that before we turn on the plotter, we put a different-colored pen in each garage in a consistent manner, such that, for example,

garage#1   is always RED
garage#2   is always GREEN

and so on. The particular association of garages to colors is unimportant. It is important that whatever the choice is, we always adhere to it.

Our plotting procedure needs a way to translate colors into garage numbers, so that when it needs to plot a green box, for example, it can tell the plotter to switch to the pen in garage#2. Such a color-to-number association is called a color map.

We can define the type COLOR_MAP as follows:

TYPE   COLOR_MAP=   {   [COLOR:COLOR   PEN:INT]   }   ;

That is, a COLOR_MAP is a set each of whose elements is a record. Each record associates a specific color with a specific garage number. This declaration uses a nested type expression, namely a record within a set. We can define the type COLOR_MAP another way, without nesting:

```
TYPE    COLOR_MAP= {  COLOR_ASSOCIATION  } ;
TYPE    COLOR_ASSOCIATION= [COLOR:COLOR    PEN:INT]  ;
```

Both specifications define COLOR_MAP equivalently, but the latter gives a name to the type of elements of the string. This subtle difference deserves some attention.

Before we consider this subtle difference, we can in either case specify a color map for a particular plotter by writing

```
VAR      THE_COLOR_MAP  =  COLOR_MAP;
THE_COLOR_MAP:=     {   [  COLOR:RED       PEN:1  ] ;
                        [  COLOR:GREEN     PEN:2  ] ;
                        [  COLOR:BLUE      PEN:3  ] ;
                        [  COLOR:YELLOW    PEN:4  ] ;
                        [  COLOR:BLACK     PEN:5  ]   } ;
```

This color map associates the color RED with pen 1, GREEN with pen 2, and so on.

Given this color map, we can translate a given color into a pen number by writing something like:

IF for each element in the string there is an element whose color matches the given color, then yield the corresponding pen number.

This search through the color map is expressed as an IF-THEN-ELSE. It is conceivable that no match will be found; for example, perhaps there are some colors that a particular plotter cannot plot.

Let us define formally the operator which, given a COLOR_MAP, maps a COLOR into a pen number:

```
COLOR_MAP    \S    COLOR        →    INT
```

so that, for example,

```
THE_COLOR_MAP    \S    GREEN    yields    2
```

(The "\S" can read like the possessive form "apostrophy s.")

```
DEFINE    S(X:COLOR_MAP  C:COLOR)  =  INT:  BEGIN VAR  Y=COLOR_ASSOCIATION;
          IF    FOR  Y  $E  X;    THERE_IS    Y.COLOR  =  C
          THEN      Y.PEN
          ELSE      0                    FI                    END      ENDDEFN
```

This function makes use of our linguistic construction (introduced at the end of Section 1.4.3)

```
Quantifier          THERE_IS    Boolean              →    Boolean  (e.g.,
FOR  Y  $E  X;      THERE_IS    (Y.COLOR=C)               is a condition
```

It can be read as

```
(IF)     FOR   Y an element of X, there is Y whose color equals C
(THEN)   …
```

If a match is found, Y will come out referring to the first such element. Thus, the expression following the THEN, the Y.PEN, refers to the pen associated with the matched color. In case no match is found, we yield pen number 0, which to many plotters means "no pen."

Let us now consider the difference between our two ways of declaring the type COLOR_MAP. The function we have just specified refers to the type COLOR_ ASSOCIATION in its declaration of the local variable Y, which is used subsequently to represent each element in the color map X. This way of writing the function therefore requires that we have declared the type COLOR_MAP the second way, the way that does give a name to the element type.

On the other hand, we can define this function a little differently, in a way that makes no use of the name COLOR_ASSOCIATION. We must let go of the variable Y therefore. Instead, we can write

DEFINE   S(X:COLOR_MAP C:COLOR) = INT: BEGIN VAR C1=COLOR; I=INT;
    IF   FOR   [COLOR:C1   PEN:I] $E X;   THERE_IS   C1=C
    THEN   I
    ELSE   0   FI   END   ENDDEFN

Here we abandon the variable Y and introduce instead two other variables which will represent not an element of the color map X, but rather the components of an element. The quantifier

FOR   [COLOR:C1 PEN:I] $E X;   as opposed to   FOR   Y $E X;

sets the variables C1 and I directly to the components of each element, and nowhere do we refer to an element as a whole. We can think of

FOR   [COLOR:C1   PEN:I] $E X;   as equivalent to
FOR   Y $E X;   each time do   [COLOR:C1   PEN:I]:= Y;

(Remember where we used the notation

[LOW:P1   HIGH:P2]:= BOX;

to extract both components of a box?)

This final version of the function will work equally well with either declaration of the type COLOR_MAP because it does not refer to the element type COL-OR_ASSOCIATION.

In general, the use of nested type expressions is fine unless you need a type name for (one of) the nested type(s). It is always easy to go back and replace a nested type expression with a nonnested declaration, for example, replacing our first declaration of COLOR_MAP with our second, nonnested declaration.

2.3 THE TYPE LAYOUT AND VARIANT TYPES

2.3.1 Type Construction 3: Variants, a Necessary Uncertainty

Our third datatype constructor gathers together unrelated types to form a new type which admits a well-defined uncertainty in representation. A given instance of the new type may be represented by any one of the other types. Such a construction can be used to define the type LAYOUT as we have sketched earlier.

For starters, let us define a type called SHAPE, which will denote either a single polygon or a single box. We formally declare SHAPE by writing

TYPE   SHAPE =   EITHER
                        STATE1 =   BOX
                        STATE2 =   POLYGON
                    ENDOR   ;

This says that a SHAPE is either a single BOX or a single POLYGON, but not both. (This declaration also introduces some seemingly irrelevant words, STATE1 and STATE2. Let us ignore these for now.)

This declaration says two things about SHAPE:

1   Any BOX is a SHAPE and any POLYGON is a SHAPE; that is, we gain the rules

BOX $\rightarrow$ SHAPE
POLYGON $\rightarrow$ SHAPE

2   It is not true that all SHAPEs are BOXes or that all SHAPEs are POLYGONs. That is, we most definitely do not have the rules

SHAPE $\rightarrow$ BOX   No!
SHAPE $\rightarrow$ POLYGON   No!

The first property about SHAPE says that

0#0   \TO   1#1,   which is a BOX,   is also a SHAPE
{ 0#0 ; 1#2 ; 2#0 },   which is a POLYGON,   is also a SHAPE

Thus, if we declare

VAR   S   =   SHAPE ;

then

S:=   0#0 \TO 1#1 ;   is legal, and so is
S:= { 0#0 ; 1#2 ; 2#0 } ;

The first assignment sets S to represent a BOX. The second assignment sets S to represent a POLYGON.

In contrast, the second property about SHAPE says that the shape S itself is uncertain. Since S is not always a BOX, the expression

S.LOW   is illegal because S might be a POLYGON

Similarly, since S is not always a POLYGON, the expression

S[5]   is illegal because S might be a BOX

Any type declared with our EITHER...ENDOR is called a variant type. The actual representation of an instance is variable in the domain of datatypes.

2.3.1.1   Creating instances of variants. We have seen already one way to create instances of a variant type. We write nothing extra. Any instance of one of the possible types passes equally well as an instance of the variant type. In general, a variant type T defined by

TYPE   T   =   EITHER
                        $STATE_1$ = T_1
                        $STATE_2$ = T_2
                                ...
                        $STATE_k$ = T_k
                ENDOR ;

introduces the rules

$$
\begin{aligned}
T_1 &\rightarrow T \\
T_2 &\rightarrow T \\
&\cdot \quad \cdot \quad \cdot \\
T_k &\rightarrow T
\end{aligned}
$$

each of which requires no specification whatsoever beyond an expression whose type is any one of $T_1, T_2, \ldots,$ or T_k.

In addition to this implicit creation of instances of a variant type, we have also a more verbose, and sometimes necessary notation. This verbose notation makes use of the "noise" words, STATE1, STATE2, and so on. That is, not only do we have the rule

T1	$\rightarrow$	T	but we have also
STATE1::T1	$\rightarrow$	T	

Thus, referring to our SHAPE example, we have not only the rules

BOX	$\rightarrow$	SHAPE
POLYGON	$\rightarrow$	SHAPE

but we have also the rules

STATE1::BOX	$\rightarrow$	SHAPE
STATE2::POLYGON	$\rightarrow$	SHAPE

For example,

STATE1:: (0#0 \TO 1#1)	is a SHAPE, and so is
STATE2:: { 0#0 ; 1#2 ; 2#0 }	but
STATE2:: (0#0 \TO 1#1)	is not a SHAPE

This verbose notation is rarely required. It is required only when an ambiguity might arise. For example, the declaration

```
TYPE    T   =    EITHER
                    STATE1  =  BOX
                    STATE2  =  POLYGON
                    STATE3  =  BOX
                 ENDOR  ;
```

refers more than once to the same type, BOX. Why we would ever make such a declaration is not yet obvious. But if we did, the BOX expression

    0#0   \TO   1#1

could be interpreted as a T in two ways: Either it is a T in STATE1 or it is a T in STATE3. Assuming that it makes a difference, we can write

STATE1:: (0#0 \TO 1#1)	or
STATE3:: (0#0 \TO 1#1)	

to specify explicitly in which state the BOX is to be represented. This kind of ambiguity cannot occur with our SHAPE type because it references no type twice.

2.3.1.2   Examining instances of variant types. Because of the inherent uncertainty in any variant type, each examination of a variant object must always first resolve the uncertainty. We provide exactly one way to do this, the CASE statement. The expression

```
CASE      variant object     OF
            STATE₁:           something₁
            STATE₂:           something₂
               …
            STATEₖ:           somethingₖ
ENDCASE
```

is something like a giant IF-THEN-ELSE sequence. It reads like

```
      IF "variant object" is in STATE₁              THEN      something₁
   else IF "variant object" is in STATE₂            THEN      something₂
…
      else IF "variant object" is in STATEₖ         THEN      somethingₖ
```

However, there is something fundamentally unique about the CASE construction which is entirely absent from any IF-THEN-ELSE.

The CASE statement maintains a very definite separation between the uncertainty associated with a variant object and the various certainties which arise only after the variant object is examined. That is, if S is a variant object (e.g., a SHAPE), the following different things are known about S at different positions throughout the CASE construction:

```
 " S is uncertain "
CASE       S      OF
     STATE1:         " S is certain, in fact, S is a BOX "
     STATE2:         " S is certain, in fact, S is a POLYGON "
ENDCASE
 " S is uncertain "
```

This separation between uncertainty and certainty is actually implemented by changing the variable S's type throughout the CASE construction:

```
 " S is of type SHAPE "
CASE       S      OF
     STATE1:         " S is of type BOX "
     STATE2:         " S is of type POLYGON "
ENDCASE
 " S is of type SHAPE "
```

For example, the actual legality of some expressions depends on where the expression appears; for example,

```
 " S.LOW and S[1] are both illegal "
CASE       S      OF
     STATE1:         " S.LOW is legal, but S[1] is illegal "
     STATE2:         " S[1] is legal,    but S.LOW is illegal "
ENDCASE
 " S.LOW and S[1] are both illegal "
```

Example. To illustrate the use of the CASE statement, let us define a function, MBB, which takes in a SHAPE and produces the MBB of that SHAPE:

```
DEFINE     MBB(S:SHAPE)  =   BOX:
         ''  We know nothing about S, and yet we need to examine S.
             There is only one way to examine S ... ''
             CASE     S      OF
                  STATE1:        '' Ah! S is a BOX. The MBB of any box is
                                     simply that box itself ''
                                 S
                  STATE2:        '' S is a POLYGON ... ''
                                 S\MBB
             ENDCASE
ENDDEFN
```

Written without comments, this reads

```
DEFINE     MBB(S:SHAPE)=  BOX:
             CASE     S      OF
                  STATE1:      S
                  STATE2:      S  \MBB
             ENDCASE                              ENDDEFN
```

2.3.1.3 Descriptive names for variant states. We have seen that the names STATE1 and STATE2 in the type SHAPE play an important role in examining a SHAPE. It is their use in the CASE statement that requires their existence at all. They merely provide a way to name the certain states within an uncertain object.

These state names may be chosen arbitrarily just like the component names in a record. We have used such dreary names only to illustrate clearly their roles as state names and not as types. We could, for example, define SHAPE by

```
TYPE     SHAPE   =    EITHER
                          BOX=        BOX
                          POLYGON=    POLYGON
                      ENDOR  ;
```

which is equivalent to our earlier form except that now the states are named ''BOX'' and ''POLYGON'' instead of ''STATE1'' and ''STATE2.''

2.3.1.4 Variant objects and the CASE statement are inseparable. To analyze a variant object, always use the CASE statement immediately. There is no other way, except by calling other functions which themselves employ the CASE statement. In general, where we might like to write

```
analyze( variant object )
```

we write instead

```
CASE     variant object     OF
             STATE₁:        analyze( certain object )
                  ...
             STATEₖ:        analyze( certain object )
ENDCASE
```

Since a variant type admits different species under its roof, analysis of a variant type always requires the willingness to consider independently each of the possible species.

2.3.2 The Type LAYOUT

We can define formally the type LAYOUT by writing

```
TYPE    LAYOUT  =   EITHER
                        BOX=        BOX
                        POLYGON=    POLYGON
                        UNION=      LAYOUTS
                        COLOR=      [ PAINT: LAYOUT      WITH:  COLOR  ]
                        MOVE=       [ DISPLACE: LAYOUT       BY:  POINT  ]
                    ENDOR  ;
```

The type LAYOUT references our previously defined types BOX, POLYGON, LAYOUTS, and COLOR. [The type LAYOUT referenced from within our earlier definition of the type LAYOUTS (plural) refers now to this definition of type LAYOUT.] This definition says that a given instance of LAYOUT is either

BOX	a single box, or
POLYGON	a single polygon, or
LAYOUTS	a union of other layouts, or
[PAINT:LAYOUT WITH:COLOR]	another layout painted some color, or
[DISPLACE:LAYOUT BY:POINT]	another layout displaced by some point

This declaration of the type LAYOUT not only gives us a representation for layouts, but actually gives us some of the notations we have been using throughout Part 1 for synthesizing layouts. This declaration in effect immediately gives us the rules

```
{ point ; point ; ... ; point }    →   LAYOUT   (polygon)
point \TO point                    →   LAYOUT   (box)
{ layout ; layout ; ... ; layout } →   LAYOUT   (union)
```

That is, independent of our LAYOUT declaration, we already have (correspondingly) the rules

```
{ point ; point ;      ... ; point }    →   POLYGON
point   \TO    point                    →   BOX
{ layout ; layout ;    ... ; layout }   →   LAYOUTS
```

simply because we have declared the types POLYGON and LAYOUTS, and because we have already defined the \TO operator which produces a BOX. However, these three forms of expression are not only of types POLYGON, BOX, and LAYOUTS, respectively, but also, due to our LAYOUT declaration, each can be interpreted as type LAYOUT. Recall that the variant type declaration

```
TYPE    LAYOUT  =   EITHER
                        ...   =   BOX
                        ...   =   POLYGON
                        ...   =   LAYOUTS
                                ...
                    ENDOR;
```

adds automatically the implicit rules

BOX	→	LAYOUT	(i.e., Any BOX is a LAYOUT)
POLYGON	→	LAYOUT	(i.e., Any POLYGON is a LAYOUT)
LAYOUTS	→	LAYOUT	(i.e., Any LAYOUTS is a LAYOUT)

Hence, the three basic forms of expression appear as LAYOUTs by the following pairs of rule applications:

{ point ; point ; ... ; point }	→	POLYGON	→	LAYOUT
point \TO point	→	BOX	→	LAYOUT
{ layout ; layout ; ... ; layout }	→	LAYOUTS	→	LAYOUT

Let us now define the three remaining layout synthesis operators,

LAYOUT	\AT	POINT	→	LAYOUT
LAYOUT	\PAINTED	COLOR	→	LAYOUT
LAYOUT	\UNION	LAYOUT	→	LAYOUT

We write

```
DEFINE   AT(L:LAYOUT   P:POINT)=  LAYOUT:
              [DISPLACE:L   BY:P]                        ENDDEFN
DEFINE   PAINTED(L:LAYOUT   C:COLOR)=  LAYOUT:
              [PAINT:L   WITH:C]                         ENDDEFN
DEFINE   UNION(A,B:LAYOUT)=  LAYOUT:
              { A ; B }                                  ENDDEFN
```

The \AT operator creates a LAYOUT in the MOVE state. The \PAINTED operator creates a LAYOUT in the COLOR state. The \UNION operator creates a LAYOUT in the UNION state. For example, the UNION operator produces a layout in the UNION state because the expression

```
{ A ; B }
```

is interpreted by the sequence of rule applications

```
{ layout ; layout }   →   LAYOUTS   →   LAYOUT
```

The "LAYOUTS → LAYOUT" produces a LAYOUT in the UNION state. This sequence of interpretations begins and ends in a way that satisfies the type information stated in the DEFINE line. That is, the sequence begins by knowing that each of A and B is of type LAYOUT. The sequence ends when it produces a LAYOUT because the DEFINE line says that this function produces an object of type LAYOUT.

At this point, we have defined completely our specification language for layouts. All our layout functions (e.g., the BB, NAND2, and NOR_UNIT functions) are supported now, so that each produces an object of type LAYOUT.

(There was one place in our specification of pull-up resistors where we used an undocumented operator, \ROT, which rotates a layout. We will come back to this shortly.)

2.3.3 Examples of Layout Analysis

Now we can freely produce objects of type LAYOUT. To make all this worthwhile, we should define procedures that perform useful functions on layouts. For example, we wish to plot layouts. We wish also to transform layouts into a very particular and low-level format that can be used to fabricate a layout in silicon. We also wish to obtain a layout's MBB to estimate its size and location. We might also wish to create an interactive graphics editor which would allow the user to modify conveniently a layout in a purely graphical setting. We might also like to check a layout to verify that it does not violate design rules. All these operations require the examination of objects of type LAYOUT.

We will show how to plot a layout, and sketch how to translate a layout into an actual pattern format for subsequent fabrication onto silicon. We will also show how to compute a layout's MBB and how to enact the heart of any interactive graphics editor. We will not show how to check a layout's adherence to design rules. Our main effort, silicon compilation, which produces layouts algorithmically, always produces correct layouts and thus relieves our need for design rule checking.

We will start with the computation of a layout's MBB. We will then show how to plot a layout. Next, we will slightly modify the datatype LAYOUT so as to admit reorientations beyond mere displacements (e.g., rotations and mirrorings). We will correspondingly touch up our MBB and PLOT functions, and then proceed with more examples.

2.3.3.1 The MBB of a layout. We define the MBB function for layouts by writing:

```
DEFINE    MBB(L:LAYOUT)=  BOX:              BEGIN     VAR    L1=  LAYOUT;
     CASE    L    OF
          BOX:      L                        "(L is of type BOX)"
          POLYGON:  L \MBB                    "(L is of type POLYGON)"
          UNION:    \MAX   (L1\MBB)   FOR    L1  $E  L;
                                             "(L is of type LAYOUTS)"
          COLOR:    L.PAINT \MBB              "(L is of type
                                                  [PAINT:LAYOUT    WITH:COLOR]  )"
          MOVE:     L.DISPLACE \MBB   \AT    L.BY
                         "(L is of type    [DISPLACE:LAYOUT    BY:POINT]  )"
     ENDCASE
END                           ENDDEFN
```

Notice how we employ the CASE statement. We find the MBB of L by considering only each possible state of any layout. If L is in the BOX state, we simply return that box itself as the MBB of the single-box layout.

If L is a polygon, we call on our MBB function for polygons:

POLYGON \MBB   →   BOX

and let that result stand as the MBB for the single-polygon layout.

In case L is a union of layouts, we yield the \MAX of the MBBs of the sublayouts. That is, our expression

\MAX   (L1\MBB)   FOR   L1 $E L;

is another example of the form

\MAX   box   Quantifier

which we have seen in Section 2.2.7.5.

In case L is in the COLOR state, we yield simply the MBB of the colorless sublayout. We ignore the color altogether because color plays no role in a layout's MBB.

Finally, in case L is in the MOVE state, we first obtain the MBB of the unmoved sublayout, with the expression

> L.DISPLACE   \MBB

which tells us the MBB of the layout before moving. We then move this box by exactly the same amount that the unmoved sublayout is meant to be moved, as represented in L itself. That is, where L represents

> the sublayout   L.DISPLACE   moved by the point   L.BY

the expression

> L.DISPLACE   \MBB   moved by the point   L.BY

reproduces the same movement, but in the domain of BOXes. Recall our \AT operator on BOXes,

> BOX   \AT   POINT   →   BOX

We now use this box \AT to move ''L.DISPLACE \MBB'' in

> L.DISPLACE   \MBB   \AT   L.BY

Does our layout MBB function always terminate? We need to ask this question because we call this layout MBB function recursively. Fortunately, each time we call the layout MBB function (in the UNION, COLOR, and MOVE states), we call it passing a sublayout of L. This is a sufficient condition to assure termination.

A fatal mistake we could have made in the MOVE clause would have been to write

> L.DISPLACE   \AT   L.BY   \MBB   instead of the practical
> L.DISPLACE   \MBB   \AT   L.BY

Both are conceptually equivalent; the first performs the movement (\AT) in the domain of layouts, and then takes the MBB, whereas the second performs the same movement but in the domain of boxes, having first acquired the MBB of the unmoved layout. The first form, however, can cause an infinite loop because it passes to MBB *not* a sublayout of L (e.g., L.DISPLACE) but a newly synthesized layout

> L.DISPLACE   \AT   L.BY

It is therefore possible that MBB can call itself infinitely many times, passing to itself each time a newly synthesized layout.

2.3.3.2 *Plotting a layout.* A plotting process interfaces between a layout and a specific plotter. A layout exists in one coordinate system and a plotter works typically in a different coordinate system. The plotter may come with the specification that its sheet of paper encompasses only points between 0#0 and 1000#1000; that is, the plotter understands only the points X#Y such that

> 0   =<   X   =<   1000   and   0   =<   Y   =<   1000

On the other hand, our layout might reside between points 2000#2000 and 3000#3000.

To make sure that our layout gets plotted on the sheet of paper, the layout must be moved so that it fits between the plotter limits 0#0 and 1000#1000. Let us therefore define a very flexible PLOT procedure which takes in not only a layout, but also a displacement that relates the layout's coordinate system to the plotter's coordinate system. Let us have it take in even a third parameter, a default color that will be adopted by all colorless boxes and polygons:

```
DEFINE    PLOT(L:LAYOUT    DISP:POINT    COLOR:COLOR):
    BEGIN       VAR   L1  =  LAYOUT  ;
          CASE    L    OF
             BOX:              plot the box displaced by DISP, with COLOR
             POLYGON:          plot the polygon displaced by DISP, with COLOR
             UNION:            FOR    L1    $E    L;    DO
                                             PLOT( L1, DISP, COLOR );      END
             MOVE:             PLOT( L.DISPLACE, DISP+L.BY, COLOR );
             COLOR:            PLOT( L.PAINT, DISP, L.WITH );
       ENDCASE                                            END          ENDDEFN
```

Our PLOT procedure takes in a LAYOUT, a displacement POINT, and a COLOR. The first thing we do, of course, is to examine the layout L. If the layout is simply either a box or a polygon, we plot it, incorporating the desired displacement and color. We will come back to these cases in a moment.

If the layout is a union of layouts, we simply plot each one in turn, using the same DISP and COLOR for each.

If the layout is in the MOVE state, notice how we plot the unmoved sublayout L.DISPLACE while simultaneously incorporating the desired movement by changing the displacement from DISP to DISP+L.BY. This will mean that all polygons and boxes within the unmoved layout L.DISPLACE will be moved by the extra amount L.BY just before they go out to the plotter.

If the layout is in the COLOR state, we plot the colorless sublayout, passing the layout's color to the PLOT procedure.

How do we plot a single box or polygon incorporating the parameters DISP and COLOR? We must know how to communicate with the plotter. Any plotter can be characterized by the low-level procedure

```
PLOT( polygon, color )
```

which plots a specific polygon in a specific color. The polygon, at this low level, is assumed to be represented in the plotter's natural coordinate system. We will sketch such a low-level plot procedure in a moment. But first let us finish our layout plot procedure by formalizing the BOX and POLYGON cases.

In the BOX case, we must first turn the box into a polygon. Then, in either the box or polygon cases, we must move that polygon by DISP so that it lands within the plotter's coordinates. We turn a box into a polygon with our PERIMETER function introduced in Section 2.2.7.5.

We will move a polygon by first defining an \AT operator for polygons as follows:

```
DEFINE    AT(PS:POLYGON    DISP:POINT)=  POLYGON:     ''(a string of POINTs)''
    BEGIN       VAR    P  =  POINT  ;
          {COLLECT    P+DISP    FOR  P  $E  PS; }
    END                                              ENDDEFN
```

This will allow us to move a polygon simply by writing

```
polygon    \AT    point
```

The result is the original polygon where each vertex is displaced by the second parameter to \AT.

Now we can write the BOX and POLYGON cases formally as

...

| BOX: | PLOT(L\PERIMETER | \AT | DISP, | COLOR); |
| POLYGON: | PLOT(L | \AT | DISP, | COLOR); |

...

These two references to PLOT refer to the plotter's low-level PLOT routine, which takes in a polygon and a color. Note that this low-level PLOT is distinguishable from our layout PLOT procedure even though they have the same names because one of them takes in the three types

LAYOUT, POINT, COLOR

whereas the other takes in a different sequence of types:

POLYGON, COLOR

Now that we have a very flexible PLOT procedure for layouts, let us provide a simpler PLOT procedure for layouts which takes in just a layout.

DEFINE   PLOT(L:LAYOUT):
        PLOT(L,   - (L\MBB).LOW, BLACK);   ENDDEFN

Our simple plot procedure calls the very flexible PLOT procedure by providing values for the extra two parameters. The "default" color is BLACK and the displacement is -(L\MBB).LOW.

This particular displacement renders the layout so that its lower-left corner lands at 0#0, presumably the plotter's lower-left corner. That is, the lower-left corner of the layout (the lower-left corner of the layout's MBB),

(L\MBB).LOW

becomes

(L\MBB).LOW   +   -(L\MBB).LOW,   or simply 0#0

in the plotter's system.

We have not yet considered what to do if the layout also requires scaling in order to fit into the plotter's coordinate system. We consider scaling and all other kinds of linear orientations in the next section.

Let us sketch how the low-level PLOT function, which takes in a polygon and a color, actually translates this information into commands for a pen plotter. We assume that our plotter, like many plotters available today, accepts its commands in textual form. The plotter understands three commands:

PEN	number		Pick up the pen in garage "number."
U	number	, number	Move to these coordinates holding the pen Up, so not to draw anything.
D	number	, number	Move to these coordinates holding the pen Down, so to draw a single line.

The second command, U, is used to prepare for drawing a new line. The third command, D, is used to draw a line from wherever the pen is now to the coordinates specified in the D command.

We can define our low-level PLOT function with:

```
DEFINE    PLOT(PS:POLYGON    C:COLOR):    BEGIN    VAR    P=POINT;  I=INT;
    "   Choose the appropriate-colored pen ...    "
        WRITE('PEN');       WRITE( THE_COLOR_MAP    \S    C   );
    "   Now plot the outline of the polygon ...    "
        FOR    P    $E    ( PS  $>  PS[1] );    &&    FOR  I  FROM  1  BY  1;
        DO         IF    I=1    THEN        WRITE('U');
                          ELSE        WRITE('D');    FI
                WRITE( P.X  \FIXR );                WRITE(',');
                WRITE( P.Y  \FIXR );                              END
                                                   END         ENDDEFN
```

This procedure first selects the appropriate-colored pen by issuing the "PEN" command, passing as pen number the result of mapping our color C to a pen number via the expression

$$\text{THE\_COLOR\_MAP} \quad \backslash S \quad \text{COLOR} \quad \rightarrow \quad \text{pen number}$$

(introduced in Section 2.2.8). Next, the procedure actually draws the outline of the closed polygon. It looks at each point in the polygon, PS, and finally looks once again at the first point in the polygon. That is, the sequence of vertices is taken not from PS alone, but from the expression

$$\text{PS} \quad \$> \quad \text{PS[1]}$$

This expression represents all the vertices of PS, but then with the first vertex PS[1] appearing again at the end of the sequence. This first-last repetition assures that the plotter closes the polygon.

Looking at the body of the loop, we see that we issue a pen-Up command on the first iteration (to move the pen from wherever it happens to be initially to the first vertex of the polygon), and then we issue a pen-Down command for each subsequent iteration. This causes the pen to draw each edge of the polygon, including that final edge, from the last vertex back around to the first vertex.

2.4 GENERAL ORIENTATIONS FOR LAYOUTS

Let us enrich the representation of layouts to provide not only for an \AT operator which displaces a layout, but also more general reorientations, such as rotation and scaling. After we enrich the datatype LAYOUT, we will provide the new operations:

LAYOUT	\ROT	REAL	→	LAYOUT	(i.e., rotation by an angle)
LAYOUT	\MIRX		→	LAYOUT	(i.e., mirror about the X-axis)
LAYOUT	\MIRY		→	LAYOUT	(i.e., mirror about the Y-axis)
LAYOUT	\SCALED_BY	POINT	→	LAYOUT	(i.e., enlarge or shrink each dimension of the layout)

We will enrich the datatype LAYOUT by replacing the old MOVE state

$$\text{MOVE} \quad = \quad \text{[DISPLACE:LAYOUT} \quad \text{BY:POINT]}$$

by the new MOVE state

$$\text{MOVE} \quad = \quad \text{[DISPLACE:LAYOUT} \quad \text{BY:MATRIX]}$$

That is, we will allow a layout to be moved by a general MATRIX instead of just a POINT.

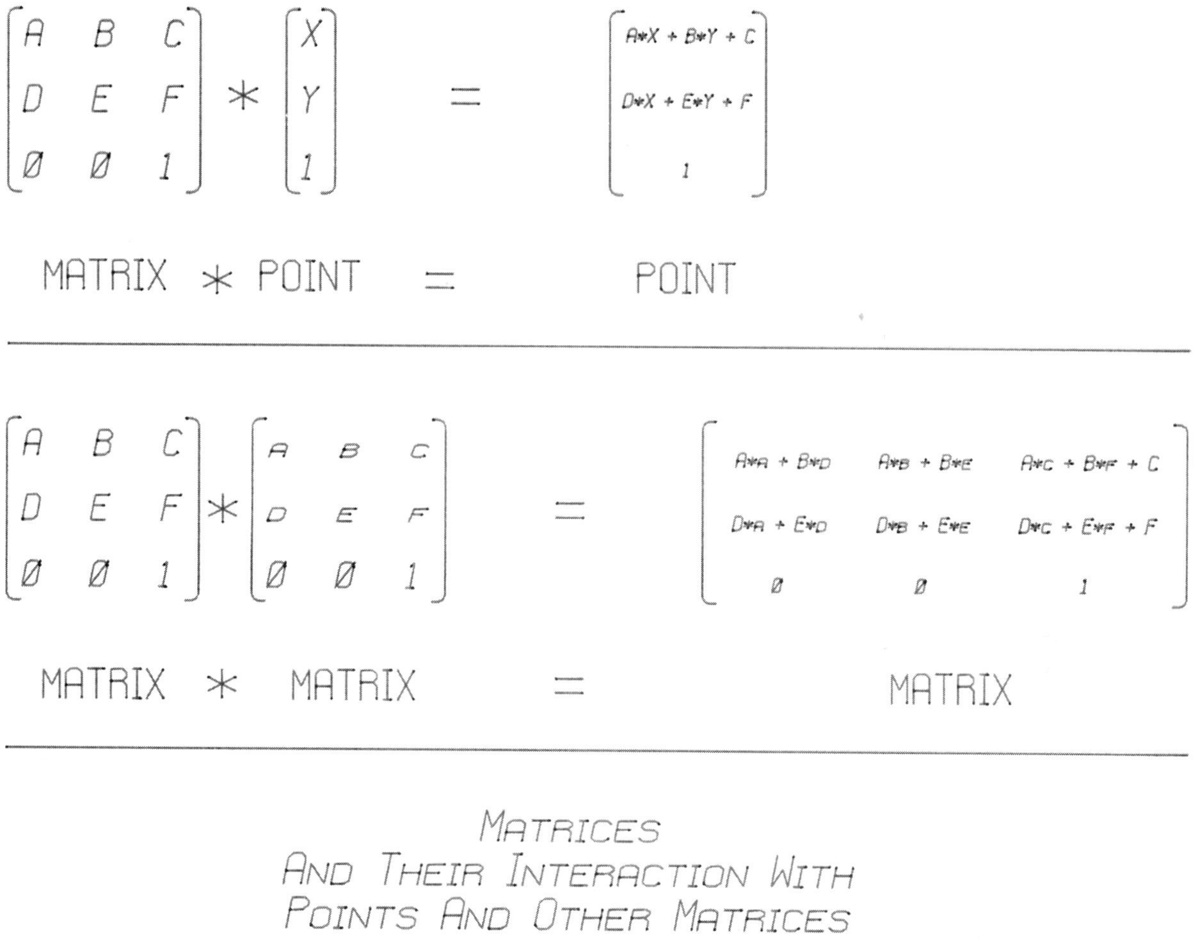

$$\begin{bmatrix} A & B & C \\ D & E & F \\ 0 & 0 & 1 \end{bmatrix} * \begin{bmatrix} X \\ Y \\ 1 \end{bmatrix} = \begin{bmatrix} A*X + B*Y + C \\ D*X + E*Y + F \\ 1 \end{bmatrix}$$

MATRIX * POINT = POINT

$$\begin{bmatrix} A & B & C \\ D & E & F \\ 0 & 0 & 1 \end{bmatrix} * \begin{bmatrix} A & B & C \\ D & E & F \\ 0 & 0 & 1 \end{bmatrix} = \begin{bmatrix} A*A + B*D & A*B + B*E & A*C + B*F + C \\ D*A + E*D & D*B + E*E & D*C + E*F + F \\ 0 & 0 & 1 \end{bmatrix}$$

MATRIX * MATRIX = MATRIX

MATRICES
AND THEIR INTERACTION WITH
POINTS AND OTHER MATRICES

FIGURE 2.5

What is a matrix? Figure 2.5 shows the common notation for matrices used in mathematics, and it shows both how a given point is transformed into a new point via a matrix, and how two matrices may be combined to form one matrix.

We use a 3 by 3 matrix even though we work only in two dimensions. The bottom row in all our 3 by 3 matrices will always be 0, 0, 1. Our restricted 3 by 3 matrix, unlike a 2 by 2 matrix, can express displacements in addition to the strictly linear transformations expressible in 2 by 2 matrices.

We apply our 3 by 3 matrix to a point by turning our two-dimensional point into a restricted three-dimensional point, always writing a 1 in the third coordinate. As Figure 2.5 shows, this technique admits the standard mathematical interpretation for multiplying matrices together and applying a matrix to a point.

We define the datatype MATRIX by

```
TYPE    MATRIX=    [  A,B,C,D,E,F:  REAL  ];
```

so to represent the six variable numbers in our matrix. We might like to rewrite this data-type definition a little more clearly to match the illustration, with

```
TYPE    MATRIX= [  A,   B,   C,
                   D,   E,   F      :       REAL
                  " 0    0    1 "                        ]  ;
```

which is entirely equivalent to the original.

We now show how each particular kind of orientation may be represented as a MATRIX by writing the following set of functions:

" A matrix may represent a simple DISPlacement by a POINT ... "

```
DEFINE     DISP(P:POINT)=   MATRIX:
    [    A:  1     B:  0     C:  P.X
         D:  0     E:  1     F:  P.Y     ]                          ENDDEFN
```

" A matrix may represent a rotation ... "

```
DEFINE     ROT(ANGLE:REAL)=   MATRIX:
    [    A:  COS(ANGLE)     B:  -SIN(ANGLE)     C:  0
         D:  SIN(ANGLE)     E:  COS(ANGLE)      F:  0  ]            ENDDEFN
```

" A matrix may represent a reflection about the X-axis ... "

```
DEFINE     MIRX  =  MATRIX:
    [    A:  1     B:  0     C:  0
         D:  0     E:  -1    F:  0              ]                   ENDDEFN
```

" A matrix may represent a reflection about the Y-axis ... "

```
DEFINE     MIRY  =  MATRIX:
    [    A:  -1    B:  0     C:  0
         D:  0     E:  1     F:  0              ]                   ENDDEFN
```

" A matrix may represent an independent scaling along each dimension "

```
DEFINE     SCALE(P:POINT)=   MATRIX:
    [    A:  P.X   B:  0     C:  0
         D:  0     E:  P.Y   F:  0              ]                   ENDDEFN
```

" A matrix can represent no change at all ... "

```
DEFINE     IDENTITY = MATRIX:
    [    A: 1      B: 0      C: 0
         D: 0      E: 1      F: 0 ]                                 ENDDEFN
```

We apply a matrix to a point with the function (Figure 2.5)

```
DEFINE     AT(P:POINT     M:MATRIX)=   POINT:
    BEGIN     VAR     A,  B,  C,  D,  E,  F,  X,  Y  =  REAL  ;
        DO    " First extract the various components ... "
              [ A:A     B:B     C:C     D:D     E:E     F:F  ]  :=     M;
              X#Y  :=  P  ;
        GIVE A*X  +  B*Y  +  C     #     D*X  +  E*Y  +  F
    END                                                            ENDDEFN
```

Thus,

```
            POINT     \AT     MATRIX          →     POINT
```

transforms a point by a matrix. For example,

Displacement:	2#2	\AT	(5#7\DISP)	is 7#9 (i.e., 2#2 + 5#7)
Rotation:	2#2	\AT	(90\ROT)	is -2#2
Mirror:	2#2	\AT	MIRX	is 2#-2
Mirror:	2#2	\AT	MIRY	is -2#2
Scale:	2#3	\AT	(5#7\SCALE)	is 10#21
Identity:	2#3	\AT	IDENTITY	is 2#3

Matrices have the wonderful property that two matrices may be combined into one matrix which will alone represent the application of both matrices. That is, where we might apply two matrices, M1 and M2, to a point P,

$$(\quad P \quad \backslash AT \quad M1 \quad) \quad \backslash AT \quad M2$$

there exists a single matrix M3 such that

$$P \quad \backslash AT \quad M3 \qquad\qquad\qquad\qquad \text{is equivalent to}$$
$$(\quad P \quad \backslash AT \quad M1 \quad) \quad \backslash AT \quad M2$$

In mathematics, M3 is the "product" of M1 and M2, written as

$$M2 \quad * \quad M1$$

Unfortunately, matrix multiplication is not commutative, that is,

$$M2 \quad * \quad M1 \qquad \text{is not always the same matrix as} \qquad M1 \quad * \quad M2$$

We must therefore be very careful about the order by which we multiply matrices. The mathematical notation we have adopted for writing matrices (Figure 2.5) chooses for us the particular order by which we multiply M1 and M2 to get the combined matrix M3:

$$M3 = M2 * M1$$

That is,

$$(\quad P \quad \backslash AT \quad M1 \quad) \quad \backslash AT \quad M2 \qquad \text{equals}$$
$$P \quad \backslash AT \quad (M2 \quad * \quad M1)$$

It appears that we have to multiply M1 and M2 in reverse order. Let us define a matrix multiplication operator,

$$\text{MATRIX} \quad \backslash THEN \quad \text{MATRIX} \quad \rightarrow \quad \text{MATRIX}$$

which will multiply two matrices in such an order that we can easily say that the resulting matrix represents the transformation rendered by applying the first matrix and THEN by applying the second matrix. Thus,

$$(\quad P \quad \backslash AT \quad M1 \quad) \quad \backslash AT \quad M2 \qquad \text{(i.e.,} \qquad \text{apply M1, then M2)}$$

is equal to

$$P \quad \backslash AT \quad (\quad M1 \quad \backslash THEN \quad M2 \quad)$$

Our \THEN operator therefore must represent matrix multiplication in the reverse order because

$$P \quad \backslash AT \quad (M1 \quad \backslash THEN \quad M2) \qquad \text{is}$$
$$P \quad \backslash AT \quad (M2 \quad * \quad M1)$$

We define \THEN with

```
DEFINE      THEN(M,N:MATRIX)=   MATRIX:
       "  The result represents the application of M and then N    "
       BEGIN              VAR     A,B,C,D,E,F,
                                  A1,B1,C1,D1,E1,F1=   REAL;
            DO            "First extract the numbers all at once ... "
                          [  A:A       B:B       C:C       D:D       E:E       F:F  ]  :=    M  ;
                          [  A:A1      B:B1      C:C1      D:D1      E:E1      F:F1 ]  :=    N  ;
            GIVE          [  A:  A1*A+B1*D   B:  A1*B+B1*E   C:  A1*C+B1*F+C1
                             D:  D1*A+E1*D   E:  D1*B+E1*E   C:  D1*C+E1*F+F1   ]
       END                         ENDDEFN
```

From now on, we will forget matrix multiplication altogether and instead remember only that

        M1   \THEN   M2

is the matrix which represents the application of M1 followed by the application of M2, so that we know simply that

        (P \AT M1)   \AT   M2   is equivalent to
        P   \AT   (M1 \THEN   M2)

2.4.1 Updating the Type LAYOUT and Its Associated Functions to Accommodate Matrices

Let us redefine the type LAYOUT, affecting the MOVE state so that it incorporates a MATRIX instead of a POINT:

```
TYPE    LAYOUT  =    EITHER
                          BOX=        BOX
                          POLYGON=    POLYGON
                          UNION=      LAYOUTS
                          MOVE=       [ DISPLACE: LAYOUT       BY:  MATRIX ]
                          COLOR=      [ PAINT: LAYOUT      WITH:  COLOR ]
                     ENDOR  ;
```

We must also modify all the layout operators that we have defined so far in order to accommodate this change to the type LAYOUT. The affected operators are

```
        LAYOUT    \AT    POINT       →      LAYOUT
        LAYOUT    \MBB               →      BOX
        PLOT(  LAYOUT  )
```

For our convenience in bringing these operators up to date, let us define the new operators:

```
        POLYGON    \AT    MATRIX     →     POLYGON
        BOX    \AT    MATRIX         →     BOX
```

to generalize our corresponding operators, which take a point instead of a matrix.

```
DEFINE    AT(PS:POLYGON    M:MATRIX)=  POLYGON:    BEGIN     VAR    P=POINT;
          {COLLECT    P  \AT  M      FOR  P  $E  PS;}           END   ENDDEFN
DEFINE    AT(B:BOX    M:MATRIX)=  BOX:
          B  \PERIMETER    \AT    M    \MBB                     ENDDEFN
```

The \AT operator for polygons forms a new polygon from the old by applying the matrix to each vertex. The \AT operator for boxes takes an easy way out; it turns the box into a polygon, then applies the matrix to that polygon, and finally takes the MBB of the transformed polygon.

Now let us update the \AT operator for layouts, and simultaneously add some other reorientation operators. First, the easiest and most basic \AT operator transforms a layout by a full-blown matrix:

```
DEFINE    AT(L:LAYOUT    M:MATRIX)=  LAYOUT:
                    [DISPLACE:L    BY:M]                    ENDDEFN
```

This takes full advantage of the new layout representation. We can specify any orientation that can be represented by a matrix. Our familiar \AT operator for points, and some other useful operators follow:

```
DEFINE    AT(L:LAYOUT    P:POINT)=  LAYOUT:
    " (Turn the point into a matrix ... ) "
            L  \AT    (P\DISP)                             ENDDEFN

DEFINE    ROT(L:LAYOUT    ANGLE:REAL)=  LAYOUT:
            L  \AT    (ANGLE\ROT)                          ENDDEFN

DEFINE    MIRX(L:LAYOUT)=  LAYOUT:
            L  \AT    MIRX                                 ENDDEFN

DEFINE    MIRY(L:LAYOUT)=  LAYOUT:
            L  \AT    MIRY                                 ENDDEFN

DEFINE    SCALE(L:LAYOUT    P:POINT)=  LAYOUT:
            L  \AT    (P\SCALE)                            ENDDEFN
```

For example,

L	\AT	3#0	still moves the layout to the right 3 units
L	\ROT	90	rotates L by 90 degrees counterclockwise, about the origin
L	\MIRX		reflects L about the horizontal X-axis
L	\SCALE	10#10	makes L 10 times bigger in each dimension.

Believe it or not, we can update our MBB function on layouts without even changing its specification. Let us look at the one place where we might have to change the MBB function, the MOVE case:

```
...
MOVE:      L.DISPLACE  \MBB    \AT    L.BY
...
```

What's new is simply that L.BY is now a matrix and not a point. However, this same old specification still makes sense. Where this specification used to interpret \AT as

```
BOX    \AT    POINT        →    BOX
```

it will now naturally interpret that \AT as

```
BOX    \AT    MATRIX       →    BOX
```

because L.BY is now a matrix, and because we have provided the new \AT operator which accepts a matrix.

Here we see an advantage which comes with our use of polymorphic operators, that is, operators of the same name which nonetheless apply in different contexts. The fact that we have the following meanings for \AT,

LAYOUT	\AT	MATRIX	→	LAYOUT
LAYOUT	\AT	POINT	→	LAYOUT
POLYGON	\AT	MATRIX	→	POLYGON
POLYGON	\AT	POINT	→	POLYGON
BOX	\AT	MATRIX	→	BOX
BOX	\AT	POINT	→	BOX
POINT	\AT	MATRIX	→	POINT

buys us two things. First, we do not have to remember many names; we have conveniently associated our single concept of movement or reorientation with a single name. We have taken advantage of the opportunity to define very specifically what \AT means in each of these different contexts. The second thing that polymorphism buys us is the ability in some cases to change \AT's parameter datatypes without having to go back and change the name AT to some other name.

To update our PLOT procedure, we need of course to reconsider the MOVE case, where L.BY is now a matrix instead of a point. If we change the type of PLOT's second parameter, DISP, from type POINT to type MATRIX, we can accommodate the L.BY matrix in the MOVE case and also provide for the specification of an initial orientation matrix, which may now include scaling.

The following rendition of PLOT differs in its literal specification from our earlier version only in that the parameter DISP is now a matrix and the MOVE case uses the \THEN operator in place of "+."

```
DEFINE    PLOT(L:LAYOUT      DISP:MATRIX      COLOR:COLOR):
      BEGIN              VAR    L1   =   LAYOUT  ;
          CASE    L    OF
              BOX:        PLOT(  L\PERIMETER    \AT     DISP, COLOR  );
              POLYGON:    PLOT(  L       \AT    DISP, COLOR  );
              UNION:      FOR    L1   $E   L;   DO
                                  PLOT(  L1,  DISP,  COLOR  );              END
              MOVE:       PLOT(  L.DISPLACE,  L.BY \THEN DISP, COLOR  );
              COLOR:      PLOT(  L.PAINT,  DISP,  L.WITH  );
          ENDCASE
      END                                                      ENDDEFN
```

The parameter DISP is now a matrix. Each of the BOX and POLYGON cases adopts the matrix DISP without any change in specification because the \AT is now interpreted as

POLYGON	\AT	MATRIX	→	POLYGON	instead of the old
POLYGON	\AT	POINT	→	POLYGON	

The UNION and COLOR cases are unchanged, even in interpretation.

The MOVE case incorporates L's reorientation matrix by plotting

L.DISPLACE   in the orientation   L.BY \THEN   DISP

Earlier, when DISP was a point, we incorporated L.BY merely by adding L.BY to DISP (Section 2.3.3.2). Now we combine the two matrices L.BY and DISP in the particular order which says:

first apply L.BY (to L.DISPLACE) to maintain accurately the meaning
        of the MOVE state, and
then apply DISP, which was meant to apply to L itself.

That is, the desire to plot L with orientation DISP is conceptually equivalent to plotting

     L   \AT   DISP

and L itself is equivalent to

     L.DISPLACE   \AT   L.BY

Together, these represent

     (L.DISPLACE \AT L.BY)   \AT   DISP   which is equivalent to
     L.DISPLACE   \AT   (L.BY \THEN   DISP)

Thus, the MOVE case specifies that we plot L.DISPLACE with the orientation

     L.BY   \THEN   DISP

    Now that we have the ability to represent scaling (as a matrix) in the PLOT procedure, we can define our simple procedure

     PLOT(LAYOUT)

so that it actually scales the layout so to fill the plotter's paper exactly. In our earlier version, where we were limited to displacements, we got only so far as to assure that the lower-left corner of the layout would land on the lower-left corner of the paper. We had no way to assure that the entire layout would fit on the paper.

    Now let us redefine PLOT as follows:

```
DEFINE     PLOT(L:LAYOUT):
        PLOT( L,    L\MBB    \FITTING_IN    (0#0  \TO  1000#1000),    BLACK  );
ENDDEFN
```

We supply as the initial orientation the matrix expression

     L\MBB   \FITTING_IN   (0#0 \TO 1000#1000)

which is meant to denote the matrix that maps the interior of

     L\MBB,   the area taken by the layout,

into the interior of

     (0#0 \TO   1000#1000),   presumably the entire area of the paper

We have expressed the transformation with the new operator

     BOX   \FITTING_IN   BOX $\rightarrow$ MATRIX

which provides the particular transformation that maps the first box into the second box.
    Such a transformation can be formed by the composition of three transformations:

1 Move the first box so that its lower-left corner resides at 0#0.
2 Enlarge or shrink this box so that its size matches the size of the second box.
3 Move the enlarged box, whose lower-left corner is still at 0#0, so that its lower-left corner comes to match the lower-left corner of the second box.

We can see that this trio of transformations maps the first box into the second box because:

1 The third step assures that the lower-left corner of the two boxes match.

2 The second step assures that the two boxes have the same size.

What is the first step for? There is something very special about the point $0\#0$. $0\#0$ is the only point that remains unaffected by scaling (step 2). (Zero times any scale factor is still zero.) Our first step moves the lower-left corner to $0\#0$ only so that we can easily predict that $0\#0$ will still be the lower-left corner after step 2 performs its scaling.

We now define the operator \FITTING_IN as follows. We will make use of the operator

BOX   \SIZE   →   POINT

which yields the size of the box, where the two dimensions are represented by the two coordinates of the point

DEFINE   SIZE(B:BOX)= POINT: B.HIGH - B.LOW   ENDDEFN

We need to know the size of each box in order to formulate the scale factor.

```
DEFINE    FITTING_IN( FROM:BOX    TO:BOX ) = MATRIX:
         BEGIN       VAR   FX, FY, TX, TY, SHRINK = REAL ;
            DO " Set FX and FY to the dimensions of the FROM box ... "
               FX # FY    :=    FROM \SIZE ;
               " Set TX and TY to the dimensions of the TO box ... "
               TX # TY    :=    TO \SIZE ;
               " The scale factor from FROM to TO ... "
               SHRINK:=    TY/FY     MIN    TX/FX ;
         GIVE " a composition of three matrices ... "
               -FROM.LOW \DISP                    \THEN
               (SHRINK#SHRINK\SCALE)        \THEN
               (TO.LOW  \DISP)                          END        ENDDEFN
```

This function first gathers the dimensions of the two boxes, FX, FY, TX, and TY. It then defines the scale factor, SHRINK, so that when multiplied by FY or FX (a dimension of the FROM box), it produces TY or TX (a dimension of the TO box). We set SHRINK to the minimum of two ratios, the x-ratio TX/FX and the y-ratio TY/FY. It is possible that these two ratios will differ; one of the boxes might be tall and thin while the other box is short and fat. The minimum of these two ratios gives us the largest uniform scaling factor which will assure that the FROM box will fit entirely within the TO box, even though one of the dimensions comes out a little short.

Finally, this function produces a matrix formed from the sequence of three matrices which implement the sequence of three steps outlined above:

1 -FROM.LOW \DISP   is a displacement that maps the point
                              FROM.LOW to $0\#0$

2 SHRINK#SHRINK \SCALE   performs the scaling

3 TO.LOW \DISP   maps $0\#0$ to TO.LOW

These three matrices are combined with the \THEN operator.

2.5 PROCESS TYPES AND GENERALIZED PLOTTING

2.5.1 Accommodating More than One Plotter and Integrated Circuit Fabrication

So far, we have assumed the existence of only one plotter, whose sheet of paper happens to be 1000 by 1000 units. In fact, there are a wide variety of plotters, some of which produce renditions on paper and others which produce an image on a color TV screen. The various plotters inevitably differ both as to the format of their interfaces and their paper or screen coordinate systems.

Let us now sketch how we can systematically accommodate all plotters. In fact, we can accommodate "plotters" that produce no immediately visible pictures, but which instead produce magnetic tapes to direct subsequently the actual fabrication of microchips from our layouts.

We have already provided for the translation from any layout into a sequence of colored polygons, each represented in the natural coordinate system of a given plotter. The only assumptions made about the plotter have been

1	The paper size	(e.g., 0#0 \TO 1000#1000)
2	The command interface	(e.g., the simple procedure PLOT(polygon,color))

If we allow these two specifics to become variables, we can accommodate any plotter.

To accommodate any plotter, we must conceive of a representation capable of representing any plotter we can imagine. We may be tempted to define such a plotter datatype with

```
TYPE    PLOTTER  =  [  PAPER:  BOX
                       INTERFACE:   a program that accepts a single-
                                    colored polygon ];
```

Any plotter is different from any other plotter in its paper size (a box), and its interface (a program that sends information in a particular format).

Thus far, none of our datatype constructors provide for the representation of programs. Let us now look at a new kind of datatype constructor which will admit the representation of programs. Such a datatype will serve as a PLOTTER's INTERFACE component.

We will characterize all plotter interfaces by the statement:

A plotter's interface is any process that takes in one polygon and one color, and which returns to us no value.

Clearly, our simple procedure PLOT(polygon,color) is a member of this class of processes. PLOT takes in one polygon and one color, and yields no value to us.

2.5.2 Type Constructor 4: Processes, or Verbs

We can declare the type that will be a plotter's interface by writing

```
TYPE    PLOTTER_INTERFACE  =    // (POLYGON,COLOR) \\    ;
```

This says that a PLOTTER_INTERFACE is a process which takes in a POLYGON and a COLOR. We use the symbols "//" and "\\" in conjunction with processes.

We might be tempted to write (which might seem more comfortable)

```
TYPE    PLOTTER_INTERFACE  =    PLOT( POLYGON,COLOR );
```

instead of using the new notation with the ''//'' and ''\\.'' The use of the ''//'' and ''\\'' in our official definition of the type PLOTTER_INTERFACE allows us to characterize all processes of interest without even suggesting that they all be named PLOT.

In general, a process datatype is characterized completely by

1 *Its input:*   the datatypes of the parameters it takes in

2 *Its output:*   the datatype of the value returned by the process

We will characterize processes not at all by their names, or the names of their parameters. Thus, all of the following hypothetical functions are members of the type PLOTTER_INTERFACE even though they use different names:

```
PLOT(   X:POLYGON      Y:COLOR   )
DRAW(   WX:POLYGON      JK:COLOR    )
FRACTURE(   A:POLYGON      B:COLOR   )
```

What isn't a PLOTTER_INTERFACE? The following are not PLOTTER_INTERFACEs because each either yields a value, or takes input parameters other than one POLYGON and one COLOR:

```
MBB(   X:POLYGON   )     =      BOX
PLOT(   L:LAYOUT   )
PLOT(   L:LAYOUT      DISP:MATRIX      COLOR:COLOR   )
BRIGHTNESS(   X:POLYGON      C:COLOR   )     =      REAL
```

We have four notations for declaring process types, three of which are simplifications of the first notation. The four notations differ only in

1 The existence of any input

2 The existence of any output

The first, and full-blown notation,

```
//   type      ( type ,  type ,     ...     , type )    \\
```

denotes all processes that take in parameters of the types specified within the parentheses, and which return an object of the first type appearing before the parentheses. Our PLOTTER_INTERFACE datatype has not been expressed with this notation simply because it yields no value.

We could imagine a different kind of plotter interface which does return a value. For example, suppose that, on occasion, our plotters ignored commands. To use such a flaky plotter effectively, we would have to know for each command whether or not the plotter acknowledges the command. We can include such an acknowledgment in a new type, FLAKY_PLOTTER_INTERFACE, by declaring

TYPE   FLAKY_PLOTTER_INTERFACE   =   //   BOOL   (POLYGON,   COLOR   )   \\;

This type of process takes in a POLYGON and a COLOR, just like our official PLOTTER_INTERFACE type, but in addition it yields to us a BOOLean, TRUE or FALSE, telling us whether or not it performed the command.

The second notation for declaring process types is the one we have used for declaring PLOTTER_INTERFACE. It differs from the first notation only in that it omits the specification of an output type. That is,

> // (type , type , ... , type) \\

denotes all processes that take in parameters of these types but produce no values.

Finally, it is possible to declare processes that take in no values at all. We use a notation that omits the sequence of types specified within the parentheses:

> // type \\

This denotes the class of processes that take in no parameters but do produce a value of the specified type. A familiar example of such a parameterless process is the computer terminal in front of which you might now be sitting. When viewed as an input device, the terminal produces to the computer the characters you type. That is, a terminal viewed as an input device is a member of the process datatype

> // CHAR \\

which yields a character. Each time we invoke this type of process, we get the next character.

It is possible to declare a process datatype which both takes in and yields no data whatsoever. We use the notation

> // \\

to denote this deaf-mute process.

For example,

1	// (POLYGON, COLOR) \\	is a process type that takes in a single polygon and a color. It yields no value.
2	// REAL (REAL) \\	is a process type that takes in a REAL and returns a REAL.
3	// INT (COLOR) \\	maps a COLOR (input) to an INT (output).

2.5.2.1 Creating instances of process types. We create instances of processes with a notation that uses the symbols "//" and "\\" much as we have done in declaring process datatypes. The notation for creating a process is

> // (input parameter specification) body \\

The "input parameter specification" matches exactly the notation we use in declaring a function's input parameters. The "body" is identical to the body of a function.

For example, the expression

> // (X:REAL) X * X \\

is similar to

> define ... (X:REAL) = real: X * X enddefn

This particular process takes in one REAL, named X, and yields the value X∗X. This particular process is certainly an instance of the process datatype

        // REAL (REAL) \\

The "input parameter specification" displays not only the datatypes of the input parameters, but also the names of variables that will represent the input values for use by the "body."

For example, we can declare

        TYPE   FUNCTION = // REAL (REAL) \\ ;
        VAR   F = FUNCTION ;

The type FUNCTION includes any process that maps a REAL to a REAL. The newly declared variable F can thus represent any function introduced in a beginning calculus course (within the limitations of computer arithmetic).

We can assign to F the function "x-squared" by writing

        F :=   // (X:REAL)   X∗X   \\ ;

We can also assign to F the function SIN(X∗3) by writing

        F :=   // (X:REAL)   SIN(X∗3)   \\;

Similarly, we can declare

        TYPE   PLOTTER_INTERFACE =   // (POLYGON,COLOR) \\ ;

to characterize all plotter interfaces. We go on to declare the type PLOTTER with

        TYPE   PLOTTER =   [PAPER: BOX
                                INTERFACE: PLOTTER_INTERFACE   ] ;

to represent the fact that any plotter has a PLOTTER_INTERFACE and also its own coordinate system, represented by a BOX. Finally, let us declare a variable which can represent any PLOTTER, with

        VAR   OUR_PLOTTER = PLOTTER ;

We can set the variable OUR_PLOTTER to represent completely the particular plotter we have been considering throughout our plotting examples:

OUR_PLOTTER:= [PAPER: 0#0   \TO   1000#1000
                INTERFACE: //(PS:POLYGON   C:COLOR)   PLOT(PS,C); \\ ] ;

The variable OUR_PLOTTER now represents the plotter whose natural coordinates lie between 0 and 1000, and whose interface is the process

        //(PS:POLYGON   C:COLOR)   PLOT(PS,C);   \\

This process takes in a polygon and a color, and calls our simple PLOT function defined earlier (Section 2.3.3.2) to send commands to the hardware plotter in its particular format.

2.5.2.2 *Examining instances of process types.* Processes do not admit examination in the same sense that all our other datatypes admit examination. We cannot examine a process to find what it is made of. Instead, we can only invoke, or execute, a process.

Where all our other datatypes are nouns, objects made out of other objects within a well-defined structure, process datatypes are verbs, arbitrary programs with no particular structure to admit their dissection. For example, we do not examine a PLOTTER_INTERFACE to determine whether or not it calls PLOT. Instead, we invoke this process and thereby perform the action of plotting.

We invoke a process with a notation that uses the symbols "< *" and "*> ." The expression

    < *   a plotter interface   *>   (some polygon, some color   )   ;

invokes a plotter interface so as to plot a polygon of some color. Referring to the variable OUR_PLOTTER, of type PLOTTER, we know that its INTERFACE component,

    OUR_PLOTTER   .   INTERFACE

is of type PLOTTER_INTERFACE. We can send a polygon and a color to our plotter by writing

    < *   OUR_PLOTTER.INTERFACE   *>   (a polygon, a color   );

This particular invocation is itself an action that produces no value in return. Linguistically, this invocation is a sentence, just like a direct call to the procedure PLOT.

In contrast, the invocation of a process that does return a value is not a sentence, but a value. The invocation does perform an action, but the culmination of that action is the production of a value. For example, the variable F, of type FUNCTION,

    //   REAL   (REAL   )   \\

produces a REAL as a result of its invocation. Linguistically, the invocation of F, for example,

    < *   F   *>   (a number   )

falls into the category for values. Such a value-producing invocation can appear anywhere that a value may appear. For example,

    VAR   R   =   REAL   ;
    R:=   < *F*>(20)   ;

shows F's invocation appearing as a value, on the right-hand side of the assignment.

Since F is a variable, we can assign it a new value. The following sequence of events can occur:

F:=   //(X:REAL)   X*X   \\   ;   " F represents the function x-squared "
R:=   < *F*>(20);   " R takes on the value 400 "
F:=   //(X:REAL)   X+1   \\   ;   " F represents the increment function "
R:=   < *F*>(20);   " R takes on the value 21 "

Example: Numerical integration. We can define an INTEGRAL function that performs numerical integration on an object of type FUNCTION. The INTEGRAL function will take in an object of type FUNCTION, the two limits of integration (LOW and HIGH), and a small increment (DX):

```
DEFINE    INTEGRAL(F:FUNCTION    LOW,HIGH:REAL    DX:REAL)  =  REAL:
        BEGIN        VAR    X  =  REAL  ;
            +   (    < *F*>(X)  *  DX  )     FOR  X  FROM  LOW  TO  HIGH  BY  DX;
        END                                              ENDDEFN
```

INTEGRAL produces as its result the sum formed by running X from LOW to HIGH, each time evaluating F at X [$< *F*>$(X)], and multiplying this result by DX.

2.5.3 Generalizing Our PLOT Procedure

Let us once again, and for the last time, redefine our PLOT procedures so that they may deal with any object of type PLOTTER. We will change

```
        PLOT(  L:LAYOUT  )
```

into

```
        PLOT(  L:LAYOUT  PL:PLOTTER  )
```

so that we may specify any plotter. We will also change our flexible

```
        PLOT(  L:LAYOUT    DISP:MATRIX    COLOR:COLOR  )
```

into

```
    PLOT(  L:LAYOUT  DISP:MATRIX  COLOR:COLOR  PL:PLOTTER_INTERFACE  )
```

so that the particular plotter interface can be known when we come down to plotting single polygons.
    We redefine our flexible PLOT procedure as follows. We change conceptually only the BOX and POLYGON cases, where we have dealt directly with the plotter. Now, instead of calling our simple PLOT procedure directly,

```
        PLOT(  ...  );
```

we invoke the plotter interface variable PL, with

```
        < *PL*>(  ...  );
```

The other cases differ from their old specifications only in that they faithfully pass the fourth parameter, PL, in their recursive calls to this flexible PLOT procedure.

```
DEFINE    PLOT(L:LAYOUT    DISP:MATRIX    COLOR:COLOR    PL:PLOTTER_INTERFACE):
    BEGIN            VAR    L1  =  LAYOUT  ;
        CASE    L    OF
            BOX:           < *PL*>(  L\PERIMETER  \AT  DISP,  COLOR  )  ;
            POLYGON:       < *PL*>(  L    \AT      DISP,     COLOR  )  ;
            UNION:         FOR   L1   $E   L  ;      DO
                                PLOT(  L1,  DISP,  COLOR,  PL  );     END
            MOVE:          PLOT(  L.DISPLACE,  L.BY  \THEN  DISP,  COLOR,  PL  );
            COLOR:         PLOT(  L.PAINT,  DISP,  L.WITH,  PL  );
        ENDCASE
    END                                              ENDDEFN
```

We now define the convenient ''high-level'' PLOT procedure as follows:

```
DEFINE     PLOT(L:LAYOUT     PL:PLOTTER):
        PLOT( L,    L\MBB \FITTING_IN    PL.PAPER,       BLACK,      PL.INTERFACE  );
ENDDDEFN
```

Notice how we specify the initial orientation using the box

PL.PAPER   in place of our old constant

0#0   \TO   1000#1000

so that no matter what plotter we are going to, we will automatically scale the layout to fit nicely on that plotter's paper or screen. We pass the process

PL.INTERFACE

to our flexible plot procedure so that each polygon and box is transmitted to the plotter in that plotter's own format.

Now if we say

PLOT(layout,   OUR_PLOTTER   );

the layout will be sent to our plotter, whose paper size is the box

0#0   \TO   1000#1000

and whose interface understands precisely the commands

PEN   number
U   number, number
D   number, number

2.5.4   Layout Fabrication

Nowhere have we made the assumption that a plotter must produce a visible picture. We have been so flexible in our definition of the type PLOTTER_INTERFACE that we can supply any program whatsoever as the plotter interface, as long as that program takes in a polygon and a color.

The fabrication of an integrated circuit maps a layout onto a real piece of silicon. To fabricate a layout, we need merely produce a magnetic tape in a particular format that is understood by the silicon foundries. The silicon foundries take in our magnetic tape and produce actual silicon chips without human regard for the particular layout.

Different fabricators use different formats; what else could be expected? All formats do have in common the ability to support the production of arbitrary polygons (within acceptable precision), but almost all formats require that each polygon be broken down into a set of very simple kinds of polygons. Some formats accept as simple polygons only rectangles that may be rotated. Other formats accept as simple polygons only trapezoids where the two parallel sides must be horizontal. All formats presently require the polygons to be sorted by color. Some require polygon sorting in the X and Y directions.

Each fabricator chooses a format that facilitates the quickest production of chips on that fabricator's particular machine.

No matter what format we use, we can represent that format as a particular instance of type PLOTTER_INTERFACE. Such a plotter interface takes in a polygon and a color, fractures the polygon into some form of simple polygons, and then sends out a series of numbers (e.g., vertices) to a file or magnetic tape.

Let us choose for illustrative purposes a format which is particularly simple from our point of view. Suppose that the fabricator would like a series of files, one for each color, where each file contains simply a very long sequence of arbitrary polygons. Let us say that each file has the format

```
polygon
polygon
   ...
polygon
   −2
```

so that the file is a sequence of polygons, terminated by a -2. Let us say also that each polygon is represented by a sequence of pairs of numbers, the x and y coordinates of each vertex, in the format

$$-1 \quad x_1 \quad y_1 \quad x_2 \quad y_2 \quad \ldots \quad x_k \quad y_k$$

We start each polygon with a -1 so that we can tell that the previous polygon has ended. Finally, we will assume also that the fabricator wants the entire layout to reside in a coordinate system whose units are tenths of micrometers (0.1 micrometer) and whose coordinates are positive (i.e., the lower-left corner of the layout is at 0#0). (It is necessary that coordinates be positive in this format so that our delimeters, -1 and -2, appear only as delimeters and never as coordinates.)

We must introduce for this example one more built-in datatype which lets us create files. The new built-in type is called OUTPUT_FILE and it participates in the following operators:

TEXT \OPEN	$\rightarrow$	OUTPUT_FILE	to open a new file whose name is TEXT
OUTPUT(OUTPUT_FILE, INTeger)			to output a single INT to the file
CLOSE(OUTPUT_FILE)			to close the file when we are done

For example, the sequence

```
VAR   F  =  OUTPUT_FILE  ;
F:=  'MRBILL'  \OPEN  ;
OUTPUT(F,5);
OUTPUT(F,10);
CLOSE(F);
```

creates a file whose name is MRBILL, and which contains the sequence of two numbers 5 and 10. The final operation, the CLOSE, is necessary on almost all computer systems to render the file complete.

We will deal with not one file, but five files, one for each color. To represent our set of "colored" files, let us declare

```
TYPE   COLORED_FILE=  [COLOR:COLOR   FILE:OUTPUT_FILE];
TYPE   COLORED_FILES=  {  COLORED_FILE  }  ;
```

The type COLORED_FILES thus represents a set of files, where each file is tagged with a particular COLOR.

Our FABRICATE function will take in a LAYOUT and also a REAL parameter called UNITS. The UNITS parameter in effect specifies the units used in constructing the layout. That is, because we have been using the "lambda" unit in all our layouts, we now specify how many of the fabricator's units (0.1 micrometer) are in one of our lambda units. Generally, the particular fabricator tells us this relationship. Some fabricators can produce chips where 1 lambda equals 2.5 micrometers, and others can produce even denser chips where 1 lambda equals 1.5 micrometers. If we are going to a fabricator whose lambda equals 1.5 micrometers (or 15 tenths of a micrometer), we produce data for the fabricator by writing

    FABRICATE(our layout, 15);

Here is a sketch of FABRICATE:

    DEFINE   FABRICATE(L:LAYOUT   UNITS:REAL):
          BEGIN   VAR   CFS= COLORED_FILES;
                CFS:=   the set of opened colored files
                PLOT(L, an appropriate matrix, BLACK; a plotter interface);
                close each of the five files in CFS
          END   ENDDEFN

FABRICATE first opens five files, one for each color, and then calls our familiar layout PLOT routine passing in a particular plotter interface. This plotter interface takes in a polygon and a color and chooses one of the five files based on the color. The plotter interface then outputs the polygon to that file. The fact that we output polygons of different colors to different files guarantees that the five files will represent all the layout's polygons, sorted by color. Our FABRICATE function finally closes the five files after the "plotting" process is complete.

In full bloom, our FABRICATE function is

    DEFINE   FABRICATE(L:LAYOUT   UNITS:REAL):
        BEGIN   VAR   CFS=COLORED_FILES; C=COLOR; F=OUTPUT_FILE;
          " Set CFS to our set of five colored files, one for each color ..."
          CFS:= {COLLECT   [COLOR:C   FILE: C\OPEN]
                          FOR   C $E   {RED;BLUE;GREEN;YELLOW;BLACK};   };

          " Output all polygons to the various files ... "
          PLOT(L, -(L\MBB).LOW \DISP   \THEN   (UNITS#UNITS\SCALE),   BLACK ,

                //(PS:POLYGON   C:COLOR) [CFS;] "(See Below)"
                      BEGIN   VAR   C1=COLOR; F=OUTPUT_FILE; P=POINT;

                      IF FOR [COLOR:C1   FILE:F] $E CFS; THERE_IS C = C1
                      THEN   " Output polygon PS to file F ... "
                                OUTPUT(F,-1);
                                FOR P $E PS;   DO   OUTPUT(F, P.X \FIXR);
                                                        OUTPUT(F, P.Y \FIXR);   END
                      FI   END \\   );
          " Finish each file by putting out a -2 and then closing it ... "
          FOR [COLOR:C FILE:F] $E CFS; DO OUTPUT(F, -2); CLOSE(F);   END
        END   ENDDEFN

The first of the three steps sets CFS to the set of colored files, each created by

    [COLOR:C   FILE: C\OPEN]

where C runs over the set of colors

{ RED ; BLUE ; GREEN ; YELLOW ; BLACK }

That is, each colored file has C as its color and C\OPEN as its output file. The expression

C \OPEN

is an OUTPUT_FILE because C, which is a COLOR, is also of type TEXT because of the definition of type COLOR (Section 2.2.2.2). Thus, we will produce files whose names are the names of our colors; that is, the files will be named RED, BLUE, GREEN, YELLOW, and BLACK, respectively.

The second of the three steps does almost all the work:

PLOT(L,   −(L\MBB).LOW \DISP   \THEN   (UNITS#UNITS\SCALE),   BLACK,
                      a plotter interface   )   ;

This plots L in a coordinate system where L's lower-left corner is 0#0 and where our lambda units are translated into 0.1-micrometer units. That is, we have specified as PLOT's initial orientation the matrix which first displaces L so that its lower-left corner resides at 0#0, and which then scales L by the specified UNITS factor.

PLOT's fourth parameter is a plotter interface, a process that takes in a single polygon and a color. As we saw earlier, an instance of PLOTTER_INTERFACE is written as

//(PS:POLYGON   C:COLOR)
                    do something with PS and C   \\

For our particular application, we must introduce one more capability of processes which has not yet been mentioned. In our FABRICATE function we have written the process as

//(PS:POLYGON   C:COLOR) [CFS;]
                    do something with PS, C, and CFS   \\

The body of our process requires access not only to the given polygon and color, but also to the colored files represented in the variable CFS.

CFS is not a parameter like PS and C. The PLOT procedure knows nothing at all about CFS; it gives us only PS and C. Rather, CFS is a parameter that comes from within FABRICATE and not from within PLOT.

We retain access to CFS within the process itself by writing, as we have, the notation

[CFS;]

as part of the process header.

In general, we can write a process as

//(variable:type ... variable:type)   [variable;   ...   variable;]
                    body   \\

We are already familiar with the parameters specified within the parentheses. These parameters are given to the process when the process is invoked, for example, when PLOT's polygon case performs

< *PL*>(polygon, color);

In contrast, the variables named within brackets (e.g., CFS) are given to the process when the process is created. The plotter interface process is created with the "//...\\" notation, where FABRICATE specifies the process as a parameter to PLOT.

We can clarify this matter with a space-age analogy. Let us think of a process as a space capsule. Information and materials are given to the space capsule in two distinct ways. First, food and astronauts are given to the space capsule at launch time. Second, radio signals are given to the space capsule once it is in orbit. Once the capsule is in orbit, the capsule has access to both the launch-time and orbit-time parameters.

Our process notation maintains this analogy in that the bracketed variables represent launch-time context and the other set of variables represents the orbit-time context. In our example, the FABRICATE function launches the process, supplying the launch-time context CFS. The PLOT function communicates with the orbiting process via the orbit-time context PS and C.

Let us look more closely at the plotter interface process given to PLOT from within FABRICATE. The body of this process has access to the variables PS, C, and CFS. The body is written in the form

> IF, looking at each colored file in CFS, there is one whose color
> matches the color of the polygon, C,
> THEN output the polygon PS to that file.

We have seen this technique in Section 2.2.8 with our example that maps a color to a pen number, given a color map as context. Whereas that example mapped a color to a pen number, our present example maps a color to an output file. By the time we reach the THEN clause, F is set to the appropriate file for the given color. The THEN clause puts out first a -1, as our file format demands, and then puts out the x and y coordinates for each of the polygon's vertices, as INTegers.

FABRICATE finishes by terminating each file in CFS. It terminates each file by putting out the final -2 demanded by our file format, and then it closes that file.

2.6 OTHER REPRESENTATIONS FOR LAYOUTS

Why have we chosen our particular representation for layouts? Could we not choose another, perhaps simpler representation? After all, in the final analysis, a layout is just a set of colored polygons. Our PLOT procedure meets this "final analysis" by turning our layout representation into a sequence of colored polygons, implemented as a sequence of calls to a plotter interface.

Perhaps we are tempted to redefine the type LAYOUT with

> TYPE LAYOUT = { [COLOR:COLOR SHAPE:SHAPE] } ;

which says that LAYOUT is simply a set of colored shapes. The type SHAPE, introduced in Section 2.3.1, might be replaced by the even simpler type POLYGON. Why not?

Let us call this newly proposed representation the "linear" representation. In contrast, let us call our standard representation the "hierarchical" or "recursive" representation. We use the term "linear" with this new representation because this representation is structurally one-dimensional; it is just one list, each of whose elements is a single atomic shape.

In contrast, our standard representation is richer. It contains lists (the UNION case) where the elements may themselves be other layouts. This representation is defined recursively; that is, the type LAYOUT refers back to the type LAYOUT within its definition. We have used recursive procedures (e.g., MBB and PLOT) to treat this recursive representation.

Let us compare the linear versus the recursive representation. The linear representation seems to favor some forms of layout analysis, certainly the plotting and fabrication of layouts. In contrast, the recursive representation seems to favor the synthesis of layouts; notice how easily we have defined the synthesis operators (e.g., \AT).

We are really free to choose either representation. We have already shown how to handle completely the recursive representation. With our general-purpose PLOT procedure, we have provided a convenient means with which to interpret our recursive representation as though it were a linear representation.

If we wanted to adopt the linear representation instead of the recursive representation, we need only redefine the synthesis operators to produce the linear representation.

Our two analysis operators, MBB and PLOT, of course would also require modification, but the result in each case would be a simplification. For example, the MBB function would be

DEFINE   MBB(L:LINEAR_LAYOUT)=   BOX: BEGIN   VAR   S=SHAPE;
          \MAX   (S\MBB)   FOR   [SHAPE:S] $ E   L;   END   ENDDEFN.

This looks much like the UNION case in our recursive MBB function.

2.6.1   The Immense Costs in a Linear Representation

Let us compare the linear versus the recursive layout representations in terms of execution time and memory consumption.

We will measure time and memory consumption in terms of "memory units" and "time units." We will use these terms loosely, in that one process's "time unit" may in practice be 10 time units to another process. However, the units of time and memory will always be independent of layouts. That is, we wish to consider only how time and memory depend on layouts, not, for example, whether it takes one or five machine instructions to perform multiplication.

We will also refer to a layout's "complexity" simply as the total number of shapes that appear on a plot of the entire layout.

2.6.2   Costs in Execution Time

Let us try to define the synthesis operator \AT to work with the linear representation. We can write the new definition for \AT easily:

DEFINE   AT(L:LINEAR_LAYOUT   P:POINT)=   LINEAR_LAYOUT:
     BEGIN   VAR   S=SHAPE; C=COLOR;
          {COLLECT   [SHAPE: S \AT P   COLOR: C]
                              FOR [SHAPE:S   COLOR:C] $E L;   }
     END   ENDDEFN

This definition forms a copy of the list L, where each element's shape S is moved by P. (It is straightforward to define the \AT operator which moves a SHAPE, the \AT applied to each shape within this example.)

Although this \AT for a LINEAR_LAYOUT is simple enough to write down, it is nonetheless very time consuming to execute. If the LINEAR_LAYOUT has 100,000 shapes in it, it takes 100,000 time units to execute this \AT, one time unit per element in the list.

In contrast, our \AT defined for the recursive type LAYOUT,

DEFINE   AT(L:LAYOUT   P:POINT)=   LAYOUT:
                    [DISPLACE: L   BY: P]   ENDDEFN

takes only one time unit, even if L represents 100,000 shapes. This \AT forms merely a single record having two components and then tags this record with the "MOVE" state.

The record references the given layout L. It does not form a copy of L nor does it geometrically transform each datum represented in L. The recursive layout \AT does not even examine L.

In general, all our synthesis operators will consume dramatically more time with the linear representation than with the recursive representation. This is because the recursive representation is capable of representing a new layout entirely in terms of a reference to the old layout, together with a tiny amount of additional data (e.g., a point or a matrix). In contrast, the linear representation has no such capability; nowhere is there a slot in which to represent a matrix or point movement. The linear representation can represent a movement only by incorporating that movement into each shape individually.

In general, where synthesis done in terms of the linear representation requires time proportional to the layout's complexity, synthesis done in terms of the recursive representation requires time that is entirely independent of the layout's complexity.

2.6.3   Costs in Memory

Not only does the linear representation consume more time to create than does the recursive representation, it also consumes more memory. The linear \AT operator forms a copy of the entire layout, whereas the recursive \AT forms no such copy. The recursive \AT refers directly to the existing layout.

For example, if L is a linear layout having 100,000 shapes, then the linear layout

        L   \UNION   (L   \AT   3#0)

contains 200,000 shapes and thus occupies 200,000 memory units. In contrast, if L is a recursive layout having 100,000 shapes, the recursive layout

        L   \UNION   (L   \AT   3#0)

contains 200,000 shapes but occupies only 100,000 (+ a small number) of memory units, only half the memory required by the linear representation. (In fact, the recursive L probably represents its 100,000 shapes in much less than 100,000 memory units, by this same kind of reasoning.)

2.6.4   Memory Sharing and Layout Regularity

How is it that the recursive representation can represent lots of shapes in only a little memory? The recursive representation can reference other layouts more than once. In the example

        L   \UNION   (L   \AT   3#0)

the layout referenced by the variable L is referenced twice within this expression. L is referenced once as the first member of the union, and L is referenced a second time from within the record produced by the \AT operator, the record

        [DISPLACE: L   BY: 3#0]

A data structure that is referenced more than once is called a ''shared'' data structure.

2.6.5   Example of Data Sharing: A 4K RAM

Let us consider another example, a 4096-bit memory. A 4096-bit memory contains 4096 individual memory cells, one for each bit of memory. Suppose that BIT is a layout for exactly one bit of memory. We form the bulk of the 4096-bit memory by forming a two-dimensional array of these BIT cells. Let us form that array. We will assume that the BIT layout has been designed to fit snugly into such an array.

If the dimensions of the BIT layout are IX in x and IY in y, we can form our 64 by 64 array (4096 elements) by writing

```
{COLLECT    BIT  \AT X#Y    ( FOR X FROM 0 BY IX; && REPEAT 64;)    !!
                            ( FOR Y FROM 0 BY IY; && REPEAT 64;)    }
```

This forms a list of 4096 BITs, each one displaced by X#Y, where X runs from 0 in increments of IX and where Y runs from 0 in increments of IY. (Refer to Sections 1.3.4 and 1.4.3 for a review of this notation.)

This array references the BIT layout 4096 times. Even if BIT itself contains 100 shapes, this array consumes not 4096 * 100 units of memory, but rather 100 + 4096 memory units. (We assume that each element in the list, each reference to BIT, consumes one memory unit.)

We can write the 4096-bit array another way, which takes even more advantage of data sharing. In fact, this expression might seem clearer than the previous one. We will first define a single row of the array,

```
ROW:=  {COLLECT    BIT  \AT X#0 FOR X FROM 0 BY IX; && REPEAT 64;}  ;
```

This ROW layout contains 64 references to BIT, each with a displacement only in x. We now form the whole array by forming 64 references to ROW, each with a displacement in y:

```
{COLLECT    ROW  \AT 0#Y FOR Y FROM 0 BY IY; && REPEAT 64;}
```

This expression represents geometrically exactly the same 4096-bit array.

How much memory does this expression require? Let us first see how much memory ROW requires. ROW requires 100 + 64 memory units, 100 for BIT and 64 for the 64 references to BIT. The representation for the entire array requires the space taken by ROW and then 64 more memory units for the 64 references to ROW.

In summary, we find that the entire array requires the following amounts of memory for each of these three ways of forming the array:

409600	for the linear representation
4196	for the recursive representation, with 4096 references to BIT
228	for the recursive representation involving ROW

The final number is so small because by using ROW as an intermediate value, we create, in fact, two levels of sharing. The array references ROW 64 times, and ROW references BIT 64 times.

It is curious perhaps that the recursive representation alone can consume different amounts of memory, depending only on the way we specify the array, that is, whether or not we introduce the ROW layout as an intermediate value. The recursive representation is very flexible. In fact, our linear representation is precisely a very special case of the recursive representation. The linear representation is realized within the recursive representation by imagining the recursive representation residing in the UNION state, where each layout referenced from the union resides always in either the POLYGON or BOX state.

The recursive representation's ability to share data allows us to take advantage of the regularity that is characteristic of all layouts to varying degrees. Because all 4096 bits in the array are identical, we can represent BIT exactly once. If all 4096 bits were entirely different from one another, we could share no data, and we would therefore have to use the 409,600 units of memory, just like the linear representation. In such very irregular situations, our flexible recursive representation adapts naturally to the structure found with the linear representation.

In fact, the recursive representation adapts very nicely throughout the continuum between total regularity and total irregularity. Suppose that all 4096 bits were not the same, but then not entirely different either. More specifically, suppose that there are four types of BITs, placed always in 2 by 2 clumps. An array 64 by 64 of these bits can be represented by a 32 by 32 array of clumps:

```
CLUMP:=  {  BIT1  \AT  0#0    ;    BIT2  \AT  IX#0    ;
            BIT3  \AT  0#IY ;    BIT4  \AT  IX#IY      }    ;
ROW:=       {COLLECT    CLUMP  \AT    X#0    FOR  X  FROM  0  BY  2*IX;  &&  REPEAT  32;}  ;
ARRAY:=  {COLLECT    ROW  \AT  0#Y    FOR  Y  FROM  0  BY  2*IY;  &&  REPEAT  32;}  ;
```

We can see how much memory this array consumes. If each of the four different BITs consumes 100 memory units, then

CLUMP	takes	400
ROW	takes	432
ARRAY	takes	464

Thus, our slightly irregular array takes 464 units, a little more than the absolutely regular 228, but much less than the absolutely irregular 409,600 units.

2.6.6 Data Sharing and the Costs of Analysis

Synthesis operators with our recursive representation operate at costs in memory and time which are very small and which are entirely independent of the complexity of layouts. Fast synthesis is essential: We will move layouts very often, often moving the same layout over and over again. Where a FORTRAN programmer does not think twice about writing

I+1

we need not think twice about writing

L \AT 1#0

How do the recursive and linear representations compare insofar as our analysis operators PLOT and MBB are concerned? Consider PLOT. Independent of representation, PLOT must always work at a cost proportional to the number of shapes in the layout simply because each shape must be drawn individually. We expect that a 4096-bit array will take 4096 times as much plotting time as a one-bit array. We therefore expect that as far as plotting is concerned, either representation serves equally well.

We will return to more plotting considerations when we consider plots that show only a small part of an entire layout. At that time, we will see how our two representations differ.

Now consider the MBB operation. How do our two representations compare for this operation? Referring to Section 2.6, we see that the MBB defined on the linear representation takes time proportional to the number of shapes in the entire layout. It forms the \MAX of the MBBs of the individual shapes.

Does our MBB function defined on the recursive representation (Section 2.3.3.1) also require time proportional to the number of shapes in the layout? That is, does the MBB computation for a 4096-bit array take 4096 times as long as for a 1-bit array? Put another way, does the MBB computation recompute the MBB of the BIT layout 4096 times, instead of conceivably computing the MBB for BIT exactly once and referring subsequently to this one-time computation 4096 times?

As written in Section 2.3.3.1, the MBB operator does in fact recompute the MBB for the BIT layout 4096 times. This MBB operator does take time which is proportional to the complexity of the layout. It takes no advantage of data sharing.

This expense can be seen clearly in a number of ways. First, the definition of MBB looks just like the definition of PLOT. Each clause in the CASE statement calls MBB for each sublayout, just as PLOT calls PLOT for each sublayout. Even if two sublayouts referenced from within a given layout are identical, MBB will call MBB independently for each reference to the same layout.

All analysis operators that yield values dependent on an entire layout will examine that layout in its entirety, without regard for data sharing. Our representation has no component which can even indicate that a given layout is a shared datum. Data sharing has arisen only as a by-product of our expression of synthesis. Although data sharing can exist, its existence is nowhere detectable.

In general, synthesis can benefit by data sharing even though the expression of data sharing is invisible. Analysis, on the other hand, cannot take advantage of data sharing because analysis can see only those intentions that can be represented explicitly.

We will soon render a much faster MBB function simply by transferring the bulk of the MBB computation away from analysis and into synthesis. This way, the MBB computation as part of synthesis can take advantage of data sharing.

2.6.7   Data Sharing in the Time Dimension

Not only can data be shared in space, they can also be shared over time. A data structure is shared over time if we perform an operation on that data structure more than once. For example, we may ask for L's MBB many times during its lifetime.

2.6.8   Transferring the MBB Computation from Analysis to Synthesis

We transfer the bulk of the MBB computation from analysis to synthesis by providing a slot in our LAYOUT representation to hold an MBB computed immediately upon synthesis. By storing precomputed MBBs with each layout, the analysis operator which obtains a layout's MBB reduces merely to the extraction of a component. Component extraction operates at a speed that is independent of the complexity of the layout.

We have the type LAYOUT, defined by (Section 2.3.2)

```
TYPE    LAYOUT  =    EITHER
                         BOX=           BOX
                         POLYGON=       POLYGON
                         UNION=         LAYOUTS
                         MOVE=          [ DISPLACE: LAYOUT    BY:  POINT  ]
                         COLOR=         [ PAINT: LAYOUT    WITH:  COLOR  ]
                     ENDOR  ;
```

Let us now introduce a new type, called MLAYOUT, to represent a LAYOUT along with its MBB:

```
TYPE    MLAYOUT = [ BODY: LAYOUT    MBB: BOX ] ;
```

Given an MLAYOUT, we can obtain its MBB instantly, by writing

    MLAYOUT . MBB

2.6.8.1 *Fusing the types LAYOUT and MLAYOUT.* How do we render a situation that offers the advantages of the type MLAYOUT within our more familiar domain of type LAYOUT? For example, we wish that given a LAYOUT, we will find each of its sublayouts represented as an MLAYOUT, so that we can obtain readily each subcell's MBB. (Notice that the LAYOUT \MBB function performs its computation based entirely on the MBBs of immediate sublayouts.)

Let us redeclare the type LAYOUT so that it references the new type MLAYOUT. We form our new definition from the old one simply by replacing each reference to LAYOUT by a reference instead to type MLAYOUT:

```
TYPE    LAYOUT  =  EITHER
                        BOX=        BOX
                        POLYGON=    POLYGON
                        UNION=      MLAYOUTS
                        MOVE=       [ DISPLACE: MLAYOUT BY: POINT ]
                        COLOR=      [ PAINT: MLAYOUT WITH: COLOR ]
                    ENDOR ;

TYPE    MLAYOUTS  =  {  MLAYOUT  } ;
```

References to the type LAYOUT in the UNION, COLOR, and MOVE states now reference only the type MLAYOUT. This means that any sublayout referenced from within a LAYOUT always comes with its own precomputed MBB.

2.6.8.2 *Retaining compatibility.* Now that we have changed the definition of type LAYOUT, we must go back and update all operators that deal with layouts. Let us first update the MBB operator.

To update the MBB operator, we need only concern ourselves with the UNION, COLOR, and MOVE cases, where we find now MLAYOUTs instead of LAYOUTs. Because each sublayout is now represented by an MLAYOUT, we have access to that sublayout's precomputed MBB, and hence we never call the MBB function recursively:

```
DEFINE   MBB(L:LAYOUT) = BOX:                  BEGIN   VAR ML = MLAYOUT ;
     CASE L OF
          BOX:        L                        " (L is of type BOX) "
          POLYGON:    L\MBB                     " (L is of type POLYGON) "
          UNION:      \MAX  ML.MBB      FOR  ML $E L;
                                                 " (L is of type MLAYOUTS) "
          COLOR:      L.PAINT .MBB      " (L is of type
                                             [PAINT:MLAYOUT  WITH:COLOR]  )"
          MOVE:       L.DISPLACE .MBB  \AT L.BY
                        " (L is of type [DISPLACE:MLAYOUT  BY:POINT]  )"
     ENDCASE                                    END        ENDDEFN
```

Where our old MBB function called itself to obtain each sublayout's MBB, this new rendition instead extracts the MLAYOUTs' precomputed MBBs. Notice also that our local variable ML has been declared to be of type MLAYOUT. This is necessary due to the use of ML in the UNION case. Within the UNION clause, L is known to be of type MLAYOUTS, and hence each element, represented by ML, is of type MLAYOUT.

Note that this new MBB operator works at an efficiency that is entirely independent of the sublayouts' complexities.

2.6.8.3   Retaining compatibility in the other LAYOUT operators. Although we now
have a fast MBB operator, we are still left in the dark because none of our other dealings
with LAYOUT know about the new representation. They expect, for example, that in the
MOVE case, the .DISPLACE component refers to a LAYOUT and not our new MLAY-
OUT.

Also, where we have expressed a union of LAYOUTs L1, L2, and L3 as

$$\{ \ \ L1 \ \ ; \ \ L2 \ \ ; \ \ L3 \ \ \}$$

we can no longer view this formally as a layout. This expression is still an instance of
type LAYOUTS, but no longer is it also an instance of type LAYOUT.

The type LAYOUTS used to be viewable as a single LAYOUT because we had the
rule

$$LAYOUTS \quad \rightarrow \quad LAYOUT$$

which came with our declaration of type LAYOUT. That rule arose because the old
definition of LAYOUT referenced LAYOUTS in its UNION state (Section 2.3.2). However, our new definition of LAYOUT refers instead to the type MLAYOUTS in its
UNION state, and thus introduces instead the rule

$$MLAYOUTS \quad \rightarrow \quad LAYOUT$$

For example, if M1, M2, and M3 were of type MLAYOUT instead of type LAYOUT,
then

$$\{ \ \ M1 \ \ ; \ \ M2 \ \ ; \ \ M3 \ \ \}$$

which is an instance of type MLAYOUTS, would now pass as an instance of type LAY-
OUT.

*Datatype coercions: hiding linguistically the distinction between MLAYOUT and LAY-
OUT.*

To maintain compatibility with everything we have done so far with the type LAY-
OUT, let us actually hide the distinction between LAYOUT and MLAYOUT so that our
attempt to store MBBs with layouts appears invisible to all other programs. The distinction between LAYOUT and MLAYOUT need be known only by the MBB operator so
that it can take advantage of the stored MBBs in MLAYOUTs.

We hide the distinction by writing two ''datatype coercions.'' We want to say

'' Any MLAYOUT can be seen as a LAYOUT ''   and

'' Any LAYOUT can be seen as an MLAYOUT ''

If both of these statements were true, the types LAYOUT and MLAYOUT would be
entirely interchangeable. For example, we could pass an MLAYOUT to a program that
expects a LAYOUT, and vice versa. The distinction between LAYOUT and MLAYOUT
would cease to make any difference as far as program specification is concerned.

We make these two statements true by writing

```
LET  MLAYOUT  BECOME  LAYOUT  BY    MLAYOUT . BODY ;
LET  LAYOUT  BECOME  MLAYOUT  BY    [BODY: LAYOUT    MBB: LAYOUT\MBB ] ;
```

The first declaration says that any MLAYOUT may also be viewed as a LAYOUT. Such
a transition from MLAYOUT to LAYOUT occurs implicitly by taking the BODY component of the given MLAYOUT.

The second coercion says that any LAYOUT may also be viewed as an MLAYOUT. Such a transition from LAYOUT to MLAYOUT occurs implicitly by forming an MLAYOUT whose BODY component is the given LAYOUT, and whose MBB component is the result of applying the MBB function on the given LAYOUT.

Notice that the first coercion operates at a speed that is independent of layout complexity. It merely extracts a field from a record.

Notice also that the second coercion operates at a speed that is dependent only on the speed of the (new) \MBB operator. The \MBB operator, and hence also this second coercion, work at a speed that is independent of the complexity of sublayouts.

These two coercion declarations augment our language by adding the rules (respectively)

MLAYOUT	$\rightarrow$	LAYOUT
LAYOUT	$\rightarrow$	MLAYOUT

These transitions occur implicitly, without any program specification whatsoever.

Linguistic context within our programs is the sole trigger of these kinds of transitions. If within a program we express a LAYOUT at a place where context demands an MLAYOUT, our language will translate implicitly our expressed LAYOUT into the demanded MLAYOUT by producing

[BODY: the layout   MBB: the layout \MBB]

FORTRAN programmers are already familiar with this kind of implicit translation. FORTRAN comes with the following two coercions built in:

LET	INTeger	BECOME	REAL	BY	FLOAT(INTeger) ;
LET	REAL	BECOME	INTeger	BY	FIX(REAL) ;

The FORTRAN programmer knows this because the assignment

R = I

where R is a REAL and I an INTeger, is legal. FORTRAN supplies implicitly a FLOAT operation upon I because FORTRAN knows from this program context that I must be viewed as a REAL so that I can be stored in R. However, FORTRAN has only these two coercions, and provides no facility for the programmer to define new ones.

How the two coercions between MLAYOUT and LAYOUT maintain compatibility.

We can understand in two different ways how the two coercions between MLAYOUT and LAYOUT are sufficient by themselves to maintain compatibility between the new and old definitions of the type LAYOUT. The first way is simple and mathematical. The second way is to understand by example.

What is the difference between the old and new definitions of the type LAYOUT? The only difference is that the type MLAYOUT appears within the new definition exactly where the type LAYOUT appears within the old definition. Therefore, the distinction between the old LAYOUT and new LAYOUT datatypes exists only in that one presents an MLAYOUT whereas the other presented a LAYOUT.

This distinction can be ignored, however, precisely because our coercions render the types MLAYOUT and LAYOUT entirely interchangeable. Old programs will now coerce appearances of MLAYOUTs into the traditionally expected LAYOUTs, and vice versa.

For example, if we wish to PLOT an MLAYOUT, say M, we still write

PLOT(M , plotter) ;

even though we have not defined a PLOT procedure that takes an MLAYOUT as a parameter. The first coercion will render the MLAYOUT M as a LAYOUT, so that this statement retains meaning.

Also, the expression

$$\{ \quad L1 \quad ; \quad L2 \quad ; \quad L3 \quad \}$$

where L1, L2, and L3 are LAYOUTs, continues now to pass as an instance of type LAYOUT. Figure 2.6 shows how the coercions apply. Each of L1, L2, and L3 is first coerced to an MLAYOUT. Each application of the coercion from LAYOUT to MLAYOUT computes the layout's MBB and installs it into the resulting MLAYOUT.

This particular programming language accommodates coercions by effectively trying all possible coercions at all points in any program specification. It guarantees that if you can even imagine a sequence of coercion applications which will render the program meaningful, it will find such and implement it.

(In case there is more than one imaginable sequence that renders meaning, this language will choose the sequence that involves a minimal number of coercions.)

Summary. We have incorporated MBBs into our layout representation and maintained compatability by a sequence of four steps:

1 Declare a new datatype (MLAYOUT) which supports our new desire in representation.

2 Modify the original datatype (LAYOUT) so that it now references the new representation as we wish.

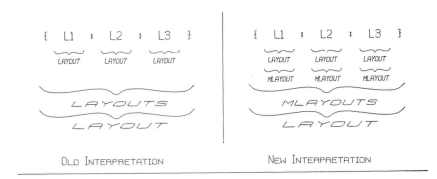

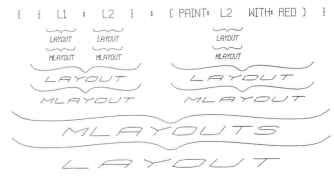

FIGURE 2.6 Interpretation of layout specification.

3 Modify the program(s) which benefit by the new representation (MBB) so to take advantage of the change.

4 Introduce a pair of coercions which render the new and old representations interchangeable.

This final step maintains compatibility with the rest of the world.

Shall we adopt one of LAYOUT or MLAYOUT as an "official" representation?

It is most efficient to carry MLAYOUTs as opposed to LAYOUTs simply because MLAYOUTs have precomputed MBBs. The difference in efficiency is minimal, however, because the type LAYOUT does have precomputed MBBs for its immediate sublayouts (each of type MLAYOUT). In other words, we might prefer MLAYOUT because the first coercion (from MLAYOUT to LAYOUT) is slightly faster than the second coercion (from LAYOUT to MLAYOUT).

In the interest of saving every microsecond of program execution time, let us, in fact, adopt MLAYOUT as our "official" layout representation. We pull a quick name change to implement this desire painlessly. (Any pain involved is limited to the following few paragraphs.)

Let us call MLAYOUT now LAYOUT, and rename LAYOUT to LAYOUT1. This way, where all our programs have referred to LAYOUT, they will now refer to the layout type that contains precomputed MBBs. The type LAYOUT1 now refers to the original variant definition.

Following is the entire program text which implements the change in representation and the subsequent improvement in the MBB function. This text replaces our original declaration of type LAYOUT, and the definition of MBB.

```
TYPE    LAYOUT1  =  EITHER
                        BOX=          BOX
                        POLYGON=      POLYGON
                        UNION=        LAYOUTS
                        MOVE=         [ DISPLACE: LAYOUT BY: POINT ]
                        COLOR=        [ PAINT: LAYOUT WITH: COLOR ]
                    ENDOR ;

TYPE    LAYOUT  =  [ BODY: LAYOUT1    MBB: BOX ] ;

LET  LAYOUT  BECOME  LAYOUT1  BY    LAYOUT . BODY ;
LET  LAYOUT1  BECOME  LAYOUT  BY   [BODY: LAYOUT1    MBB: LAYOUT1\MBB ];

DEFINE   MBB(L:LAYOUT1)  =  BOX:         BEGIN   VAR ML = LAYOUT ;
    CASE L OF
        BOX:    L             " (L is of type BOX) "
        POLYGON:  L\MBB        " (L is of type POLYGON) "
        UNION:  \MAX ML.MBB    FOR ML $E L;
                              " (L is of type LAYOUTS) "
        COLOR:  L.PAINT .MBB " (L is of type
                              [PAINT:LAYOUT  WITH:COLOR] )"
        MOVE:   L.DISPLACE .MBB \AT L.BY
                              " (L is of type [DISPLACE:LAYOUT  BY:POINT] )"
    ENDCASE                                END    ENDDEFN
```

We add one nicety, an MBB function that takes in a LAYOUT (not LAYOUT1):

```
DEFINE    MBB(L:LAYOUT)  =  BOX:    L.MBB           ENDDEFN
```

In the absence of this nicety, all would still work, but a LAYOUT given to \MBB would always be coerced to type LAYOUT1 first. This would always strip off a LAYOUT's precomputed MBB, requiring therefore a quick reexamination of the layout's immediate sublayouts.

2.6.8.4 *All sublayouts now have their own particular MBBs.*

Not only have we reduced the time taken to compute MBBs, but we have also given each and every sublayout its own particular MBB. This does take more storage, but this extra storage is proportional only to the storage taken by the layout in the absence of stored MBBs. This extra storage is of little concern if we do in fact make extensive use of all those varied sub-MBBs.

We can strip off any layout's MBB (e.g., coercing from LAYOUT to LAYOUT1) without suffering a great loss. That layout's MBB can be recomputed very quickly (e.g., coercing from LAYOUT1 to LAYOUT) because each of that layout's sublayouts still has readily available its own precomputed MBB.

We will make extensive use of all sub-MBBs for a particular class of applications. These MBBs serve as a heuristic that can dramatically focus searches through layouts, thus reducing all kinds of search times. Figure 2.4 illustrates how sub-MBBs are used in layout searching. Whole sections of layouts can be ignored in the search just by quick MBB examinations. We will come back to this point as we present the outline and heart of an interactive graphics editor.

2.6.8.5 *Time efficiency in the MBB computation.*

The time consumed for the MBB computation of an entire layout is now proportional to the memory consumed by the layout and not the complexity of the layout. For example, our rendition of the 4096-bit array which consumes 228 memory units now expends only 228 time units to define its MBB, not the 409,600 time units that would occur with the old MBB function. In other words, where the old MBB function would recompute 4096 times the MBB of BIT, the new MBB function computes BIT's MBB only once. This computation occurs implicitly as we assign initially to the variable BIT the set of shapes that make up the BIT layout.

We can understand this time invariant by noting that each sublayout represented in memory has its MBB computed only once, in its coercion from LAYOUT1 to LAYOUT. The MBB computation for each sublayout expends time that is independent of the complexity of the sublayout. Finally, the number of sublayouts is bounded above by the number of memory units consumed by the entire layout.

In fact, the time taken to compute the MBB for a given sublayout does depend on how many sub-sublayouts it references. This number may be more than one, in the UNION case. However, proportionality is still preserved because for each iteration taken in MBB's UNION case, there corresponds exactly one memory unit used to represent that reference.

2.6.9   Using the Disk: Introducing the \SWAPPABLE Operator for LAYOUTs

Layouts can require lots of storage, more than might be available in the computer's main memory. Let us refer to the main memory as "core" and the mass storage device as "disk."

2.6.9.1 *Type construction 5: DISK structures.*

Let us define a datatype for a layout that resides on disk:

        TYPE   DLAYOUT =   DISK LAYOUT ;

This declaration not only defines a new type DLAYOUT, but also gives us the rules

        LAYOUT \DISK   →   DLAYOUT
        DLAYOUT   →   LAYOUT

The first rule says that the \DISK operator maps a LAYOUT to a DLAYOUT. We can imagine that \DISK writes immediately an image of the LAYOUT to the disk. The resulting DLAYOUT is simply a pointer to a disk address. The second rule maps a DLAYOUT to a LAYOUT by swapping in the layout from disk.

In general, the declaration

    TYPE   DX   =   DISK X ;

makes DX a disk pointer type and supplies the rules

    X \DISK   →   DX
    DX   →   X

The first rule creates a disk object, and the second rule examines a disk object.

The core memory required to represent a disk object (e.g., DLAYOUT) is very tiny. We can therefore think of the \DISK operator simply as a space saver:

    big thing \DISK   →   little thing

2.6.9.2 *One more state in the LAYOUT datatype.* Let us augment the datatype LAYOUT so that it may reference a DLAYOUT. Referring to Section 2.6.8.3, we redefine the type LAYOUT1.

TYPE   LAYOUT1 =   EITHER
                          BOX=   BOX
                          POLYGON=   POLYGON
                          UNION=   LAYOUTS
                          MOVE=   [DISPLACE: LAYOUT BY: POINT]
                          COLOR=   [PAINT: LAYOUT WITH: COLOR]
                          DISK=   DLAYOUT
                      ENDOR ;

We have added one more state to the type LAYOUT1.

It is now possible for a layout to reside partly on disk and partly in core. For example, the LAYOUT

    { L1 ; L2 \DISK ; L3 }

appears in the UNION state, and the second element in the union resides on disk even though the other elements reside in core.

Once again, having changed the type LAYOUT1, we must update all operators that deal with layouts. Fortunately, we need not even consider our synthesis operators. All synthesis operators presented so far never examine layouts, and they always produce layouts residing in non-DISK states, states that we have not modified. We need consider only our two analysis operators, MBB and PLOT.

Let us first consider \MBB. If we give MBB a LAYOUT1 residing in the DISK state, how does \MBB obtain the MBB of the DLAYOUT? As things stand now, \MBB must swap in the DLAYOUT and then yield the swapped-in LAYOUT's MBB. It is unfortunate that an MBB computation requires interaction with the disk.

We could avoid this swap operation if the DISK state in a LAYOUT1 referenced not a DLAYOUT, but instead a DLAYOUT together with its MBB. Let us define the type DISK_LAYOUT,

    TYPE   DISK_LAYOUT = [BODY: DLAYOUT MBB: BOX] ;

which represents a DLAYOUT together with its MBB. The nice thing about

DISK_LAYOUT is that the DLAYOUT is disk resident, whereas the MBB is core resident.

For the last time, we redefine the type LAYOUT1 with

```
TYPE    LAYOUT1  =  EITHER
                        BOX=          BOX
                        POLYGON=      POLYGON
                        UNION=        LAYOUTS
                        MOVE=         [ DISPLACE: LAYOUT BY: POINT ]
                        COLOR=        [ PAINT: LAYOUT WITH: COLOR ]
                        DISK=         DISK_LAYOUT
                    ENDOR  ;
```

We define MBB with

```
DEFINE    MBB(L:LAYOUT1)  =  BOX:            BEGIN    VAR  ML  =  LAYOUT  ;
      CASE  L  OF
            BOX:       L
            POLYGON:   L\MBB
            UNION:     \MAX  ML.MBB    FOR  ML  $E  L;
            COLOR:     L.PAINT  .MBB
            MOVE:      L.DISPLACE  .MBB  \AT  L.BY

            DISK:      L.MBB
      ENDCASE                                        END        ENDDEFN
```

Now the MBB operator never refers to a DLAYOUT; it just grabs the MBB from the DISK_LAYOUT.

With our substitution of DISK_LAYOUT for DLAYOUT within LAYOUT1's definition, the expression

```
{  L1  ;  L2 \DISK  ;  L3  }
```

no longer makes formal sense. L2\DISK produces an object of type DLAYOUT (not DISK_LAYOUT), and the type LAYOUT1 now harbors only a DISK_LAYOUT (not DLAYOUT). The \DISK operator came to life only as a by-product of the declaration of the type DLAYOUT.

Let us define an operator that can serve as the official synthesis operator associated with the disk. Where the \DISK operator maps a LAYOUT to a DLAYOUT (different types), let us have our new operator always map a LAYOUT to a LAYOUT so that layout specification can be done without any awareness of the DLAYOUT type. We introduce this operator, called \SWAPPABLE, by writing

```
DEFINE    SWAPPABLE(L:LAYOUT)  =  LAYOUT:
              [ BODY: L\DISK    MBB: L\MBB ]         ENDDEFN
```

SWAPPABLE transforms any layout L into a layout residing in the DISK state. The body of this function specifies a DISK_LAYOUT whose BODY is a disk resident L and whose MBB is L's MBB. This DISK_LAYOUT is viewed as a LAYOUT because SWAPPABLE has been written so that it returns an object of type LAYOUT, and because we have the pair of rules

```
DISK_LAYOUT     →     LAYOUT1        (by definition of LAYOUT1), and
LAYOUT1         →     LAYOUT         (by our coercion declaration)
```

In summary, we have added one more synthesis operator

LAYOUT \SWAPPABLE   →   LAYOUT

which is effectively an identity function as far as geometry is concerned, but which nonetheless reduces core memory consumption.

Finally, we update our PLOT function (Section 2.5.3) by adding one more clause to the CASE statement:

. . .

DISK: PLOT(L.BODY, DISP, COLOR, PL);

. . .

Within this clause, L appears as a DISK_LAYOUT, so L.BODY is thus a DLAYOUT. Since a call to PLOT requires a LAYOUT as parameter, the DLAYOUT L.BODY is coerced to a LAYOUT, thus swapping in the disk resident layout implicitly.

2.6.10   Comparing the Linear versus the Recursive Representation

Notice how easily we have provided for disk resident data within our recursive type LAYOUT. We merely added another state to the original five states in LAYOUT1's definition.

In contrast, the linear representation for layouts (Section 2.6) admits no such modification. The linear representation insists that any layout is represented by exactly one (long) list, each of whose elements is a single polygon or box. If we try to incorporate the disk into such a representation, we can either

1   Make each individual shape disk resident, or
2   Make the entire list as a whole disk resident

That is, we have an all-or-nothing situation. Either all or nothing is disk resident. Swapping individual shapes is usually of little help because shapes are primarily boxes or simple polygons, either of which already takes only little memory.

2.7 INTERACTIVE GRAPHICS: MORE EXAMPLES OF LAYOUT ANALYSIS

Layouts may be produced in a setting very different from the textual means we have provided so far. While we have specified layouts via programs that produce objects of type layout, we can also specify layouts in a purely graphical setting.

In a purely graphical setting, the designer specifies layouts by pointing to and "drawing" on a video screen. For example, the designer specifies polygons by pointing to the screen at the places where the vertices are desired.

The entire input from the designer can appear to the computer as a sequence of characters (commands) each of which comes with a screen position, that is, the position of the pointing device taken at the time the character is typed.

We present an overview of an interactive graphics editor. Reasons for bringing up interactive graphics include:

1   To see how easy it is to implement interactive graphics on top of a system that provides for programmable textual specification for layouts
2   To see how the MBBs stored with sublayouts play a substantial role in quickly plotting small portions of layouts, and in splitting layouts

3   To see what roles interactive graphics can play in the design process

4   To introduce the specification of polygons in terms of "wires"

2.7.1   Overview of an Interactive Graphics Editor

There are four kinds of operations available in a graphics editor. They are:

1   Creating new objects

2   Selecting objects of interest for subsequent modification

3   Modifying the selected objects

4   Changing viewing parameters

It might seem at first that the first category, the creation of objects, is sufficient for creating layouts graphically. However, users change their minds often and therefore require an ability to modify existing layouts. To modify objects, the user requires a means by which to specify the subset of all objects intended for subsequent modification.

Finally, because TV screens are small and low in resolution, we simply cannot view the entire layout with complete and utter detail. Instead, we use the screen as a window that can be manipulated. The user can look in detail at a small portion of the layout, or the user can step back and see a larger portion of the layout, losing resolution.

2.7.2   Creation of Objects Initially

How do we specify graphically the creations of boxes and polygons? A box is defined by two points, the parameters to our \TO operator. A box therefore requires two characters, or two button pushes. For example, a box may be specified with the pair of characters

B∗

Typing a B indicates both the user's choice to create a box, and the position of one of the four corners. (The user moves the pointing device to the desired position before typing the B.) The subsequent ∗ indicates the other corner, assumed by convention to be the corner diagonally opposite the first corner. (Again, the user moves the pointing device before typing the ∗.)

A polygon is defined by a sequence of vertices, whose length is variable. The character sequence

P∗∗∗∗   carriage return

can be used to indicate a five-sided polygon, one vertex per character. (The carriage return is used to indicate not another vertex, but rather the end of the variable-length sequence.) Similarly, a seven-sided polygon can be specified by the sequence

P∗∗∗∗∗∗   carriage return

The command interpreter provides feedback to the user upon each character typed. In the case of the polygon, each asterisk draws one more edge onto the screen, thus indicating the entire set of edges so far specified in this one polygon.

If we ignore feedback altogether, we can easily write down the command interpreter presented so far. Let us assume that we have a function that yields the next character typed at the terminal together with the position of the pointing device at that moment. That is, we have

```
TYPE    CP  =  [CHAR:CHAR   POSITION:POINT];
DEFINE    NEXT=  CP:
                     DO          Query the terminal for a character and position
                     GIVE        these two pieces of information
ENDDEFN
```

Let us declare a variable ALL of type LAYOUT that will always represent the entire layout built up so far.

```
VAR    ALL  =  LAYOUT;
ALL:=  NIL;                        " Set ALL to be empty initially "
```

Here is a loop that repeatedly accepts commands, augmenting ALL with each new
object. We add one more command, the character E, which ends the edit session.

```
VAR    C=CHAR;  P,P1=  POINT;
WHILE    DO [CHAR:C  POSITION:P]  :=  NEXT;
         GIVE    C  <>  'E'      ;
DO    IF  C='B'  THEN     ALL:=  ALL  \UNION  (P  \TO  NEXT.POSITION);  FI
      IF  C='P'  THEN     ALL:=  ALL  \UNION
                    P  <$     {COLLECT  P1   WHILE
                                     DO          [CHAR:C  POSITION:P1]:=  NEXT;
                                     GIVE        C='*'  ;      }  ;      FI
END
```

Paraphrased, this reads

> WHILE   the next character, C, is not 'E'   ...
> (first define both C and P by querying the terminal)
>
> DO   IF that character was a 'B' THEN
> augment ALL to include the box containing the point P
> (given with the character 'B') and the point specified
> with the next button push (NEXT.POSITION)
>
> IF that character was not a 'B', but a 'P' instead, THEN
> augment ALL to include a new polygon. This polygon
> contains as vertices the point P already given with
> the 'P' character, and then each point specified
> subsequently with the '*'.
>
> END

This loop collects polygons and boxes until the user types an 'E'.

Unfortunately, this loop gives absolutely no feedback to the user. Even after each
shape is completely specified, that shape does not appear on the screen. In fact, the
screen remains blank forever. We can provide some feedback if we replace each of the
two statements that contain the \UNION operator:

```
ALL  :=  ALL  \UNION  a new layout  ;
```

with a procedure call

```
ADD(  the new layout  );
```

We then define ADD with

```
DEFINE    ADD(L:LAYOUT):
          ALL:=  ALL  \UNION  L;
          DRAW(L);                          ENDDEFN
```

Now, each time we add a new shape, not only do we augment ALL, but we also draw the new shape on the screen. We assume that the DRAW procedure referenced here is defined so that it calls our familiar PLOT procedure with appropriate parameters. We now go on to consider what these parameters ought to be.

2.7.3 Viewing Parameters and Their Specification

Because the display cannot always show an entire layout with sufficient resolution, we will add commands with which the user can zoom into close-up views of small portions of the layout.

As we discovered when considering our PLOT procedure (Section 2.3.3.2), a layout generally resides in a coordinate system other than the plotter's or screen's natural coordinate system. Any plot process thus involves a coordinate transformation.

Sitting between the layout and the screen, therefore, is a matrix. The matrix transforms from the layout's coordinate system into the screen's coordinate system. We use this matrix to plot the layout onto the screen. We accommodate changes in viewing parameters (e.g., changes in magnification) simply by incorporating these changes into the transformation matrix.

Let us consider how the user may wish to specify changes in the viewing parameters. Here are some possibilities:

1 ZI   Zoom In. These two characters indicate a box contained within the screen. The intent is to magnify the picture so that this box grows to fill the entire screen.

2 ZO   Zoom Out. These two characters again define a box contained within the screen. The intent is to shrink the picture so that all which now appears on the screen subsequently shrinks to fill only this box, a small portion of the screen. As a result, portions of the layout presently outside the screen also contract so to appear subsequently on the screen.

3 ZF   Zoom to Fill. Simply shrink or expand the picture so that the entire layout fills the screen.

4 SH   Scroll Here. Rather than changing the magnification, instead preserve the present magnification but slide the window laterally across the layout so that S moves to H.

Let us consider how each of these viewing specifications affects the matrix that relates the layout's coordinates to the screen coordinates. Let us declare the variable that will represent this pivotol matrix:

```
VAR    FROM_LAYOUT_TO_SCREEN  =  MATRIX  ;
       '' We assume that this matrix maps a layout coordinate to the
       corresponding screen coordinate ''
```

By the stated convention, this matrix does not map a screen coordinate to a layout coordinate. However, the following matrix does:

```
FROM_LAYOUT_TO_SCREEN  \INVERSE
```

Let us declare one more variable to represent the extent of the screen itself, in the screen's natural coordinate system:

VAR   THE_SCREEN = BOX ;
       '' In screen coordinates ''

This variable plays exactly the same role that a plotter's PAPER component plays in type PLOTTER (Section 2.5). If our screen is 512 pixels on a side, we might write

THE_SCREEN:= 0#0 \TO 511#511;

This value is a constant from now on.

We might be tempted to imagine that changes in magnification could be implemented simply by changing this variable, that is, changing the screen's natural coordinates so to correspond precisely to the interesting portion of the layout. However, the screen's natural coordinate system comes built in with the screen and is therefore simply not subject to change.

How do we affect this matrix to implement the Zoom In command, for example? We write the following assignment statement. Assume that the variables Z and I are of type POINT and contain the screen coordinates of the box specified by the user:

FROM_LAYOUT_TO_SCREEN:=   FROM_LAYOUT_TO_SCREEN \THEN
                           (Z \TO I \FITTING_IN THE_SCREEN);

This says that the new transformation applies conceptually in two steps:

1 Map the layout to the screen as it stands now.
2 Provide further expansion such that the ZI box comes to fill the screen (refer to Section 2.4.1).

The Zoom Out operator affects the matrix via the following assignment (having access to the screen coordinates Z and O):

FROM_LAYOUT_TO_SCREEN:= FROM_LAYOUT_TO_SCREEN \THEN
                         (THE_SCREEN \FITTING_IN Z \TO O);

The Zoom to Fill operator does

FROM_LAYOUT_TO_SCREEN:= ALL\MBB \FITTING_IN THE_SCREEN;

Finally, the Scroll Here operator does (with the variables S and H)

FROM_LAYOUT_TO_SCREEN:=   FROM_LAYOUT_TO_SCREEN \THEN
                           (H - S \DISP);

2.7.3.1 *Plotting only the visible portion of a layout.* A graphics editor responds to each user action by modifying the picture on the screen. Certainly, it must augment the picture to show each new object as it is created.

We can plot a new piece of layout by using our flexible PLOT procedure (Section 2.5.3):

PLOT(piece of layout, FROM_LAYOUT_TO_SCREEN, BLACK, the screen as a
                                                         plotter);

We use this flexible form so that we may directly specify our particular transformation FROM_LAYOUT_TO_SCREEN. We need this flexibility; our standard rigid PLOT procedure, left to its own, takes the liberty to define its own transformation, always cramming the entire layout onto the screen. Such liberty cannot be tolerated when we want to have control explicitly over magnification.

This method of plotting, where we allow the layout to be larger than the screen, even in screen coordinates, deserves some attention. Many plotters will tolerate coordinates off screen. These plotters clip the object so that only the visible part appears. Some older plotters, in contrast, may produce undefined results.

Even if our screen tolerates off-screen coordinates, our program may waste lots of time sending invisible coordinates to the screen. For example, if we zoom in to view just one of 4096 memory cells in a RAM, our PLOT procedure will compute and send all 4096 memory cells even though we will see only one.

Let us define a new PLOT procedure which takes in one additional parameter, a box outside of which the layout can be ignored. Let us call this box LIMITS. The new PLOT procedure will differ from our flexible PLOT procedure only in that:

1 It takes the extra parameter, LIMITS.
2 There is one IF statement introduced.
3 The MOVE case does a tiny bit more than merely pass the LIMITS parameter onward.

The new PLOT follows:

```
DEFINE    PLOT(L:LAYOUT DISP:MATRIX  COLOR:COLOR  PL:PLOTTER_INTERFACE
                 LIMITS:BOX   ):
          BEGIN    VAR  L1=LAYOUT;
IF        L\MBB  \TOUCHES  LIMITS      THEN
          CASE  L  OF
                 BOX:       <*PL*>(  L\PERIMETER \AT  DISP,   COLOR);
                 POLYGON: <*PL*>(   L  \AT  DISP,   COLOR);
                 UNION:    FOR  L1  $E  L;  DO
                                      PLOT(L1,  DISP,  COLOR,  PL,  LIMITS);  END
                 MOVE:     PLOT(L.DISPLACE,  L.BY  \THEN DISP,  COLOR,  PL,
                                      LIMITS  \AT  INVERSE(L.BY)  );
                 COLOR:    PLOT(L.COLOR,  DISP,  L.WITH,  PL,  LIMITS);
          ENDCASE              FI           END        ENDDEFN
```

The IF statement effectively ignores L immediately if L lies entirely off screen (i.e., outside LIMITS). Only if L's MBB touches the LIMITS box does further computation begin.

This filtering based on MBBs applies not only for the entire layout as a whole, but also applies recursively. Each sublayout passed to PLOT will be checked to see if that sublayout itself can be ignored. Where a given sublayout's MBB might be so big as to intersect LIMITS, that sublayout's sub-sublayouts have individual and smaller MBBs, many of which do not touch LIMITS. So even when a given sublayout survives the filter, it is quite possible that many of its immediate sub-sublayouts will be rejected by the filter.

Beware of the MOVE case. Whereas all the other cases merely pass LIMITS onward in their recursive calls to PLOT, the MOVE case actually modifies LIMITS. Our PLOT procedures have always implemented movements by simultaneously:

1 Concentrating only on the unmoved layout L.DISPLACE
2 Compensating for this switch in coordinate systems by incorporating L.BY into the parameter DISP

This osmosis of movement away from the layout and into DISP implies that the L given to PLOT is really

    L \AT DISP

in a coordinate system that is invariant throughout all recursive calls to PLOT.
  The MOVE case passes

    LIMITS \AT INVERSE(L.BY)

as the new limits for the recursive PLOT. This maintains the following sequence of equivalent relations:

	LIMITS			is to L
as	LIMITS			is to L.DISPLACE \AT L.BY
as	LIMITS	\AT	INVERSE(L.BY)	is to L.DISPLACE

Thus, when working with L.DISPLACE, the given LIMITS box must compensate for the loss of the L.BY transformation. In fact, we see that DISP and LIMITS are affected in opposite directions within the MOVE case. DISP is transformed by some matrix, whereas LIMITS is transformed by that matrix's inverse. This implies a delightful and expected result:

    LIMITS \AT DISP

is invariant throughout all recursive calls. In other words, if we were to plot the LIMITS box on any recursive call to PLOT, we would plot this expression, as in the BOX case, and hence always see an unmoving LIMITS box.
  We define the DRAW procedure (referenced in Section 2.7.2 within the ADD procedure) by defining two DRAWs:

```
DEFINE    DRAW(L:LAYOUT):
     DRAW(L,  THE_SCREEN  \AT  INVERSE(  FROM_LAYOUT_TO_SCREEN  )  );
ENDDEFN
DEFINE    DRAW(L:LAYOUT  LIMITS:BOX):
     PLOT(L,  FROM_LAYOUT_TO_SCREEN,  BLACK,  the screen as a plotter
                                                interface   ,
          LIMITS  );                                         ENDDEFN
```

The first DRAW calls the second DRAW, passing THE_SCREEN rendered in layout coordinates as the second DRAW's LIMITS parameter.

2.7.4 The Selection Process

We have seen two of the four parts of a graphics editor, the creation of objects and the manipulation of view. We finish the editor by providing for the modification of the existing layout.
  No matter what modification operators we may provide, we generally desire their application to affect only a portion of the entire layout. For example, if we notice two objects residing too close together on the screen, we will wish to move one of the shapes while leaving the other shape unaffected.
  We will define and implement all modification operators in a way which is independent of the fact that the operator applies only to a selected portion of the entire layout. Each modification operator will be defined simply as a function that maps a LAYOUT to another LAYOUT. The modification operators will then be trivial to implement.

"Selection" refers to the specification of portions of layout subject to subsequent modification. We will implement selection by actually splitting the entire layout into two pieces:

1 SEL: All that which is to be subject to modification
2 REST: All that which will remain unaffected

The layouts SEL and REST always satisfy the following:

1 SEL \ UNION REST is the entire layout.
2 SEL and REST include no shape in common.

We implement a modification, F, by the following surgery:

1 "Scalpel"   Split the entire layout into SEL and REST.
2 "Fixit"   SEL:= F(SEL).
3 "Sutures"   The entire layout becomes SEL   \ UNION   REST.

How might we specify layout selection? We can point to a place on the screen and ask for the shape(s) that contains it. We might wish to choose at once all shapes contained inside a box, specified with two button pushes. We may then want to refine our choice by adding or subtracting from it. The following is a set of character sequences for specifying the intended selection:

1 .   Select those shapes that contain the point
2 +   Add to selection shapes that contain the point.
3 −   Subtract from selection shapes that contain the point.

4 [.   Select those shapes that reside entirely inside the box.
5 [+   Add to selection shapes that reside inside the box.
6 [−   Subtract from selection shapes inside the box.

7 x   Invert selection.
8 0   Clear selection.
9 1   Select all.

Let us represent the result of any selection by a new datatype:

TYPE   SPLIT_LAYOUT = [SEL, REST: LAYOUT] ;

The SEL component represents all that is selected, and the REST component represents everything else. With this datatype in hand, we can implement easily each of the selection operators simply in terms of two fundamental functions:

LAYOUT \SPLIT_BY POINT   →   SPLIT_LAYOUT
LAYOUT \SPLIT_BY BOX   →   SPLIT_LAYOUT

The first \SPLIT_BY, called the point splitter, selects all shape(s) that contain the point. The second \SPLIT_BY, called the box splitter, selects all shape(s) that are contained entirely within the box.

To implement selection, let us reconsider how we represent the entire layout. Let us represent the entire layout, not by the variable ALL, but instead by two variables that will represent the selected and unselected portions of the entire layout:

VAR   SEL,   REST   =   LAYOUT ;

ALL is simply the value of the expression

SEL   \UNION   REST

Following is the complete implementation for each selection operator, written in terms of the \SPLIT_BY operators:

8   0   Clear selection: REST:=   SEL   \UNION   REST;
                               SEL:=   NIL;
7   x   Invert selection: Exchange REST and SEL
1   .   [SEL:SEL   REST:REST]:=   SEL   \UNION   REST   \SPLIT_BY   P ;
2   +   [SEL:S   REST:REST]:=   REST   \SPLIT_BY   P;
            SEL:=   SEL   \UNION   S;
3   −   [SEL:R   REST:SEL]:=   SEL   \SPLIT_BY   P;
            REST:=   REST   \UNION   R;
4   [.   [SEL:SEL   REST:REST]:=   SEL   \UNION   REST   \SPLIT_BY
                                         (P1   \TO   P2);

Character sequences 5 and 6 are the same as 2 and 3 if we write (P1   \TO   P2) in place of P.

2.7.4.1 *Splitting the layout.* The two \SPLIT_BY operators are nearly identical in specification:

```
DEFINE    SPLIT_BY(L:LAYOUT  P:POINT)  =  SPLIT_LAYOUT:
    BEGIN        VAR  L1=LAYOUT;
        IF  P  \IN  (L\MBB)     THEN
            CASE  L  OF
                BOX:     [SEL:L]
                POLYGON:    IF  P  \IN  L  THEN  [SEL:L]
                                          ELSE  [REST:L]  FI
                UNION:  {COLLECT  L1  \SPLIT_BY  P  FOR  L1  $E  L;}
                MOVE:   L.DISPLACE  \SPLIT_BY  (P  \AT  INVERSE(L.BY))
                                    \AT  L.BY
                COLOR:  L.COLOR  \SPLIT_BY  P  \PAINTED  L.WITH
                DISK:   L.BODY  \SPLIT_BY  P    \SWAPPABLE
            ENDCASE
        ELSE     [REST:L]          FI              END        ENDDEFN
DEFINE    SPLIT_BY(L:LAYOUT  B:BOX)  =  SPLIT_LAYOUT:
    BEGIN        VAR  L1=LAYOUT;
        IF  (L\MBB)  \IN  B    THEN     [SEL:L]
        EF  (L\MBB)  \TOUCHES  B       THEN
            CASE  L  OF
                BOX:     [REST:L]
                POLYGON:  [REST:L]
                UNION:  {COLLECT  L1  \SPLIT_BY  B  FOR  L1  $E  L;}
```

```
                  MOVE:    L.DISPLACE \SPLIT_BY (B \AT INVERSE(L.BY))
                                      \AT L.BY
                  COLOR:   L.COLOR \SPLIT_BY B \PAINTED L.WITH
                  DISK:    L.BODY \SPLIT_BY B   \SWAPPABLE
          ENDCASE
 ELSE      [REST:L]              FI              END        ENDDEFN
```

In each operator, we always perform first a gross check based on the given layout's MBB alone. The point splitter asks simply if the given layout, L, includes P within its MBB. If not, the entire L as a whole is returned as the REST component; nothing is selected. The box splitter asks two questions. First, if the layout as a whole resides entirely inside B, then L as a whole is returned as the SEL component; all of L is selected. If L's MBB does not even touch B, then none of L is selected.

Each split operator examines L further only if these gross checks yield no certainties. Let us consider the BOX and POLYGON states for L. The point split operator yields L as selected if L is a single shape and L contains P. (We will define the \IN operator for polygons used in the POLYGON case.) The box split operator yields L as not selected if L is a single shape. (If that single shape were contained entirely inside B, that shape's MBB would also lie inside B, and thus L would be SELected due to the first IF.)

Consider now the recursive states, UNION, MOVE, COLOR, and DISK. These cases are specified identically in each of the two split operators, even though one uses the variable P exactly where the other uses B. The UNION case applies \SPLIT_BY to each sublayout in the union, and yields a list of these SPLIT_LAYOUTs. The MOVE, COLOR, and DISK cases each apply \SPLIT_BY to the referenced sublayout, and then yield that SPLIT_LAYOUT reconstructed so to include the implied movement, the implied color, and the implied disk residency, respectively.

These specifications for the recursive cases assume the existence of the following rules, so that the expression in each case can be returned as a SPLIT_LAYOUT:

```
SPLIT_LAYOUTS                      →     SPLIT_LAYOUT      (UNION)

SPLIT_LAYOUT \AT MATRIX            →     SPLIT_LAYOUT      (MOVE)

SPLIT_LAYOUT \PAINTED COLOR        →     SPLIT_LAYOUT      (COLOR)

SPLIT_LAYOUT \SWAPPABLE            →     SPLIT_LAYOUT      (DISK)
```

For example, the UNION case produces a SPLIT_LAYOUTS (declared by

```
TYPE    SPLIT_LAYOUTS = { SPLIT_LAYOUT } ;                        )
```

However, the function header requires a single SPLIT_LAYOUT as the result. We introduce these assumed rules by defining operators (e.g., \AT and \PAINTED) for SPLIT_LAYOUTs:

```
DEFINE    AT(S:SPLIT_LAYOUT    M:MATRIX) = SPLIT_LAYOUT:
     [SEL:    S.SEL \AT M         REST:   S.REST \AT M ]               ENDDEFN
DEFINE    PAINTED(S:SPLIT_LAYOUT    C:COLOR) = SPLIT_LAYOUT:
     [SEL: S.SEL \PAINTED C        REST: S.REST \PAINTED C ]           ENDDEFN
DEFINE  SWAPPABLE(S:SPLIT_LAYOUT) = SPLIT_LAYOUT:
     [SEL: S.SEL \SWAPPABLE        REST: S.REST \SWAPPABLE ]           ENDDEFN
LET  SPLIT_LAYOUTS BECOME SPLIT_LAYOUT BY
     BEGIN        VAR S = SPLIT_LAYOUT;
        [SEL:    {COLLECT S.SEL    FOR S $E SPLIT_LAYOUTS;}
        REST:    {COLLECT S.REST   FOR S $E SPLIT_LAYOUTS;} ]         END ;
```

With these four new declarations, the two split operators become well defined.

The three layout operators \AT, \PAINTED, and \SWAPPABLE are defined on SPLIT_LAYOUTs simply by operating on each of the SEL and REST layouts independently. For example, we move a SPLIT_LAYOUT by moving the SEL and REST components each by the same amount. The UNION case is accommodated by providing the coercion from the plural SPLIT_LAYOUTS to the singular SPLIT_LAYOUT. The resulting SPLIT_LAYOUT has as SEL the union of the SEL components, and it has as REST the union of the REST components. That is, looking at the UNION case in either split operator, we are saying that the selected layout resulting from a union is simply the union of the selected portions of each sublayout. This interpretation is consistent with our notion that a union represents the superposition of its elements.

2.7.4.2   A note about NIL layouts, and records and strings.   Let us look back over the two split operators and the new operators defined on SPLIT_LAYOUTs. Within the two split operators, we have specified SPLIT_LAYOUTs using the record constructors

[SEL: a layout   ]

and

[REST: a layout   ]

That is, we have not always explicitly specified both components of the record.

In general, it is okay to omit components of a record. Omitted components will always produce the value NIL upon subsequent examination. For example,

[SEL: a layout   ]

is a SPLIT_LAYOUT whose REST component is NIL.

Let us look at the coercion from SPLIT_LAYOUTS to SPLIT_LAYOUT. That coercion forms two strings, one made up of SEL components and one made up of REST components. What happens when some of these elements are NIL?

A NIL value specified as an element of a string is always dropped from the string. In other words, every element in a finished string is non-NIL, even if the specification of that string included NIL values. For example, the two strings formed in the coercion may have different lengths. If, for example, all the SPLIT_LAYOUTs in the given SPLIT_LAYOUTS had NIL SEL components, the SEL component of the SPLIT_LAYOUT resulting from this coercion would have no elements at all; in fact, the resulting SEL component would itself be simply NIL.

Thus, where it might appear that our SPLIT_LAYOUT operators consume exactly twice as much memory as the original layout, this appearance is just an illusion. Although the coercion appears to form two lists from one list, each of these lists is typically shorter than the one list.

Consider now any one of the three other operators defined on the type SPLIT_LAYOUT (e.g., \AT). The SPLIT_LAYOUT \AT operator applies the LAYOUT \AT operator to each of the SEL and REST components. What happens if one of these components was originally NIL? We would like to think that

a NIL layout \AT matrix   yields a NIL layout

However, the layout \AT operator produces the record

[DISPLACE: the NIL layout   BY: the matrix   ]

This record will not be NIL; the matrix is non-NIL.

Fortunately, as far as plotting and fabrication are concerned, this record will introduce no additional shapes; it will act as though it were not there at all. (The CASE statement within the PLOT procedure will execute none of its clauses; a NIL resides in no state. The CASE statement as a whole acts as a no-op when given NIL.)

While it is okay to have NIL sublayouts, this is not optimal as far as memory consumption is concerned. Now that we have a real example where we might pass a NIL layout to \AT, we might wish to redefine all our layout synthesis operators so that they check for NILs. We can redefine \AT, for example, so that it does yield a NIL if given a NIL.

Let us redefine \AT with

```
DEFINE    AT(L:LAYOUT  M:MATRIX)  =  LAYOUT:
          IF  DEFINED(L)  THEN
                    [DISPLACE:L  BY:M]      " (as before) "
          ELSE    NIL                            FI      ENDDEFN
```

This new rendition of \AT yields NIL if given a NIL L. We test for NIL by using the built-in function

```
DEFINED(  any type  )    →    BOOLean
```

The other layout synthesis operators can benefit by the same treatment. We need redefine only the basic synthesis operators: the \AT that takes a matrix, the \PAINTED, and the \SWAPPABLE operators. (The \UNION operator requires no modification because it produces a string. \UNION will therefore naturally return NIL if both of the given layouts are NIL.)

As long as we are redefining the layout synthesis operators, we can provide further optimizations. For example, we can define a very efficient \AT by

```
DEFINE    AT(L:LAYOUT  M:MATRIX)  =  LAYOUT:
          IF  DEFINED(L)  THEN
                    CASE  L  OF
                         MOVE:    L.DISPLACE  \AT  (L.BY  \THEN  M)
                         ELSE:    [DISPLACE:L   BY:M]
                    ENDCASE
          ELSE    NIL                FI                    ENDDEFN
```

This rendition actually examines the given layout. It avoids the creation of nested MOVE states. That is, if L happens itself to be in the MOVE state, this new \AT does not reference L. Instead, it references L.DISPLACE directly, and represents both L's matrix and the new matrix M at once as a single matrix. (If L is not in the MOVE state, this function yields the standard record, as before.) This new \AT not only saves memory, it also saves time for all subsequent examinations of its resulting layout; the two matrices now appear only as one.

2.7.4.3 Efficiency in layout splitting. The intimate use of all the MBBs stored with all sublayouts serves as a powerful heuristic for splitting layouts efficiently, both in time and memory. As Figure 2.4 illustrates, the MBBs serve to focus the layout examination directly to the areas of interest. The uninteresting areas are left unexamined. They are treated as indivisible wholes; for example, the split functions yield all of L as entirely selected or not selected based simply on MBB examination.

Consider Figure 2.7. Figure 2.7A shows the MBBs for each cell in an 8 by 8 array. The red box shows an intended selection; the goal is to isolate the six cells inside the red box. Part B shows what this layout looks like to the first recursive call to the box splitter. The box splitter sees only the MBBs of the eight immediate sublayouts. [This rendition

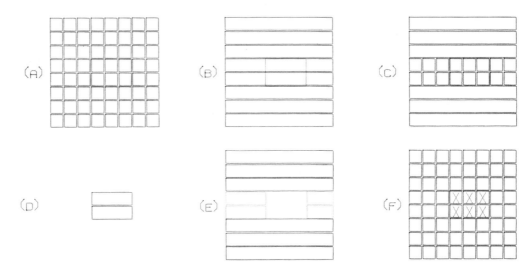

SPLITTING A LAYOUT

FIGURE 2.7   Selecting part of a layout.

assumes that the layout was originally specified in terms of rows (Section 2.6.5).] With just these eight sub-MBBs, the box splitter knows immediately that it can ignore entirely six of them; only two rows intersect the red box.

However, each of these two rows straddles the red box. The box splitter therefore examines each of these two rows by calling the box splitter recursively. Within this second recursion, the box splitter sees sub-sub-MBBs (Figure 2.7C), that is, the immediate sublayouts in each of the two interesting rows. The box splitter examines no further; in this example, no visible MBB straddles the area of interest. The box splitter now yields SPLIT_LAYOUTs. Part D shows the selected portion in terms of its immediate sub-MBBs (one for each row). Part E shows the sub-MBBs for the unselected portion. (The blue boxes are actually sub-sub MBBs; part B shows the unselected portion strictly in terms of its immediate sub-MBBs.) Finally, part F shows both the selected and unselected portions, with the X's in the selected portion.

This entire scenario applies verbatim no matter how complex each cell in the array might be. It makes no difference whether the entire layout represents 100,000 shapes or just 22 shapes.

Figure 2.8 shows the entire examination required for a different split. In this case, the cutting box does straddle two of the cells in the 8 by 8 array. The complexity of this split operation exceeds that of the previous example in that two of the cells require more detailed examination.

The MBB heuristics not only save lots of time, they also save lots of memory. Because uninteresting chunks are not even examined, they are treated as individual wholes and they become shared data structures. These gross chunks become referenced not only from the original layout, but also from the new SEL and REST. For example, the memory consumed to represent the splitting shown in Figure 2.7 is proportional only to the complexity you see in both parts D and E.

This data sharing provides for an efficient implementation of an UNDO command, with which the user can undo the effects of the previous command. A change in the SEL-REST status due to selection or modification generally requires only a small amount of additional memory, to represent the difference. All that remains unchanged is shared among various SEL-REST states. The UNDO command requires merely the sav-

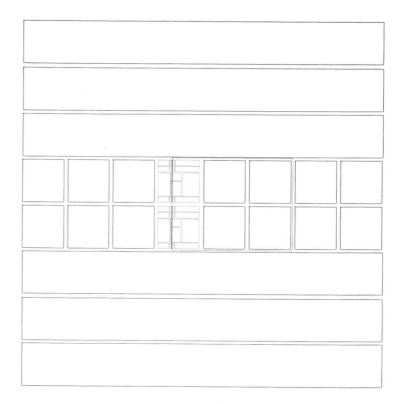

FIGURE 2.8   Example of more refined splitting.

ing of the previous SEL-REST states and their subsequent restoration via assignments to the variables SEL and REST.

Note also that the MBB heuristics nearly minimize disk communications. A disk resident sublayout is not swapped-in if it is not examined (i.e., if its MBB resides entirely outside the area of interest or if it lies entirely within the area of interest). The splitters communicate with the disk only if the area of interest straddles the disk resident sublayout.

Finally, note that the selection process reshapes the layout's hierarchy. A layout's hierarchy is the recursive grouping implied by nested UNION states. Consider what happens when we split a layout into SEL and REST, and subsequently put these two pieces back together (e.g., by clearing the selection):

```
[SEL:SEL   REST:REST]   :=   all   \SPLIT_BY   BOX   ;
all   :=      SEL   \UNION   REST   ;
```

The entire layout appears unchanged, but that layout's hierarchy is changed. Now the layout has as direct sublayouts SEL and REST.

This change in hierarchy affects subsequent examinations of the layout. The gross MBB compares will now be applied to the gross chunks (old) SEL and REST instead of the original direct descendants in the original layout. For example, even if a given split operation must cut deeply into the original layout, a second application of that same split operation will occur very quickly. The second application requires only a shallow cut because it finds the desired split already implemented in the hierarchy. The MBBs of the direct descendants, old SEL and REST, fall perfectly inside and outside the splitting box.

2.7.4.4 *When is a point inside a polygon?* We made use of an operator

$$\text{POINT} \quad \backslash \text{IN} \quad \text{POLYGON} \qquad \rightarrow \qquad \text{BOOLean}$$

in the POLYGON case within the point split operator. We define this new \IN operator with the following text. Conceptually, we imagine a half-line starting at the given point and extending infinitely far to the right. We deduce the "insidedness" of the point relative to the given polygon by counting the number of polygonal edges which cross that half-line. More precisely, we form our count by considering each edge, and

1 Adding one if the edge crosses going upward

2 Subtracting one if the edge crosses going downward.

If this count comes out to zero, the point is outside. (Try an example where the point lies outside the polygon.) A nonzero result implies insidedness. This algorithm works for arbitrary polygons even if some edges intersect other edges. The following text makes use of a new kind of quantifier which gives us easy access to the sequence of edges.

```
DEFINE    IN(P:POINT  POLY:SP)=  BOOL:     BEGIN     VAR  P1,P2=POINT;
     0  <>  +  IF  P2.Y  >  P1.Y  THEN  1  ELSE  -1  FI
            FOR  {P1;*P2}  $C  POLY;
               WITH  P1.Y  <>  P2.Y;
               WITH  (P.Y  >  P1.Y)  <>  (P.Y  >  P2.Y);
               WITH  (P.Y-P1.Y)/(P2.Y-P1.Y)*(P2.X-P1.X)  +  P1.X  >  P.X;
        END     ENDDEFN
```

The first line in this function compares 0 against the sum of plus and minus ones. Each plus or minus one is the result of the IF expression, which chooses +1 if P2 is above P1 in Y, and chooses -1 otherwise. The point variables P1 and P2 are set to each adjacent pair of vertices in the polygon via the quantifier

$$\text{FOR} \quad \{ \quad \text{P1} \quad ;* \quad \text{P2} \quad \} \quad \text{\$C} \quad \text{POLY} \quad ;$$

Each edge is represented very conveniently by its two endpoints, the adjacent pair of vertices. The appearance of the asterisk in this quantifier specifies that P2 is to wrap around back to the beginning of the polygon (while P1 contains the last vertex in the polygon). Refer to Figure 2.9.

This quantifier is modified by three occurrences of the WITH clause, which filters out some of the iterations. The first WITH says that we want to consider only edges that are not horizontal. The second requires that P1 and P2 lie on opposite sides of the half-line. The third asserts that this edge intersects the half line; that is, the intersection appears to the right of P.

2.7.5 Modification Operators

Following is a set of useful modification operators. Each command is described here by three things:

1 The sequence of characters with which the user invokes the command. (Remember that each command character comes with the position of the pointing device taken at the time the user actually types the character.)

2 A short description of the command's effect.

3 The implementation of that command, that is, its effect on the variable SEL.

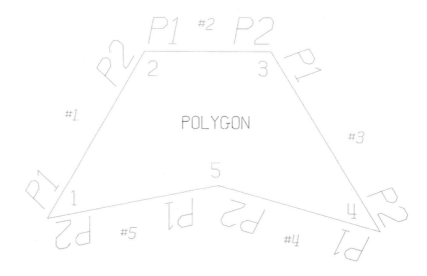

FOR { P1 ;* P2 } $C POLYGON ;

FIGURE 2.9   Notation for visiting edges of a polygon.

The commands follow:

> **1** MH   Move Here: Move the selected portion from M to H:
>
> SEL:=   SEL   \AT   H-M   ;
>
> **2** MC   Move Copy: Move a copy of the selected portion from M to C:
>
> SEL:=   SEL   \UNION   (SEL   \AT   C-M);
>
> **3** M<   Mirror left-right about the point M:
>
> SEL:=   SEL   \AT   -M   \MIRY   \AT   M;
>
> **4** M/   Mirror top-bottom about the point M:
>
> SEL:=   SEL   \AT   -M   \MIRX   \AT   M;
>
> **5** O<   Orient Left: Rotate 90 degrees (counterclockwise):
>
> SEL:=   SEL   \AT   -O   \ROT   90   \AT   O;
>
> **6** O>   Orient Right: Rotate −90 degrees:
>
> SEL:=   SEL   \AT   -O   \ROT   −90   \AT   O;
>
> **7** D   Delete selection:
>
> SEL:=   NIL;
>
> **8** !   Arbitrary Modification (see below)

These operators provide for moving, copying, mirroring, 90-degree rotations, and deleting. The final command is a catch-all. It allows the user to specify any modification whatsoever by leaving the graphics mode and entering our language interpreter. The user can then modify SEL however desired.

(As certain kinds of modification become commonly used, it is a good idea to promote these new kinds of modifications to full-fledged commands, thus lengthening this list.)

2.7.6 Keeping the User Informed

Each modification operator requires its effect to be shown on the screen. An easy but nonoptimal method is to:

1 Erase old SEL   (before modification).
2 Draw new SEL   (after modification).

This pair of operations keeps the screen updated for the application of any conceivable modification operator.

The nonoptimality of this erase-draw technique can be seen easily with the copy command. The copy command requires no erasing. Copy can work much more efficiently by not erasing old SEL and by drawing only the new copy (only part of new SEL). In general, each particular form of modification can make use of its own special circumstances to update the screen as quickly as possible.

A quick way to erase the old SEL is to erase completely the MBB of old SEL. This generally requires only one short communication with the screen. However, erasing completely the MBB of old SEL will erase not only SEL, but also elements in REST that happen to lie (even partially) within SEL's MBB. Therefore, the erase should be followed by redrawing REST within SEL's MBB:

DRAW(REST,   SEL\MBB);

Not only should the screen reflect changes due to modification, but it should also provide a visible distinction between the selected and nonselected portions of the entire layout. That is, each selection operator should affect the screen to reflect the change in selection status. Let us say that selected portions will be "highlighted."

The operation of highlighting can be implemented by a variety of means, depending on the capabilities of the screen device. Some color screens have spare memory planes for colors not used in layouts. Highlighting can be implemented by drawing the newly selected layout to one of these unused planes. The screen will show the highlighting by an apparent change of color. The highlighting can be changed (e.g., erased) simply by clearing that one special memory plane, without affecting the original layout visible on the screen.

2.7.7 Color in Interactive Graphics

So far all our examples in interactive graphics ignore color. Shapes are created without color, selection splits layouts without regard for color, and no modification operator considers color. Viewing parameters provide no means by which to see objects of a given color in isolation.

Object creation can incorporate color by painting each new box and polygon with the color present in a variable. We provide for the setting of that "default" color by introducing a new, nongeometric command which simply sets that color variable.

Color can apply to selection in that the user might wish to specify

"Of all that is selected, keep only those objects of a particular color."

It is possible that there can be shapes identical in every respect, including location, but which differ only in color. To distinguish such shapes requires the specification of color in selection. A layout can be split on the basis of color by introducing the operator

LAYOUT   \SPLIT_BY   COLOR   →   LAYOUT

This operator differs from our geometric split operators in that MBBs play no role whatsoever. Splitting by color is best performed after splitting by geometry. Geometric splitting works quickly, with the aid of MBBs, and its result is typically a relatively small portion of layout.

Color can also apply to modification. We may want a command that changes the color of all shapes selected.

2.7.8 A Convenient Specification for "Wire" Polygons

We have provided for the representation of boxes and polygons. Even though a box is merely a special kind of polygon, we support its explicit representation because

1 Boxes are by far the most common shapes.
2 Boxes admit to much faster examination than do general polygons.

For example, it is much easier to determine whether a given point lies inside a box than it is to determine the same for a general polygon.

There is another special kind of polygon besides boxes. Figure 2.10 shows a wire. A wire is defined by a thickness and a path:

TYPE   WIRE = [WIDTH:REAL   PATH:POINTS] ;
TYPE   POINTS = { POINT } ;

The concept of wire is most useful as a convenient means for polygonal specification, particularly within an interactive graphics editor.

Unfortunately, there are many different interpretations for how a WIRE becomes a POLYGON. Figure 2.10 shows three interpretations. Different groups of people use different interpretations; one group's wire is not a wire to another group. We have avoided the consideration of geometric wires precisely for this reason. Also, silicon compilers can generate polygons as easily as wires.

In fact, the silicon compiler presented in this text makes no use of wires. Although it does produce sets of shapes which together look like wires, the generation of these "wires" occurs in very distinct and almost independent steps. No single routine thinks of a wire as a single geometric entity. Silicon compilers generally produce layouts in terms of very small pieces (e.g., segments of a wire), pieces much smaller than a graphics user cares to think about. (In fact, a silicon compiler may produce even a single segment from smaller subsegments.)

Nonetheless, we can incorporate WIREs into our system if we wish. The bulk of this effort centers on the translation of a WIRE to a POLYGON. We will introduce a coercion,

WIRE   →   POLYGON

so that any wire can be also viewed as a polygon, without extra specification.

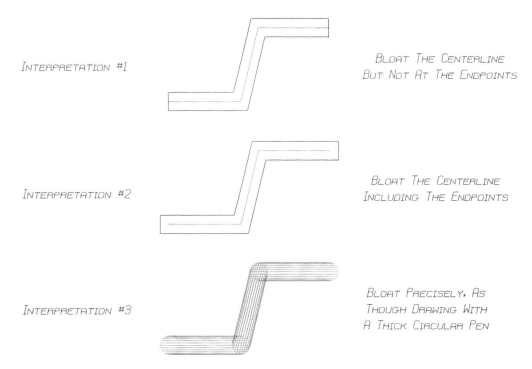

INTERPRETATION #1 — BLOAT THE CENTERLINE BUT NOT AT THE ENDPOINTS

INTERPRETATION #2 — BLOAT THE CENTERLINE INCLUDING THE ENDPOINTS

INTERPRETATION #3 — BLOAT PRECISELY, AS THOUGH DRAWING WITH A THICK CIRCULAR PEN

FIGURE 2.10   Many interpretations for wires.

Armed with this coercion, we have a choice as to how intimately we incorporate WIREs. Do we want to change the type LAYOUT to include another state besides BOX and POLYGON, a WIRE state? Or is it sufficient merely to specify a polygon in terms of the WIRE datatype, and continue to represent only polygons in the type LAYOUT?

If we chose to introduce a new state to the type LAYOUT, we would introduce the WIRE state by redeclaring the type LAYOUT1:

```
TYPE    LAYOUT1  =  EITHER
                         BOX  =      BOX
                         WIRE  =     WIRE
                         POLYGON  = POLYGON
                              ...
                      ENDOR  ;
```

If we do this, we must change all our analysis operators so as to consider this new state. We can make this change simply by augmenting each analysis operator as follows:

1   Wherever the CASE statement appears, add to it a clause for the WIRE state.

2   The text for that new WIRE clause can be copied verbatim from the text of the POLYGON clause.

That is, where we see

```
CASE    L  OF
             ...
             POLYGON:        f(L)
             ...
```

we form

```
CASE     L   OF
              ...
              POLYGON:         f(L)
              WIRE:            f(L)
              ...
```

This easy manipulation always works because:

1 Since L is a POLYGON within the POLYGON clause, we know that f works with POLYGONs.

2 f will work even if L is a WIRE because L will be coerced to type POLYGON, thanks to our new coercion.

Let us now write that coercion from WIRE to POLYGON. This program renders the first interpretation shown in Figure 2.10. Figure 2.11 illustrates the steps involved.

```
LET  WIRE     BECOME  POLYGON  BY
     BEGIN      VAR  P,P1,P2,N1,N2,BI,E  =  POINT;
                  PATH,  NORMALS,  ELBOWS  =  POINTS;     WIDTH  =  REAL;
     DO         [PATH:PATH  WIDTH:WIDTH]  :=  WIRE;     WIDTH:=  WIDTH/2  ;
                NORMALS:=  {COLLECT  P2-P1  \NORMAL    FOR  {P1;P2}  $C  PATH;}  ;
                ELBOWS:=  {COLLECT        DO        BI:=  N1  +  N2;
                                            GIVE     BI  *  (WIDTH  /  (N1  \DOT  BI)  )
                            FOR  {N1;N2}  $C  NORMALS;  }  ;
                    " (Add the extreme elbows ... ) "
                ELBOWS:=            NORMALS[1]   *   WIDTH
                               <$       ELBOWS        $>
                           REVERSE(NORMALS)  [1]    *   WIDTH    ;
     GIVE       {COLLECT  P+E    FOR  P  $E  PATH;  &&  FOR  E  $E  ELBOWS;}
                $$
                REVERSE(  {COLLECT  P-E    FOR  P  $E  PATH;  &&  FOR  E  $E  ELBOWS;}  )
     END        ;
```

This coercion first forms a list of vectors, called NORMALS. NORMALS is formed by considering each segment in the wire, represented by the pair of adjacent points P1 and P2. Each element in NORMALS is a vector perpendicular to the corresponding edge. Note that the NORMALS list is one element shorter than the PATH list; where PATH represents vertices, NORMALS corresponds to edges.

Having NORMALS in hand, we go on to form another list called ELBOWS. We envision that ELBOWS corresponds to the set of vertices, excluding both the first and last vertices of PATH. Note in the final GIVE clause of this coercion that we form the polygon in two pieces, one of which is PATH + ELBOWS and the other the reverse of PATH - ELBOWS. ELBOWS is therefore intended to represent the displacement from each vertex required to thicken the path into a polygon.

ELBOWS is formed by considering pairs of adjacent edges, or more precisely, pairs of adjacent edge normals. Each elbow is formed by summing the normals N1 and N2, followed by an application of an appropriate scale factor which involves WIDTH. Finally, since the ELBOWS list is two elements shorter than the PATH list, we add an additional elbow to both the front and tail of ELBOWS. [The difference between the first and second interpretations of wires (Figure 2.10) is implemented precisely in the definition of these two extreme elbows.]

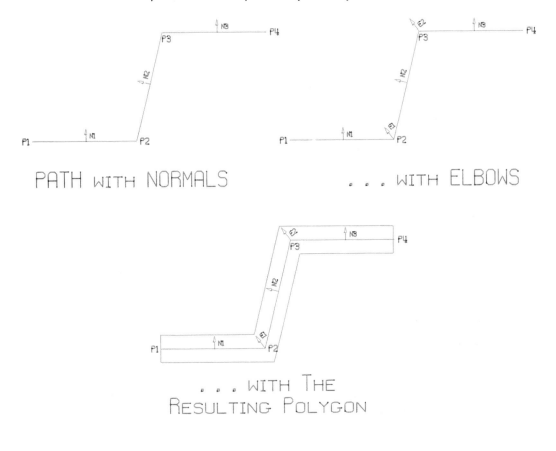

PATH WITH NORMALS   . . . WITH ELBOWS

. . . WITH THE
RESULTING POLYGON

THE WIRE -> POLYGON COERCION

FIGURE 2.11   Wire-to-polygon translation.

Figure 2.12 shows a phenomenon that deserves some attention. Acute angles in the path will give rise to sharp and lengthy extensions in the resulting polygon. Figure 2.12 also shows a solution to this problem. We can get rid of acute angles simply by affecting the wire's path infinitesimally. The vertex at an acute angle is replaced by two vertices "infinitely" close to the original vertex. Although the path is affected only infinitesimally, the resulting polygon has a dramatically different appearance.

2.7.9   Pros and Cons for Interactive Graphics

Interactive graphics is useful primarily for the specification of small, constant layouts. Large layouts tend to be difficult to create; they require too much view manipulation to overcome low display resolution. Consider, for example, the creation of a single long shape, a wire meant to span a large distance. Just to create that one wire may take three changes in viewing. Assuming that the layout appears initially in its entirety on the screen, the user must first zoom in close to one of the two endpoints of the proposed wire. This magnification is required just so the user can accurately specify that one endpoint. Having specified that endpoint, the user then zooms out, to see the other endpoint. Finally, the user zooms in close to that other endpoint to specify its position accurately.

Some interactive graphics editors provide for multiple views simultaneously. They split the screen into pieces so that each view occupies a different portion of the screen. The user must still define each of the multiple views. However, this technique has the

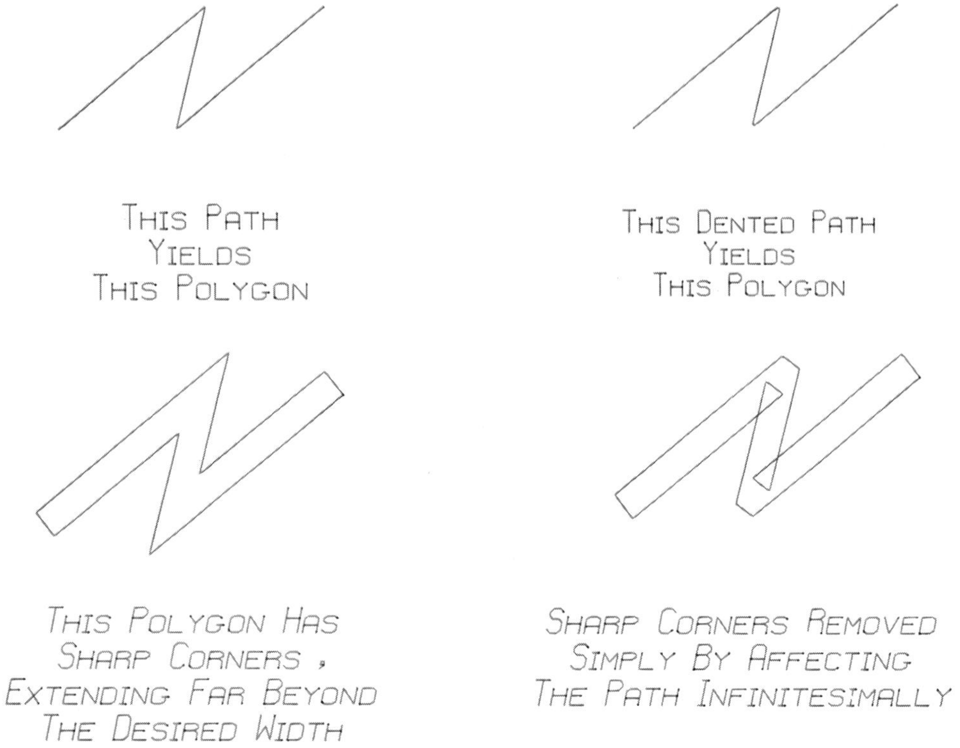

THIS PATH
YIELDS
THIS POLYGON

THIS DENTED PATH
YIELDS
THIS POLYGON

THIS POLYGON HAS
SHARP CORNERS ,
EXTENDING FAR BEYOND
THE DESIRED WIDTH

SHARP CORNERS REMOVED
SIMPLY BY AFFECTING
THE PATH INFINITESIMALLY

FIGURE 2.12   Removing sharp corners.

advantage that the user can produce several wires without having to change the view several times for each wire. Unfortunately, each small window now has even less resolution than the screen as a whole.

Even if all viewing problems were resolved (e.g., the screen were 10 feet on a side), a more fundamental drawback remains. Each layout produced with a graphics editor is absolutely constant. Specification via graphics admits no variables. In contrast, all of our layout specification done textually in Part 1 made extensive use of variables. In effect, we specified not constant layouts, but rather, entire classes of layouts. For example, we defined many NOR gates all at once, simply by defining the NOR function once. We even produced the class of all simple NOR planes, each programmable directly from a logical (not geometric) specification (a NOR_PLANE_LOGIC).

Interactive graphics does serve well to produce small constant layouts, and more. Graphics can be used very effectively for nonlayout tasks. Graphics can serve as an interface for an automatic process that requires coarse geometric suggestions from the user.

For example, a place-and-route program might engage human participation by allowing the user to move individual cells. The cells can be displayed simply as large boxes. As long as the program does not require precise geometric information, the user can make suggestions via coarse movements, without the need for extensive view manipulation.

In general, interactive graphics serves well as long as the complexity of the graphical information is minimized. The best domains tend to be abstractions.

Finally, interactive graphics can be used very effectively for producing illustrations. Illustrations tend to be simple, because they are intended for human consumption. Accuracy in position is far less critical than with formal layouts.

EXERCISES

Section 2.2.2.1

1. What is (10#6)   −   (33#5)   \MAX   −(4#6)∗2 ?

2. (a) For any three points A, B, and C, is it always true that

(A \MAX B) \MAX C   =
A \MAX (B \MAX C)?

(b) Do the point operators +, \MAX, and \MIN conform to the commutative and associative laws (as does "+" for ordinary numbers)?

(c) Is "<" for points transitive; that is, does

A < B   and   B < C   imply that   A < C?

Section 2.2.3.2

3. How many elements are in each of the following strings?

(a) {COLLECT I   FOR I FROM 1 TO 10;}

(b) {COLLECT I-1 FOR I FROM 1 TO 10;} $> 10

(c) {COLLECT I-J FOR I FROM 1 TO 10; !! FOR J FROM 1 TO
(Refer to Sections 1.4.3 and 1.3.4.)

4. What are the largest and smallest numbers in the third string shown in Problem 3?

5. Specify a string of points that trace out a circle (or, more precisely, a regular N-sided polygon, where N is a parameter). [*Hint:* Use the SIN and COS functions.]

6. Given a string of points, PATH, specify a new string that represents PATH displaced by 6 in X and 5 in Y. [*Hint:* Use a variable P of type POINT.]

7. Given a string of points, PATH, specify a new string that represents PATH displaced uniformly, so that its first point resides at 0#0.

8. Given PATH again, specify a new string that represents PATH enlarged by a factor of 2.

Section 2.2.7.4

9. Write the definition for an operator

box \IN box   →   boolean

which yields TRUE when the first box resides entirely within the second box.
Fill in the "…":

DEFINE   IN(A, B: BOX) = BOOL: …   ENDDEFN

10. Given a box B, what value for a point P should we choose so that the box

B \AT P

appears with its lower-left corner (B.LOW) at the point 0#0?

11. Define an operator to find a box's center:

box \CENTER   →   point

    Fill in the "…":

DEFINE   CENTER(B: BOX) = POINT: …   ENDDEFN

12. If B is a box, what is the center of the box

B \AT - (B \CENTER)?

Section 2.2.8

13. Define the operator

point \DOT point   →   real

    so as to represent vector dot product.

14. Define the operator

point \NORMAL   →   point

    so as to represent the given point (vector) rotated 90 degrees counterclockwise.

15. Write a program to compute the Euclidean distance between two given n-dimensional vectors. Assume that each vector is represented by the type VECTOR:

TYPE   VECTOR = { REAL } ;

    Fill in the "…":

DEFINE   DISTANCE(V1, V2: VECTOR) = REAL:
    BEGIN VAR A,B = REAL;
        SQRT(…)   END   ENDDEFN

16. Write a program to find the greatest distance between any pair of VECTORs in a given set of VECTORs:

TYPE   VECTORS = { VECTOR } ;

    Fill in the "…":

DEFINE   GREATEST_DISTANCE(VS: VECTORS) = REAL:
    BEGIN   VAR V1, V2, = VECTOR ; … END   ENDDEFN

Section 2.3.3.2

17. If B is a box, consider the layout

B \PAINTED RED \PAINTED GREEN

    What color will appear in a plot of this layout? [*Hint:* Consider the PLOT procedure given in Section 2.3.3.2. Consider its COLOR parameter and also the "COLOR" clause of its CASE statement.]

Section 2.4.1

18. Write a MATRIX that will slant a picture (layout) so to transform text into italics. That is, define an operator

real \SLANT   →   matrix

so that a parameter of 0 yields no slant (the identity matrix), and a parameter of 1.0 yields a 45-degree slant (up and right). [*Hint:* We slant a point X#Y by transforming it to X + S∗Y # Y, so that the new X coordinate slides to the right as Y increases.] Fill in the ''…'':

DEFINE   SLANT(S: REAL) = MATRIX   …   ENDDEFN

19. Write an operator that takes in a FUNCTION and yields a FUNCTION that is the derivative of the given FUNCTION:

function \PRIME   →   function

Fill in the ''…'':

DEFINE   PRIME(F: FUNCTION) = FUNCTION:
           // (R: REAL) [F ;]   …   \\   ENDDEFN

Assume that there is a variable EPSILON which contains a small value.

Part 2

INTEGRATED CIRCUIT BEHAVIOR

3

The Language of Synchronous Logic: A Behavioral Specification

3.1 OVERVIEW AND ESSENTIAL SEMANTICS OF SYNCHRONOUS LOGIC

Synchronous logic is a language in which one can specify the digital function of an IC. In many IC designs, there exists at some time a synchronous logic specification so that the design can be simulated before the more detailed layout work proceeds.

The language of synchronous logic admits any set of equations written in terms of boolean expressions and variables, under certain constraints. In addition, synchronous logic admits the specification of a unit delay in time.

Put in terms of logical devices, synchronous logic encompasses all dynamic circuits that can be built out of AND and OR gates, inverters, and unit memories (D flipflops). This includes all digital computers. Refer to Figure 3.1. We use the term "unit memory" to denote a device that remembers one bit of information for one unit of time.

Example 1

We specify a two-input AND gate in terms of synchronous logic by writing

OUT = IN1 and IN2

This specifies that the output of the AND gate is the logical AND of two inputs, named IN1 and IN2 (Figure 3.2A). OUT will be true precisely when each of IN1 and IN2 are true.

We specify a three-input AND gate with (Figure 3.2B)

OUT =   IN1 and IN2 and IN3

Example 2: The IF-THEN-ELSE Abbreviation

Let us specify a steering circuit, which has the popular names "multiplexer," "MUX," and "IF-THEN-ELSE." Figure 3.2C shows a schematic for this circuit. The IF-THEN-ELSE circuit connects exactly one of two inputs so that that input alone appears as the output. A third input,

145

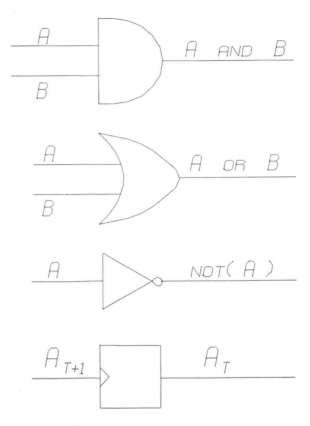

FIGURE 3.1 Elements of synchronous logic.

CHOICE, is introduced to direct the steering. We specify the if-then-else's behavior in terms of synchronous logic by writing

OUT = if CHOICE then IN1 else IN2   or

OUT = (CHOICE and IN1) or (not(CHOICE) and IN2)

We see two notations here. The first notation is the easiest of the two for us to write down and to read subsequently. The second notation, however, tells the story strictly in terms of AND and OR gates and inverters.

Let us adopt the if-then-else notation as an abbreviation for the implementation in terms of AND and OR gates and inverters. This example shows precisely how any if-then-else construction can be decomposed into standard gates.

Example 3: The "=next" Notation and the D Flip-flop

The equation

OUT =next   IN

specifies that OUT follows the input IN but with a unit delay in time. That is, a change appearing on IN will show up on OUT one unit of time later. This is the function performed by a D flip-flop (D for "delay"). Figure 3.3A shows a graph over time of how OUT responds to IN.

This is different from the equation

OUT = IN

which specifies that OUT follows IN instantaneously, or in other words, OUT is identical to IN in all respects.

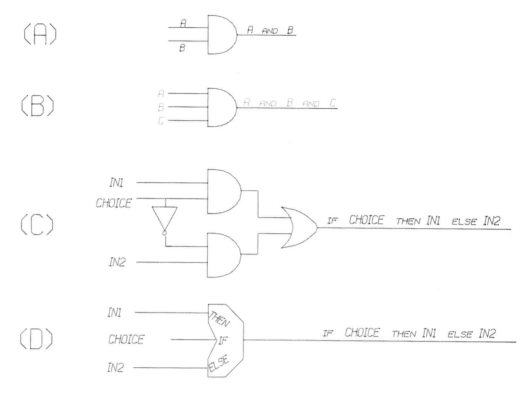

FIGURE 3.2   Examples and notations for logic.

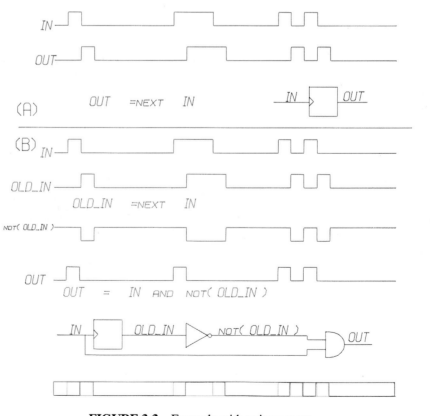

FIGURE 3.3   Example with unit memory.

Equations specified with "=next" as opposed to "=" define future values, that is, the equation reads present values (the right-hand side) but defines a future value (the left-hand side). Only upon the next unit of time does the old "future" value become a present value.

Figure 3.3B shows the graph over time for the behavior specified in the following set of equations:

OLD_IN   =next   IN

OUT   =   IN and not(OLD_IN   )

These equations can be paraphrased as:

1   OLD_IN is what IN was a moment ago.

2   OUT is true precisely when IN is true and IN was not true a moment ago.

With these assertions, it is clear that OUT cannot be true for two consecutive time units. Even if IN stays true over many time units, OUT will become true for only the first of these time units. In other words, OUT goes true exactly when IN goes true, but OUT shuts off immediately upon the next time unit, independent of IN's activity.

Example 4: A 1-Bit Register

We define the behavior of a 1-bit register, which unlike a unit memory, can remember 1 bit of information for many units of time. Any memory takes an input and produces an output, but in addition, a 1-bit register requires another input, called LOAD, which directs the register to begin remembering a new value.

We define the behavior of the 1-bit register in terms of synchronous logic by writing

OUT   =next   if LOAD then IN else OUT

(Figure 3.4A shows a schematic.)

This defines OUT for the next unit of time. If LOAD is true, OUT will take on the present value of IN for the next unit of time. If we keep LOAD set at false, OUT will take on the present value of OUT for the next unit of time. In other words, as long as LOAD is false, OUT remains unchanged, that is, the register propagates its present value forward in time, and hence it "remembers." As soon as LOAD becomes true, the value of IN at this same moment will appear on OUT for the next unit of time.

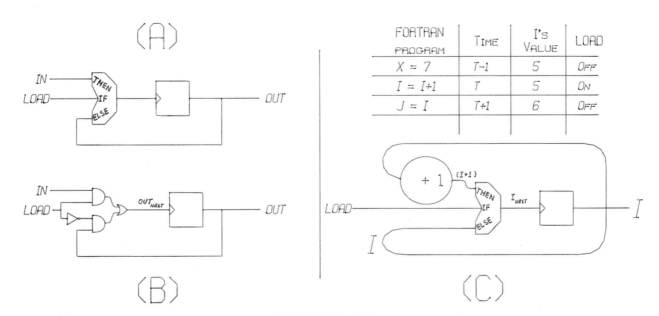

FIGURE 3.4   Unit memory in assignment statement.

Figure 3.4C shows how this mechanism can be viewed as the implementation for a FORTRAN assignment statement (e.g., I=I+1). The LOAD signal goes high during the execution of this assignment. Notice how the variable I does not change during this time unit. I changes only upon the next time unit.

This delay is of great importance. If I were to change immediately during the LOAD pulse, we can imagine that I will change from 5 to 6, and then immediately change from 6 to 7, and then from 7 to 8, and so on, all of this occurring during the single, short LOAD pulse. The value of I would be infinity upon termination of the assignment statement.

Example 5: A 1-Bit Counter

The following equations define the synchronous logic for a single bit of a resettable counter:

RESET_OUT   =   RESET_IN
CARRY_OUT   =   CARRY_IN and VALUE
VALUE   =next   (if CARRY_IN then not(VALUE) else VALUE) and not(RESET_IN)

The inputs are RESET_IN and CARRY_IN. The outputs are RESET_OUT, CARRY_OUT, and VALUE. The first equation specifies that RESET_OUT is simply RESET_IN. The second equation specifies that CARRY_OUT is 1 precisely when the VALUE of this counter bit is 1 and when the CARRY_IN is 1. The third equation specifies the subsequent VALUE for this counter bit; it is written with =next as opposed to =. This equation does not affect VALUE now; rather, it specifies which value VALUE will take on one unit of time in the future. The new VALUE is defined in terms of the present VALUE and the input parameters RESET_IN and CARRY_IN. The new VALUE is not(VALUE) if CARRY_IN is 1, and if CARRY_IN is 0, VALUE remains unchanged. The final "and not(RESET_IN)" in the third equation specifies that VALUE becomes 0 unconditionally if RESET_IN is 1.

3.1.1 Comparing the Two Kinds of Equations: "=" versus "=next"

Let us return to the register example. If it seems awkward and unintuitive that our register delays one unit of time before exposing a new value, consider also that the notation

I   =   I+1

makes no sense in the mathematical interpretation. Mathematically, this "equation" is never true. It is mathematically an impossibility, yet FORTRAN programmers write this text profusely.

This FORTRAN text makes sense to programmers and mathematicians alike when we write more specifically what it really means:

I   =next   I+1

FORTRAN programmers understand that this equation defines only a future value for I, not the present value for I. This assignment reads the present value of I and defines the value for I that is to become apparent one unit of time in the future.

Mathematicians cannot object to this notation because it is not an equation. It relates I and I+1 not at one moment in time, but over at least two different times.

In summary, synchronous logic provides a distinction between the two kinds of equations

A   =   B
A   =next B

The first kind of equation is the mathematician's native territory, and the second kind of equation is the programmer's native territory. The first kind implies simultaneity whereas the second kind implies a separation in time.

3.1.2 The Time Dimension in Computation Provides for the Tolerance of Contradictions

Let us point out another distinction between the two kinds of equations. Whereas the "=next" equation

$$I \quad =\text{next} \quad I+1$$

is well defined, the "=" equation

$$I \quad = \quad I+1$$

is not well defined. The latter equation is known as a "race" condition. If we were to try to "execute" it, the value of I would change infinitely many times instantaneously, thus yielding a nonsense result.

Similarly, the equation

$$X \quad =\text{next} \quad \text{not}(X)$$

is valid, whereas the equation

$$X \quad = \quad \text{not}(X)$$

is not valid. The first equation specifies that X inverts on each time unit. The second equation specifies that X inverts infinitely many times simultaneously, and no one knows whether X will be true or false on the next unit of time.

The latter equation corresponds to the popular paradox

" This sentence is false. "

The truth of this sentence is necessarily undefined: If we were to believe that this sentence were true, then believing in its truth, we would conclude what it says (i.e., this sentence is in fact false). (We can never assume that this sentence is true.) Similarly, if we were to believe that this sentence were false, we would conclude (in our strictly true/false logic) that whatever this sentence says, the opposite must be true (i.e., this sentence must be true). In summary, we cannot assign a truth value to this sentence.

The correspondence between this paradox and the equation

$$X \quad = \quad \text{not}(\ X\ )$$

can be seen by replacing X with a more descriptive name, for example,

$$\text{THE\_TRUTH\_OF\_THIS\_SENTENCE} = \text{not}(\ \text{THE\_TRUTH\_OF\_THIS\_SENTENCE}\ )$$

or, equivalently,

$$\text{THIS\_SENTENCE\_IS\_TRUE} = \text{if THIS\_SENTENCE\_IS\_TRUE then FALSE else TRUE}$$

Another amusing example of this kind of paradox, or race condition, appears in an episode of the TV show *Star Trek*, where Captain Kirk tells a robot (named Norman)

" I am a liar. "

The robot thinks about this, concluding alternately that Kirk is a liar and that Kirk is not a liar. Of course, Kirk knows that a strictly logical being cannot resolve the truth of this statement, and as expected, the robot enters a race condition and burns up and "dies" in the process.

Mathematicians outlaw such paradoxes simply by forbidding self-referential assertions; that is, an admissible assertion does not refer to itself. The language of synchronous logic outlaws race conditions by forbidding "=" equations which read the same variable as it defines.

We avoid race conditions by separating the logical "contradiction" in time; for example, we write

$$X \quad =next \quad not(X)$$

which corresponds to either

" This sentence will be false in a moment. "   or

" I will be a liar in a moment. "

(If Kirk is presently a liar, he will be truthful in the next time unit, but not now. Similarly, if Kirk is presently truthful, he will remain truthful during the present time unit and will emerge in the next time unit as a liar.)

Notice that the "=next" equation

$$X \quad =next \quad not(\quad X \quad)$$

and its corresponding sentence

" This sentence will be false in a moment. "

are entirely admissible in both mathematics and synchronous logic. The equation does both define and read the signal X, but the "=next" implies that these two "X"'s are not the same variable at the same time. The two "X"'s are separated in the time dimension. Similarly, the corresponding sentence is not self-referential. The sentence refers only to a future existence of itself. Again, the self-reference is separated, or insulated, in the time dimension.

3.1.3 The Glitch: A Subtle Form of Race Condition or Contradiction

Consider our 1-bit register example:

$$OUT \quad =next \quad if \ LOAD \ then \ IN \ else \ OUT$$

Because we wrote it with the "=next" notation, we know unconditionally that this equation is admissible (i.e., it introduces no contradictions). You might wonder if we could write this particular equation with the "=" as opposed to the "=next":

$$OUT \quad = \quad if \ LOAD \ then \ IN \ else \ OUT$$

Does this "=" equation introduce any contradictions? It states merely:

1   If LOAD is true at the moment, then OUT=IN.
2   If LOAD is false, then OUT remains unchanged (i.e, OUT=OUT).

The second equation is certainly not a contradiction; in fact, it is a tautology. The first equation introduces a contradiction only if IN depends on OUT, for example,

$$IN \quad = \quad not(\ OUT \ ) \qquad or$$
$$IN \quad = \quad OUT+1 \qquad \text{(as in the FORTRAN example)}$$

Either of these two dependencies would render the OUT=IN equation as

OUT =   not (OUT)   or

OUT =   OUT+1

However, we can imagine situations where IN does not depend on OUT (e.g., where the register serves only as a variable delay in a linear pipeline architecture). Assuming that IN does not depend on OUT, this analysis shows that replacing the "=next" by the "=" introduces no contradictions. In fact, omitting the "=next" delay appears to have the advantage of faster execution; that is, the register can expose on OUT its new value on IN immediately when LOAD becomes true, without enduring a unit delay in time.

As stated earlier, this "=" equation would be forbidden because it both defines and reads the variable OUT (at the same time). Perhaps that restriction is too strong? Maybe, for simplicity of expression, we outlawed too much.

In fact, we really do need that restriction as stated. The "=" rendition of the 1-bit register suffers from a subtle form of contradiction, sometimes called a glitch, which appears when LOAD changes from true to false. In our strictly logical domain, LOAD can never be between true and false; it is exactly one or the other.

However, any physical implementation must tolerate a nonzero span of time during which LOAD does take on an indeterminant value. During this indeterminent time, OUT will also be undefined. So even when LOAD finally reaches false, the value of OUT will be found to hold an undefined value, perhaps true, perhaps false, or neither. Even if OUT resolves to true or false, the particular value will be unrelated to the value of OUT previously, when LOAD (and OUT) entered the undefined state.

Figure 3.5 shows how undefined, or unsteady, states propagate through "=" equations. The following is clear for any "=" equations:

1   The output is unsteady if any input is unsteady.

2   The output is steady only after all inputs are steady.

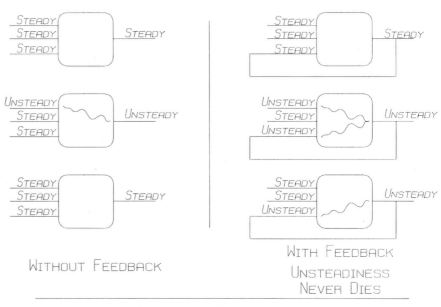

WITHOUT FEEDBACK

WITH FEEDBACK

UNSTEADINESS NEVER DIES

STEADY / UNSTEADY PROPAGATIONS

FIGURE 3.5

An "illegal" equation, which defines a signal it also reads, appears as follows when we consider that the output is also an input:

1 The output is unsteady if the "output" is unsteady.
2 The output is steady only after the "output" is steady.

This implies that the output is never steady if we even so much as allow just one input to change just once. At the moment the input changes (i.e., becomes unsteady), the output becomes unsteady. In fact, the output remains unsteady forever; it can become steady only after it is already steady. In other words, an "illegal" equation can never render a stable output if we ever allow an input to change. (If we were to forbid changing inputs, the equation would be useless; it would be used only to define a constant for all time.)

We must point out that this analysis is overly simplified. Whereas an output becomes steady only after all the inputs have been steady for a short while, unsteadiness also takes time to propagate from an input to the output. Therefore, it is possible that the output will remain steady for a very short while even after an input becomes unsteady. Some circuit designers take advantage of this fact and produce circuits that correspond to "illegal" equations. These circuits can be a risky business because they make detailed assumptions about the electrical characteristics of the silicon. Such assumptions have caused many circuits to fail in practice because amid this detail, approximate calculations sometimes fail. On the other hand, there are some circuits that do work reliably, where the electrical assumptions can be stated and maintained easily.

We will continue to forbid "illegal" equations because:

1 Our notation provides no way to specify these subtle differences in delays due to electrical properties very dependent on a detailed layout.
2 Such delay specifications would destroy the abstract simplicity provided by synchronous logic (i.e., the user would have to become aware of unsteady states).

Synchronous logic has been developed because of its abstract simplicity, which is appropriate for reliable and clear behavioral specifications.

3.1.4 How the "=next" Equations Suppress Race Conditions and Glitches

Synchronous logic gains its simplicity by supporting the belief that each signal is exactly true or false, and never in between these two states, or unsteady. We have had to forbid feedback in "=" equations for two reasons:

1 *Purely theoretical:* Avoid simultaneous contradictions.
2 *Practical:* Acknowledge the impossibility of instantaneous change, that is, a signal must go through an undefined state during a transition.

    a Feedback would introduce "black holes," periods of time during which all information would be lost, due to unending propagations of unsteadiness (Figure 3.5).

    b In the absence of feedback, the duration of unsteadiness is finite, and we produce a practical implementation by expanding the duration of a "time unit" so that it is longer than the longest finite duration of unsteadiness.

We have not restricted "=next" equations because

1 Purely Theoretical: An "=next" equation cannot express a contradiction.
2 Practical: We can handle all cases, as we will see.

An "=next" equation differs from an "=" equation because it defines a future value while reading only present values. Even if the future value becomes unsteady, it in no way affects the present values being read by the equation.

We can practically tolerate feedback in "=next" equations precisely because the "=next" concept introduces the notion of time units (i.e., separable quanta of time). This convenient quantization of time provides for the existence of physical time "between" adjacent time units. Whereas we will maintain the consistency of all equations during all time units, we can in between time units tolerate a loss of consistency. (Synchronous logic does not include this physical time between time units in its domain of discourse. Hence, we are free to do whatever we please during these vacations, as long as each vacation is finite in duration.)

Figure 3.6 shows that the output of a unit memory remains steady during each and every time unit, even while its input is unsteady. From the end of one time unit to the commencement of the next time unit, that output appears to change instantaneously.

Figure 3.7A shows what happens around a unit memory between time units. This figure shows feedback in order to illustrate the most worrisome of situations. Notice that whenever the unit memory's output is unsteady, this figure shows appropriately the propagation of this unsteadiness around back to the input.

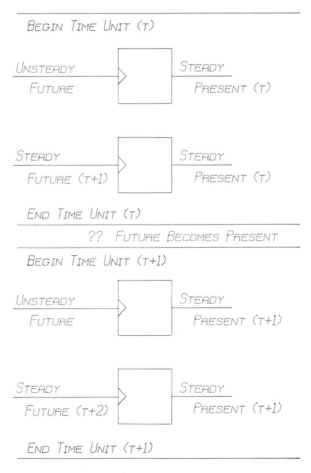

FIGURE 3.6 Close look at time units.

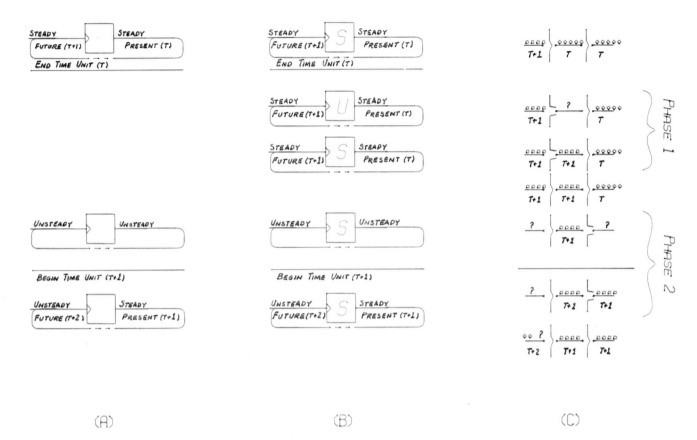

FIGURE 3.7 Close look between time units.

We need to look more closely at the transition from the second step to the third step in Figure 3.7A. The memory unit as a whole recovers from an entirely unstable situation back to a well-defined stable situation. We have noted already such a recovery is impossible, unless there is a hidden stability inside that survives the entire duration of this external instability. Figure 3.7B shows the stability of the hidden state, which does remain entirely stable while the external world goes through its unsteadiness.

Figure 3.7C shows an implementation of a unit memory in terms of two gates, together with its evolution through time. The period during which the input gate is opened is called phase 1; similarly, phase 2 corresponds to the open output gate. It works like the two locks in a canal for ships, or the two major phases of your heartbeat.

3.1.5 Implementation in Silicon for the Unit Memory

Figure 3.8A shows a way to visualize and implement the unit memory in silicon. We use a single transistor to implement a gate (Section 1.2.2). The control for the gate (signal phase1 or phase2) rides on the red and thus either makes or breaks the connectivity along the green (data) wire. Notice that immediately following the red gate, we place a capacitor. This capacitor provides the actual storage capacity of each stage in the unit memory. The capacitor is required because we have assumed that even after the gate shuts, the internal state remains intact for at least a little while. (Without the capacitor, shutting the front gate would isolate the internal state from its definition, and thus electrical charge which represents true or false would dissipate, having no place to stay.)

Beyond the capacitor, we show an amplifier that quietly reads the state (the charge stored on the capacitor) and shouts this value forward. We use the amplifier only to provide electrical isolation, so the capacitor can keep its charge and not use up that charge

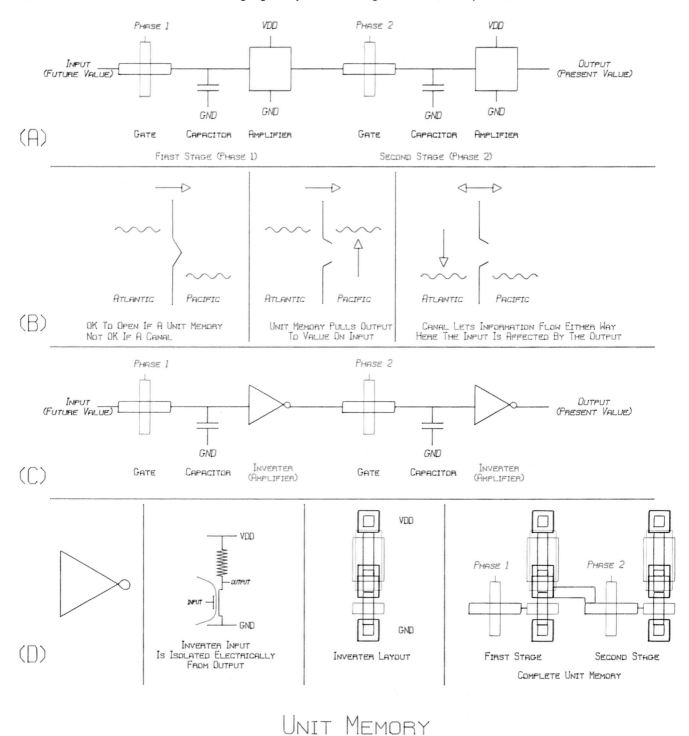

UNIT MEMORY

FIGURE 3.8   Implementation of the unit memory.

in the effort to transmit its value forward. The amplifier reads the charge nondestructive-
ly, and acquiring its power from an independent source, the amplifier maintains on its
output a very secure rendition of the value read from the capacitor.

In the water canal analogy, where are the capacitor and amplifier? Figure 3.8B
shows how our unit memory differs dramatically from the water canal. It shows what our
memory must do in order to propagate a true forward. Whereas the canal opens a door

only when both sides of the door have the same water level, our unit memory opens a door even when the water levels differ. The unit memory is supposed to change the water level of the external world (i.e., raise the entire Pacific Ocean to the level of the Atlantic Ocean). (If the unit memory were to work exactly like the Panama Canal, it would have no effect on the external world.)

To make the canal work like our unit memory, it is clear that it would take an enormous amplifier (pump) on its output to raise the entire Pacific Ocean. It is also clear that the water in the internal state (the capacitor) left to its own without an amplifier (i.e., without isolation) would quickly lose its information and simply drain to the level of the Pacific Ocean.

Figure 3.8A shows a capacitor-amplifier pair at each of the two stages. The internal pair, which resides between the gates, serves to maintain securely the internal state. The pair to the right of both gates serves to maintain the output value of the unit memory. It is this second pair that holds the world steady during the unsteadiness of the internal state.

Figure 3.8C shows the same implementation with the use of inverters (Section 1.3.1). Forgetting for a moment that an inverter inverts its signal, we can see that the inverter serves as both the capacitor and amplifier (Figure 3.8D). The input to the inverter is electrically isolated from the output, and it has a nonzero capacitance. The output of the inverter derives its power not from the input, but rather from the VDD and GND sources at the two extreme vertical endpoints.

Contributions to the inverter's input capacitance come from the horizontal green and red wires, and also the intersection of the red wire and the vertical green wire, the pull-down transistor. This capacitance is sufficient to hold its charge in isolation for at least 1 millisecond. Empirically, it has been seen to hold charge for as long as 4 seconds at room temperature.

Since the capacitor cannot remember forever, we must definitely run the circuit fast enough so that the capacitor's forgetfulness never has a chance to appear. In other words, we must separate our time units by no more than 1 millisecond. This places a lower bound on the speed of the chip. Fortunately, we intend to run chips at a rate of 1 million (or more) time units per second, 1000 times as fast as the lower bound.

An upper bound on the rate of execution is imposed by the fact that all the transitions from unsteady to steady states shown in Figure 3.7 must occur within the physical time from the start of one time unit to the start of the next time unit. It is this consideration that will limit the speed of the chip. As long as the lower and upper bounds on rate of execution do not cross, any rate of execution between these two limits will produce the desired behavior.

In summary, we implement a unit memory with two stages. We maintain for each stage that its input and output are never both unsteady. (This assertion by itself requires the existence of two stages.) We implement each stage with a pass transistor (gate) followed by an inverter. The inverter contributes both the necessary capacitance and the isolation required to hold a value securely. Although each inverter inverts the value, the pair of inverters in both stages together render overall no inversion whatsoever.

3.2 FORMALIZING THE LANGUAGE OF SYNCHRONOUS LOGIC

Let us formalize the language of synchronous logic in much the same way as we formalized the language of LAYOUTs. Recall that we defined the language of layouts by:

1 Introducing datatypes (e.g., LAYOUT, BOX, POLYGON, COLOR, etc.) to denote the kinds of objects we talk about

2 Introducing operators that relate these datatypes (e.g., \AT, \PAINTED, \TO, \FITTING_IN, etc.).

The definitions of these datatypes and operators were specified in terms of the programming language ICL. We used ICL's TYPE statement to declare new datatypes, and we used the DEFINE statement to declare the new operators.

What are appropriate datatypes for the language of synchronous logic? We certainly want to talk about SIGNALs (e.g., RESET_IN, RESET_OUT, and CARRY_IN). We want also to talk about an EQUATION, for example,

CARRY_OUT =   CARRY_IN   and   VALUE

To talk about equations, we will consider signal expressions, such as the expression on the right-hand side of this equation.

Let us introduce the following types:

1   EQUATION   to denote an equation
2   SIGNAL   to denote a signal
3   SIGNAL_EXPR   to denote a boolean combination of SIGNALs

We will form an equation using either of the two rules:

signal \EQU   signal_expr   →   equation
signal \NEXT signal_expr   →   equation

The first rule corresponds to equations written with the =, and the second corresponds to equations written with the =next. For example, we can begin to write our counter equations with

RESET_OUT \EQU   RESET_IN
CARRY_OUT \EQU   CARRY_IN and VALUE
VALUE   \NEXT   (if CARRY_IN then not(VALUE) else VALUE)
                            and not(RESET_IN)

The right-hand side of each equation (the text following the \EQU or \NEXT) is a boolean combination of signals (i.e., an object of type SIGNAL_EXPR). We include the following rules to form any SIGNAL_EXPR:

signal   →   signal_expr
signal_expr \AND   signal_expr   →   signal_expr
signal_expr \OR   signal_expr   →   signal_expr
NOT(signal_expr)   →   signal_expr
[IF: signal_expr   THEN: signal_expr
                      ELSE: signal-expr] →   signal_expr

The first rule says that any SIGNAL by itself is a valid SIGNAL_EXPR. It is this rule which allows us to write the first of the three counter equations. Where the \EQU operator demands a SIGNAL_EXPR to its right, we can write simply a SIGNAL (RESET_IN). The remaining rules for SIGNAL_EXPRs provide for the logical AND, OR, and NOT operations which we need for forming useful SIGNAL_EXPRs. The final rule, the IF-THEN-ELSE, is not essential, but it does allow us to proceed with the counter example most easily.

We can now write each counter equation formally with

```
RESET_OUT  \EQU      RESET_IN
CARRY_OUT  \EQU      CARRY_IN  \AND  VALUE
VALUE      \NEXT     [ IF:  CARRY_IN  THEN:  NOT(VALUE)  ELSE:  VALUE  ]
                         \AND  NOT(RESET_IN)
```

3.2.1 The Datatypes and Operators for Synchronous Logic

To provide a complete definition and implementation for the language of synchronous logic, we now define in detail the representations for the types SIGNAL, EQUATION, and SIGNAL_EXPR. Subsequently, we define in detail all the operators introduced above, so that their meanings are defined in terms of the chosen representations.

Let us declare the datatypes of our synchronous logic language with

```
TYPE   EQUATION    =     [ LHS:  SIGNAL  RHS:  SIGNAL_EXPR  DELAY:  BOOL  ];
TYPE   SIGNAL_EXPR  =    EITHER
                            SIMPLE  =   SIGNAL
                            AND     =   SIGNAL_EXPRS
                            OR      =   SIGNAL_EXPRS
                            NOT     =   SIGNAL_EXPR
                         ENDOR  ;
```

These declarations define the types EQUATION and SIGNAL_EXPR, and the following define their plurals.

```
TYPE   SIGNAL_EXPRS  =  {  SIGNAL_EXPR  }  ;
TYPE   EQUATIONS     =     {  EQUATION  }  ;
```

We will come back shortly to define the datatype SIGNAL.

An equation has a left-hand side (LHS), a right-hand side (RHS), and a DELAY indicator. The LHS is a SIGNAL, the signal being defined by the equation. The RHS is a SIGNAL_EXPR, the expression that the LHS will follow. The DELAY component is a BOOLean which indicates whether or not the equation is to have a unit delay.

This representation may become clearer if we now define the \EQU and \NEXT operators, which produce EQUATIONs:

```
DEFINE  EQU(  X:SIGNAL    Y:SIGNAL_EXPR  )  =  EQUATION:
              [ LHS:  X    RHS:  Y    DELAY:  FALSE  ]      ENDDEFN
DEFINE  NEXT( X:SIGNAL  Y:SIGNAL_EXPR  )  =  EQUATION:
              [ LHS:  X    RHS:  Y    DELAY:  TRUE  ]      ENDDEFN
```

These two operators differ only in the resulting EQUATION's DELAY component.

The datatype SIGNAL_EXPR is a variant. A SIGNAL_EXPR is one of the following:

1 Simply a SIGNAL

2 An AND over a set of SIGNAL_EXPRs

3 An OR over a set of SIGNAL_EXPRs

4 The NOT of a SIGNAL_EXPR

Let us define the \AND, \OR, and NOT operators:

DEFINE   AND(X,Y: SIGNAL_EXPR) =   SIGNAL_EXPR:
                   AND:: {   X   ;   Y   }   ENDDEFN
DEFINE   OR(X,Y: SIGNAL_EXPR) =   SIGNAL_EXPR:
                   OR:: {   X   ;   Y   }   ENDDEFN
DEFINE   NOT(X:SIGNAL_EXPR) =   SIGNAL_EXPR:
                   NOT:: X   ENDDEFN

The \AND operator produces a SIGNAL_EXPR which resides in the AND state. It produces the list of two SIGNAL_EXPRs X and Y, with the {X;Y} notation, and then prefixes this list explicitly with the AND state. (Refer to Section 2.3.1.1 for a review of this notation.) We need to specify the state, AND, together with the set of signals, to distinguish this list from the OR state. The \OR operator specifies the OR state. The NOT operator specifies the NOT state.

Let us finally introduce the IF-THEN-ELSE construction into the language, as another way to express a SIGNAL_EXPR. We do this not by augmenting the representation for SIGNAL_EXPR, but instead by:

1   Accommodating the IF-THEN-ELSE notation
2   Producing a translation into our existing representation for the type SIGNAL_EXPR

We first declare a new datatype to represent the IF-THEN-ELSE construction:

TYPE   IF_EXPR = [IF, THEN, ELSE: SIGNAL_EXPR] ;

For example, the expression

[IF: CARRY_IN   THEN: NOT(VALUE)   ELSE: VALUE]

is an instance of type IF_EXPR. We allow this IF_EXPR to be interpreted as a SIGNAL_EXPR by writing the following coercion:

LET IF_EXPR BECOME SIGNAL_EXPR BY
         (IF_EXPR . IF   \AND   IF_EXPR . THEN)   \OR
         (NOT(IF_EXPR . IF)   \AND   IF_EXPR . ELSE)   ;

This says that to interpret an IF_EXPR as a SIGNAL_EXPR, form the expression

if \AND then   \OR   not(if) \AND else

This expression reduces to "then" if "if" is TRUE, and it reduces to "else" if "if" is FALSE.

3.2.2   The Datatype SIGNAL

Let us now declare the datatype SIGNAL. We will declare SIGNAL as a record having a variety of components. Unlike our other record structures, the set of components will look almost entirely unrelated. Each component is included to satisfy the information requirements of a computation that will be oblivious to the other components.

For example, a logical simulator would like to think of a SIGNAL as a place to store a boolean value. That is, the logical function denoted by the equation

X   \EQU   A \AND B

can be discovered if we have a means to "set" each of A and B to a specific boolean value, and from there derive the boolean value intended for X.

Another process, one that manipulates and optimizes equations, might like to think of a SIGNAL as a place to store some SIGNAL_EXPR. For example, if we are given the equations

$$
\begin{aligned}
X \ \backslash EQU \qquad & A \ \backslash AND \ B \\
D \ \backslash EQU \qquad & X \ \backslash AND \ C
\end{aligned}
$$

we might like to remove the variable X and hence define D simply as

$$
D \ \backslash EQU \qquad (\ A \ \backslash AND \ B \ ) \ \backslash AND \ C
$$

This kind of optimization is facilitated by the ability to store the SIGNAL_EXPR

$$
A \ \backslash AND \ B
$$

in the SIGNAL X.

Let us declare the type SIGNAL with

```
TYPE    SIGNAL  =    [    VALUE:      BOOL
                          EXPR:       SIGNAL_EXPR
                          MARK:       BOOL
                          INDIRECT:   SIGNAL      ]  ;
```

The VALUE component provides storage for a BOOLean value, and the EXPR component provides storage for a SIGNAL_EXPR. Two more fields appear, an INDIRECT and a MARK. The INDIRECT field will be used by a process that changes "variables" under equations; for example, the equation

$$
C \ \backslash EQU \qquad (\ A \ \backslash AND \ B \ ) \qquad \backslash OR \qquad (\ NOT(A) \ \backslash AND \ NOT(B) \ )
$$

can be transformed into

$$
Z \ \backslash EQU \qquad (\ X \ \backslash AND \ Y \ ) \qquad \backslash OR \qquad (\ NOT(X) \ \backslash AND \ NOT(Y) \ )
$$

by a process that:

1 "Indirects" the SIGNAL A to the SIGNAL X, and
    SIGNAL B to the SIGNAL Y, and
    SIGNAL C to the SIGNAL Z, and then

2 Forms a copy of the equation in which every SIGNAL is replaced by its INDIRECT field

This ability to change "variables" is essential, as we will desire to replicate entire sets of equations. For example, we will want to replicate 16 times the set of equations for our 1-bit counter so that we can form easily a 16-bit counter. It is not appropriate to form 16 copies, all of which share the same CARRY_IN signal, for example. If we do not change the variables for each copy, the 16 copies will represent 16 counterbits, all of which are shorted together on a per signal basis. [Once the 16 counterbits are rendered in terms of independent signals, we can subsequently specify any additional relations we might desire (e.g., equating the seventh bit's CARRY_OUT with the eighth bit's CARRY_IN).]

The MARK field will be used by a simple process which shortens a list of SIGNALs by removing duplicate appearances of the same signal.

This choice of this SIGNAL record is somewhat arbitrary. We may choose to augment this record with additional fields if we conceive new processes that wish to store other information in SIGNALs.

We go on now to discuss a small set of notations and concepts designed especially to deal with "storage" or "variable" objects such as the SIGNAL record.

3.2.3 Objective versus Subjective Data: The "@" Operator in ICL

We intend that a SIGNAL will serve as a place of storage. We imagine that whenever some process stores a value into a SIGNAL, this effect will become apparent to all points of view (i.e., to all processes which reference that SIGNAL). For example, given the equation

$$X \ \backslash EQU \quad (\ CARRY\_IN \ \backslash AND \ NOT(VALUE) \ ) \quad \backslash OR$$
$$(\ NOT(CARRY\_IN) \ \backslash AND \ VALUE \ )$$

we notice two references to the signal CARRY_IN. We assume that if a simulator stores some boolean value in CARRY_IN, this boolean value will appear in both references to CARRY_IN.

This section explores two subtly different interpretations for what "modification" means. We classify the two interpretations as "subjective" and "objective" modifications. In all popular programming languages, modification on numbers always fall under the "subjective" category. (We make note of one rare occasion where FORTRAN violates this regularity, which is a great mystery to FORTRAN programmers who happen upon it.)

ICL maintains the notion of "subjective" modification for all datastructures, besides numbers. This uniform treatment provides for the simplicity of the language, as we have seen so far.

This section introduces a notation with which the programmer can override ICL's default "subjective" interpretation and instead specify explicitly an "objective" modification. We introduce this concept now because it goes hand in hand with our desire that the type SIGNAL serve as a storage location.

In summary, this section introduces two new operators in ICL, the "@" and "==" operators. We will use them as follows:

1　To modify the VALUE field in an existing SIGNAL, we will write

@(signal) . VALUE := boolean ;

instead of the more familiar

signal . VALUE := boolean ;

2　To compare the identities of two SIGNALs (not merely their contents) we write

signal == signal

which yields TRUE if the two signals represent the same storage location.

3　To create a new signal and assign it to the SIGNAL variable X, we write

X := NEW ;

This makes X reference a brand new SIGNAL, which is referenced presently from nowhere else. In other words, X now references a storage location unknown presently to any other structure (e.g., no existing EQUATION references this new SIGNAL).

You may wish to skip the rest of this section on the first reading.

3.2.3.1 Two interpretations. We have two closely related concepts of what the text

CARRY_IN

means. On one hand, CARRY_IN is a variable. We can write

CARRY_IN := X ;

This makes CARRY_IN reference the signal referenced by X. This assignment does not affect the SIGNAL referenced originally by CARRY_IN. With this assignment, CARRY_IN merely ceases to reference its original SIGNAL; instead, CARRY_IN comes to reference the SIGNAL referenced by X. After this assignment is executed, CARRY_IN and X reference the same SIGNAL.

On the other hand, we sometimes imagine that CARRY_IN is always associated with the same SIGNAL. We imagine that any modification we specify on CARRY_IN will in fact appear as a modification to the SIGNAL referenced by CARRY_IN. With this conception, we might expect that the assignment

CARRY_IN := X ;   (which in ICL is written   @(CARRY_IN) := X;)

affects not the variable CARRY_IN, but rather the SIGNAL referenced by CARRY_IN. We might imagine that this assignment affects the SIGNAL referenced by CARRY_IN, so that it inherits all the attributes of the SIGNAL referenced by X. With this interpretation, the variables CARRY_IN and X will continue to reference distinct SIGNALs, even though the two SIGNALs have identical attributes.

These two interpretations of the text CARRY_IN are different and not interchangeable. The first interpretation implies that the modification affects only the variable CARRY_IN. The second interpretation implies that the modification affects not the variable CARRY_IN, but rather it affects the SIGNAL referenced from CARRY_IN. Put another way:

1   The first interpretation affects only a variable.
2   The second interpretation affects an existing datastructure.

We will say that the first interpretation denotes a ''subjective'' modification, while the second interpretation denotes an ''objective'' modification. The entire distinction between these two interpretations revolves around the simple question:

From which point(s) of view does the modification become apparent?

A subjective modification, which affects only a single variable, makes the modification apparent to exactly one point of view, the single variable's point of view. In contrast, an objective modification, which affects an existing datastructure, makes the modification apparent to all points of view, that is, to all existing structures (and variables) that reference the modified datastructure.

The terms ''subjective'' and ''objective'' are easy to remember by noting that:

1   An objective fact is true from all points of view (i.e., all people agree to its truth).
2   A subjective perception is true from the point of view of a single person (i.e., no two people need agree about subjective perceptions).

Examples. Most programming makes subjective modifications. For example, the sequence of assignments

       I:=   3;
       I:=   4;

affects only the variable I. If the second assignment were objective,

       @(I)   :=   4   ;

it would affect not the variable I, but instead the object "3" presently represented by I. This would change the entire notion of "3" so that "3" now means "4." For example, a subsequent assignment

       K:=   3;

would really put a "4" in K.

It is amusing to note where the language FORTRAN confuses subjective and objective modification, most notably at subroutine calls. Many implementations of FORTRAN will leave the variable N containing a 12 in the following example:

```
SUBROUTINE     ADD(I,J,K)
        I  =  J  +  K
        RETURN
        END
CALL     ADD(333333,5,7)
        N= 333333
```

Although we assign N the value 333333 in our specification, the preceding call to ADD modifies the first parameter objectively, thus rendering all 333333s as 12s.

3.2.3.2   *Subjective modification is default in ICL.*   ICL extends the notion of subjective modification to apply not only to numbers, but also to all datatypes. This simple and intuitive interpretation provides for very reliable programming. For example, if we write

```
VAR     A,  B  =  BOX  ;
A:=  [  LOW:  0#0     HIGH:  1#1  ]  ;
B:=  A  ;
```

we establish among other things that A and B represent (and reference) the same box. Subsequently, the assignment

       B   .   HIGH   :=   2#2   ;

will affect B, and it will have no effect whatsoever upon A:

A	.	HIGH	remains	1#1	even though
B	.	HIGH	is now		2#2

At this point, A and B reference different BOXes.

The assignment to B.HIGH affects the variable B and not the box referenced from B. ICL affects the variable B by assigning to B a new box which is a copy of the original box except that its HIGH field differs; it contains 2#2. The cost of this "copy on write" implementation is minimal due to extensive use of pointers in the actual implementation. In fact, even though A and B now reference different boxes, both boxes continue to share their LOW fields; that is, the memory taken to represent the 0#0 is shared between the two boxes.

This principle of subjective modification applies uniformly throughout ICL. Even if we pass the box A to a complex function, we can rest assured that this box will remain unchanged. For example, we can define a function

```
DEFINE     STRETCH(  U:BOX  P:POINT  )  =  BOX  :
     DO        U.HIGH  :=  P  ;
     GIVE      U                                        ENDDEFN
```

Internally, this function affects the local variable U, and it leaves unchanged the original box. When we call STRETCH, passing in A as a parameter,

```
     B  :=  STRETCH(  A,  2#2  )  ;
```

we will detect no side effect on the variable A.

In analogy, if our FORTRAN example were implemented in ICL, the variable N would contain a 333333, as specified, and the ADD subroutine, as written, would have no effect whatsoever. In ICL, we would define ADD as a function that returns a value:

```
DEFINE    ADD(  J,  K:  INT  )  =  INT  :      J  +  K        ENDDEFN
```

Unlike FORTRAN, ICL admits functions that return any data, even arrays, or entire layouts.

3.2.3.3 *An objective treatment for SIGNALs.* If we try to modify the SIGNAL variable CARRY_IN with

```
     CARRY_IN  .  VALUE  :=  TRUE  ;
```

ICL will affect the variable CARRY_IN so that from the variable CARRY_IN's point of view, CARRY_IN references a SIGNAL whose VALUE component is TRUE. This assignment does not affect the particular SIGNAL referenced originally by CARRY_IN. This assignment causes the variable CARRY_IN to reference a brand new SIGNAL whose components are identical to the original SIGNAL except that the VALUE component now appears to contain TRUE. (Refer to the BOX example given earlier.)

To illustrate this further, the assignment

```
     X  :=  CARRY_IN  ;
```

sets X to reference the same SIGNAL referenced by CARRY_IN. A second assignment,

```
     CARRY_IN  .  VALUE  :=  TRUE  ;
```

affects the variable CARRY_IN, and it has no side effects on either the variable X or the SIGNAL referenced from X. Thus, following this second assignment, X and CARRY_IN cease to reference the same SIGNAL. This assignment has not affected any existing SIGNAL.

We now introduce the @ operator, which allows objective modifications in ICL. Except for this operator, all modifications in ICL are subjective; that is, they are free of side effects in existing datastructures. We affect the SIGNAL referenced by the variable CARRY_IN with the notation

```
     @(  CARRY_IN  )  .  VALUE  :=  TRUE  ;
```

The @ notation

  @(variable) ... := ... ;

specifies that this assignment affects directly the datastructure referenced by the variable, and leaves the variable itself unchanged. For example, the sequence

  X := CARRY_IN ;
  @(CARRY_IN).VALUE:= TRUE ;

first makes X reference the same SIGNAL referenced by CARRY_IN. The second assignment affects this SIGNAL itself, setting its VALUE component to TRUE. As a result, the variables X and CARRY_IN continue to reference that same SIGNAL. Now that SIGNAL's VALUE component contains TRUE, whether we look at that SIGNAL from the point of view of X or from the point of view of CARRY_IN:

  not only is CARRY_IN.VALUE now TRUE
  but also   X.VALUE is TRUE

  It is appropriate that we depart from ICL's default tendency toward subjective modification in the case of SIGNALs. We declared the type SIGNAL with the intention that a SIGNAL serve as a storage location for many processes. As soon as we think in terms of a storage location, we intend very definitely that the action of modifying that storage location be vividly apparent to all points of view; that is, we expect that any access to that SIGNAL will see the effects of the most recent modification.

3.2.3.4 Comparing the identities of storage locations: the "==" operator. We will want to ask whether or not two given SIGNALs are identical, in the sense that they both reference the same storage location. This question is different from asking whether or not two SIGNALs contain the same contents. For example, two SIGNALs, A and B, can both contain the value TRUE even though A and B reference distinct storage locations.
  We already know how to compare the contents of two SIGNALs A and B. We write

  A.VALUE = B.VALUE

This comparison can yield TRUE even if A and B are different SIGNALs. In contrast, we introduce the == operator so that

  A == B

is TRUE only if A and B reference the identical SIGNAL (i.e., A and B reference the same storage location).
  Consider this distinction. If A==B, then

  @(A).VALUE := FALSE ;

also sets B to FALSE, always. In general, A==B always implies that

  A.VALUE = B.VALUE

On the other hand, if A==B is FALSE, then

  @(A).VALUE := FALSE ;

does not affect B at all. In other words, if A==B is FALSE, and even if now

$$A.VALUE = B.VALUE$$

the action

$$@(A).VALUE := TRUE ;$$
$$@(B).VALUE := FALSE ;$$

renders the comparison above FALSE.

3.2.3.5 Why must we even consider objective versus subjective modification? One may wonder why we have had to introduce the "@" operator for synchronous logic while we never needed it in Part 1 in our presentation of layouts. What is different about these two domains? Could we have avoided the "@" operator simply by presenting synchronous logic differently?

In fact, the "@" operator is rarely needed. Its use is to be discouraged, or at least minimized. The "@" operator introduces global side effects; existing data structures can be changed behind your back, opening the potential for devastating surprises that can take enormous effort to discover.

The "@" operator exposes the existence of pointers in the implementation. In its absence, the programmer can actually believe that there are no pointers, even for recursive datatypes, and hence believe that all assignments produce fresh copies of entire structures. This belief is supported in its entirety in ICL (less the "@" operator), with ICL's uniform subjective interpretation for modification.

We can use a popular buzzword to illustrate the danger in programming with pointers:

1   "Structure programming" discourages the use of "GOTO"'s in programming because they make little or no conceptual sense. (Whereas the computer understands GOTOs well, people do not.)

2   "Pointers" are GOTOs, that is, structureless references from one point in memory to another. What is worse, pointers are dynamic, whereas GOTOs are merely static.

The latter point refers to the fact that the total number and placement of GOTOs in a program is constant throughout program execution. In contrast, the placement and number of pointers varies during execution.

For analogy, consider that unstructured GOTOs correspond to a map containing roads that crisscross and start and end with no regularity. The programmer uses this incomprehensible map to debug programs. Consider now that unstructured pointers correspond to the same kind of map, except that this map changes in time. Every second of program execution affects the map by changing, adding, or deleting 1000 or 1,000,000 roads.

So far, we have used the "@" operator in a very limited way. We have used the "@" operator to affect only the fields in one datatype, SIGNAL. This use does not affect EQUATIONs or SIGNAL_EXPRs, that is, what the user expresses in synchronous logic. This use affects only the contents of SIGNALs, not their identities. The worst bugs we might encounter would involve invalid data in the fields of SIGNALs. Fortunately, each field is used by a process that is oblivious to other fields. For example, any bug in the VALUE field can be attributed to the simulation process, and any bug in the

INDIRECT field would be attributed to the process that changes logical "variables" of equations.

Let us answer two questions: First, could we implement synchronous logic without objective modifications? Second, what is it about synchronous logic that attracts the use of objective modification? The answer to the first question is yes, and the answer to the second question is found in many formal mathematical treatments of axiomatic logic.

We could avoid the use of the "@" operator in our implementation of synchronous logic by doing the following:

1 Declare the type SIGNAL to be simply an INTeger.
2 Define the function NEW so that it yields a unique INTeger on each call.
3 Compare the identities of SIGNALs simply by comparing INTegers.
4 Store values "into" SIGNALs by affecting not the SIGNALs themselves, but by maintaining a separate "context," or association list, which serves to map a SIGNAL to a value.

This final step relieves the need to use a SIGNAL as a storage location. Instead, for each field we maintain a separate lookup table, a list of pairs, where each pair represents a signal/value association. Each and every store or read operation on a SIGNAL now requires a search through such a table, and this table is as long as the number of existing SIGNALs. The disadvantage with this technique is mostly a loss of efficiency for storing into and reading from SIGNALs.

To answer the second question, there is a mathematical precedence for the careful distinction between subjective and objective modification. Whereas the logician uses mathematics to study mathematics itself, we have used a programming language to describe objects (EQUATIONs) which are themselves programs (i.e., objects subject to their own execution). In both cases, one is confronted with objects which themselves contain variables; then, in addition, one is confronted with a whole new class of variables, our program variables, which refer to the objects under study.

The logician has to be careful to distinguish between:

1 Objective "variables," variables that belong to the mathematical objects themselves
2 Subjective (or meta-) "variables," variables that the logician uses to refer to the mathematical objects

It is clear from this description that nowhere does a metavariable appear as part of any object.

We have distinguished between two kinds of variables:

1 *Objective variables:* These are variables that occur as parts of EQUATIONs. Equations relate variables, variables of type BOOLean (i.e., they take on only the values TRUE and FALSE).
2 *Subjective (meta-) variables:* These are our program variables (i.e., they refer to the objects under study). These are variables of type SIGNAL, EQUATION, or SIGNAL_EXPR. A SIGNAL refers to a BOOLean variable, not a BOOLean value. The variation afforded by a SIGNAL variable spans the domain of logic variables, whereas the variation afforded by logic variables (type BOOLean) spans the domain of TRUE and FALSE.

This distinction has required our careful attention about what

```
CARRY_IN  :=  X  ;
```

means; that is, does this assignment transfer a logic variable or the contents of a logic variable? We have used the "@" operator to specify the latter.

The temptation to use objective modifications comes from the fact that synchronous logic refers to objects that themselves contain variables. Whereas subjective modification provides us with the ability to change our program variables, objective modification provides the ability to affect the variables of the objects.

3.2.4 Operations on SIGNALs

3.2.4.1 Initializing a SIGNAL variable. Let us declare some variables and generate as data the equations for our 1-bit counter example. First, we want to write equations in terms of SIGNALs, which we declare with

```
VAR    CARRY_IN,  CARRY_OUT,  RESET_IN,  RESET_OUT,  VALUE  =  SIGNAL;
```

Let us now initialize each SIGNAL, so that each of these variables will reference a distinct storage location:

```
CARRY_IN:=  NEW;       CARRY_OUT:=  NEW;       VALUE:=  NEW;
RESET_IN:=  NEW;       RESET_OUT:=  NEW;
```

For these statements to be valid, we must define the NEW function:

```
DEFINE    NEW  =  SIGNAL:    [VALUE:  FALSE]          ENDDEFN
```

This NEW function, when executed, creates a new SIGNAL, whose VALUE is initially FALSE.

3.2.4.2 The counter example. We now declare a variable to hold our counter equations:

```
VAR        COUNTER_BIT  =  EQUATIONS  ;
```

The following assigns our counter equations to this variable:

```
COUNTER_BIT:=  {  RESET_OUT          \EQU      RESET_IN  ;
                  CARRY_OUT          \EQU    ( VALUE \AND  CARRY_IN )  ;
                  VALUE    \NEXT   [ IF:  CARRY_IN  THEN:  NOT(VALUE)
                                        ELSE:  VALUE ]  \AND  NOT(RESET_IN) };
```

COUNTER_BIT now refers to three equations.

This set of equations as a whole refers to five signals (storage locations) from 11 different places. The first equation contains two references, the second equation contains three references, and the last equation contains six references. The last equation contains two references to CARRY_IN, due to the implicit translation from the IF-THEN-ELSE (type IF_EXPR) to the type SIGNAL_EXPR. All 11 references refer to five SIGNALs: the NEW storage locations assigned to the signal variables RESET_OUT, RESET_IN, CARRY_OUT, CARRY_IN, and VALUE.

It is important that we initialized the five signal variables prior to assigning the set of equations to COUNTER_BIT. As a result, COUNTER_BIT now refers to a structure that shares these five storage locations in precise correspondence with the multiple appearances of each signal variable within the specification of this set of equations. This sharing maintains the mathematical assertion that a modification to CARRY_IN's VALUE will be visible from all references to this signal (e.g., from within the second and third equations).

3.2.4.3 *Setting the VALUE of a SIGNAL.* Let us define a procedure

        SET(a SIGNAL , a BOOLean value);

As discussed in Section 3.2.3, we wish to make an "objective" modification to the given SIGNAL. We write

        DEFINE   SET(S:SIGNAL B:BOOL):
                            @(S).VALUE := B;   ENDDEFN

Thus,

        SET(CARRY_IN , TRUE);

sets the SIGNAL referenced by CARRY_IN to hold the value TRUE.

The effect of this objective modification is also apparent in the existing SIGNAL_EXPR

        VALUE \AND CARRY_IN

For example, if we perform

        SET(VALUE, TRUE);

then the boolean value represented by that SIGNAL_EXPR,

        (VALUE \AND CARRY_IN)   \VALUE

yields TRUE. We will shortly define this \VALUE operator,

        signal_expr \VALUE   →   boolean

which computes a boolean value based on the signals and logical combinations present within the SIGNAL_EXPR (Section 3.2.5.1).

In fact, the following scenario occurs:

        VAR   SE = SIGNAL_EXPR;
        SE:= VALUE \AND CARRY_IN;
        WRITE(SE \VALUE);   " Prints TRUE "
        SET(CARRY_IN, FALSE);
        WRITE(SE \VALUE);   " Prints FALSE "

This is the first real example shown so far which exposes unambiguously the existence of an objective modification. In the absence of objective modifications (the "@" operator in SET), we would deduce that the two WRITE statements should print the same value. That is, between the WRITE statements, we see no modification specified on the variable SE. Without the "@" operator in SET, we could deduce unconditionally that no existing data are changed, and hence SE's entire meaning must remain unchanged.

The two WRITE statements do, in fact, print different values because the SET procedure does use the "@" operator, affecting the signal referenced by CARRY_IN, which is also referenced from within the data referenced by SE.

To better understand the role of objective modification, we present another example. We declare a new SIGNAL variable, W, and assign it the signal CARRY_IN with

```
VAR     W  =  SIGNAL  ;
W   :=   CARRY_IN
```

Let us now modify the variable CARRY_IN, say, by assigning a new signal to this variable:

```
CARRY_IN  :=  NEW  ;
WRITE(  SE  \VALUE  );        "  Still prints FALSE  "
SET(  W,  TRUE  );
WRITE(  SE  \VALUE  );        "  Prints TRUE  "
```

Notice that W now references the original "carry-in" signal, and so can be used to affect the value of the SIGNAL_EXPR SE. The following shows that the variable CARRY_IN now plays no role in SE anymore:

```
SET(  CARRY_IN,  FALSE  );
WRITE(  SE  \VALUE  );          "  Still prints TRUE  "
```

Finally, the following shows how ICL's default subjective modification (notice the absence of the "@") causes the variable W to reference a new SIGNAL:

```
W.VALUE  :=  FALSE  ;
WRITE(  SE  \VALUE  );        "  Still prints TRUE  "
SET(  W,  FALSE  );
WRITE(  SE  \VALUE  );        "  Still prints TRUE  "
```

3.2.4.4 *Comparing the identities of two SIGNALs: the \EQ operator.* Let us specify

```
DEFINE  EQ(  A,B:  SIGNAL  )  =  BOOL:     A  ==  B        ENDDEFN
```

so that we can write

```
A  \EQ  B
```

to compare the identities of SIGNALs, forgetting the fact that SIGNALs are storage, or objective, data.

3.2.5 Operations on SIGNAL_EXPRs and EQUATIONs

To become more familiar with our logic domain, let us consider several kinds of operations we might like to perform on EQUATIONs, SIGNAL_EXPRs, and SIGNALs. We will consider how to simulate a set of EQUATIONs, that is, how to see what function the EQUATIONs, as specified, really perform. Simulation is useful in order to gain confidence that a set of equations perform as intended.

As we consider simulation, we will see how to detect the existence of "race" conditions. A "race" condition is a phenomenon that occurs in poorly designed circuits, rendering them highly unreliable. We can verify the absence of electrical race conditions in a silicon implementation by proving a simple property about sets of EQUATIONs.

Finally, we will consider the transformation of a set of EQUATIONs into disjunctive normal form. Disjunctive normal form is just one of the many equivalent ways of writing the same set of equations. Equations written in disjunctive normal form can be translated easily into the type NOR_PLANE_LOGIC (Section 1.4.3), from which we can obtain a silicon implementation of the logic equations via a programmable logic array structure (PLA).

3.2.5.1 Evaluating a SIGNAL_EXPR. Suppose that we set the VALUE field in each SIGNAL referenced by a SIGNAL_EXPR. We could then ask what boolean value is represented by that SIGNAL_EXPR as a whole. For example, if we consider the SIGNAL_EXPR

> VALUE \AND CARRY_IN

we can ask what boolean value is represented by this expression if we set VALUE and CARRY_IN each to a specific boolean value.

Let us write a function, \VALUE, so that

> signal_expr \VALUE $\rightarrow$ boolean

\VALUE will evaluate a SIGNAL_EXPR within the context supplied by its constituent signals. We will write this function in a manner that considers each of the four possible states in which any SIGNAL_EXPR resides. (Refer to our MBB computation on LAYOUTs in Section 2.3.3.1 for another example of this kind of programming.)

```
DEFINE     VALUE( S:SIGNAL_EXPR )  =  BOOL:     BEGIN  VAR  S1=SIGNAL_EXPR;
           CASE  S  OF
                 SIMPLE:  S.VALUE                        " (S  is  a  SIGNAL) "
                 AND:     ALWAYS  S1\VALUE  FOR  S1  $E  S;
                                                         " (S  is  a  SIGNAL_EXPRS) "
                 OR:      THERE_IS  S1\VALUE  FOR  S1  $E  S;
                                                         " (S  is  a  SIGNAL_EXPRS) "
                 NOT:     - (S\VALUE)                    " (S  is  a  SIGNAL_EXPR) "
           ENDCASE                                               END       ENDDEFN
```

This evaluation of a SIGNAL_EXPR can be paraphrased as follows:

1   If S is simply a SIGNAL, the value of the SIGNAL_EXPR S is the value of the SIGNAL S.

2   If S is the AND over a set of SIGNAL_EXPRs, the value of the SIGNAL_EXPR S is TRUE precisely if each and every SIGNAL_EXPR in the set evaluates to TRUE.

3   If S is the OR over a set of SIGNAL_EXPRs, S is TRUE if there is at least one SIGNAL_EXPR in the set which evaluates to TRUE.

4   If S is the NOT of another SIGNAL_EXPR, the value of S is the boolean negation of the value of the other SIGNAL_EXPR.

3.3 SYNCHRONOUS LOGIC SIMULATION

A set of EQUATIONs (e.g., COUNTER_BIT) can be simulated, or "executed," to expose its behavior, just as a computer program can be executed, exposing its behavior.

Let us write a procedure that "executes" an equation:

```
DEFINE    EXECUTE( E:EQUATION )  :
                    SET( E.LHS , E.RHS \VALUE );          ENDDEFN
```

This procedure evaluates the equation's RHS (right-hand side) and then stores this value into the SIGNAL referenced by the equation's LHS.

For example, we can execute the first EQUATION in the COUNTER_BIT set (i.e., COUNTER_BIT[1]) by writing

EXECUTE(COUNTER_BIT[1]);

This action leaves the signal RESET_OUT holding the same value held presently by RESET_IN. Similarly,

EXECUTE(COUNTER_BIT[2]);

sets the signal CARRY_OUT to the evaluation of

VALUE \AND CARRY_IN

If we set values to signals with

SET(RESET_IN, FALSE);
SET(CARRY_IN, TRUE);
SET(VALUE, TRUE);

then

EXECUTE(COUNTER_BIT[1]);

affects the world as would

SET(RESET_OUT, FALSE);

and

EXECUTE(COUNTER_BIT[2]);

affects the world as would

SET(CARRY_OUT, TRUE);

3.3.1 EQUATIONs and Order of Evaluation

The EXECUTE function provides a convenient means to treat an equation exactly as though it were a FORTRAN assignment statement. EXECUTE evaluates the right-hand side of the equation and finally SETs the left-hand signal of this equation to the new value. Can we simulate a set of equations simply by EXECUTing each equation, one at a time, like a sequence of assignment statements?

With the COUNTER_BIT example as shown, we could simulate that set of three equations as a sequence of three assignment statements. The first equation sets RESET_OUT, the second equation sets CARRY_OUT, and the third equation finally sets VALUE for the next time unit.

One such scan through the entire set of equations corresponds to one time unit. We simulate the behavior over many time units by scanning the set of equations many times. Each scan leaves new values in the signals, so subsequent scans may in fact produce different values; that is, this technique of simulation does expose a behavior evolving in time.

Unfortunately, this simple technique would simulate incorrectly the following equations:

```
C      \EQU      B
B      \EQU      A
```

We can deduce that C should always equal A. However, if we set A to TRUE and B to FALSE initially, we can see that the first scan will render C=FALSE and B=TRUE. In general, the value we assign to the A input for each time unit will show up on C only on the next time unit, thus contradicting our simple mathematical deduction.

As long as we wish to execute equations as though they were FORTRAN programs, we will have to adopt FORTRAN's criterion of well-formedness. For example, the FORTRAN text

```
R:=    SQRT(   X*X   +   Y*Y   );
X:=    3;
Y:=    5;
```

should be rewritten as

```
X:=    3;
Y:=    5;
R:=    SQRT(   X*X   +   Y*Y   );
```

to reflect R's dependence on X and Y. [Although the first piece of program might be valid within a larger program, its validity depends on the assumption that there exist other assignments to X and Y prior to that piece of program. However, synchronous logic (like mathematics) admits only one equation per signal, so in analogy, this sequential program can have no other, previous, assignment to X and Y.]

In other words, in order to treat a set of equations like a FORTRAN program, we must impose the following condition on the order of equations:

For any two equations in the set, say Equation1 and Equation2,

Equation1 must appear before Equation2

if

Equation2 reads the signal defined by Equation1

For example, the set of equations

```
C  \EQU      B        (Equation2)
B  \EQU      A        (Equation1)
```

violates this order requirement because

1　 Equation2 reads the signal defined by Equation1, B, yet
2　 Equation1 does not appear before Equation2.

We will say that a set of equations is "levelized" if it satisfies this order requirement. For another example, note that of the two pieces of FORTRAN text shown above, the second piece is "levelized" whereas the first piece is not.

We need to consider two more things. First, considering the \EQU equations alone, is it always possible to order the equations so to be levelized? Second, where do \NEXT equations fit in? That is, \NEXT and \EQU equations are fundamentally different, and whereas we have shown an order requirement to be placed on \EQU equations (so that they may be treated like a FORTRAN program), we have not yet mentioned how \NEXT equations fit in.

To answer the first question, we will write a program called LEVELIZE:

equations   \LEVELIZE   →   equations

which will put a given set of \EQU equations into levelized order. We will see where this algorithm can get stuck, and we will prove that such a disaster happens precisely when the given equations are "illegal" in the sense that they express feedback (i.e., when they impose mathematical contradictions or infinite propagations of unsteadiness). Thus, the \LEVELIZE operator will both

1 Verify the legality of a set of \EQU equations, and

2 Render this (legal) set in levelized order, so that we can evaluate these \EQU equations as simply as a FORTRAN program.

The only requirement placed on a correct evaluation of \EQU equations is that upon completion of their evaluation, all signals contain values that satisfy all the equations simultaneously. We can execute a levelized set of equations like a sequential FORTRAN program and be assured that upon completion of the scan, all signals will contain values that are consistent with the entire set of equations because:

1 Upon completing the execution of any one equation, this equation alone is certainly consistent with the values of the signals on both its LHS and RHS.

2 The execution of any one equation does not affect the consistency of any equation executed previously.

    a The execution of this equation affects only this equation's LHS signal.

    b Because the equations are levelized, no previous equation depends on this LHS signal; that is, the previous equation's consistency is independent of the value we now put into this LHS signal

To answer the second question, we must consider how \NEXT equations differ from \EQU equations. \NEXT equations are supposed to provide insulation in the time dimension (e.g., via unit memories). This implies that although we evaluate their RHSs now, we must wait until the end of the present time unit before we actually transfer these computed values to the \NEXT equations' LHS signals. In other words, looking at Figure 3.6, we evaluate \NEXT equations' RHSs now so that the input to each unit memory becomes steady during this time unit, but we transfer these new values to the outputs of the unit memories, the \NEXT equations' LHS signals, only between time units, that is, during the physical time between the completion of this time unit and the commencement of the next time unit.

It is interesting to note that we may evaluate \NEXT equations in any order, or more precisely, evaluate their RHSs in any order, because these evaluations affect no signals.

3.3.1.1 Levelizing a set of \EQU equations and the detection of race conditions. To
begin writing the \LEVELIZE operator, we need first an operator

$$\text{signal\_expr} \quad \text{\\INPUTS} \qquad \rightarrow \qquad \text{signals}$$

to extract the set of signals read by a signal_expr. For example, we would like

$$(\quad \text{CARRY\_IN} \quad \text{\\AND} \quad \text{VALUE} \quad) \qquad \text{\\INPUTS}$$
$$\text{to be} \qquad \{ \quad \text{CARRY\_IN} \quad ; \quad \text{VALUE} \quad \}$$

and

$$\text{[IF:CARRY\_IN} \quad \text{THEN:NOT(VALUE)} \quad \text{ELSE:VALUE]} \qquad \text{\\INPUTS}$$
$$\text{to be} \qquad \{ \quad \text{CARRY\_IN} \quad ; \quad \text{VALUE} \quad \}$$

In fact, let us tolerate duplicate signals within the resulting list; for example, we will
accept the list

$$\{ \quad \text{CARRY\_IN} \quad ; \quad \text{VALUE} \quad ; \quad \text{VALUE} \quad \}$$

as the result of the latter example. We define the \INPUTS operator with

```
DEFINE  INPUTS(  S:SIGNAL_EXPR  )  =  SIGNALS:
     BEGIN        VAR  S1  =  SIGNAL_EXPR;
          CASE  S  OF
               SIMPLE:     { S }              "(S is a SIGNAL)"
               AND:        $$ S1\INPUTS  FOR  S1  $E  S;
                                               "(S is a SIGNAL_EXPRS)"
               OR:         $$ S1\INPUTS  FOR  S1  $E  S;
               NOT:        S\INPUTS           "(S is a  SIGNAL_EXPR)"
          ENDCASE
     END                                              ENDDEFN
```

In the SIMPLE clause, S is of type SIGNAL. We enclose it in braces to yield an instance
of type SIGNALS, as demanded by the function header. The AND and OR clauses each
forms the concatenation of the inputs required by its subexpressions.

This \INPUTS operator yields the set of signals referenced by a SIGNAL_EXPR.
An equation, E, reads precisely those signals that are referenced from its right-hand side.
That is,

$$\text{E} \quad . \quad \text{RHS} \qquad \text{\\INPUTS}$$

denotes precisely the entire set of signals read by the equation E.

We will need another operator,

$$\text{equation} \qquad \text{\\DEPENDS\_ON} \qquad \text{signals} \qquad \rightarrow \qquad \text{boolean}$$

which will yield TRUE precisely if the equation reads a signal that appears in the second
parameter. For example,

$$(\quad \text{CARRY\_OUT} \quad \text{\\EQU} \qquad \text{CARRY\_IN} \quad \text{\\AND} \quad \text{VALUE} \quad)$$
$$\text{\\DEPENDS\_ON} \{ \quad \text{CARRY\_OUT} \quad ; \quad \text{RESET\_IN} \quad \}$$

yields FALSE, because the equation reads neither CARRY_OUT nor RESET_IN. In
contrast,

$$\text{the same equation}$$
$$\text{\\DEPENDS\_ON} \qquad \{ \quad \text{CARRY\_IN} \quad ; \quad \text{RESET\_IN} \quad \}$$

yields TRUE because the equation does read CARRY_IN.
We define this operator by writing

DEFINE   DEPENDS_ON(E:EQUATION   X:SIGNALS   )   =   BOOL:
E   .   RHS   \INPUTS   \INTERSECTS   X   ENDDEFN

This yields TRUE precisely if E.RHS\INPUTS, the set of signals read by E, intersects the set of signals X. In other words, we say that E depends on X if there is a signal that is shared by both E.RHS\INPUTS and X. (We will define the \INTERSECTS operator in Section 3.3.1.2 as an example of complex quantification.)

We now sketch the \LEVELIZE operator, which will map a set of equations into a list of equations adhering to the levelized order requirement:

DEFINE   LEVELIZE(ES:EQUATIONS   )   =   EQUATIONS:
BEGIN   VAR   ANSWER   =   EQUATIONS;   HAVENT_BEEN_DEFINED=SIGNALS;
DO   Transfer equations from ES to ANSWER.
(Initially, ANSWER is NIL).

(Do this iteratively. For each iteration:
1   HAVENT_BEEN_DEFINED:=   the LHS of each equation
in ES.
2   Transfer those equations that do not depend
on HAVENT_BEEN_DEFINED.

(These transfers shorten the length of ES)

Do this until ES defies reduction in length)
GIVE   ANSWER   END   ENDDEFN

This sketch indicates that we will move an equation onto ANSWER only when this equation depends on no signal which is defined by an equation yet to appear in ANSWER (i.e., an equation in ES).

Let us take a brief digression into ICL's quantifiers, so that some new notations can serve to make the levelize operator easier to write and understand.

3.3.1.2   More about quantifiers. A ''quantifier'' is a loop generator. We have already seen a variety of quantifiers (Sections 1.3.4 and 1.4.3), for example,

FOR   element $E   list;   and
FOR   variable   FROM   number   TO   number;   etc.

We have introduced quantifier operators, for example,

Quantifier   &&   Quantifier   →   Quantifier
Quantifier   !!   Quantifier   →   Quantifier

These form a new quantifier from two given quantifiers by respectively lock-stepping the two or nesting the two (Cartesian product).
We have also introduced some ''unary'' quantifier operators, for example,

Quantifier   WITH   boolean;   →   Quantifier

This filters out those iterations for which the boolean yields FALSE.
We now introduce a few more quantifier operators which allow us to specify side effects right alongside any quantifier. First, we can specify an action that is to occur before the quantifier starts up:

Quantifier   INITIALLY   action   ;   →   Quantifier

For example, in the levelize function, we will have a quantifier that continues looping while "progress is being made," that is, while the previous iteration has augmented ANSWER:

> WHILE MAKING_PROGRESS;
> > INITIALLY MAKING_PROGRESS:=TRUE; ;

This quantifier loops while MAKING_PROGRESS is TRUE, and it also initially sets this variable to TRUE so that at least one iteration will occur.

We can append a quantifier with an action that is to occur upon each iteration:

> Quantifier EACH_DO action ; → Quantifier

The resulting quantifier is the original quantifier together with the side effect of performing the specified action on each iteration, immediately after the original quantifier steps. For example, we can append an EACH_DO to our complex WHILE quantifier shown above:

> WHILE MAKING_PROGRESS;
> > INITIALLY MAKING_PROGRESS:=TRUE; ;
> > EACH_DO   MAKING_PROGRESS:=FALSE; ;

This quantifier sets MAKING_PROGRESS to FALSE on each iteration (after the WHILE reads this variable). This quantifier is useful in many applications. It loops as long as some other action sets MAKING_PROGRESS to TRUE on each iteration. As soon as an entire iteration passes during which nobody sets MAKING_PROGRESS to TRUE, this quantifier terminates.

We can append a quantifier with an action that will be performed only upon the first iteration:

> Quantifier FIRST_DO action ; → Quantifier

The specified action is performed after the quantifier sets up for the first iteration. This is like an EACH_DO, except that the action is performed only for the first iteration. Note, however, that the FIRST_DO is very different from the INITIALLY construction, in that

> FIRST_DO   is executed after the first iteration is set up, whereas
>
> INITIALLY   is executed before the quantifier even prepares for the first iteration

Thus, the quantifier

> FOR E $E EQUATIONS;
> > FIRST_DO   EQUATIONS:= NIL; ;

sets E to each element in EQUATIONS, but it also sets EQUATIONS to NIL upon the first iteration. The original quantifier reads the variable EQUATIONS before the FIRST_DO clause sets it to NIL.

This quantifier is useful in applications where we want to read through a set, and also have that set cleared so that the body of the loop can append elements onto the NIL set. The result of the entire execution is to affect the variable EQUATIONS.

We have also an OTHER_DO clause:

> Quantifier OTHER_DO action ; → Quantifier

The action is performed on all nonfirst iterations, that is, on the second, third, and so on, iterations. The OTHER_DO complements the FIRST_DO, and together, these two clauses form the equivalent of an EACH_DO:

Quantifier   FIRST_DO   action   ;   OTHER_DO   action   ;   is equivalent to
Quantifier   EACH_DO   action   ;

if the actions are all identical.

We conclude this section with an example that makes use of the ''!!'' operator, the Cartesian product of quantifiers. We wish to define the operator

signals   \INTERSECTS   signals   →   boolean

so that we can determine whether or not two sets of signals have a signal in common. We might like to express this condition as

there is a signal X such that X is a member of both sets

or we can say, equivalently,

there is an X in A, and a Y in B   such that   X\EQ Y

We write this condition in ICL with

THERE_IS   X   \EQ   Y   FOR   X $E   A;   !!   FOR   Y $E   B;

or with

FOR   X $E   A;   !!   FOR   Y $E   B;   THERE_IS   X   \EQ   Y

(The very end of Section 1.4.3 shows another example of the THERE_IS notation.) The quantifier

FOR   X $E   A;   !!   FOR   Y $E   B;

sets X and Y to elements in A and B, respectively, in a two-dimensional manner, so that each X in A appears against each Y in B, during some iteration. We define the \INTER-SECTS operator with

```
DEFINE    INTERSECTS(  A,B:  SIGNALS  )  =  BOOL:    BEGIN  VAR  X,Y=SIGNAL;
          THERE_IS    X  \EQ  Y    FOR  X  $E  A;  !!  FOR  Y  $E  B;
    END   ENDDEFN
```

3.3.1.3 *The LEVELIZE function.* The following defines the LEVELIZE operator:

```
DEFINE    LEVELIZE(  ES:EQUATIONS  )  =  EQUATIONS:
          BEGIN    VAR HAVENT_BEEN_DEFINED=  SIGNALS;    X,  Y=  SIGNAL;
                   E=  EQUATION;    ANSWER=  EQUATIONS;
                   MAKING_PROGRESS=  BOOL;
    DO
          WHILE  MAKING_PROGRESS;
                        INITIALLY              MAKING_PROGRESS:=TRUE;
                                               ANSWER:=NIL;   ;
                        EACH_DO     MAKING_PROGRESS:=FALSE;   ;
```

```
DO      HAVENT_BEEN_DEFINED:=  {COLLECT  E.LHS  FOR  E  $E  ES;}  ;
        FOR    E  $E  ES;      FIRST_DO      ES:=NIL;  ;
        DO              IF        E   \DEPENDS_ON    HAVENT_BEEN_DEFINED
                        THEN    ES:=  ES  $>  E;  "(Throw the fish back
                                                        into the water)"
                        ELSE    ANSWER:=  ANSWER  $>  E;
                                MAKING_PROGRESS:=  TRUE;    FI
                                                        END
END
IF  DEFINED(ES)  THEN      HELP;    FI
GIVE    ANSWER                                        END    ENDDEFN
```

This function loops while progress is being made. Each iteration considers all equations in ES. Each of those equations is appended to either ANSWER or to ES. (ES is cleared upon beginning the equation scan.) An equation is put onto ANSWER only if it depends on no signal in HAVENT_BEEN_DEFINED. MAKING_PROGRESS is set to TRUE precisely when an equation is appended to ANSWER.

In case progress ceases and there are equations remaining in ES, this function calls HELP, to complain.

3.3.1.4 *Why LEVELIZE works.* We can deduce the following facts about the execution of LEVELIZE:

1 No equation is lost:

   Whenever ES is cleared, the elements of ES are distributed over ES and ANSWER.

2 No equation appears twice on ANSWER:

   When an equation is appended to ANSWER, it is not put back onto ES, and hence E will never refer to this equation again.

3 ANSWER contains a levelized list of equations at all times:

   Choose any pair of equations in ANSWER, say A and E, where A appears before E in answer. We wish to show that A does not depend on E.
       At the moment we put A onto ANSWER, we know (by looking at the program text) that
   a. E was not on ANSWER (E was put on ANSWER only after A was, because by assumption, E now appears on ANSWER following A),
   b. A \DEPENDS_ON HAVENT_BEEN_DEFINED was FALSE.

Since E was not on ANSWER, it was in ES at the time HAVENT_BEEN_DEFINED was defined. Hence, the second assertion here implies that A does not read E.LHS. Therefore, A does not depend on E.

4 This program terminates:

All loops besides the outer loop

   WHILE   MAKING_PROGRESS   ;

are finite in duration because they scan finite sets. This outer loop is also finite because it iterates once more only if ANSWER has grown since the previous iteration. Since ANSWER can grow to at most a finite length (the total number of equations given initially), this WHILE loop can iterate at most this finite number of times.

These assertions assure us that ANSWER is levelized, and that the program terminates. They do not, however, assure us that ANSWER contains all the given equations. The program does finally check that ANSWER does contain all the equations, by crying HELP if any equations remain in ES after all processing terminates.

What if \LEVELIZE terminates and leaves some equations remaining in ES? Does this mean that our program does not work, or does it mean simply that there exists no levelized order for the given set of equations?

Let us take a closer look at what we mean by "illegal" equations. We have had to forbid feedback in \EQU equations because such equations introduce contradictions or unending propagations of unsteadiness; for example, we have forbidden the \EQU equation

OUT   \EQU   [IF: LOAD   THEN: IN   ELSE: OUT]

We must consider feedback which spans over several equations; for example, there is still feedback in the set of equations

OUT   \EQU   [IF: LOAD   THEN: IN   ELSE: X]
X   \EQU   OUT

even though each equation in isolation does not show feedback.

Let us say that an equation participates in feedback if it defines a signal that affects any signal it reads (albeit the effect is propagated through other \EQU equations). We will show that any "legal" set of equations, that is, any set of equations in which no equation participates in feedback, will be levelized successfully by the LEVELIZE operator.

We first show that any set of equations devoid of feedback contains at least one equation that depends on no signal defined by any (other) equation in the set: The assumed lack of feedback in the set implies the existence of no infinite propagations of unsteadiness. Therefore, all equations become steady in finite time, so we can choose an equation E in the set which becomes steady at the earliest moment. This equation, E, cannot depend on any equation in the set because such a dependency would imply that the other equation (or E itself) must have become steady strictly before E has become steady, thus contradicting our choice of E. Thus, E is an equation that depends on no (other) equation in the set.

This fact about a "legal" set of equations, say ES, implies that there is at least one equation, E, in ES which depends on no equation in ES; that is, it is false that

E   \DEPENDS_ON   HAVENT_BEEN_DEFINED

Thus, E will be placed onto ANSWER (and hence removed from ES) during the first WHILE-iteration.

In fact, as long as ES contains at least one equation, we can repeat this argument: Although each iteration replaces ES by a subset of ES, ES remains "legal." (Feedback is never introduced into a set of equations by removing equations from the set.) Thus, ES always contains an equation, E, which depends on no equation in ES, and hence each iteration will remove E from ES and put it into ANSWER. This transfer of equations stops only when ES contains no equations (i.e., when ANSWER contains all equations).

We can imagine that LEVELIZE actually computes the propagations of steadiness in its formation of ANSWER. LEVELIZE puts an equation onto ANSWER as soon as all the equation's inputs become steady. Placing the equation on ANSWER (and hence removing it from ES) is the action that stablizes the output of that equation. Thus, some equations previously unsteady may now find their inputs entirely steady, so the steadiness propagates. Initially, of course, all equations' outputs are considered unsteady.

3.3.2 The SIMULATE Procedure

Let us define a procedure called SIMULATE which will implement an entire simulation. As we consider the simulation of a set of equations, we must accommodate the fact that an external source will define absolutely the values for input signals (e.g., CARRY_IN and RESET_IN) for each cycle in the simulation. We also want to accommodate the external detection of signal values for each cycle. We can accommodate both kinds of external intervention by representing such intervention as a process, i.e.,

$$\text{TYPE}\quad \text{EXTERNAL\_INTERVENTION}\ =\ //\ \backslash\backslash\ \ ;$$

(See Section 2.5.2 for process datatypes.) Our choice to use process datatypes to represent the external world frees us from specifying immediately how the external world goes about setting and reading values.

We can sketch the SIMULATE procedure with

```
DEFINE      SIMULATE( ES:EQUATIONS     INPUT,OUTPUT: EXTERNAL_INTERVENTION):
            Set up
            Repeat forever . . .
              " Begin Time Unit . . . "
              1   Invoke INPUT so to place values in the input signals
              2   Execute the \EQU equations
              3   Invoke OUTPUT so that the external world can read
                  signals' values now
              " End Present Time Unit . . . "
              4   Prepare for the next time slice; that is, evaluate the
                  RHSs of all \NEXT equations, and then transfer these
                  values to the LHSs.
            End of Loop                              ENDDEFN
```

Let us go ahead and define this function without considering yet how we might define the INPUT and OUTPUT processes.

Let us introduce one more parameter for SIMULATE, a parameter that will tell SIMULATE when to terminate the simulation. Again, we will let this parameter be a process type. This process, however, will yield a boolean value on each iteration, telling whether or not to stop the simulation. The use of processes as parameters facilitates a great deal of flexibility, as we will see shortly. We will use the following datatype to represent the simulation stop parameter:

$$\text{TYPE}\quad \text{SIMULATION\_STOPPER}\ =\ //\ \text{BOOL}\ \backslash\backslash\ \ ;$$

A SIMULATION_STOPPER will be invoked on each cycle, and its BOOLean result, if TRUE, will stop the simulation.

A SIMULATE procedure follows:

```
DEFINE      SIMULATE( ES:EQUATIONS     INPUT,OUTPUT: EXTERNAL_INTERVENTION
                                       DONE:  SIMULATION_STOPPER   ):
BEGIN  VAR  EQU,NEXT=  EQUATIONS;  E=EQUATION;  TEMPORARY=  {BOOL};  B=BOOL;
    " Set up:     Separate the equations into two parts, the EQU and
                  the NEXT equations. . . "
EQU:=  {COLLECT      E     FOR  E  $E  ES;  WITH  -(E.DELAY);  }  ;
NEXT:={COLLECT       E     FOR  E  $E  ES;  WITH  E.DELAY;  }  ;
EQU:=  EQU  \LEVELIZE;
    " Cycle: . . . "
```

```
WHILE -  < *DONE*>   ;          " (While not done . . . ) "
     DO   " Begin Time Unit . . . "
          < *INPUT*> ;          " Set input values "
          FOR  E  $E  EQU;  DO      EXECUTE(E);      END      "(Do EQUs)"
          < *OUTPUT*> ;        " Allow detection of values "

          " Now, evaluate the RHS of each \NEXT equation, and remember
                  these values in TEMPORARY . . . "
          TEMPORARY:=  {COLLECT      E.RHS \VALUE    FOR  E  $E  NEXT;  }  ;
          " End Present Time Unit "

          " Transfer these TEMPORARY values to the \NEXT equations' LHSs"
          FOR  E  $E  NEXT;  &&  FOR  B  $E  TEMPORARY;
              DO      SET( E.LHS, B  );          END
     END
END                       ENDDEFN
```

Figure 3.9 illustrates this procedure graphically. Refer to Section 1.4.3 for a review of our quantifier notations, for example,

> the quantifier FOR E $E ES; WITH E.DELAY;
>
> the quantifier FOR E $E ES; && FOR B $E TEMPORARY;

3.3.3 Specifying the INPUT, OUTPUT, and DONE Parameters for SIMULATE

Let us consider a variety of ways by which we might specify the external world to the SIMULATE procedure. Let us start with the DONE parameter.

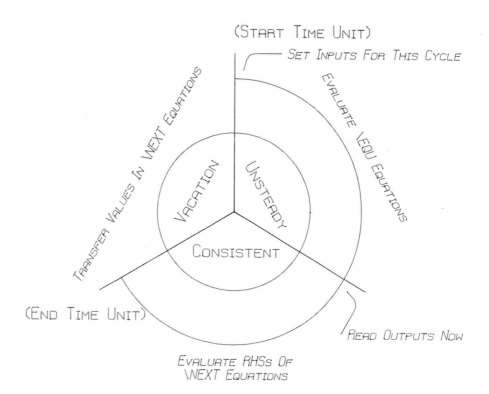

FIGURE 3.9 Simulation cycle.

We may wish to specify the duration of the simulation simply in terms of an INTeger number, namely the total number of cycles to pursue. For example, we might like to specify as the DONE parameter simply

        25   \CYCLES

We can specify the DONE parameter literally as shown, if we have the rule

        integer   \CYCLES   →   SIMULATION_STOPPER

We introduce this rule by writing

    DEFINE   CYCLES(N:INT   )   =   SIMULATION_STOPPER   :
            //   [N;]   ``   (A process which has access to the number N)''
                    DO   N:=   N-1;
                    GIVE   N   <   0   \\   ENDDEFN

The process yielded by this CYCLES function decrements N upon each invocation, and yields TRUE only when N reaches zero. Refer to the end of Section 2.5.4 for an explanation of the [N;] notation.

How else might we specify termination? We may wish to terminate simulation as soon as a certain SIGNAL_EXPR evaluates to TRUE. For example, if our set of equations defines among other things a DONE signal, we may wish to stop simulation as soon as the signal DONE evaluates to TRUE. We might choose to stop simulation for another reason, when an ''illegal'' situation occurs. For example, we might have formulated our set of equations, having removed perhaps some complicated logic because we ''knew'' that certain situations would never occur. Many ''illegal'' situations can be characterized simply by a special SIGNAL_EXPR, for example,

> if we ''know'' that the signals A and B will never both be TRUE, then
> the SIGNAL_EXPR   A \AND B
> becomes TRUE precisely upon a violation.

We accommodate termination dependent on a SIGNAL_EXPR by supplying the rule

        SIGNAL_EXPR   →   SIMULATION_STOPPER

With this rule, we can specify termination literally as a SIGNAL_EXPR itself, for example,

        A   \AND   B

We introduce this rule by writing the coercion

        LET   SIGNAL_EXPR   BECOME   SIMULATION_STOPPER   BY
            //[SIGNAL_EXPR;]   `` (We retain access to the SIGNAL_EXPR) ''
                    SIGNAL_EXPR   \VALUE   \\   ;

This says that a SIGNAL_EXPR can be viewed as a SIMULATION_STOPPER via the process that yields the evaluation of the SIGNAL_EXPR.

3.3.3.1 *Describing the INPUT parameter.* The INPUT parameter to SIMULATE is supposed to set all the input signals to new values on each invocation (i.e., on each cycle). Let us start with a simple case where there is only one input signal.

We can specify the sequence of values to be adopted by an input signal simply with a list of BOOLean values. For example, if we want the input signal to take on the values

FALSE   for the first three cycles, then
TRUE   for the fourth and fifth cycles, then
FALSE   for the sixth cycle, and then
TRUE   for the seventh cycle,

we can write simply

{FALSE; FALSE; FALSE; TRUE; TRUE; FALSE; TRUE}

to represent the input sequence.

Let us associate such a boolean sequence with a particular input signal, via the rule

signal \TAKES_ON booleans   →   EXTERNAL_INTERVENTION

We introduce this useful rule by defining the TAKES_ON function with

DEFINE   TAKES_ON(S:SIGNAL BS:BOOLS) = EXTERNAL_INTERVENTION:
    //[S;BS;]   '' (A process which retains access to S and BS) ''
        SET(S,   BS[1]   ); '' Set S to first value ''
        BS:= BS[2-];   '' Remove first value from sequence ''
                                      \\   ENDDEFN

We can specify very complicated sequences of booleans with notations we have in hand already. For example, we can specify that the short pattern

{ FALSE ; TRUE ; FALSE }

be repeated 100 times simply by concatenating ($$) this pattern 100 times, i.e.,

$$ { FALSE ; TRUE ; FALSE }   REPEAT 100;

In general, we may write programs to specify boolean sequences.

Suppose, for example, that we wish to define the input for a machine that accepts 8-bit instructions serially. Let us assume that the machine always expects the 8-bit chunk to be divided as follows:

2 bits for op code, followed by 6 bits of data.

It is most natural to specify this serial input as a sequence of instructions, as opposed to a sequence of booleans. If we have names for the four instructions, say, LOAD, STORE, ADD, SUB, we might like to specify an input sequence as

LOAD(23) $$ ADD(10) $$ STORE(22)

We can accommodate this expression if we provide the rules

LOAD(integer)   →   booleans
STORE(integer)   →   booleans,   etc.

[The concatenation ($$) operator shown above will then form a sequence of BOOLeans of length 24.] We can introduce these rules by writing

```
DEFINE    LOAD(I:INT)=  BOOLS:
          {  FALSE  ;  TRUE  }  $$  (  I  \FIELD  6  )          ENDDEFN
DEFINE    STORE(I:INT)=  BOOLS:
          {  TRUE  ;  FALSE  }  $$  (  I  \FIELD  6  )          ENDDEFN
```

Each of these functions produces a sequence of eight BOOLeans by supplying explicitly the first 2 bits, the op code, followed then by the 6-bit interpretation of the integer parameter. (This \FIELD operator is not defined here.)

Another way we might like to specify a long sequence of booleans is by writing a list of integers, for example,

$$\{ 3 ; 5 ; 2 ; 1 ; 1 ; 10 ; 5 \}$$

which will designate the durations between changes in value. For example, this list of integers can be interpreted as

3	FALSEs	followed by
5	TRUEs	followed by
2	FALSEs	followed by
1	TRUE	etc.

We accommodate this form of specification by writing

```
LET  INTEGERS  BECOME  BOOLS  BY          BEGIN    VAR  I=INT;  B=BOOL;
     $$    {COLLECT  B  REPEAT  I;}    FOR  I  $E  INTEGERS;
                                       FIRST_DO  B:=TRUE;;
                                       OTHER_DO  B:=-B;;          END  ;
```

The result is the concatenation ($$) of constant sequences, one for each integer I in INTEGERS. Each constant sequence is obtained by first flipping the boolean B and then forming a list of the constant B whose length is I. B is set to TRUE on the first iteration (in the FIRST_DO clause), and B is flipped for each subsequent iteration (in the OTHER_DO clause).

Now that we have a flexible means by which to specify an input sequence for a single input signal, let us accommodate the input specifications for many input signals. For example, we might like to specify the input sequences for both RESET_IN and CARRY_IN with

```
{  RESET_IN  \TAKES_ON    {FALSE;FALSE;FALSE;TRUE}  ;
   CARRY_IN  \TAKES_ON    {TRUE;FALSE;TRUE;TRUE}      }
```

Here we specify many inputs by forming a list of their individual specifications. With the mechanism provided so far, this specification can certainly be viewed as

```
{  EXTERNAL_INTERVENTION  ;
   EXTERNAL_INTERVENTION      }
```

However, the SIMULATE procedure wants one EXTERNAL_INTERVENTION, not a list of them. We can satisfy this requirement by providing a coercion from such a list to a single EXTERNAL_INTERVENTION. We write

```
TYPE    EIS  =  {  EXTERNAL_INTERVENTION  }  ;
```

to provide the representation for such a list (type EIS). Then we write a coercion from type EIS to type EXTERNAL_INTERVENTION by writing

```
LET  EIS  BECOME  EXTERNAL_INTERVENTION  BY
      //[EIS;]                          BEGIN    VAR  X  =  EXTERNAL_INTERVENTION;
      DO     <*X*> ;        FOR  X  $E  EIS;  END\\    ;
```

The list (EIS) is interpreted as a single EXTERNAL_INTERVENTION by forming a single process which, upon invocation, will invoke each element in the EIS list. For example, the first invocation of the EXTERNAL_INTERVENTION

```
{  RESET_IN  \TAKES_ON    {FALSE;FALSE;FALSE;TRUE}  ;
   CARRY_IN  \TAKES_ON    {TRUE;FALSE;TRUE;TRUE}    }
```

will set RESET_IN to FALSE and CARRY_IN to TRUE. The second invocation will set RESET_IN to FALSE and CARRY_IN to FALSE, and so on.

3.3.3.2 *Describing the OUTPUT parameter.*

The OUTPUT parameter to SIMULATE is invoked upon each cycle as soon as all SIGNALs are defined for that cycle. The OUTPUT parameter does not affect the simulation at all. Its purpose is to provide for us a report of the simulation results.

Let us consider the simplest of all reports, a cycle-by-cycle view of the values held by some set of signals. We might wish to specify the subset of signals

```
{  CARRY_IN  ;  VALUE  ;  CARRY_OUT  }
```

and obtain a report like

1	TRUE	FALSE	FALSE
2	TRUE	TRUE	TRUE
3	TRUE	FALSE	FALSE
4	FALSE	TRUE	FALSE

which shows each cycle number and the values held by the three specified signals, upon entry to each cycle.

We can obtain such a report by specifying as the OUTPUT parameter something like

```
{  CARRY_IN  ·  VALUE  ;  CARRY_OUT  }  \REPORT
```

We accommodate this form of specification by introducing the rule

```
signals  \REPORT        →        EXTERNAL_INTERVENTION
```

We introduce this rule by writing

```
DEFINE    REPORT(  X:SIGNALS  )  =  EXTERNAL_INTERVENTION:
      BEGIN          VAR    I  =  INT ;
         DO      I:=  0;
         GIVE    //[X;I;]       ''(Retain access to X and I)''
                       BEGIN    VAR    S=SIGNAL;
                          I:=I+1;    CRLF;    WRITE(I);
                          DO    TAB;  WRITE(S.VALUE);    FOR  S  $E  X;
                          END                            \\
      END          ENDDEFN
```

The resulting process, when invoked, will write a carriage return and the (incremented) cycle number. It will then write the value of each signal in X preceded by a tab.

Such reports generally become too long for large simulations. We could introduce an operator \REPORT_IF:

signals \REPORT_IF signal_expr   →   EXTERNAL_INTERVENTION

which would report only those cycles for which the signal_expr evaluates to TRUE. This serves to shorten the report, and the signal_expr can be chosen so that it evaluates to TRUE only when an "interesting" condition arises. For example, if we are interested in only those cycles that find both RESET_IN and CARRY_IN TRUE, we would supply as the signal_expr

RESET_IN \AND CARRY_IN

We define the \REPORT_IF operator with

```
DEFINE      REPORT_IF( X:SIGNALS  WHEN:SIGNAL_EXPR)=  EXTERNAL_INTERVENTION:
       BEGIN          VAR   I=INT;
            DO       I:=0;
            GIVE     //[X;WHEN;I;]                        BEGIN    VAR   S=SIGNAL;
                         I:=  I+1;
                     IF  WHEN\VALUE      THEN
                              write the data, as before   FI  END\\
       END          ENDDEFN
```

Other forms of reporting might be desired, such as the creation of a plot of this same information, represented as step functions. Another, more sophisticated form of report might include pattern matching, so that information would be printed only when certain sequences of values are detected over time. All of these forms of reporting can be implemented in terms of the EXTERNAL_INTERVENTION datatype, as in the examples above.

Example. We can simulate our COUNTER_BIT equations with

```
SIMULATE(  COUNTER_BIT  ,
                  {  RESET_IN  \TAKES_ON  {FALSE;FALSE;FALSE;FALSE}  ;
                     CARRY_IN  \TAKES_ON  {FALSE;TRUE;FALSE;TRUE}    }  ,
                  {  CARRY_IN  ;  VALUE  ;  CARRY_OUT  }  \REPORT    ,
                  4  \CYCLES      );
```

This will write the following:

1	FALSE	FALSE	FALSE
2	TRUE	FALSE	FALSE
3	FALSE	TRUE	FALSE
4	TRUE	TRUE	TRUE

If we want to verify that the COUNTER_BIT resets immediately upon RESET_IN (i.e., not on the subsequent cycle), we write

```
SIMULATE(  COUNTER_BIT  ,
                  {  RESET_IN  \TAKES_ON  {FALSE;FALSE;FALSE;TRUE;FALSE}  ;
                     CARRY_IN  \TAKES_ON  {TRUE;FALSE;FALSE;FALSE;FALSE}  },
                  {  CARRY_IN  ;  RESET_IN  ;  VALUE  }     \REPORT_IF
                                                  VALUE  \AND  RESET_IN  ,
                  5  \CYCLES      );
```

This will write

4   FALSE   TRUE   TRUE

We have thus discovered a cycle where VALUE and RESET_IN are TRUE at the same time; that is, RESET_IN does not reset the COUNTER_BIT immediately.

This effect is understood by noticing that RESET_IN participates in defining the next value for VALUE in the equation

VALUE   \NEXT   .   .   .   \AND   NOT(RESET_IN)

We see therefore that VALUE may be TRUE at the same time that RESET_IN is TRUE, even though VALUE will certainly become FALSE immediately upon the next cycle.

If we really do desire an immediate reset, we replace COUNTER_BIT's third equation,

VALUE \NEXT   [IF:CARRY_IN   THEN: NOT(VALUE)   ELSE:VALUE   ]
                                              \AND   NOT(RESET_IN)

with the pair of equations

V \NEXT   [IF:CARRY_IN   THEN: NOT(VALUE)   ELSE:VALUE   ]
VALUE \EQU   V \AND   NOT(RESET_IN)

This new specification defines a new signal V which represents the next value, as computed from the present, visible VALUE. The present, visible VALUE is the previously computed "next" value, V, ANDed with NOT(RESET_IN).

3.3.3.3 Can the INPUT parameter depend on signal outputs? As presented thus far, the INPUT and OUTPUT specifications are specified and treated separately. All forms of input specification have made no reference to output signals. Although it is indeed possible to write an EXTERNAL_INTERVENTION that provides inputs dependent on output signals, this technique is to be discouraged.

The user can nonetheless gain the effect of inputs dependent on outputs in a safe manner. The user removes these dependent "inputs" from the conceived set of inputs, and instead:

1 Writes equations that define each dependent "input" signal in terms of the output signals
2 Concatenates this new set of equations onto the orginal set of equations subject to simulation

Thus, the dependent "inputs" cease to be inputs and instead become part of the now enlarged set of equations subject to simulation.

It is important that all logical dependencies be present within the set of equations because all logical dependencies must be considered together in the process of levelizing the logic.

3.3.4 Summary

We have provided for the synthesis of synchronous logic, and its representation. We have provided some forms of analysis, namely simulation and the evaluation of SIGNAL_EXPRs. We have seen how the datatype SIGNAL is distinguished from all other datatypes in that we affect SIGNALs via "objective modification," so that our simulator can affect not only program variables, but also object variables, the variables (SIGNALs) that are directly part of the objects under consideration (synchronous logic equations).

We have seen how to detect race conditions in equations within the \LEVELIZE operator. We have seen how to implement unrestricted \NEXT equations, without glitches. The unit memory, together with our programmable NOR plane (Section 1.4.3), could now be used to implement reliably any set of synchronous logic equations.

4

A PLA Implementation
for Synchronous Logic

4.1 DISJUNCTIVE FORM FOR SIGNAL_EXPRs

In this section we consider the translation of any SIGNAL_EXPR into "disjunctive form." Disjunctive form is just one of many equivalent ways to write a SIGNAL_EXPR. Disjunctive form allows for a straightforward silicon implementation in terms of pairs of NOR_PLANEs (Section 1.4.3).

We say that a SIGNAL_EXPR is in disjunctive form (DF) if it is represented as an \OR of \ANDs or, more precisely, if the SIGNAL_EXPR is

> the \OR of a set of terms,
> where each term is the \AND of a set of atoms,
> where each atom is either a SIGNAL or the negation of a SIGNAL

For example, the SIGNAL_EXPR

(CARRY_IN \AND NOT(VALUE))   \OR   (NOT(CARRY_IN) \AND VALUE)

is in DF. It is the \OR of two terms, namely,

(CARRY_IN \AND NOT(VALUE))
(NOT(CARRY_IN) \AND VALUE)

Each term is the \AND over atoms; the atoms are

CARRY_IN,   NOT(VALUE),   NOT(CARRY_IN), VALUE

In contrast, the following SIGNAL_EXPR is not in DF:

(A \OR B) \AND C

One parameter to the \AND is not an atom; the first parameter itself contains an \OR. In DF, each parameter to any \AND must be an atom (i.e., simply a SIGNAL or the negation of a SIGNAL).

191

In analogy, we see in algebra a process of "expanding" an arithmetic expression into a sum-of-products form, using the distributive law, for example,

we "expand"   (x + 1) * (x + 2)
into   x*x + 3*x + 2

The original expression contains a "+" within a parameter to "*," and hence is not in DF, but the second expression is in DF because all parameters to "*" contain no "+"s. We might note that to simplify algebraic expressions, it is very often necessary to expand various portions into DF so that individual terms may be found to cancel out, for example,

the expression   (x + 1) * (x + 2) + (1 − x) * (x + 4)
expands to   x*x + 3*x + 2   +   −x*x − 3*x + 4
which reduces nicely to   6

How do we render a SIGNAL_EXPR into DF? Shall we choose a new representation just for DF, or shall we represent DF simply as a SIGNAL_EXPR? It is clearly possible to represent DF as a SIGNAL_EXPR because DF is just a restricted form of SIGNAL_EXPR. If it were difficult for us to define a more restricted datatype especially for DF, we might proceed to use the type SIGNAL_EXPR to represent DF.

However, whereas any DF SIGNAL_EXPR is clearly also a SIGNAL_EXPR, not every SIGNAL_EXPR is in DF. The type SIGNAL_EXPR is a recursive datatype, allowing arbitrary SIGNAL_EXPRs to participate under ANDs and NOTs. Suppose that we were to write a procedure to map DF into a layout. In the absence of a special representation for DF, this procedure would have to take in its logic as an unrestricted SIGNAL_EXPR, forgoing an enforced guarantee that the logic is already in DF.

The generality of the type SIGNAL_EXPR manifests itself in an apparent clumsiness required for the access of the SIGNAL_EXPR when we "know" that it is in DF. For example, given a SIGNAL_EXPR alledged to be in DF, the function would still have to perform a CASE statement to begin examining it:

CASE   SIGNAL_EXPR   OF
      OR: . . .

We would expect, of course, that the OR state would always be chosen (because of the DF assumption), but nonetheless we would have to write the examination allowing for the possibility of a violation. (Recall that we must always use the CASE statement to even begin examining a variant type such as SIGNAL_EXPR. See the \VALUE operator in Section 3.2.5.1 for an example.) It is actually very appropriate for the programming language to require such explicit accommodation for possible violations, because as far as the programming language can guarantee, the given SIGNAL_EXPR might in fact be in violation.

Let us therefore define a new datatype just for the representation of DF SIGNAL_EXPRs. We will define three datatypes, in correspondence to the three lines of DF's characterization shown at the beginning of this section:

TYPE   DF_EXPR = { DF_TERM } ;   " An 'OR' of terms "
TYPE   DF_TERM = { DF_ATOM } ;   " An 'AND' of atoms "
TYPE   DF_ATOM = [SIGNAL:SIGNAL NOT:BOOL];
                                        " A SIGNAL with possible NOT "

A DF_ATOM represents a single SIGNAL (not a SIGNAL_EXPR) or its negation. A DF_TERM represents the AND over a set of DF_ATOMs, and a DF_EXPR represents the OR over a set of DF_TERMs.

The type DF_EXPR can represent only expressions in DF. Now, given an object of type DF_EXPR, not only are we guaranteed that the object is already in DF, but also we may access it without any CASE statements and without any provisions for possible violations. To expose the ease of access, let us define a useful coercion,

DF_EXPR $\rightarrow$ SIGNAL_EXPR

This coercion will also lend confidence right away to the fact that any DF_EXPR can be interpreted as a SIGNAL_EXPR:

```
LET  DF_EXPR  BECOME  SIGNAL_EXPR  BY
     BEGIN        VAR  T  =  DF_TERM;  A  =  DF_ATOM;
   \OR
         (  \AND
            IF    A.NOT    THEN    NOT( A.SIGNAL )    ELSE    A.SIGNAL  FI
            FOR   A    $E    T;  )
     FOR    T    $E    DF_EXPR;                       END  ;
```

This coercion translates a DF_EXPR into a SIGNAL_EXPR, and in fact, it is here that we give meaning to the type DF_EXPR in terms of the familiar SIGNAL_EXPR datatype.

Let us look closer at this coercion in order to understand the "cumulative" notations used. (See Sections 1.4.3 and 2.2.7.5 for other examples.) The body of the coercion produces an \OR of SIGNAL_EXPRs, where each of these SIGNAL_EXPRs is itself an \AND of atomic SIGNAL_EXPRs. In other words, we view this body initially as

\OR   of terms interpreted as signal_exprs   FOR   term $E DF_EXPR;

This alone exposes our convention that the elements in the DF_EXPR (DF_TERMs) are meant to be OR'd together. As we now look more closely, we see that each term in the \OR is formed via

\AND   of atoms interpreted as signal_exprs   FOR   atom $E   term;

This alone shows that the elements of a DF_TERM are meant to be AND'ed together. Finally, each atom in the \AND is formed into a SIGNAL_EXPR via

IF A.NOT   THEN   NOT(A.SIGNAL)   ELSE A.SIGNAL   FI

That is, the atom A becomes a SIGNAL_EXPR simply by extracting its SIGNAL component and then possibly applying the NOT operator on this simple SIGNAL_EXPR.

We will return shortly to provide the coercion going in the other direction, that is, the translation from an arbitrary SIGNAL_EXPR into the rigid DF_EXPR representation.

4.1.1   Implementation of DF in Terms of NOR_PLANEs and Inverters

Before we consider how to render a SIGNAL_EXPR into a DF_EXPR, let us jump ahead for a moment and see how a DF_EXPR is even useful in our endeavor to provide a silicon implementation for SIGNAL_EXPRs. We have in hand (Chapter 1) the layouts for

1   An inverter
2   A general NOR_PLANE

We will use the NOR_PLANE twice, once as an AND plane and once as an OR plane. To see how a NOR_PLANE, or more specifically, a single NOR gate, can be used to implement either an AND gate or an OR gate, we resort to DeMorgan's laws of boolean algebra. First, we always find that

$$
\begin{aligned}
A \text{ and } B &= \text{not}(\quad \text{not}(A) \text{ or } \text{not}(B) \quad) \\
&= \text{not}(A) \text{ nor } \text{not}(B)
\end{aligned}
$$

We also find that always

$$
\begin{aligned}
A \text{ or } B &= \text{not}(\text{ not}(\quad A \text{ or } B \quad)\ ) \\
&= \text{not}(\quad A \text{ nor } B \quad)
\end{aligned}
$$

In other words, we can implement \AND and \OR strictly in terms of NOR gates with some additional inverters. [We choose to use NOR logic because the silicon accommodates NOR gates especially well (Section 1.3.6).]

We can write these laws in another, equivalent way:

$$
\begin{aligned}
\text{not}(\ A \text{ or } B\ ) &= \text{not}(A) \text{ and } \text{not}(B) \\
\text{not}(\ A \text{ and } B\ ) &= \text{not}(A) \text{ or } \text{not}(B)
\end{aligned}
$$

The latter rendition of the laws indicates directly how to move a NOT from the outside of an expression to deeper within the expression. Note how the NOT does not get lost; rather, it causes an \AND to become an \OR, and vice versa.

Let us restate DeMorgan's laws in a cumulative manner. Recall that a DF_EXPR is given meaning via the SIGNAL_EXPR

\OR (\AND atom   FOR atom $E term;)   FOR term $E DF_EXPR;

This expression can be prefixed with two applications of NOT, without changing its meaning:

NOT(NOT(
   \OR (\AND atom FOR atom $E term;) FOR term $E DF_EXPR;))

Let us take the inner of the two NOTs, and bring it inside the \OR loop using DeMorgan's laws:

NOT(
   \AND   NOT(
            \AND atom FOR atom $E term;) FOR term $E DF_EXPR;)

Let us take that same NOT and move it even deeper, inside the innermost loop:

NOT(
   \AND (\OR NOT(atom) FOR atom $E term;) FOR term $E DF_EXPR;)

Finally, let us move the outer NOT inward one level:

```
\OR
    NOT(  \OR
                    NOT(atom)  FOR  atom  $E  term;  )
        FOR  term  $E  DF_EXPR;
```

At this point, we have very nearly an implementation in terms of NOR logic. Let us put one more pair of NOTs on the front of this expression:

```
NOT(
        NOT(    \OR
                NOT(  \OR
                            NOT(atom)  FOR  atom  $E  term;  )
            FOR  term  $E  DF_EXPR;  )  )
```

This logic manipulation begins to show how we can implement our "OR of ANDs" logic in terms of "NOR of NORs" logic. This final logic derivation contains two occurrences of

```
NOT(  \OR    ...        )
```

instead of one occurrence of \OR and one occurrence of \AND. This NOT(\OR...) represents a multiple-input NOR gate. This entire derivation indicates simply that we can replace each of the AND and OR gates with a NOR gate, as long as we invert each input (notice the NOT introduced around the atom) and also invert the output (notice the outermost NOT).

Figure 4.1A shows how we would implement a DF_EXPR in terms of an AND plane followed by an OR plane. (An AND plane is a set of AND gates that produce an output for each DF_TERM.) Figure 4.1B shows how the same is implemented in terms of two NOR planes; notice the inverters placed on both the inputs and the output.

This form of silicon implementation for logic, done in terms of a pair of NOR planes, is called a programmable logic array (PLA). The name PLA comes from the fact that it implements logic in a very regular array structure, the two NOR planes. It is said to be programmable because different PLAs differ only in their dimensions and in their placement of the pulldown transistors in each plane (called LINKs in Section 1.4.3). We will return to the PLA after we provide the translation from SIGNAL_EXPR to DF_EXPR.

4.1.2 Translation from SIGNAL_EXPR to Disjunctive Form

We have now two representations for boolean logic, the SIGNAL_EXPR and DF_EXPR datatypes. Before we provide the translation from SIGNAL_EXPR to DF_EXPR, let us duplicate the \AND, \OR, and NOT operators that already exist for SIGNAL_EXPRs, but let us define them now to apply directly in the DF_EXPR representation. The new \AND, \OR, and NOT operators will take in and produce DF_EXPRs instead of SIGNAL_EXPRs. We will use these ultimately to provide the translation from SIGNAL_EXPR to DF_EXPR; that is, we will implement the translation by examining a SIGNAL_EXPR and by simultaneously building up an equivalent DF_EXPR using these new operators.

We will provide first the following limited set of operators:

```
df_expr  \OR  df_expr      →    df_expr
df_term  \AND  df_term      →    df_term
```

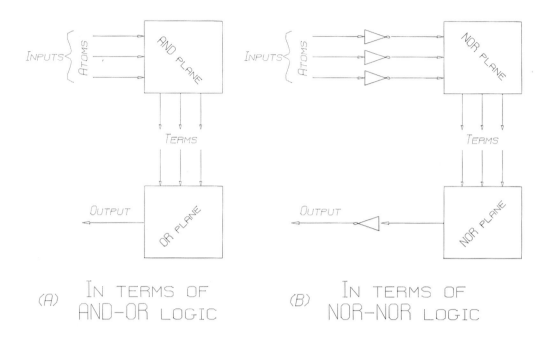

(A) IN TERMS OF AND–OR LOGIC   (B) IN TERMS OF NOR–NOR LOGIC

IMPLEMENTING A DF_EXPR

FIGURE 4.1

that is, \OR upon DF_EXPRs and \AND upon DF_TERMs. (We do not provide \OR upon DF_TERMs because the resulting DF_TERM could not express a logical OR.) We will then provide for DF_EXPRs the remaining logical operators, \AND and NOT.

We could define these first two operators as simply:

DEFINE   OR(X,Y: DF_EXPR) = DF_EXPR: X \$\$ Y   ENDDEFN

DEFINE   AND(X,Y: DF_TERM) = DF_TERM: X \$\$ Y   ENDDEFN

That is, we could from the logical OR of two DF_EXPRs as the concatenation of the two sets of DF_TERMs, for example,

> if X is A or B and if Y is C or D,
> then X or Y is
>> (A or B) or (C or D),
> which becomes (by concatenation)
>> A or B or C or D

Concatenation on DF_EXPRs implies by definition the logical OR. Similarly, concatenation on DF_TERMs implies by definition the logical AND, for example,

> if X is A and B and if Y is C and D,
> then X and Y is
>> (A and B) and (C and D),
> which becomes (by concatenation)
>> A and B and C and D

This great simplicity arises only because we have chosen to define \OR on DF_EXPRs and \AND on DF_TERMs, and not vice versa.

Let us instead put more meat in these two "trivial" operators in order to provide an "optimized" result. (We will use the term "optimized" to denote an "improved," if not perfectly optimized, result.) This optimization is not necessary, but an optimized result will produce much more efficient layouts. For each of these \AND and \OR operators, we will consider the following optimizations:

1 For \OR, consider that

(A and B) or (A and B and C)

is equivalent to the simpler

(A and B)

2 For \AND, consider that

(A and B) and (not(A))

is equivalent simply to

FALSE

and that

(A and B) and (A and C)

is equivalent to

A and B and C

The optimization for \OR suggests that we may omit some of the terms in the concatenation:

if term1 implies term2, we do not need term1

That is, since we are forming a logical OR, we can omit a term, term1, if there is some other term, term2, which contributes a TRUE at least whenever term1 contributes a TRUE.

The optimization for \AND (on DF_TERMs) suggests two things:

1 If in the concatenation there are two atoms which represent the same signal and simultaneously have opposing specifications for NOT, this term is always FALSE.

2 We may remove duplications of atoms.

Let us define \OR as follows:

```
DEFINE  OR(  X,Y:  DF_EXPR  )  =  DF_EXPR:
       BEGIN     VAR  T,T1  =  DF_TERM;
    DO   '' Remove terms in X which imply Y   ''
         X:=  {COLLECT  T  FOR  T  $E  X;.
                                   WITH   NEVER   T  \IMPLIES   T1
                                     FOR  T1  $E  Y;  ;  }  ;
```

```
                    '' Remove terms in Y which imply X ''
                    Y:=  {COLLECT   T   FOR   T  $E  Y;
                                          WITH   NEVER   T  \IMPLIES   T1
                                                  FOR   T1  $E   X;  ;  }  ;
          GIVE '' the concatenation ''     X   $$   Y                          END       ENDDEFN
```

This rendition still forms the concatenation of X and Y, but it first removes from X any term that implies a term in Y, and then vice versa. We retain a term T in X only when

```
          NEVER      T  \IMPLIES   T1      FOR   T1  $E   Y;
```

that is, when for every T1 in Y, it is never true that T implies T1. We have placed this condition in a WITH clause, attached to the quantifier

```
          FOR   T   $E   X;
```

so to omit T when this condition fails.

We have made use of an \IMPLIES operator, i.e.,

```
          df_term   \IMPLIES   df_term      →     boolean
```

A term implies another term precisely when the first term includes at least all the atoms of the other term. Mathematically, this condition is stated

```
          term X implies term Y        when
                    for all atom1 in X, there exists atom2 in Y such that
                                                  atom1 = atom2.
```

We write this a little more precisely with

```
DEFINE    IMPLIES(  X,Y:  DF_TERM  )   =  BOOL:
     BEGIN    VAR  S,S1   =  SIGNAL;  N,N1   =  BOOL;
          ALWAYS
                THERE_IS   (S1  \EQ  S)  &  (N1  =  N)   FOR  [SIGNAL:S1   NOT:N1]  $E   X;
          FOR    [SIGNAL:S   NOT:N]  $E   Y;                         END       ENDDEFN
```

(Each atom is viewed directly in terms of its signal S and its negation N. Two atoms are identical when both the signals and the negations match.)

At this point, we can see that the optimized \OR will remove terms which imply other individual terms. This will not optimize, for example

```
          ( A and B ) or ( A and not(B) )        into simply A
```

because neither of the two terms implies the other term. This form of optimization will occur via another means.

Let us now write the optimized \AND operator for DF_TERMs. This operator will do two things. First, it will detect the "contradiction" situation where an atom and its inverse are both members of the AND concatenation. In this case, it will return NIL, that is, a DF_TERM containing no atoms. [NIL is the appropriate representation for a permanently FALSE DF_TERM because when this DF_TERM becomes a member of a DF_EXPR, it should contribute nothing logically, and it will fortunately contribute nothing to the DF_EXPR. NILs are always dropped from lists (Section 2.7.4.2).] The only other thing \AND need look out for is duplicate atoms, removing duplicate appearances.

The optimized \AND operator will therefore look like the following, where X and Y are the two given DF_TERMs:

IF   there_is an atom, A1, in X, and an atom, A2, in Y such that
        A1   =   not(A2),
   THEN   yield   NIL
   ELSE   yield the concatenation with duplicates removed FI

The program text follows:

```
DEFINE    AND( X,Y:  DF_TERM  )  =  DF_TERM:
      BEGIN    VAR  S,S1=  SIGNAL;  N,N1=  BOOL;  A,A1=  DF_ATOM;
          IF  FOR  [SIGNAL:S1  NOT:N1]  $E  X;    !!
              FOR  [SIGNAL:S   NOT:N ]  $E  Y;
                   THERE_IS       (S  \EQ  S1)  &  (N  < >  N1)
          THEN  NIL
          ELSE   X  $$    {COLLECT  A  FOR  A  $E  Y;
                                WITH  NEVER  A.SIGNAL  \EQ  A1.SIGNAL
                                    FOR  A1  $E  X;  ; }
                                                                        FI
      END           ENDDEFN
```

We have now an optimized \AND defined for DF_TERMs and an optimized \OR defined for DF_EXPRs. This is the last of the difficult optimizations that we will program directly. Other optimizations which we will consider will take no effort to implement.

Let us now finish the translation from SIGNAL_EXPR to DF_EXPR. We have defined \OR for DF_EXPRs; let us now define \AND for DF_EXPRs:

```
DEFINE    AND( X,Y:  DF_EXPR  )  =  DF_EXPR:
      BEGIN          VAR  T,T1  =  DF_TERM;
          \OR   { T1 \AND T }    FOR  T1  $E  X;  !!  FOR  T  $E  Y;
      END        ENDDEFN
```

This forms the \OR over the pairwise \AND of the Cartesian product of the lists X and Y. That is, each term in X is AND'ed with each term in Y, for example,

    (X1 or X2 or X3) and (Y1 or Y2 or Y3)   is
    (X1 and Y1) or (X1 and Y2) or (X1 and Y3)
    (X2 and Y1) or (X2 and Y2) or (X2 and Y3)
    (X3 and Y1) or (X3 and Y2) or (X3 and Y3)

The expression " { T1 \AND T } " invokes the \AND for DF_TERMs, and the braces in this expression turn the resulting DF_TERM into a DF_EXPR for consumption by the cumulative \OR (which expects DF_EXPRs as its parameters). Because of the optimization performed by the \AND upon DF_TERMs, some of the resulting terms may drop out, for example,

    if   T1   is   A and not(B)
    and   T   is   C and D and B,
    then   T1   \AND   T   yields a NIL   DF_TERM

Also, because of the optimization performed by \OR, some more terms may be removed because they imply other terms, for example,

    (A or not(B)) and (A or B) yields the set of terms
    (A) or (A and B) or (not(B) and A)
    which are then reduced by \OR to
    A

We define the one remaining operator for DF_EXPRs, NOT, with

```
DEFINE    NOT(  X:DF_EXPR  )  =  DF_EXPR:
    BEGIN           VAR  S=SIGNAL;  N=BOOL;  T=DF_TERM;
        \AND
            \OR  {{  [SIGNAL:S  NOT:  -N  ]  }}  FOR  [SIGNAL:S  NOT:N]  $E  T;
    FOR  T  $E  X;                                END      ENDDEFN
```

This turns the outer \OR into an \AND, and the inner \AND into an \OR, and negates each atom, as derived by DeMorgan's laws. Notice that each negated atom is enclosed within a pair of braces, so to elevate that atom from type DF_ATOM to type DF_TERM and finally to type DF_EXPR, the type demanded by the enclosing \OR operator.

Finally, we can provide the translation from SIGNAL_EXPR to DF_EXPR. We examine the SIGNAL_EXPR (recursively) and simultaneously build up a DF_EXPR:

```
DEFINE  DF(  S:SIGNAL_EXPR  )  =  DF_EXPR:    BEGIN  VAR  S1=SIGNAL_EXPR;
        CASE  S  OF
            SIMPLE:      {  {  [SIGNAL:S  NOT:FALSE]  }  }
            OR:          \OR      DF(S1)     FOR  S1  $E  S;
            AND:         \AND     DF(S1)     FOR  S1  $E  S;
            NOT:         NOT(  DF(S)  )
        ENDCASE                                          END      ENDDEFN
```

The SIMPLE case, where S is just a SIGNAL, produces a DF_EXPR by forming an atom, and then enclosing it in two pairs of braces to raise it from an atom to a DF_TERM, and then to a DF_EXPR. All the other cases reconstruct the intent, first translating each element into DF. (All the \AND and \OR and NOT operators seen here are those defined on the DF_EXPR domain, as can be deduced by context.) The following renders this translation as a coercion:

```
LET  SIGNAL_EXPR  BECOME  DF_EXPR  BY    DF(  SIGNAL_EXPR  )  ;
```

4.1.3 A Loose End: Representing TRUE in DF_EXPRs and in SIGNAL_EXPRs

Whereas the type DF_EXPR can represent equivalently any SIGNAL_EXPR, let us look closely at how we represent the simple value TRUE. We may write

```
A   or   not(A)
```

What happens if we invert this expression, that is,

```
not(    A   or   not(A)   )         becomes
not(A)    and   A
```

This result certainly represents FALSE, and if we used our optimized \AND, we would get simply

```
NIL
```

which we have agreed represents FALSE. We have assumed that NIL represents FALSE for both DF_TERMs and DF_EXPRs.

FALSE and TRUE are the only signal expressions that need not involve signals. We have chosen NIL, for convenience, to be our signal-less representation for FALSE. What about TRUE; that is, what is

```
NOT(  NIL  )  ?
```

If we look at NOT defined for DF_EXPRs, we find that NOT(NIL) yields NIL, because there are no loops generated by the quantifiers. This result would imply that

NOT(FALSE   )   =   FALSE   !

We used NIL, an artifact of this programming language, to represent a signal-less FALSE. We must be careful about using NIL to represent a valid value, as opposed to ICL's intended meaning for NIL as "undefined." (It is the \AND operator which can yield NIL, as the result of optimizing a term containing a contradiction). We now embark on this consideration.

Let us continue to use NIL to represent FALSE, and let us introduce yet another artifact to represent a signal-less TRUE, again, to accommodate optimization. In a moment, we will think about safely handling both artifacts. We invent an artificial signal especially for TRUE with

VAR   THE_TRUE_SIGNAL   =   SIGNAL;
THE_TRUE_SIGNAL:=   NEW;
SET(THE_TRUE_SIGNAL,   TRUE   );

Thus, THE_TRUE_SIGNAL is a new signal whose value is set to TRUE. We will treat this signal drastically differently from any other signal in that

1   We will never SET THE_TRUE_SIGNAL to a boolean value (e.g., during simulation).

2   THE_TRUE_SIGNAL will never appear in any DF_ATOM (and hence in any DF_TERM or DF_EXPR) except for what follows:

VAR   THE_TRUE_ATOM   =   DF_ATOM;
VAR   THE_TRUE_TERM   =   DF_TERM;
VAR   THE_TRUE_EXPR   =   DF_EXPR;

THE_TRUE_ATOM:=   [SIGNAL: THE_TRUE_SIGNAL   NOT: FALSE   ];
THE_TRUE_TERM:=   {   THE_TRUE_ATOM   };
THE_TRUE_EXPR:=   {   THE_TRUE_TERM   };

That is, THE_TRUE_EXPR will be our representation for a signal-less TRUE, and in no other DF_EXPR will THE_TRUE_SIGNAL appear.

Let us redefine \AND, \OR, and \NOT so that they take into account both artifacts, that is, the possibility that this signal-less TRUE or the signal-less FALSE (NIL) itself may appear as a parameter, or as a result. To test easily whether or not a given DF_EXPR is THE_TRUE_EXPR, we define the \IS_TRUE predicate:

DEFINE   IS_TRUE(A: DF_ATOM   )   =   BOOL: A.SIGNAL   \EQ   THE_TRUE_SIGNAL
                                                                       ENDDEFN
DEFINE   IS_TRUE(T: DF_TERM   )   =   BOOL: T[1]   \IS_TRUE   ENDDEFN
DEFINE   IS_TRUE(E: DF_EXPR   )   =   BOOL: E[1]   \IS_TRUE   ENDDEFN

The following redefinitions of the logical operators account for both artifacts, the signal-less TRUE and NIL:

DEFINE   OR(X,Y: DF_EXPR   )   =   DF_EXPR:
                    IF   (X   \IS_TRUE   )   !   (Y   \IS_TRUE   )   THEN   THE_TRUE_EXPR
                    ELSE   as before   FI   ENDDEFN

```
DEFINE    AND( X,Y: DF_TERM )  =  DF_TERM:
                   IF   X  \IS_TRUE       THEN      Y
                   EF   Y  \IS_TRUE       THEN      X
                   ELSE      as before                        FI                    ENDDEFN
DEFINE    AND( X,Y: DF_EXPR )  =  DF_EXPR:
                   IF   X  \IS_TRUE       THEN      Y
                   EF   Y  \IS_TRUE       THEN      X
                   ELSE      as before                        FI                    ENDDEFN
DEFINE    NOT( X: DF_EXPR )  =  DF_EXPR:
                   IF   X  \IS_TRUE   THEN       NIL
                   EF   -DEFINED(X)   THEN       THE_TRUE_EXPR
                   ELSE      as before                   FI                         ENDDEFN
DEFINE    IMPLIES( X,Y: DF_TERM )  =  BOOL:
                   IF   Y  \IS_TRUE              THEN     TRUE
                   EF   -DEFINED(X)             THEN     TRUE
                   ELSE      as before                   FI                         ENDDEFN
```

[The program word ''EF'' is short for ''Else If''].

Notice how each of these new definitions does ''as before'' only when it is assured that neither X nor Y is THE_TRUE_EXPR. This check guarantees therefore that THE_TRUE_SIGNAL appears in no result, unless that result is precisely THE_TRUE_EXPR. In fact, each function should also check for NIL (FALSE) inputs, so to accommodate both of the artifacts. NOT is careful to turn NIL into THE_TRUE_EXPR. The other functions need not check for NIL because, as noted earlier, NIL participates in the representation exactly the way FALSE participates logically.

   We now have bulletproof operators for DF which accommodate both artifacts. It is interesting to note that we have not yet provided a means to specify literally TRUE or FALSE as a SIGNAL_EXPR. That is, until now, a user could specify

   a TRUE only with something like   X \OR   NOT(X)   and
   a FALSE only with something like   X \AND   NOT(X)

Let us now provide a direct translation from the boolean type (i.e., the literal values TRUE and FALSE) to the type SIGNAL_EXPR:

```
LET  BOOL  BECOME  SIGNAL_EXPR  BY
          IF  BOOL  THEN  THE_TRUE_SIGNAL  ELSE  NOT(THE_TRUE_SIGNAL)  FI  ;
```

This accommodates the expression of literal values in the formulation of SIGNAL_EXPRs, and hence EQUATIONS, just as FORTRAN permits the specification of literal numbers in its expressions (e.g., 1 or 2.6, not just X or J). This use of THE_TRUE_SIGNAL in SIGNAL_EXPRs, as opposed to a different representation for TRUE, lets us leave unchanged those functions that relate DF_EXPRs and SIGNAL_EXPRs. (In the translation from SIGNAL_EXPR to DF_EXPR, the DF_EXPR is built from scratch, so our assertion about the limited appearance of THE_TRUE_SIGNAL is maintained.)

4.1.4 A Possible Optimization for Free

Implicit in the functions as they now stand is the property that any DF_TERM that represents FALSE logically is in fact guaranteed to be NIL. This property is supported by the fact that any DF_TERM is created either by the \AND operator on DF_TERMs, or that term contains at most one atom. If the term contains only one atom, it is never permanently FALSE, by simple mathematical reasoning: That one atom is a logical variable that may be set to TRUE or FALSE, one of which settings will certainly render this one-atom DF_TERM TRUE. Nontrivial terms, those which come from \AND, always come out NIL if they represent FALSE (i.e., if they contain a contradiction), due to the optimization performed by \AND.

We can conclude not only that a permanently FALSE DF_TERM is represented only by NIL, but we can conclude also the same for DF_EXPRs: If a DF_EXPR represents FALSE logically, that DF_EXPR has only DF_TERMs each of which represents FALSE. Therefore, all the DF_TERMS of the DF_EXPR are represented by NIL, and hence the DF_EXPR is itself represented by NIL.

In summary, NIL is the only representation produced for a FALSE DF_EXPR.

In contrast, there are many DF representations produced for TRUE besides THE_TRUE_EXPR, for example,

   A or not(A)   produced by \OR

We see here a representation for TRUE, produced by our functions, which is not perfectly optimized (i.e., it is not precisely THE_TRUE_EXPR).

This lack of symmetry in the uniqueness of representation for TRUE and FALSE DF_EXPRs suggests a new trick for obtaining tighter optimizations. If we apply NOT to this nonoptimal TRUE, we get FALSE, which we know will always be represented by NIL. This (first) application of NOT has turned a nonoptimized representation into a perfectly optimized representation, although it is the negation of the original. If we now apply NOT a second time, we get back our original meaning, but now it is represented optimally by THE_TRUE_EXPR. (Notice that NOT translates NIL directly to THE_TRUE_EXPR.) We see therefore that two applications of NOT serve to focus the many representations of TRUE into the one optimized representation THE_TRUE_EXPR.

For example, the DF_EXPR resulting from \OR

   (A and not(B))   or   (A and B)

is not optimized to ''A'' by \OR because neither term implies the other term. However, let us negate this DF_EXPR twice, thus leaving its value unchanged:

not(not((A and not(B)) or (A and B))   )   becomes
not((not(A) or B) and (not(A) or not(B))   )   which becomes
not((not(A) and not(A)) or (not(A) and not(B))
        or (not(A) and B) or (B and not(B))   )

This last rendition will be optimized by \AND for each term to produce

   not(not(A) or (not(A) and not(B)) or (not(A) and B)   )

The \OR operator then finds that each of the second and third terms implies the first term, and hence we really get

   not(not(A)   )   which gives us simply A

This example suggests that we can achieve a new degree of optimization simply by applying NOT twice. If we are sure that the double NOT always yields no decrease in optimization, we would always desire to apply the double NOT to any DF_EXPR. However, since we are not sure that this technique yields no loss in optimization, but we do know that it succeeds very nicely in the examples considered so far, we play it safe by defining the following operator, which attempts to optimize a DF_EXPR via the double NOT:

```
DEFINE    OPTIMIZE( E:DF_EXPR )  =  DF_EXPR:
      BEGIN    VAR E1 = DF_EXPR; T = DF_TERM ;
      DO  " Try the double NOT  ...  "
          E1:=  E \NOT \NOT ;
      GIVE     " either E1 or E, whichever has the fewest number of
                              DF_TERMs  ...  "
          IF    ( + 1 FOR T $E E; )   <   ( + 1 FOR T $E E1; )
          THEN  E          ELSE E1 FI                            END      ENDDEFN
```

4.2 FROM EQUATIONS TO PLA_LOGIC

We see in Figures 4.1 and 4.2 that a silicon implementation for a set of equations consists basically of two NOR_PLANEs. Let us construct a translation from EQUATIONS to a new type, PLA_LOGIC, defined by

```
TYPE    PLA_LOGIC  =  [  AND, OR:            NOR_PLANE_LOGIC
                         INPUTS, OUTPUTS:  SIGNALS
                         CLOCKS:             NOR_COLUMN_LOGIC  ]  ;
```

A PLA_LOGIC contains the information required to produce two NOR_PLANEs (Section 1.4.3), namely the logical placement of the pulldown transistors for each of the OR and the AND planes. The AND and OR fields alone, each a NOR_PLANE_LOGIC, completely specify the two NOR_PLANEs; however, they alone do not specify which signals go to which inputs (for the AND plane) nor which signals come from which outputs (from the OR-plane). The type NOR_PLANE_LOGIC does not even mention SIGNALs; it mentions only BOOLeans that guide the "programming" of the PLA.

The INPUTS and OUTPUTS fields of PLA_LOGIC are introduced to bring signals back into the picture. The order of signals in each of these two lists corresponds with the order of BOOLeans contained in NOR_COLUMN_LOGICs and the order of NOR_COLUMN_LOGICs contained in NOR_PLANE_LOGICs. That is:

1 The order of INPUTS corresponds to the order of BOOLeans contained in each NOR_COLUMN_LOGIC contained in the AND field's NOR_PLANE_LOGIC.

2 The order of OUTPUTS corresponds to the order of NOR_COLUMN_LOGICs (outputs of OR gates) contained in the OR field's NOR_PLANE_LOGIC.

3 Finally, between the AND and OR planes, there is an order correspondence between each output of the AND plane and the corresponding input to the OR-plane.

Where it might feel unpleasant to think about all this ordering, it is even less pleasant to produce a PLA from a PLA_LOGIC which confuses its signals and hence does not work. (The translation from EQUATIONS to PLA_LOGIC will contain no extra specification to enforce this ordering; it just happens to come out very naturally. However, we now want to specify these order correspondences so to assure that the PLA programming matches the input and output signals.)

Finally, PLA_LOGIC contains the CLOCKS field, a list of BOOLeans. This corresponds with the OUTPUTS field (and hence the OR field). A TRUE indicates that the corresponding output is to be clocked. That is, where each equation contributes a signal to OUTPUTS, the DELAY field of that equation appears correspondingly in CLOCKS.

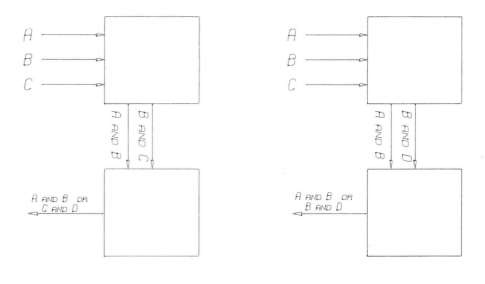

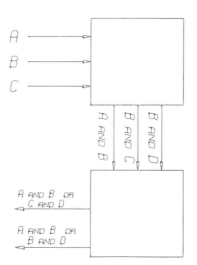

FIGURE 4.2   Implementing two equations at once.

Thus, the PLA_LOGIC type represents any set of equations simplified so to direct in a straightforward manner the entire programming of both NOR planes and the clocking (to implement \NEXT equations). In addition, the PLA_LOGIC tells the order of signals (INPUTS and OUTPUTS) as they will appear on the finished PLA.

4.2.1   The Translation

Let us provide an intermediate step in the translation from EQUATIONS to PLA_LOGIC. We introduce the type DF_EQUATION and its plural to represent EQUATIONs where each SIGNAL_EXPR (the RHS field) is replaced by the type DF_EXPR:

```
TYPE   DF_EQUATION  =  [ LHS: SIGNAL    RHS: DF_EXPR    DELAY: BOOL ] ;
TYPE   DF_EQUATIONS  =  {  DF_EQUATION  } ;
```

Any set of EQUATIONS is translated to a set of DF_EQUATIONS via

```
LET   EQUATIONS  BECOME  DF_EQUATIONS  BY
      BEGIN        VAR    L=SIGNAL;  R=SIGNAL_EXPR;  D=BOOL;
           {COLLECT    [ LHS: L    RHS: R  \DF  \OPTIMIZE    DELAY: D  ]
                            FOR  [LHS: L  RHS: R  DELAY: D]  $E  EQUATIONS;}
      END     ;
```

(The RHS field of each DF_EQUATION is the RHS of the corresponding EQUATION, R, translated into DF and then optimized.)

Figures 4.1 and 4.2 show how to implement DF_EXPRs in terms of their atoms. These figures do not show how to form the atoms from the atoms' signals, which require possibly the inversion of signals. In contrast, Figure 4.3 shows a PLA for logic which does contain atoms, some of whose NOT fields are TRUE:

(A and not(B)) or (not(A) and B)

We accommodate inverted atoms by bringing into the AND plane each signal and also that signal's inverse, for example, so that each of

the atom   A
and the atom   not(A)

enter the AND plane as independent signals. In other words, we build the AND plane by

1   Forming the set of signals referenced from all atoms, ignoring the NOT field in each atom, and then

2   Forming the AND plane to take in twice as many signals (i.e., each signal and also its inverse)

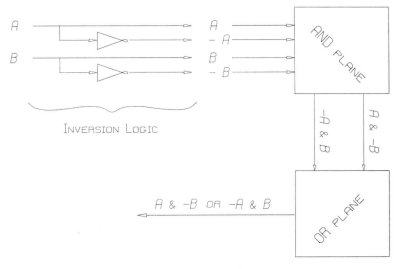

INVERSION LOGIC ON THE FRONT
OF THE AND PLANE
TURNS SIGNALS INTO ATOMS

FIGURE 4.3

The following translates DF_EQUATIONS into a PLA_LOGIC under the assumption that each adjacent pair of inputs to the AND plane will ultimately have the inversion structure shown in Figure 4.3 attached to the front.

```
LET  DF_EQUATIONS  BECOME  PLA_LOGIC  BY
     BEGIN          VAR TERMS= DF_EXPR; D= DF_EQUATION; INPUTS= DF_TERM;
                        S= SIGNAL; T=DF_TERM;
     DO   " First, form the collection of all DF_TERMs referenced by
            all equations ... "
          TERMS:= $$ D.RHS    FOR  D $E  DF_EQUATIONS; ;

          " (For optimization, we may remove duplicates) "
          TERMS:=  TERMS \NO_DUPLICATES;

          " Form the set of all input SIGNALs (for all terms of all
            equations). (The following removes duplicate appearances
            of input signals by using the \AND operator upon all
            signals S where each signal appears without inversion)... "
          INPUTS:=  \AND  {  [SIGNAL:S]  }  FOR  T  $E  TERMS;  !!
                                             FOR  [SIGNAL:S]  $E  T; ;

     GIVE      " The PLA_LOGIC ... "
          [  INPUTS:      {  COLLECT  S  FOR  [SIGNAL:S]  $E  INPUTS;  }
             OUTPUTS:     {  COLLECT  D.LHS  FOR  D  $E  DF_EQUATIONS;  }
             CLOCKS:      {  COLLECT  D.DELAY  FOR  D  $E  DF_EQUATIONS;  }
             AND:  {  FOR  T  $E  TERMS;  COLLECT       " one term ... "
                           $$    {  [SIGNAL:S NOT:FALSE]  \APPEARS_IN  T;
                                    [SIGNAL:S NOT:TRUE]  \APPEARS_IN  T  }
                      FOR  [SIGNAL:S]  $E  INPUTS;      }
             OR:   {  FOR  D  $E  DF_EQUATIONS;  COLLECT     " one output ... "
                      {COLLECT    T  \APPEARS_IN  D.RHS
                                     FOR  T  $E  TERMS;  }    }  ]
     END    ;
```

Let us look closely at the definition for the AND plane. Recall that the AND component is of type NOR_PLANE_LOGIC, and that a NOR_PLANE_LOGIC is simply a list of NOR gates (AND gates). We see the formulation of the set of AND gates, one for each term in TERMS via

```
{  FOR  T  $E  TERMS;  COLLECT    a  NOR_COLUMN_LOGIC  }
```

Each NOR_COLUMN_LOGIC in this list is formed by

```
$$    {    a pair of inputs, i.e., a signal and its inverse }
           FOR each signal in the set of all INPUTS
```

That is, each AND gate has as potential inputs all of INPUTS, and this expression forms merely a list of booleans in correspondence with each input and its inverse, for all inputs in the list INPUTS. This list of booleans is therefore always twice as long as the list of INPUTS. [The doubling in length is deduced from the fact that this expression forms the concatenation ($$) of one pair of booleans per signal in INPUTS.]
Each boolean in these lists is formed by

```
[SIGNAL:S  NOT:FALSE]  \APPEARS_IN  T        or by
[SIGNAL:S  NOT:TRUE]  \APPEARS_IN  T
```

That is, we wish an input (or its inverse) to be an input to the AND gate precisely if that input (or its inverse) appears in the term T. The \APPEARS_IN operator is defined by

DEFINE   APPEARS_IN(A: DF_ATOM   T: DF_TERM   )   =   BOOL:
                    T   \IMPLIES   {   A   }   ENDDEFN

The OR plane is formed just like the AND plane, except that the inversion consideration is absent (i.e., only atoms, and not terms, may specify inversion). The OR plane NOR_PLANE_LOGIC is formed by

{   FOR   D $E   DF_EQUATIONS;   " i.e., for each output "   COLLECT
                    a NOR_COLUMN_LOGIC   }

Thus, we specify one NOR gate (OR gate) per output. Each OR gate has as potential inputs each and every DF_TERM (outputs of the AND plane). The NOR_COLUMN_LOGIC list of booleans therefore specifies which DF_TERMs are to be inputs to the OR gate in

{   COLLECT   T \APPEARS_IN D.RHS   FOR   T $E   TERMS;   }

This list of booleans corresponds in order with the list of all terms, TERMS, and shows a TRUE only when T is to be an input for the OR gate which implements the DF_EQUATION D.
We define the \APPEARS_IN for DF_TERMs in DF_EXPRs with

DEFINE   APPEARS_IN(T: DF_TERM   E: DF_EXPR   )   =   BOOL:
        BEGIN   VAR   T1   =   DF_TERM;
          THERE_IS   T   \IMPLIES T1   FOR   T1 $E   E;   END   ENDDEFN

That is, we say that a term appears in a DF_EXPR precisely if it implies the DF_EXPR (or at least one of the DF_EXPR's own terms). We can view this operator more simply as yielding TRUE precisely when the given term T is actually one of the terms in E. As written, this \APPEARS_IN operator yields the set of all terms that imply the DF_EXPR E, so we have the following guarantees:

1   The \OR over this set of terms itself implies E.
2   The \OR over this set of terms actually equals E.

The second guarantee exists because the terms are taken from the set TERMS, which includes, among other things, all the terms that make up E.

4.2.2   Symbolic and Functional PLAs

Figure 4.4A shows a symbolic representation for a PLA that implements the COUNTER_BIT equations from Section 3.2.4.2. This picture is not a working layout for a PLA; it represents an abstraction that is most useful for much of our subsequent discussion because unlike a real PLA layout, this symbolic form shows clearly and simply all the information contained in our PLA_LOGIC type. The symbolic PLA is itself the clearest way to show and check all our programs concerning disjunctive form and PLA_LOGIC.

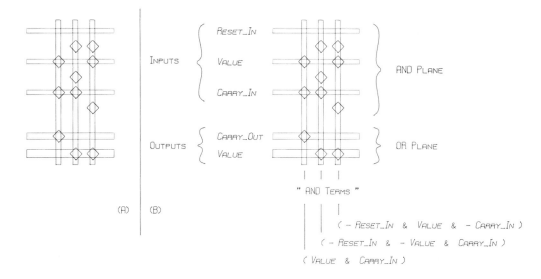

Symbolic PLA

FIGURE 4.4

Figure 4.4B shows the same symbolic PLA with its parts labeled. The inputs come into the PLA horizontally from the upper left. The outputs leave the PLA horizontally from the lower left. The vertical lines represent the DF_TERMs. Where the inputs and DF_TERMs intersect, we find the AND plane. This AND plane reads the inputs and defines the values of the DF_TERMs. The lower half, the OR plane, reads the DF_TERMs and defines the outputs. The diamonds in each plane denote which inputs (DF_TERMs) are read by which DF_TERMs (outputs). The diamonds represent the PLA's programming and in fact correspond precisely to the actual pulldown transistors (called LINKs in Section 1.4.3) in a functional PLA.

Some of the diamonds in the AND plane lie just below input lines and not right on the input lines. These lowered diamonds denote that the negation of the input line is an input to the DF_TERM. Thus, where our symbolic PLA shows one input line, in a real PLA there are two, the lower of which is the negation of the upper (visible) input line. The symbolic PLA does not show explicitly the inverter which takes in one input (at the far left) and turns it into two inputs for the AND plane (Figure 4.3).

In other words, the visible input lines correspond to the INPUTS field of our PLA_LOGIC, and the doubly dense vertical positions for the diamonds in the AND plane correspond to the doubly dense AND field of the PLA_LOGIC. (The OR plane in contrast has no such implicit, inverted inputs.)

Finally, the symbolic PLA represents the CLOCKS field of PLA_LOGIC by modulating the width of each output line as a function of the corresponding boolean in the CLOCKS field. The wide outputs represent clocked outputs (i.e., the outputs defined for \NEXT equations) and the thinner outputs correspond to unclocked outputs, for \EQU equations. In addition, we have chosen to make all inputs even thinner than the thinner of the two kinds of outputs so to help us determine the orientation of the symbolic PLA (i.e., distinguish the inputs from the outputs no matter how we might rotate the PLA).

Where the symbolic PLA exposes most clearly the essential information that defines the behavior of a PLA, this form hides the actual implementation of the PLA. Figure 4.5 shows two different functional layouts for the same PLA_LOGIC. These two

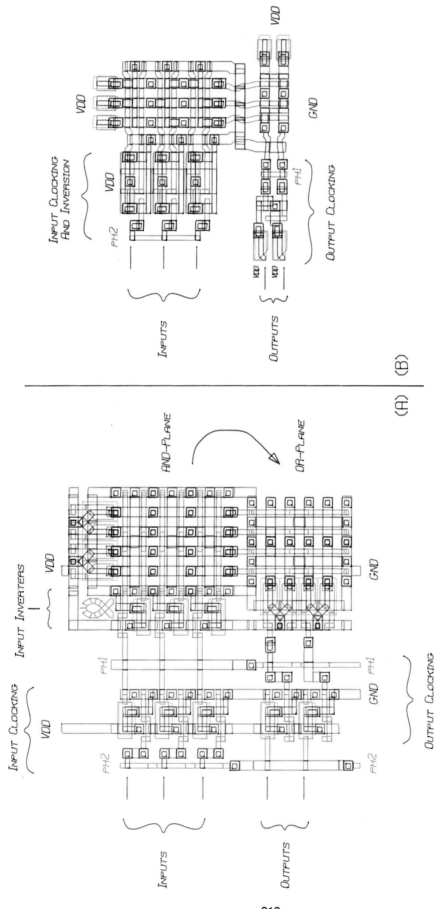

FIGURE 4.5 Effect of changing conventions (*see also color plate*).

TWO FUNCTIONAL PLAs

PLA layouts have identical anatomies even though they look different. We can describe this anatomy by following an input signal on its journey through the PLA:

1 The input enters at the upper left.

2 The input passes through a clock/inverter unit. In Figure 4.5A we see two distinct stages:

    a The input passes through a clocking unit.

    b The output of the clocking unit then enters an inverter.

    The output of this unit is now a pair of inputs: the original input and its negation. At this point, we have translated input signals into DF_ATOMS.

3 The input pair enters the AND plane and thereby feeds a subset of the AND (NOR) gates.

4 The outputs of the AND (NOR) gates travel downward and enter as inputs to the OR plane. The OR plane is rotated so to accommodate the vertical inputs. The inputs to the OR plane are of course DF_TERMs (outputs from AND gates), and they feed a subset of the OR (NOR) gates.

5 The OR plane produces as outputs our DF_EXPRs, and these outputs each enters another clocking element on its way out.

Although this description is accurate, it can use some clarification to accommodate descriptions provided in Sections 3.1.5 and 4.1.1.

4.2.3 A Closer Look at the Functional PLA

Let us consolidate the information contained in Sections 3.1.5 and 4.1.1 so to understand how the clocking works (Section 3.1.5) and how we can continue to call one NOR plane the AND plane and call the other NOR plane the OR plane (Section 4.1.1). We have considered each of these separately, but we must consider these together now because in the implementation of the PLA, they scratch each other's back.

We will answer two questions. First, we see in the PLA two clocking elements, one on input and one on output. Our earlier discussions mentioned nothing about input clocking. All clocking was supposed to occur on output. Second, Figure 4.1 indicates that we can talk of AND and OR planes instead of NOR and NOR planes only if we invert all inputs and all outputs.

As described in Section 3.1.5, there is definitely a need for two stages of clocking in order to implement reliably unit memories (for \NEXT equations). Figure 3.7 shows the two phases required. As our symbolic PLA shows, the entire implementation of clocking appears conceptually on output, and in fact on only some of the outputs (those for \NEXT equations).

Figure 4.6 shows how our original concept of clocking can be transformed into the implementation where clocking appears on both inputs and outputs. Figure 4.6A shows our initial concept, with the addition of an extra wire to connect an output of the PLA back around to an input of the PLA. For example, consider the COUNTER_BIT PLA. The signal VALUE appears as both an input and an output simply because the COUNTER_BIT equations both read and define the VALUE signal. In fact, the equations read VALUE and define VALUE(next). The clocking element is there precisely to transform the OR plane's output, VALUE(next), into the present VALUE.

Figure 4.6B shows that we can bend the wire that connects the two clocking stages together, so that the second stage appears to be associated with the input. This simple and obvious transformation explains the appearance of clocking distributed over both inputs and outputs, but it does not explain why our functional PLA layout includes

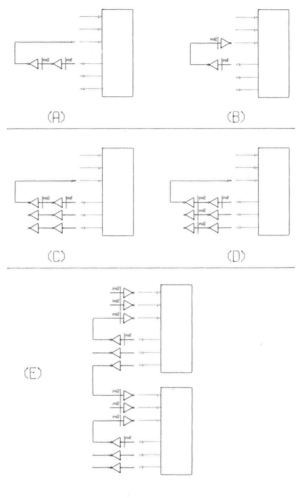

DISTRIBUTED CLOCKING

ALL INPUTS CLOCKED ON PH2,
\NEXT OUTPUTS CLOCKED ALSO ON PH1

FIGURE 4.6

clocking for all inputs and outputs, even for those outputs that are meant not to be clocked.

In fact, if you look closely at the output in the functional PLAs (Figure 4.5), you will see a tiny difference between the output clocking units of the VALUE(next) signal and the other two "unclocked" signals. The "unclocked" signals bypass the ph1 pass transistor by crossing the red ph1 signal not in green, but in blue instead (or in addition). That subtle difference alone determines whether the output clocking unit functions as a clocking stage or merely as a simple inverter devoid of any clocking mechanism. The CLOCKS field of a PLA_LOGIC manifests itself precisely in this subtlety; a FALSE in the CLOCKS field introduces this blue jumper, whereas a TRUE adds no jumper. (In the symbolic PLA, this subtle manifestation is represented much less subtly; it shows up as a variation in the width of the entire output line.)

Let us return to Figure 4.6C, which shows all the clocking implemented once again entirely at the outputs. The two "unclocked" outputs appear to have clocks, but these clocks have been "neutered" in that they bypass the ph1 and ph2 clock signals, and hence these two outputs are not subjected to clocking.

Before we bend wires again to associate the second stages with inputs, let us make one more transformation in our way of thinking. This change is more subtle and requires a reexamination of Figure 3.7C, where the two-staged clocking technique is shown in detail. Notice that ph2 (phase 2) is active not only between time units, but it is also active during the beginning of an actual time unit (at the bottom of the figure). We can, and now will take the liberty to leave ph2 active not only during the beginning of a time unit, but also throughout the entire time unit.

We can leave ph2 active during an entire time unit because the internal state of the unit memory, which resides between the two gates, is stable during the entire time unit. Also, the internal state matches the value meant to be shown on the output of this memory for the entire time unit. (Look at the top of Figure 3.7C, which shows the end of a time unit.) The only real restriction on ph2 is that it closes before ph1 opens, and this must happen after the time unit ends. (In contrast, ph1 can be open only between time units.)

Once we agree that ph2 will remain active during an entire time unit, we can put the ph2 gate back into all second stages (Figure 4.6D) without affecting the function.

When we model this layout for electrical performance, we will find, as we expect, that ph2 will need to be active for more time than does ph1. However, the extended duration of ph2 does not degrade the ph1/ph2 cycle time; it merely consumes time which would otherwise be consumed by a period when both ph1 and ph2 are inactive. For example, ph2 will have to remain active during entire propagations of carry chains, in contrast to another model, where such propagations occur during a (long) period when neither ph1 nor ph2 is active.

Figure 4.6E again shows the bending of wires and the return of the second stages to the input positions. The two unclocked signals (CARRY and RESET) are shown feeding a second COUNTER_BIT PLA. We now establish the convention that all PLA inputs include ph2 clocking elements and that all outputs include ph1 clocking elements for \NEXT equations and neutered ph1 clocking elements (inverters) for \EQU equations. This convention justifies our functional PLA layouts and places the sole distinction between \EQU and \NEXT equations precisely at the outputs (and not the inputs), as we are accustomed.

This clocking arrangement brings with it a solution to the second question posed at the beginning of this section. The clocking introduces inverters precisely at the inputs and the output, thus clearing the way for us to think of the first NOR plane as an AND plane and the second NOR plane as an OR plane (Figure 4.1). This implies that we must think of the PLA programming in terms of AND and OR planes (as we have) as opposed to programming in terms of NOR-NOR logic.

Our symbolic PLA abstracts away all these clocking and inversion details. However, if we were actually to measure the signals that enter the AND plane (e.g., the pair consisting of an input and its negation), we would find them each inverted relative to our expectations. The top input line carries the negation of the original input signal and the lower line of the pair (the invisible line in the symbolic PLA) carries the original input signal (inverted twice). These extra inversions exist, of course, because of the input clocking elements, and simultaneously because the AND plane strictly speaking is not an AND plane but rather a NOR plane.

In conclusion, if we measure our functional PLA only by looking at inputs and outputs, and not its insides, we find that they behave exactly as expected with AND-OR logic and with the intended clocking. Henceforth, we will present illustrations primarily with symbolic PLAs because they expose the intended function most clearly. This will facilitate understanding of interconnected sets of PLAs.

4.2.4 What Follows

Before we build layouts for large systems of equations, we will first extend the language of synchronous logic so to accommodate modular, or organized, behavioral specifications. Whereas we now know how to translate equations into PLAs, the extended logic language will utilize these services and will contribute interconnection services. In fact, our PLA generators will be used not only to implement both small and large sets of equations, but it will also be used to generate PLAs for sets of equations never specified manually.

After we add modularity to synchronous logic specification, we will introduce the notion of a layout cell, a datatype that includes not only layout information but also some behavioral information. At that point, we will introduce the program that generates the symbolic PLA from PLA_LOGIC. That program will generate not only a layout (which we could do right now), but instead a complete layout cell. The layout cell will naturally contain the information that will guide interconnect programs (e.g., to provide the VALUE feedback in our COUNTER_BIT PLA example). PLA feedback thus does not come with the PLA; rather, it is supplied by interconnection processes, which do not distinguish between feedback in a single PLA versus interconnections among separate PLAs.

We will also consider the generation of the functional PLA shown in Figure 4.5B. That will be generated in part from general principles that apply not only to PLAs. It contrasts a more conventional method of PLA layout generation done via programs specialized solely for PLAs.

EXERCISES

Section 4.2.1

1. Define the operator \NO_DUPLICATES used in the coercion

    DF_EQUATIONS → PLA_LOGIC

    That is, fill in the "..." so that the result will have no two DF_TERMS which are identical:

    DEFINE   NO_DUPLICATES(TS:DF_EXPR)= DF_EXPR:
        BEGIN   VAR   T,T1=DF_TERM; REST=DF_EXPR;
                            ...   END   ENDDEFN

    (Recall that the type DF_EXPR is just plural for DF_TERM.)

2. Define an operator \MINIMAL to be used in place of \NO_DUPLICATES within the coercion

    DF_EQUATIONS   →   PLA_LOGIC

    so to remove not only duplicates, but also to remove a term T if there is a subset of terms whose OR equals T itself. For example, suppose that

    T   = A
    T1   = A \AND B
    T2   = A \AND NOT(B)

    We could remove T because

    T1 \OR T2 = T

That is, any output dependent on the term T may now depend instead on both of T1 and T2.

Fill in the "...":

```
DEFINE     MINIMAL(TS:DF_EXPR=   DF_EXPR:
BEGIN      VAR   REST=  DF_EXPR;   T,T1=DF_TERM;
           ...                                            END        ENDDEFN
```

(Recall that the type DF_EXPR is just plural for DF_TERM.)

5

Organized Synchronous Logic

5.1 ORGANIZED, OR HIERARCHICAL, FUNCTIONAL SPECIFICATION

How do we go about forming large behavioral specifications maintaining a good margin of confidence? We can either make the silicon "smarter," that is, render the silicon closer to our way of thinking, or reduce the complexity of the problem, or both. In both cases, we increase confidence by reducing the apparent size of problems.

Programming languages show us many ways to reduce the apparent sizes of problems. We resort to a divide-and-conquer methodology. We organize a solution by imagining the solution to be made up of smaller, subsolutions, each of which solves a subproblem. We have exercised this method throughout this text, where we have solved many subproblems, each with a small function definition.

What is it about a programming language that makes this divide-and-conquer organization actually work in practice? The programming language provides a bulletproof insulation around each and every function definition.

Whereas we can invoke a function and pass to it parameters and take its result, we can in no way detect the insides of that function. For example, we cannot determine what other subfunctions are called, or the names or number of local variables used in the definition, or the method by which the function produces its output. Functions are simply not subject to analysis.

In all domains outside the function definition itself, the function is known only by its header, that is, the interface specified in the first line of text, the DEFINE line. This interface includes precisely

1 The function name (or none in case of a coercion)

2 The sequence of datatypes for input

3 The datatype for the one output

and nothing else. This header establishes precisely the set of contexts within which the function can be used. The rest of the function (the "body") serves to relate the input and output parameters. The function body is entirely invisible to users of this function.

216

This insulation, the separation of appearance from implementation, provides us with a very practical illusion. Each function we define augments our language so that we may believe, in fact, that this function is actually part of the computer's native wisdom. This function becomes a black box which we can just use, even as we forget the insides of that box. Each new function definition we introduce brings the computer closer and closer to our way of thinking. The basis of this illusion is the burial of details, enforced completely by the programming language.

For example, television sets are used effectively by people who see only its interface (e.g., a couple of knobs and a screen), who know nothing of its definition (i.e., its very complex insides). The television's interface insulates the audience from the television's implementation. We see various forms of insulation everywhere: between human nerve cells, between physical quantum states, between distinct locations in computer memories, and in the silicon design rules that specify the minimum separation required to establish a well-defined insulation between components. Insulation provides an essential privacy, much like the kind of privacy required for citizens in order to minimize a "big brother" role of government.

The use of subsolutions introduces a valuable side benefit. We gain enormous leverage from the fact that subsolutions can participate as subsolutions to many different large problems; that is, a subsolution can be shared, much as data may be shared. For example, the layout \AT function serves as a subsolution to many different layout generation problems. This benefit of sharing of subsolutions can be seen in another light: We need write the subsolution only once, yet we can reference it many times and from many places.

5.1.1 Organized Specification for Synchronous Logic: LOGIC_CELLs

We can provide for an insulated burial of details in the domain of synchronous logic specification by introducing the concept of a logic cell. A logic cell appears to the outside world as a black box with an interface. Figure 5.1A shows a complete interface for a logic cell. The outside world sees a logic cell simply as an entity that accepts inputs, produces outputs, and has a name. The interface of a logic cell, like a membrane of a biological cell, protects the inside world from the outside world, and vice versa; it presents the cell to the outside world as a single, functional entity.

Let us peer inside a logic cell (Figure 5.1B). Besides the interface, we see inside the cell a set of equations, and even possibly a set of subcells. The equations define the function of the logic cell, that is, the relation between the inputs and the outputs, employing possibly some subcells to aid in this definition.

This inclusion of subcells introduces the notion of hierarchy, or recursive grouping. Since each subcell may itself contain subcells of its own, this kind of grouping supports many levels of hierarchy.

For example, we can define a 16-bit counter as a logic cell by:

1   Including as subcells 16 distinct copies of our COUNTER_BIT

2   Including as equations things like

seventh subcell's CARRY_IN   \EQU   eighth subcell's CARRY_OUT,

which serve to connect the subcells together

3   Defining as the interface for the 16-bit counter cell the set of signals that are relevant to users of this cell, for example, the 16 VALUE signals of the 16 subcells and the least significant bit's CARRY_IN, but not "local" (irrelevant) signals such as the fifth bit's CARRY_IN or CARRY_OUT signals

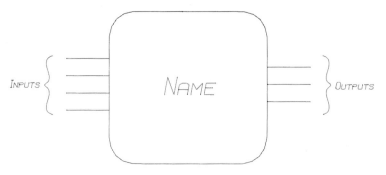

(A): LOGIC_CELL INTERFACE

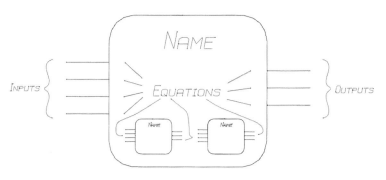

(B): LOGIC_CELL WITH INTERNALS

FIGURE 5.1   The logic cell.

This 16-bit counter example exposes the need to include equations which reference not only this logic cell's inputs and outputs, but also the inputs and outputs of the immediate subcells. We form the counter's "carry chain" by writing 15 equations, each of which reads an output (CARRY_OUT) from one subcell and defines an input (CARRY_IN) of another subcell. Each of these equations references the interface signals of subcells.

The need to reference interface signals from logic (sub)cells suggests that we include with each interface signal a name, simply to provide a means for selecting unambiguously one desired signal in the interface. We will represent a signal together with a name by using the datatype NAMED_SIGNAL:

TYPE   NAMED_SIGNAL   =   [NAME: NAME   SIGNAL: SIGNAL];

We will represent the inputs and the outputs of an interface each by a set of NAMED_SIGNALs, that is, by the datatype

TYPE   NAMED_SIGNALS   =   { NAMED_SIGNAL } ;

Thus, given a logic cell's inputs, a NAMED_SIGNALS, we can select a desired signal by name. (We will later define the datatype NAME, but for now, think of the type NAME simply as TEXT.)

We declare the entire LOGIC_CELL datatype (and its plural) with

```
TYPE    LOGIC_CELL  =  [ NAME:        NAME
                         INPUTS:      NAMED_SIGNALS
                         OUTPUTS:     NAMED_SIGNALS
                         EQUATIONS:   EQUATIONS
                         SUBCELLS:    LOGIC_CELLS  ]  ;
TYPE    LOGIC_CELLS = { LOGIC_CELL } ;
```

The first three fields, the NAME, INPUTS, and OUTPUTS, make up the entire interface. The remaining two fields, the EQUATIONS and SUBCELLS fields, define completely the behavior of the logic cell.

Example 1: A 1-Bit Counter as a LOGIC_CELL

Let us construct our counter bit as a LOGIC_CELL. Sections 3.1.1 and 3.2.4 show the construction of the set of equations that defines the behavior of our 1-bit counter. We present now the construction of not only the behavior, but also everything involved in making a LOGIC_CELL.

We will use abbreviated names for SIGNAL variables in this example to help expose the difference between the program variable names for signals and the names that participate as part of the LOGIC_CELL's interface:

```
DEFINE    COUNTER_BIT  =  LOGIC_CELL:
     BEGIN    VAR CI, CO, V, RI, RO  =  SIGNAL;  " (Declare Variables) "
DO        " Initialize each SIGNAL variable to reference a distinct signal "
          CI:= NEW;   CO:= NEW;   V:= NEW;   RI:= NEW;   RO:= NEW;
GIVE      " Here is the LOGIC_CELL ... "

          [ INPUTS:       { CI \NAMED 'CARRY_IN' ;
                            RI \NAMED 'RESET_IN' }
            OUTPUTS:      { CO \NAMED 'CARRY_OUT' ;
                            RO \NAMED 'RESET_OUT' ;
                            V  \NAMED 'VALUE'     }
            EQUATIONS:    { RO \EQU RI ;
                            CO \EQU ( CI \AND V ) ;
                            V  \NEXT [IF: CI THEN: NOT(V) ELSE: V]
                                     \AND  NOT(RI)             } ]
END       ENDDEFN
```

This function COUNTER_BIT yields a logic cell for a 1-bit counter. Figure 5.2A shows graphically this logic cell, complete with its interface.

This COUNTER_BIT specification shows a general style with which we specify LOGIC_CELLs in this programming language. We first declare variables to hold the signals used in the definition of the logic. Second, we initialize each signal so that each signal is distinguished from the other signals. These first two specifications together form what we call the "inventory" or "ingredients." Finally, we yield as the value of COUNTER_BIT a logic cell, which in this example includes as inputs the two signals CI and RI (named CARRY_IN and RESET_IN), and includes as outputs the signals CO, RO, and V (CARRY_OUT, RESET_OUT, and VALUE), and which finally includes the desired equations.

We formed each interface NAMED_SIGNAL from a SIGNAL and a name via the rule

```
signal  \NAMED  text        →     named_signal
```

This operator is defined by

```
DEFINE    NAMED( S:SIGNAL  N:NAME )  =  NAMED_SIGNAL:
               [NAME:N  SIGNAL:S]                              ENDDEFN
```

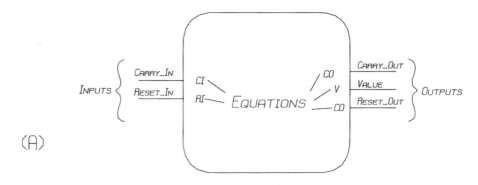

(A)

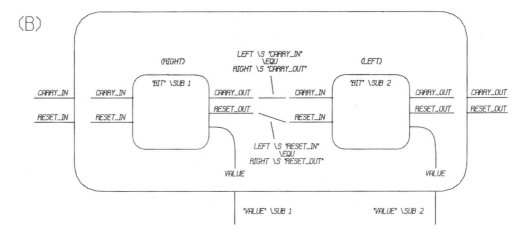

(B)

(A): COUNTER_BIT

(B): TWO_BIT_COUNTER

FIGURE 5.2   Examples of logic cells.

We will come back shortly to see all notations used in forming LOGIC_CELLs.

We did not define the SUBCELLS or the NAME fields in this LOGIC_CELL example. We will see later why we even have a NAME field, and when it is we will wish to supply it a name. We have included no SUBCELLS because the counter-bit equations refer to no LOGIC_CELLs. All examples of synchronous logic presented so far have referred to no subcells.

Example 2: A 2-Bit Counter

Let us look at a logic cell that does contain subcells. We form a 2-bit counter from two 1-bit counters as follows:

```
DEFINE    TWO_BIT_COUNTER  =  LOGIC_CELL:
     BEGIN       VAR    LEFT,  RIGHT  =  LOGIC_CELL;      " Declare Variables "
DO        " Let LEFT and RIGHT be two distinct COUNTER_BITs "
     LEFT:=  COUNTER_BIT;     RIGHT:=  COUNTER_BIT;
     " Let us agree that RIGHT is the least significant bit "
```

```
GIVE      '' Here is the LOGIC_CELL ... ''
          [   INPUTS:  {      RIGHT   \S   'CARRY_IN'    ;
                              RIGHT   \S   'RESET_IN'          }
                                             '' (The \S reads like apostrophe s) ''
              OUTPUTS:  {      LEFT   \S   'CARRY_OUT'    ;
                              RIGHT   \S   'VALUE'  \NAMED  ('VALUE'  \SUB  1)   ;
                               LEFT   \S   'VALUE'  \NAMED  ('VALUE'  \SUB  2)  }
              EQUATIONS:  {  LEFT  \S  'RESET_IN'  \EQU  (  RIGHT  \S  'RESET_OUT'  )  ;
                             LEFT  \S  'CARRY_IN'  \EQU  (  RIGHT  \S  'CARRY_OUT'  )  }
              SUBCELLS:  {   RIGHT  \NAMED  ('BIT'  \SUB  1)   ;
                              LEFT  \NAMED  ('BIT'  \SUB  2)       }      ]
END       ENDDEFN
```

Figure 5.2B shows graphically this logic cell.

There are two new notations embedded in this text. First, the \S notation has been used to identify signals from LEFT's and RIGHT's interfaces. The \S reads like 's (apostrophe s) and does play the role of English's possessive 's. The \S operator yields the signal which goes by the given name (e.g., 'CARRY_IN') from within the given LOGIC_CELL (e.g., RIGHT). For example, the first line in the INPUTS field specifies that the 'CARRY_IN' signal of the RIGHT subcell is itself to be an input to this 2-bit counter LOGIC_CELL.

Second, note that two of TWO_BIT_COUNTER's outputs are RIGHT's and LEFT's 'VALUE's. These signals have been given new names (with the \NAMED operator) lest they become indistinguishable. RIGHT \S 'VALUE' becomes an output of this 2-bit LOGIC_CELL and it goes by the name 'VALUE' \SUB 1, for users of this 2-bit LOGIC_CELL. Similarly, LEFT \S 'VALUE' becomes an interface signal and goes by the new name 'VALUE' \SUB 2. We will see shortly (in Section 5.2) this \SUB formulation of NAMEs.

Finally, this logic cell makes use of the SUBCELLS field, which references the two subcells LEFT and RIGHT. Thus, this logic cell stands alone as an integral whole; that is, it contains not only equations but also all the subcells referenced within the equations.

Each subcell is given a name so that it may be referenced ultimately by name. It is this naming of subcells that defines the NAME field in a LOGIC_CELL; that is, we define the NAME field of a LOGIC_CELL typically as the LOGIC_CELL becomes a subcell.

The EQUATIONS in this logic cell effectively connect the carry and reset signals between the two counter bits.

Example 3: An n-Bit Counter

The next example of LOGIC_CELL specification is a function that generates an n-bit counter, where n is an INTeger parameter. This example exposes some abbreviated notations useful for dealing easily with arrays of signals.

```
DEFINE     COUNTER(N:INT)  =  LOGIC_CELL:
          '' The function COUNTER takes in an INTeger and produces a LOGIC_CELL ''
                      '' Declare variables local to this function ''
          BEGIN     VAR   SUBCELLS  =  LOGIC_CELLS;
                          LEFT,  RIGHT,  L,  R  =  LOGIC_CELL;
          DO        SUBCELLS:=  {COLLECT  COUNTER_BIT  REPEAT  N;}   ;
                          '' Form a list of N distinct counter bits ''
                    LEFT:= SUBCELLS[1];        RIGHT:= SUBCELLS[N];
                          '' For naming convenience, let LEFT identify the
                            most significant bit, and RIGHT identify
                            the least significant bit ''
```

```
                              '' The resulting LOGIC_CELL follows: ''
          GIVE   [  INPUTS:  {  RIGHT  \S  'CARRY_IN'  ;
                               RIGHT  \S  'RESET_IN'        }
                 OUTPUTS:  {LEFT  \S  'CARRY_OUT'  ;
                           SUBCELLS  \SS  'VALUE'       }
                                        '' (See below about \SS) ''
                 EQUATIONS:
                      {  FOR  {  L  ;  R  }  $C  SUBCELLS;     COLLECT
                           {  L  \S  'CARRY_IN'  \EQU  (R  \S  'CARRY_OUT')  ;
                             L  \S  'RESET_IN'  \EQU  (R  \S  'RESET_OUT')  }  }
                 SUBCELLS: SUBCELLS \NAMED 'BIT' ]
          END          ENDDEFN
```

As in our previous LOGIC_CELL examples, we have first written the inventory [i.e., the declarations and initialization of program variables (SUB_CELLS, LEFT, and RIGHT)] and then we wrote the desired LOGIC_CELL expression.

The OUTPUTS field of this LOGIC_CELL expression uses a new notation, the \SS notation, to form a set of named signals. This expression,

SUBCELLS \SS 'VALUE'

represents the VALUE of each subcell renamed to ('VALUE' \SUB I) for I from 1 to the number of subcells. (Recall that in our 2-bit counter we renamed each of the two value signals explicitly.)

The EQUATIONS have been specified with the aid of the quantifier

FOR { L ; R } $C SUBCELLS;

which sets L and R to each pair of adjacent subcells. (Refer to Section 2.7.4.4 for another example of this quantifier.) The collected equations specify the connections for the carry and reset signals between adjacent cells.

Finally, the SUBCELLS field is specified as a set of named logic cells where each cell in SUBCELLS is given the name ('BIT' \SUB I) for I from 1 to the number of subcells.

5.2 ALL LOGIC_CELL NOTATIONS, THE TYPE NAME, AND CABLE OPERATORS

Let us now show a complete set of notations useful for the specification of LOG-IC_CELLs. Many of these notations have already been used in examples shown so far. We now present these notations formally.

5.2.1 The Type NAME and Formation of Names

First, we define the type NAME so to accommodate an index:

TYPE   NAME = [ROOT: TEXT   SUB: INT] ;

We include the following ways to form a NAME:

```
     text                    →     name
     text      \SUB    int   →     name
```

The first rule supports our assumption made so far that TEXT by itself can act as a NAME. The second rule introduces the \SUB notation, for making a NAME with an index, (e.g., the second and third outputs in our TWO_BIT_COUNTER example).

We provide for the comparison of NAMEs with

```
DEFINE    EQ(  A,B:  NAME  )  =  BOOL:
          (  A.ROOT  =  B.ROOT  )    &
          (           (  A.SUB  =  B.SUB  )  !
                      (  A.SUB  =  0  )      !
                      (  B.SUB  =  0  )          )        ENDDEFN
```

In other words, two NAMEs are equal when their ROOTs match and either their SUBs match or at least one of these SUBs is zero. (A SUB of zero is considered to be a non-existent subscript, and will therefore match any subscript.)

Finally, we have already defined the operator

$$\text{signal} \quad \backslash\text{NAMED} \quad \text{name} \quad \rightarrow \quad \text{named\_signal}$$

which forms a named_signal from a single signal and a name. For convenience, let us now extend the \NAMED operator to provide names for a set of signals all at once, i.e.,

$$\text{signals} \quad \backslash\text{NAMED} \quad \text{text} \quad \rightarrow \quad \text{named\_signals}$$

This operator takes in many signals and text (not a full name) and produces a set of named_signals by naming each signal

$$\text{text} \quad \backslash\text{SUB} \quad i \qquad \text{for i from 1 to the number of signals}$$

as defined in

```
DEFINE    NAMED(  SS:SIGNALS  T:TEXT  )  =  NAMED_SIGNALS:
BEGIN     VAR  S=  SIGNAL;  I=  INT;
{COLLECT     S  \NAMED  (T  \SUB  I)
          FOR  S  $E  SS;  && FOR  I  FROM  1  BY  1;}      END
                                                                 ENDDEFN
```

5.2.2 The Use of NAMEs for Extracting Interface Signals from LOGIC_CELLs

We use NAMEs primarily to select SIGNAL(s) from a set of NAMED_SIGNALS, as in:

$$\text{named\_signals} \quad \backslash\text{S} \quad \text{name} \quad \rightarrow \quad \text{named\_signal}$$
$$\text{named\_signals} \quad \backslash\text{SS} \quad \text{text} \quad \rightarrow \quad \text{named\_signals}$$

The first rule selects a single NAMED_SIGNAL from a set of NAMED_SIGNALS (e.g., from a LOGIC_CELL's interface). The second rule selects not one, but potentially several NAMED_SIGNALs from a set of NAMED_SIGNALS, that is, all NAMED_SIGNALs whose names match the text, disregarding subscripts contained in the names. These operators are defined as follows:

```
DEFINE    S(  NS:  NAMED_SIGNALS  Q:  NAME  )  =  NAMED_SIGNAL:
     BEGIN  VAR  N  =  NAMED_SIGNAL;
          IF  THERE_IS     N.NAME  \EQ  Q  FOR  N  $E  NS;
          THEN    N
          ELSE    DO      HELP;
                         GIVE  NIL  FI  END          ENDDEFN
```

```
DEFINE   SS(  NS:NAMED_SIGNALS  T:TEXT)   =   NAMED_SIGNALS:
    BEGIN  VAR  N  =   NAMED_SIGNAL;
       {COLLECT      N      FOR  N  $E  NS;
                                    WITH    N.NAME.ROOT   =   T;  }
    END                                                          ENDDEFN
```

In the examples shown so far, we have actually applied these \S and \SS operators directly upon LOGIC_CELLs (as opposed to the type NAMED_SIGNALS), as provided by the rules

logic_cell	\S	name	→	named_signal
logic_cell	\SS	text	→	named_signals
logic_cells	\SS	text	→	named_signals

Each of these (except for the third) views the LOGIC_CELL as a NAMED_SIGNALS and applies the \S or \SS on all the LOGIC_CELL's NAMED_SIGNALs, for example,

```
DEFINE     S(  L:  LOGIC_CELL     N:  NAME  )  =   NAMED_SIGNAL:
    L.INPUTS  $$  L.OUTPUTS    \S  N                          ENDDEFN
```

The third rule operates on the plural form LOGIC_CELLS. It forms its result by taking the desired NAMED_SIGNAL from each of the individual LOGIC_CELLs, and then presenting all these signals with names distinguished by the introduction of indices:

```
DEFINE     SS(  LS:  LOGIC_CELLS    T:  TEXT  )  =   NAMED_SIGNALS:
    BEGIN     VAR  L  =   LOGIC_CELL;    I  =   INT;
    {COLLECT    L  \S  T  \NAMED  (T  \SUB  I)
                     FOR  L  $E  LS;  &&  FOR  I  FROM  1  BY  1;  }
    END                                          ENDDEFN
```

For example, the OUTPUTS field of the n-bit counter contains the specification

```
    SUBCELLS   \SS   'VALUE'
```

which synthesizes the set of NAMED_SIGNALs with the names

```
    'VALUE'  \SUB  I          for I from 1 to n
```

where each signal comes from one of the LOGIC_CELLs in SUBCELLS.

Since we so often think of a NAMED_SIGNAL simply as a SIGNAL, we provide the following coercions:

| named_signal | → | signal |
| named_signals | → | signals |

(The latter coercion forms its result by applying the first coercion to each NAMED_SIGNAL in the given set.)

5.2.3 Cable or Array Operators

Let us go on now to accommodate arrays (or cables) of SIGNALS, SIGNAL_EXPRS, and EQUATIONS so that we may specify operations on cables as easily as we make single-signal specifications. (Subsequent examples will make use of these notations.) We already have the type SIGNALS and EQUATIONS; let us add the type SIGNAL_EXPRS (plural):

TYPE   SIGNAL_EXPRS = { SIGNAL_EXPR } ;

We include the EQUATION-producing operators for cables:

signals	\EQU	signal_exprs	→	equations
signals	\NEXT	signal_exprs	→	equations

For example, we define the new \EQU with

```
DEFINE   EQU( X: SIGNALS    Y: SIGNAL_EXPRS  ) = EQUATIONS:
    BEGIN    VAR  S  =  SIGNAL;  SE  =  SIGNAL_EXPR;
       {COLLECT            S  \EQU  SE
                              FOR  S  $E  X;  &&  FOR  SE  $E  Y;  }
    END                                                ENDDEFN
```

Thus, the new \EQU and \NEXT operators take in the plural forms and produce not one equation, but a set of equations. Each equation relates one corresponding SIGNAL/SIGNAL_EXPR pair.

Just as we have a coercion from SIGNAL to SIGNAL_EXPR (so that we may write just a SIGNAL and have it pass as a SIGNAL_EXPR), let us put in a similar coercion for the plural form:

signals   →   signal_exprs

We go on to provide boolean logic for cables:

signal_exprs	\AND	signal_exprs	→	signal_exprs
signal_exprs	\OR	signal_exprs	→	signal_exprs
NOT(	signal_exprs	)	→	signal_exprs

Just like the plural \EQU operator, these boolean operators for cables proceed element-wise (using the && lock-step relation for the quantifiers).

Finally, to extend the IF-THEN-ELSE notation to cables, we introduce

TYPE   IF_EXPRS = [IF: SIGNAL_EXPR   THEN, ELSE: SIGNAL_EXPRS] ;

and the coercion

if_exprs   →   signal_exprs

These operators allow us to use all the notations we are accustomed to not only for individual signals and equations, but also for arrays of signals, thereby producing arrays of equations.

5.2.4 NAMEs and Sub-LOGIC_CELLs

The following rules facilitate the use of names with LOGIC_CELLs, in much the same manner that we have used names with signals:

logic_cell	\NAMED	name	→	logic_cell
logic_cells	\S	name	→	logic_cell
logic_cells	\NAMED	text	→	logic_cells

The first rule fills in the NAME field of the LOGIC_CELL, and the second rule selects one out of many LOGIC_CELLs by name. The third rule gives to each LOGIC_CELL in the set the name

> text　\SUB　I　　　　　for I from 1 to n

This third rule has been used in the SUBCELLS field of our n-bit counter example.
　　For example, the expression

> TWO_BIT_COUNTER　\S　　(　'BIT'　\SUB　2　)

can denote TWO_BIT_COUNTER's second subcell (a single COUNTER_BIT). Similarly,

> COUNTER(16)　　\S　　(　'BIT'　\SUB　7　)

denotes the seventh subcell of the 16-bit counter.

5.2.5　Subtle Rules of Grammar Necessary to Complete the Language of LOGIC_CELL Specification

We include for completeness a few nonobvious rules which must be present to accommodate even the few examples shown so far. We have taken the liberty to specify a set of NAMED_SIGNALS (e.g., the OUTPUTS of the n-bit counter) as a set each of whose elements is a NAMED_SIGNAL or even a NAMED_SIGNALS (plural). That is, the expression making up the OUTPUTS field of the n-bit counter,

> {　LEFT　\S　'CARRY_OUT'　;
> 　SUBCELLS　\SS　'VALUE'　　}

parses (is interpreted) as

> {　a named_signal　;
> 　a set of named_signals　　}

We wish, as context demands, that this expression be viewed simply as a NAMED_SIGNALS, instead of as a set containing two elements, the latter of which is itself a set of NAMED_SIGNALs.
　　Whereas it is very convenient to use sets within sets to specify a set, as in this example, the representation (a single set) requires a completely flattened set, that is, a set each of whose elements is precisely a single NAMED_SIGNAL. This rigidity of the NAMED_SIGNALS datatype serves to standardize the LOGIC_CELL representation. This standardization eases substantially the subsequent analysis of any LOGIC_CELL because the programs we will write to perform analysis will not have to consider these varied forms of specification (synthesis).
　　We accommodate this kind of nested-set specification by first accommodating the initial capture of such specification. We declare a double-plural type:

> TYPE　　NAMED_SIGNALSS　=　{　NAMED_SIGNALS　}　;

This provides for the initial representation of a set containing sets of NAMED_SIGNALs. We then provide two coercions, both of which yield our desired plural NAMED_SIGNALS. These two coercions differ in that one takes in the singular form and the other takes the double-plural representation:

```
LET    NAMED_SIGNAL  BECOME  NAMED_SIGNALS  BY    {  NAMED_SIGNAL  }  ;
LET    NAMED_SIGNALSS  BECOME  NAMED_SIGNALS  BY
          BEGIN    VAR  X  =  NAMED_SIGNALS;
             $$    X    FOR  X  $E  NAMED_SIGNALSS;           END  ;
```

The latter coercion turns a double plural (set of sets) into a set by concatenating the subsets.

With these two rules, our sample specification (the OUTPUTS field of the n-bit counter) is interpreted via the following sequence of interpretations:

```
original:       {    named_signal    ;    named_signals    }

(coercion  1): {    named_signals    ;    named_signals    }
                    named_signalss

(coercion  2): named_signals
```

The two coercions provide not only for the interpretation of this particular use of nested sets, but these two coercions alone are sufficient to accommodate NAMED_SIGNALS specifications given with any kind of nesting whatsoever, for example,

```
original:       {  {  {    named_signal    }  }  }
                {  {    named_signals    }  }
                {    named_signalss    }

(coercion  2)  {    named_signals    }
                    named_signalss

(coercion  2):      named_signals
```

(The choice of interpretation sequence is done at compile time, when the program is translated into machine language, so the choice of interpretation sequence does not introduce overhead at run time.)

We have used this same kind of nested specification for EQUATIONS as well as for NAMED_SIGNALS. The n-bit counter has as its EQUATIONS the specification

```
{    FOR  {  L  ;  R  }  $C  SUBCELLS;        COLLECT
                                    a set of EQUATIONS        }
```

This specifies a set of sets of equations. We accommodate this nested-set form of specification for EQUATIONS just as we did for NAMED_SIGNALS, for example, with the type declaration

```
TYPE    EQUATIONSS  =  {  EQUATIONS  }  ;
```

and the rules

```
EQUATION          →        EQUATIONS
EQUATIONSS        →        EQUATIONS
```

The ability to use nested sets in EQUATIONS specification also accommodates very nicely EQUATIONS specifications involving cables, e.g.,

```
{    cable  \EQU  cable    ;
     cable  \NEXT  cable    }
```

This specification initially forms a set of two sets of equations, and then our coercions provide for the simple EQUATIONS interpretation, as demanded by context.

In summary, the considerations embraced in this section facilitate the specification of LOGIC_CELLs. These considerations arise whether or not one uses a programming language like ICL. If we choose to implement a brand-new language just for the capture of behavioral specification, independent of any programming language, the considerations of representation and grammar shown in this section must still be dealt with.

If we try to embed this kind of specification in a programming language which does not provide for user-defined coercions (as ICL does), the resulting behavioral language becomes very awkward, simply because the user has to specify explicitly all these subtle translations via function calls. As an unfortunate result, we find that a vast majority of such a behavioral specification has nothing to do with behavior, but appears only to cope with the awkwardness imposed by the artificially detailed language.

Example 4: A Programmable Frequency Divider

We wish to emphasize the logical insulation provided with LOGIC_CELLs and its benefit. We will therefore define a programmable frequency divider by using parts that we have not yet defined. We will now decide the interfaces for these undefined parts, and come back in later examples to define the implementations completely. This example will clarify the firm separation between interface and implementation.

A frequency divider takes in a signal that pulses (becomes TRUE for one clock cycle) at regular intervals (i.e., at some frequency). The frequency divider produces as output a sloweddown version of the input signal; the output pulses at a frequency n times as slow as the input. This factor of n is a dynamic parameter of the frequency divider (i.e., n may be changed).

Such a frequency divider consists of a register, a counter, and a comparator. The register holds the divisor. The counter is incremented by the input frequency. A TRUE output is generated precisely when the counter attains the value in the register. This output signal is also used to reset the counter, to prepare for the next output cycle. Thus, it takes n pulses in the input frequency to produce each output pulse, where n is the value held in the register.

We already have the counter logic cell; we also need the logic cells for the comparator and register. Fortunately, we need to know only their interfaces in order to specify the frequency divider. Let us assume that an n-bit register, say REGISTER(N), has an interface with inputs named

'LOAD'	(to load the register), and
'IN' \SUB I	for I from 1 to N,

and outputs named

'OUT' \SUB I	for I from 1 to N.

Assume that an n-bit comparator, say EQ(N), has an interface with inputs named

'A' \SUB I	for I from 1 to N,	and
'B' \SUB I	for I from 1 to N,	

and outputs named

'EQ_OUT'	TRUE when input A equals input B

We create a 6-bit frequency divider called FD with the following text:

```
VAR    FD, COUNTER, EQ, REG = LOGIC_CELL;    " Declare variables "
         " Get the three subcells "
COUNTER  :=COUNTER(6);   EQ:= EQ(6);   REG:= REGISTER(6);
         " The frequency divider as a LOGIC_CELL ... "
```

```
FD:=  [ INPUTS:  {  REG  \S  'LOAD'  \NAMED  'LOAD_DIVISOR'  ;
                    REG  \SS  'IN'  \NAMED  'DIVISOR'  ;
                    COUNTER  \S  'CARRY_IN'  \NAMED  'FREQ_IN'  }
      OUTPUTS:  {     EQ  \S  'EQ_OUT'  \NAMED  'FREQ_OUT'      }
      EQUATIONS:  {   EQ  \SS  'A'  \EQU  (COUNTER  \SS  'VALUE')  ;
                      EQ  \SS  'B'  \EQU  (REG  \SS  'OUT')  ;
                      COUNTER  \S  'RESET_IN'  \EQU  (EQ  \S  'EQ_OUT')  }
      SUBCELLS:  {    COUNTER  \NAMED  'COUNTER'  ;
                      EQ  \NAMED  'COMPARATOR'  ;
                      REG  \NAMED  'REGISTER'          }        ]  ;
```

This frequency divider accepts three inputs: a divisor (fed to the register), a LOAD_divisor command (to change the divisor), and of course, the input frequency (fed to the counter's carry_in). The one output is the output of the comparator, the output frequency. The EQUATIONS in FD define the two inputs for the comparator, and the third equation specifies that the counter be reset when the comparator yields TRUE. Figure 5.3 shows graphically this frequency divider.

As in previous examples, the \SS notation is used to specify arrays of signals; for example, REG \SS 'INPUT' represents six signals because REG has signals named 'INPUT' \SUB I for I from 1 to 6. Similarly, the left- and right-hand sides of the first two equations in EQUATIONS each specify an array of six signals. Thus, each of the first two equations in EQUATIONS actually represents six equations. [All of the operators \EQU, \NEXT, and \AND, \OR, and NOT() are defined not only for single signals, but also for arrays of signals. They operate bitwise.]

Example 5: A 1-Bit EQual and Greater-Equal Comparator

Figure 5.4A shows graphically the following LOGIC_CELL. This LOGIC_CELL is a one-bit "EQual comparator" and will be used to form an n-bit EQ-comparator in Example 6.

```
DEFINE   EQ_BIT=  LOGIC_CELL:        BEGIN    VAR  A,  B,  IN,  OUT=  SIGNAL;
     DO        A:=NEW;       B:=NEW;       IN:=NEW;       OUT:=NEW;
```

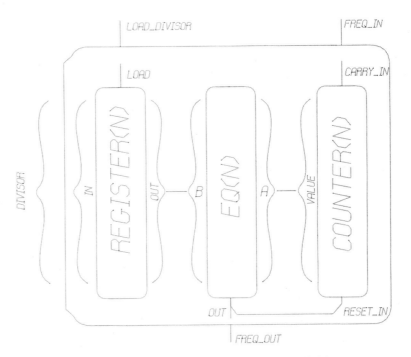

FIGURE 5.3   Logic cell for a frequency divider.

(A)   ONE-BIT EQ COMPARATOR

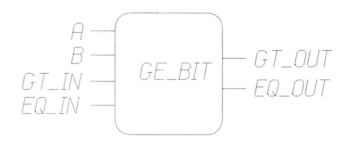

(B)   ONE-BIT GE COMPARATOR

FIGURE 5.4

```
GIVE      [INPUTS:        {  A    \NAMED   'A'  ;
                             B    \NAMED   'B'  ;
                             IN   \NAMED   'EQ_IN'  }
           OUTPUTS:       {  OUT \NAMED   'EQ_OUT'    }
           EQUATIONS:     {  OUT \EQU      IN    \AND
                                (A \AND  B \OR  (NOT(A) \AND  NOT(B)))  }
           ]                                    END      ENDDEFN
```

The signals EQ_IN and EQ_OUT are intended to participate in an AND chain between adjacent EQ_BITs in a set of EQ_BITs, so that the EQ_OUT signal of the extreme bit position yields TRUE precisely when all corresponding pairs of bits (A and B) in the chain are equal. In other words, this logic cell yields a TRUE EQ_OUT when A and B are equal and EQ_IN is TRUE. The assertion that EQ_IN be TRUE can be seen as asserting that the other EQ_BIT logic cells in a chain of EQ_BITs all find their As and Bs equal.

Figure 5.4B shows graphically the following "Greater-or-Equal" (GE) comparator. This LOGIC_CELL will participate in two chains, one of which senses EQuality and the other of which senses strict Greater-Than (GT).

```
DEFINE    GE_BIT  =  LOGIC_CELL:
    BEGIN    VAR  A,  B,  GT_IN,  GT_OUT,  EQ_IN,  EQ_OUT  =  SIGNAL;
    DO       A:=NEW;           B:=NEW;              GT_IN:=NEW;
             GT_OUT:=NEW;      EQ_IN:=NEW;          EQ_OUT:=NEW;
    GIVE     [INPUTS:      {   A       \NAMED     'A'  ;
                               B       \NAMED     'B'  ;
                               GT_IN   \NAMED     'GT_IN'  ;
                               EQ_IN   \NAMED     'EQ_IN'     }
              OUTPUTS:     {   GT_OUT    \NAMED    'GT_OUT'
                               EQ_OUT    \NAMED    'EQ_OUT'    }
              EQUATIONS:   {   EQ_OUT \EQU      EQ_IN    \AND
```

```
                                       (A  \AND  B  \OR  (NOT(A)  \AND  NOT(B)))  ;
                    GT_OUT  \EQU    GT_IN     \OR
                                       (EQ_IN  \AND  A  \AND  NOT(B))        }
        ]                                         END                    ENDDEFN
```

The EQ-chain (EQ_IN and EQ_OUT) is defined as in the EQ_BIT logic cell. The GT-chain yields TRUE when, scanning from left to right in a chain of GE_BITs, either GT_IN is TRUE or both EQ_IN is TRUE and A is greater than B. In other words, GT_OUT is TRUE when either

1 "Greater than" has been determined already from higher-order bits (GT_IN), or

2 "Equal" has been determined from higher-order bits (EQ_IN) and A is greater than B

The latter condition occurs at the highest-order bit position for which A and B are not equal.

Example 6: An n-Bit EQual and Greater-Equal Comparator

Let us use our LOGIC_CELL EQ_BIT to form an n-bit EQual comparator (Figure 5.5A). This specification is very similar to the n-bit counter example. Where we defined a carry chain between adjacent COUNTER_BITs, we now define the EQ-chain between adjacent EQ_BITs.

```
DEFINE      EQ(N:INT)  =  LOGIC_CELL:
     BEGIN    VAR  BITS=LOGIC_CELLS; LEFT, RIGHT, L, R  =LOGIC_CELL;
     DO       BITS:=  {COLLECT    EQ_BIT    REPEAT N; } ;
              LEFT:=  BITS[1];        RIGHT:=  BITS[N];
     GIVE     [INPUTS:        {    BITS \SS 'A' ;
                                   BITS \SS 'B'        }
               OUTPUTS:    {    RIGHT \S 'EQ_OUT'    }
               EQUATIONS: {    LEFT \S 'EQ_IN'    \EQU    TRUE  }        $$
                          {    FOR { L ; R } $C BITS;    COLLECT
                                        R \S 'EQ_IN'  \EQU  L \S 'EQ_OUT' }
               SUBCELLS:    BITS \NAMED 'BIT'      ]      END      ENDDEFN
```

Notice that the A and B signals of all the single-bit comparators are made available in the INPUTS field. The EQ_OUT signal of the extreme right comparator is the output of this full comparator. Note also that the leftmost comparator is given TRUE to its EQ_IN signal, so as to initiate the AND-chain optimistically.

Figure 5.5B shows graphically the following n-bit GE-comparator (Greater-or-Equal).

```
DEFINE      GE(N:INT)  =  LOGIC_CELL:
     BEGIN    VAR  BITS=LOGIC_CELLS; LEFT, RIGHT, L, R  =LOGIC_CELL;
                   GE_OUT  =  SIGNAL;
     DO       BITS:=  {COLLECT    GE_BIT REPEAT N; } ;
              LEFT:=  BITS[1];        RIGHT:=  BITS[N];        GE_OUT:=  NEW;
     GIVE     [INPUTS:   {    BITS \SS 'A' ;
                             BITS \SS 'B'        }
               OUTPUTS:  {    GE_OUT \NAMED 'GE_OUT'    }
               EQUATIONS{    LEFT \S 'EQ_IN'    \EQU    TRUE ;
                            LEFT \S 'GT_IN'    \EQU    FALSE ;
                            GE_OUT    \EQU
                                    RIGHT \S 'EQ_OUT'    \OR
                                            (RIGHT \S  'GT_OUT') }        $$
                          { FOR { L ; R } $C BITS;    COLLECT
                             { R \S 'EQ_IN'    \EQU    L \S 'EQ_OUT' ;
                               R \S 'GT_IN'    \EQU    L \S 'GT_OUT' }
                          }
               SUBCELLS:    BITS \NAMED 'BIT'      ]      END      ENDDEFN
```

The interface of this LOGIC_CELL matches the interface of the n-bit EQ-comparator (except that the output signal here is named GE_OUT). The first two equations initialize the two chains, and if

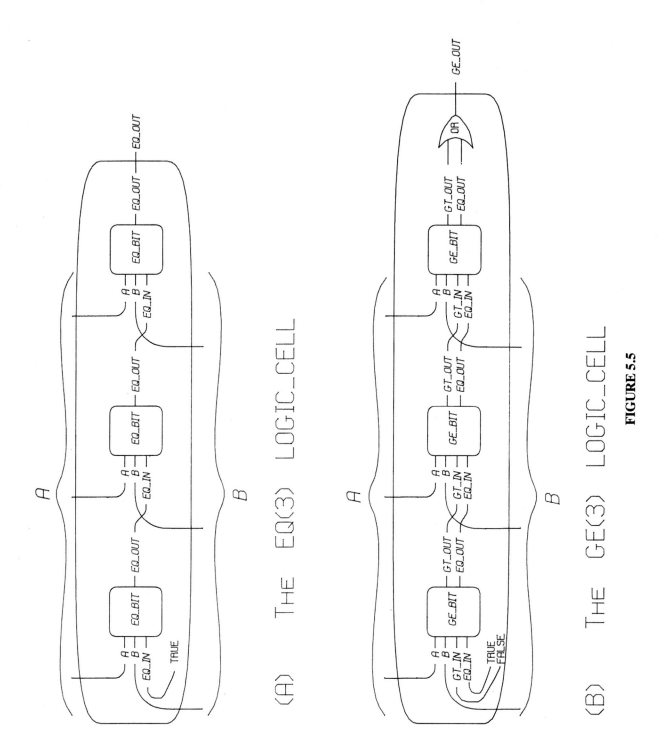

(A)   THE EQ(3) LOGIC_CELL

(B)   THE GE(3) LOGIC_CELL

FIGURE 5.5

232

we skip the third equation, we see a set of equations that forms the two independent chains. The third equation forms the output GE_OUT by forming the OR of the rightmost element's EQ_OUT and GT_OUT, thus yielding greater OR equal.

Example 7: A Register and a Shift Register

Figure 5.6A shows graphically the following LOGIC_CELL for a single-bit register. (The one equation appearing in this LOGIC_CELL has been taken from Section 3.1, Example 4.)

```
DEFINE    REG_BIT  =  LOGIC_CELL:          BEGIN    VAR  IN,  OUT,  LOAD  =  SIGNAL;
    DO       IN:=  NEW;          OUT:=  NEW;        LOAD:=NEW;
    GIVE     [INPUTS:    {    IN     \NAMED    'IN'  ;
                              LOAD   \NAMED    'LOAD'    }
              OUTPUTS:    {  OUT    \NAMED    'OUT'      }
              EQUATIONS:  {  OUT  \NEXT    [IF:  LOAD  THEN:  IN  ELSE:  OUT]  }
              ]                                  END       ENDDEFN
```

The following constructs an n-bit parallel-in, parallel-out register.

```
DEFINE    REGISTER(N:INT)  =  LOGIC_CELL:
    BEGIN     VAR    BITS=LOGIC_CELLS;  LEFT,  X  =  LOGIC_CELL;
    DO        BITS:=  {COLLECT  REG_BIT    REPEAT  N; }  ;
              LEFT:=  BITS[1];
    GIVE      [INPUTS:    {    LEFT  \S  'LOAD'  ;
                              BITS  \SS  'IN'      }
               OUTPUTS:  {    BITS  \SS  'OUT'        }
               EQUATIONS:  {  FOR  X  $E  BITS[2-];      COLLECT
                                        X  \S  'LOAD'    \EQU    LEFT  \S  'LOAD'  }
               SUBCELLS:      BITS  \NAMED  'BIT'        ]        END        ENDDEFN
```

Finally, the following (Figure 5.6B) forms an n-bit serial-in, parallel-out, left-to-right shift register. This example uses the REG_BIT logic cell just shown.

```
DEFINE    SHIFTER(N:INT)  =  LOGIC_CELL:
    BEGIN     VAR    BITS=LOGIC_CELLS;  LEFT,  RIGHT,  L,  R=  LOGIC_CELL;
    DO        BITS:=  {COLLECT  REG_BIT    REPEAT  N; }  ;
              LEFT:=  BITS[1];        RIGHT:=  BITS[N];
```

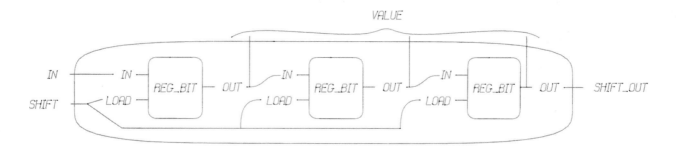

(A)   THE REG_BIT LOGIC_CELL

(B)   THE SHIFTER(3) LOGIC_CELL

FIGURE 5.6

```
GIVE      [INPUTS:    {    LEFT  \S  'IN'  ;
                            LEFT  \S  'LOAD'    \NAMED  'SHIFT'  }
           OUTPUTS:  {    RIGHT  \S  'OUT'    \NAMED  'SHIFT_OUT'  ;
                            BITS  \SS    'OUT'    \NAMED  'VALUE'        }
           EQUATIONS:  { FOR  {L;R}  $C  BITS;      COLLECT
                              {    R  \S  'LOAD'      \EQU    L  \S  'LOAD'  ;
                                    R  \S  'IN'        \EQU    L  \S  'OUT'  }
                      }
           SUBCELLS:    BITS  \NAMED  'BIT'        ]          END        ENDDEFN
```

5.3 NECESSARY AND SUFFICIENT CONDITIONS FOR A WELL-FORMED LOGIC_CELL

Unfortunately, it is possible to specify a LOGIC_CELL which is ill formed in the sense that some signals which require definition might be left undefined accidentally. For example, our COUNTER_BIT LOGIC_CELL would be ill formed if we left out any of the three equations. For example, if we were to remove the first equation, the signal RO would be unassigned, and hence the 'RESET_OUT' interface signal would be undefined logically.

A well-formed LOGIC_CELL certainly provides a definition for each of its output signals. It also provides a definition for each of its subcells' inputs, so that the subcells can perform their functions properly. In addition, all signals read by the equations must be defined, either by other equations, or by subcells' outputs, or as an input signal to this LOGIC_CELL.

We present an operator

```
logic_cell    \STRUCTURALLY_OK        →      bool
```

to verify the well-formedness of a LOGIC_CELL. The definition of this operator initially forms two sets of signals: those signals which must be defined logically and those signals which are known to be defined logically:

```
DEFINE    STRUCTURALLY_OK( L:  LOGIC_CELL )  =  BOOL:
    BEGIN          VAR    WE_HAVE, WE_NEED  =  SIGNALS;    S  =  SIGNAL;
                          SUB=  LOGIC_CELL;  E=  EQUATION;  OK=  BOOL;
    IF  DEFINED(L)    THEN
    DO    WE_NEED:=
                        L.OUTPUTS      $$
                        (  $$ SUB.INPUTS  FOR  SUB  $E  L.SUBCELLS;  )      $$
                        ($$ E.RHS  \INPUTS  FOR  E  $E  L.EQUATIONS;)
                        \LESS  {  THE_TRUE_SIGNAL  }    ;
          WE_HAVE:=
                        L.INPUTS      $$
                        (  $$ SUB.OUTPUTS  FOR  SUB  $E  L.SUBCELLS;  )      $$
                        {COLLECT      E.LHS    FOR  E  $E  L.EQUATIONS;}    ;
          OK:=  FOR  S  $E  WE_NEED;  ALWAYS    S  \IN  WE_HAVE    ;
    GIVE    IF  OK  THEN      ALWAYS  SUB  \STRUCTURALLY_OK
                                      FOR  SUB  $E  L.SUBCELLS;
            ELSE          FALSE    FI
    ELSE    TRUE  FI                                    END        ENDDEFN
```

This function notes that

1   We need to define

    a   Our OUTPUTS

    b   The inputs to each subcell

    c   All signals read by the equations

2   We have at our disposal

    a   Our INPUTS

    b   The outputs of all subcells

    c   All signals defined by equations

This function asserts that we have all the signals we need, and finally that our subcells are themselves STRUCTURALLY_OK.

Notice that we removed from WE_NEED the artificial signal THE_TRUE_SIGNAL. Equations may read this signal if they contain the constants TRUE or FALSE in their specifications (Section 4.1.3). However, nobody is going to think to put THE_TRUE_SIGNAL in the interface. It is not an input whose value can change. In addition, where the input interface to a logic cell carries with it the implication that the signals contained therein must be made available as inputs, we in fact never need THE_TRUE_SIGNAL as an input. SIGNAL_EXPRs (the RHS of equations) which reference THE_TRUE_SIGNAL will cease to reference that signal when they are translated into (DF_EXPRs). (The \LESS operator,

$$\text{signals} \quad \backslash \text{LESS} \quad \text{signals} \quad \rightarrow \quad \text{signals}$$

removes from the first set all signals that appear in the second set.)

The \STRUCTURALLY_OK operator makes use of the rule

$$\text{signal} \quad \backslash \text{IN} \quad \text{signals} \quad \rightarrow \quad \text{boolean}$$

in the assignment to OK. This yields TRUE if the signal is a member of the set of signals.

Let us consider another rule which asserts not only that a signal is in a string of signals, but also that it appears exactly once in that string:

$$\text{signal} \quad \backslash \text{UNIQUELY\_IN} \quad \text{signals} \quad \rightarrow \quad \text{boolean}$$

If we replace the appearance of \IN by \UNIQUELY_IN, STRUCTURALLY_OK will assert not only that each needed signal is defined, but also that it is defined only once.

A well-formed logic cell must contain at most one definition per signal, lest that signal's definition be ambiguous. This restriction comes from synchronous logic itself, where it is required that no two equations define the same signal.

Let us in fact incorporate this uniqueness check in STRUCTURALLY_OK, so that it will check against the existence of multiple definitions for a given signal. This check will thus note violations due to a signal being defined as

1   An output from more than one subcell

2   The LHS of more than one equation, or

3   In general, from more than one source in the entirety of sources: our inputs, our equations, and our subcells' outputs

We incorporate the uniqueness check by replacing the assignments to WE_HAVE and OK with

```
WE_HAVE:=
        ( L.INPUTS  \UNIQUE )        $$
        ( $$  ( SUB.OUTPUTS \UNIQUE )    FOR SUB $E L.SUBCELLS; ) $$
        {COLLECT    E.LHS    FOR E $E L.EQUATIONS;}    ;
OK:= FOR S $E WE_NEED; ALWAYS    S \UNIQUELY_IN WE_HAVE    ;
```

We have applied yet another new operator,

signals \UNIQUE   →   signals

to L.INPUTS and each SUB.OUTPUTS, independently. This \UNIQUE operator renders the same set of signals devoid of duplicate appearances.

Have we gone back on our intentions? That is, just as we are about to assert uniqueness in the definitions of signals, do we first explicitly remove all duplicates? We would render our uniqueness check ineffective if we applied \UNIQUE to the entire string WE_HAVE. However, we have applied \UNIQUE only to independent subsets. The appearance of \UNIQUE serves only to soften the uniqueness assertion so that a single subcell may in fact contain two or more appearances of the same signal on its outputs without causing alarm. Note, however, that the existence of two subcells, each of which produces the same signal, will continue to be detected as a violation.

The multiple appearances of a signal on a single subcell's interface does not by itself violate the uniqueness of that signal's definition. That signal may appear twice on the subcell's interface and nonetheless be defined only once within that subcell. If we suspect that a duplicate appearance of signal on a given subcell's interface is cause for alarm, we need merely look inside that subcell itself and verify therein the uniqueness of definition. The STRUCTURALLY_OK operator does assert all of these conditions on each subcell individually, looking at the GIVE clause.

Why even tolerate duplicate appearances of the same signal in a single subcell's interface? A signal will appear twice on an interface if we desire to give that signal two different names. For example, our SHIFTER(N) logic cell contains two names for the rightmost bit's output:

'SHIFT_OUT'   and   'VALUE' \SUB N

We consider later (Section 7.2) one more phenomenon that must be checked to verify completely the structural well-formedness. This involves the appearance of the same signal on both of a single subcell's inputs and outputs. So far, we have specified no logic cells that have this property. We will not change the definition of STRUCTURALLY_OK; rather, we will provide an operator which will legitimately remove this phenomenon, so that the complete well-formedness can then be checked with our present definition for STRUCTURALLY_OK.

5.3.1 One More Condition for LOGIC_CELL Well-Formedness

There is one more condition which must hold in order to guarantee that a LOGIC_CELL makes complete sense in the domain of synchronous logic. We refer to the LEVELIZED condition imposed on sets of EQUATIONS (independent of the LOGIC_CELL concept, Section 3.3.1).

Recall that we applied the \LEVELIZE operator to a set of EQUATIONS prior to its simulation. The \LEVELIZE operator ordered the equations for simulation and also reported if such an order could not be attained, implying then that the EQUATIONS themselves could not make sense in the abstract domain of synchronous logic.

We must impose this condition on LOGIC_CELLs as well. Unfortunately, this LEVELIZED condition cannot be computed independently for each LOGIC_CELL in isolation (as could be done for the STRUCTURALLY_OK condition). It is possible to violate this condition overall even when the EQUATIONS in each subcell satisfy this condition independently. (Feedback may be introduced simply by wiring cells together). Hence, we will verify this condition by first translating a LOGIC_CELL into a single (large) set of EQUATIONS, and then verify this condition on the entire set of EQUATIONS as a whole.

5.3.1.1 *Translating a LOGIC_CELL into EQUATIONS.* We provide for the translation of a LOGIC_CELL into pure EQUATIONS with the rule

> logic_cell   \EQUATIONS   →   equations

We introduce this rule by writing

DEFINE   EQUATIONS(L: LOGIC_CELL) = EQUATIONS:
     BEGIN   VAR   SUB = LOGIC_CELL ;
       L.EQUATIONS $$
       ($$ SUB \EQUATIONS   FOR SUB $E L.SUBCELLS;)
END   ENDDEFN

This function transforms each subcell into pure equations so that each subcell is represented by a logically equivalent set of equations. This function yields all the equations of the subcells and also the EQUATIONS field of this LOGIC_CELL, so that this result represents the subfunctions related together as implied in this LOGIC_CELL.

The EQUATIONS resulting from this operator represent the logical function of the entire LOGIC_CELL. These equations may be simulated, thus providing for the simulation of LOGIC_CELLs. These equations can be levelized, hence verifying the well-formedness of the entire LOGIC_CELL.

Example 8: A Light Dimmer Chip

The next example LOGIC_CELL utilizes the LOGIC_CELLs defined so far. This LOGIC_CELL, in conjunction with a triac, implements a digitally controlled light dimmer. Such a device might be used in a theater or discotheque, where it may be desirable to have a computer control the brightness of each of a large number of light bulbs.

A high-power device called a triac, which is readily available, transforms wall current (110 volts, 60 Hz) into a current whose total power may be weakened by variable amounts. Figure 5.7A shows the 60-Hz waveform of wall current, and Figure 5.7B shows one "half-cycle" of such current. A low-voltage input to the triac tells the triac how much to weaken the high-power output.

Figure 5.8 shows that a triac transforms a half-cycle into a partially suppressed half-cycle. Figure 5.8B shows how the timing of the input pulse affects the amount of half-cycle that is suppressed. (The half-cycle has been divided into 64 intervals, numbered 0 through 63.) Thus, the

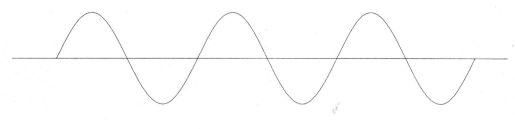

(A)   WALL PLUG: 60-CYCLE, 110 VOLTS

(B)   ONE "HALF CYCLE"

1 / 120 OF A SECOND

FIGURE 5.7

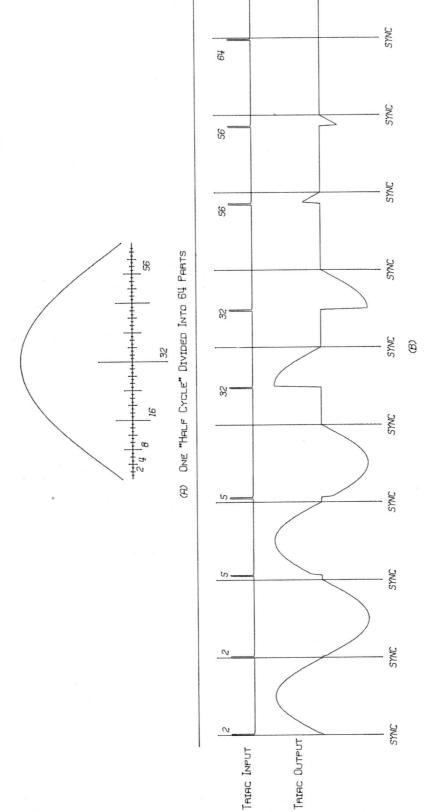

(A) One "Half Cycle" Divided Into 64 Parts

(B)

FIGURE 5.8 Triac function.

time of pulse determines the power output from the triac, and hence the brightness of the light bulb. (Figure 5.8B shows that a pulse occurring in the middle of the half-cycle produces one-half total power. A late pulse yields very little power and an early pulse yields nearly full power.)

The example LOGIC_CELL, called LD (light dimmer), is meant to generate such pulses for a triac. LD must in fact generate such a pulse for each and every half-cycle because the triac itself does not remember pulses given for previous half-cycles.

LD takes a brightness specification in quite a different, and more convenient form. LD takes a brightness specified simply as a 6-bit binary number. A low 6-bit value indicates a brighter light, and a high value indicates a dimmer light. LD remembers the 6-bit value and translates it into a pulse for the triac which occurs in the specified time interval (0 to 63) for each half-cycle.

Figure 5.9 shows how such a 6-bit brightness value can be translated into the desired pulse. At the top we have a counter, called TIME, which has on its VALUE outputs always the present time, as labeled in Figure 5.8A. That is, we assume the counter to be at 0 in the beginning of a half-cycle, and that it counts up to 63 by the end of the half-cycle. (The 6-bit counter wraps around back to 0 upon commencement of the next half-cycle.)

In addition to the counter, we have a register called BRIGHTNESS, which holds the 6-bit brightness number. Sitting between the counter and register is a comparator, which yields TRUE as soon as the counter attains the brightness value. This output from the comparator is the desired pulse, rising at the appropriate time as represented in the BRIGHTNESS register.

We have chosen to make the comparator a GE (greater or equal) comparator and not an EQ comparator. An EQ comparator would generate the appropriate pulse, lasting only for the duration of the one matching time interval. However, we have instead chosen a GE comparator so that the pulse will stay on until the completion of the half-cycle. This extended pulse does not affect the operation of the triac, except that it does assure certainly that the pulse is long enough to be detected by the triac.

The correct operation of this entire circuit rests heavily on the fact that the counter counts at a frequency exactly 64 times as high as the wall frequency. This requires that the clock fed to the LD chip be generated with careful regard for the wall frequency. (This clock defines for synchronous logic the physical period of its "time unit.")

The circuit that generates the clock for the LD chip may be insufficiently precise. It must, in effect, multiply the wall frequency by 64. Slight variations in the durations of half-cycles can render such a predictive multiplication slightly inaccurate.

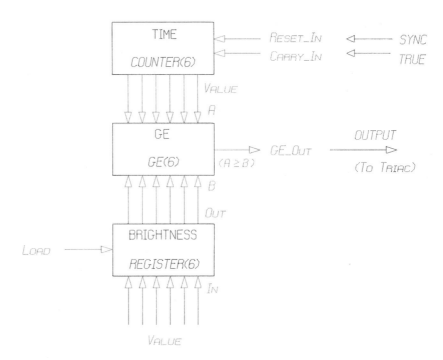

FIGURE 5.9   Pulse generator for triac.

We include therefore an input signal for LD, called SYNC, which realigns LD upon the start of each half-cycle. That is, we intend SYNC to pulse on the commencement of each half-cycle, so that LD has a reliable, independent knowledge of these crucial zero crossings. Figure 5.9 shows that SYNC resets the counter. Thus, even if the clock drifts so much as to render the counter nonzero upon the commencement of the next half-cycle, SYNC will by brute force reset the counter so that the next half-cycle may be treated more accurately.

We intend to drive many different light bulbs with independent light dimmers, and hence we need a means by which to load the BRIGHTNESS register of any one of these light dimmers. Figure 5.10 shows many light dimmers, strung together on a single bus. We use one set of wires (the bus) to communicate with all light dimmers at once. We place at the front of the bus a computer that will issue instructions to the light dimmers. (This bus implementation for communications is much easier to install than would be an implementation done in terms of independent wires between each dimmer and the computer.) The computer will change the brightness of one light bulb at a time; it will select a light dimmer and then feed to its BRIGHTNESS register a new brightness value.

The computer will place instructions on the bus, and all dimmers will see them, but only one dimmer will actually respond. The computer will affect the brightness of a light bulb via two steps:

1 Select one dimmer: `" Hey you ... "`

2 Send a new brightness value: `" Change your brightness "`

We provide a way to distinguish one dimmer from another by associating a distinct address with each dimmer. The computer thus selects a dimmer by putting on the bus the address of the desired dimmer. This address is seen, of course, by all dimmers. However, each dimmer compares this specified address with its own internal address. The one dimmer whose internal address matches the address on the bus notes this fact by setting an internal state called ENABLE. All the other dimmers, which sense a mismatch, render themselves not ENABLEd.

The computer will then place on the bus a new brightness value. All dimmers will see this new value, but only the dimmer with ENABLE=TRUE will actually respond and thereby adopt this new brightness value.

Let us formalize each dimmer as a little computer which accepts basically two kinds of instructions:

1 ENABLE   address

2 LOAD_BRIGHTNESS   brightness value

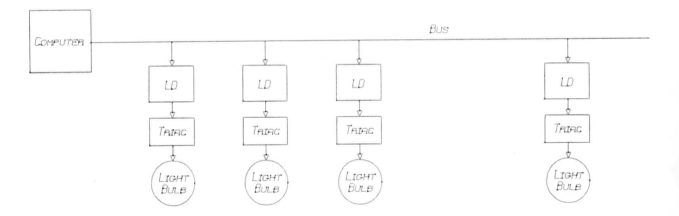

EACH LD IS RESIDES ON A BUS
AND IS DISTINGUISHED BY AN ADDRESS STORED INTERNALLY

FIGURE 5.10   Role of light dimmer (LD) chip.

The ENABLE instruction tells each dimmer which single dimmer shall respond to subsequent non-ENABLE instructions. The LOAD_BRIGHTNESS instruction issues a new brightness value, which is to be adopted by the dimmer presently enabled.

    We will represent each instruction as an 8-bit entity:

OPERAND   (6-bits)   OP   (2-bits)

We include a total of four instructions, assigned the following (arbitrary) 2-bit codes:

01)	ENABLE	(operand is an address)
10)	LOAD_BRIGHTNESS	(operand is a brightness value)
00)	LOAD_ADDRESS	(operand is an address)
11)	ABSOLUTE_LOAD_ADDRESS	(operand is an address)

The last two instructions are much less useful than the first two, but they will serve to illustrate a slightly more complex design. The LOAD_ADDRESS instruction tells the enabled chip to adopt a new address (the operand). The ABSOLUTE_LOAD_ADDRESS tells all chips, enabled or not, to adopt the new address. (This last instruction is intended to initialize the address of dimmers whose internal states are unknown. It will be useful when only one dimmer resides on the bus, that is, when all but one dimmer has been disconnected from the bus temporarily.)

    To minimize the number of bus wires, these 8-bit instructions will be transmitted serially, so that only one wire is required. Figure 5.11 shows in detail how an LD chip is connected to the bus. LD's interface takes in DATA_IN for instructions and SYNC for synchronization. (The two clocks also enter the chip, but these are supplied implicitly to all LOGIC_CELLs.)

    Figure 5.12 shows a schematic for the LD logic cell, augmented from Figure 5.9. Besides the top three components already seen in Figure 5.9, we have included the instruction interpreter. The instruction interpreter consists of an 8-bit serial-in shift register (OPERAND and OP together) to capture the 8-bit instructions supplied serially. Instruction bits shift in from the left to the right.

    Below the instruction shift register is an EQ-comparator and an address register. The EQ-comparator compares this internal address with the operand, and the result goes into the enable

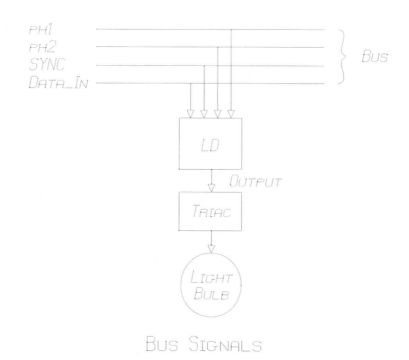

BUS SIGNALS

FIGURE 5.11

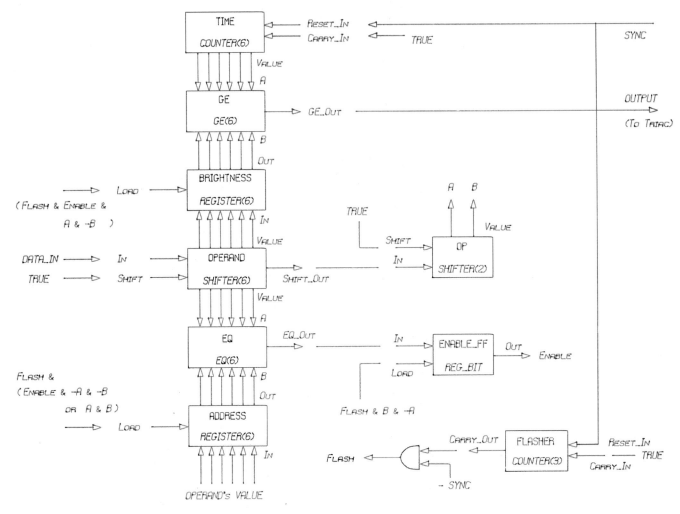

LIGHT DIMMER SCHEMATIC

FIGURE 5.12

flip-flop on the right. At the bottom, we have a 3-bit counter that divides the clock by 8, so to indicate when a complete 8-bit instruction has arrived into the OPERAND/OP shift register.

The 2-bit operation code, resident in the OP shift register, has its outputs named A and B for convenience. Judging by the 2-bit codes presented earlier, we can sense which instruction has been received:

1 NOT(A)   \AND   B   implies the ENABLE instruction.
2 A   \AND   NOT(B)   implies LOAD_BRIGHTNESS.
3 NOT(A)   \AND   NOT(B)   implies LOAD_ADDRESS.
4 A   \AND   B   implies ABSOLUTE_LOAD_ADDRESS.

In addition to these signals, A and B, we will use two other signals, FLASH and ENABLE, to determine which registers are to be affected at any moment. FLASH, the carry-out signal from the 3-bit counter, occurs once every eight cycles, and indicates when a complete instruction resides in the OPERAND/OP shift register. Like the flashbulb of a camera, the FLASH signal indicates that it is time to see the ripe instruction. The signal ENABLE is the output of the enable flip-flop and indicates that this chip should respond to the present instruction.

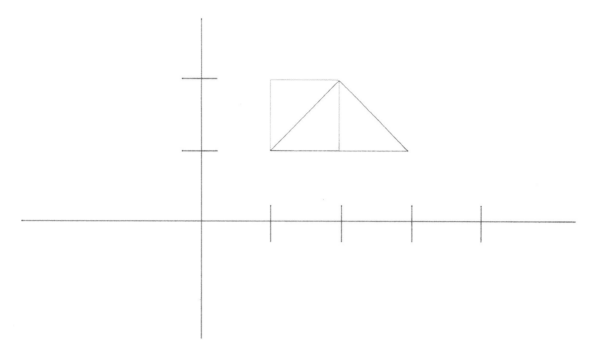

FIGURE 1.3

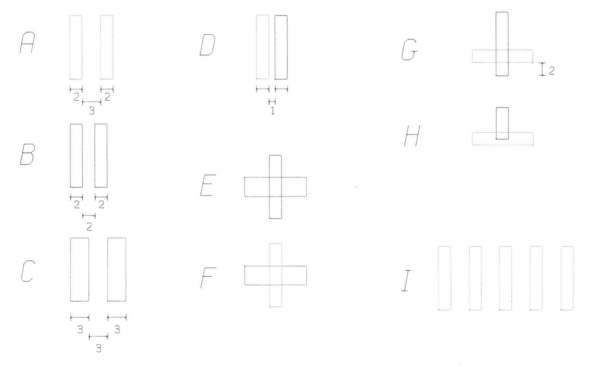

FIGURE 1.4

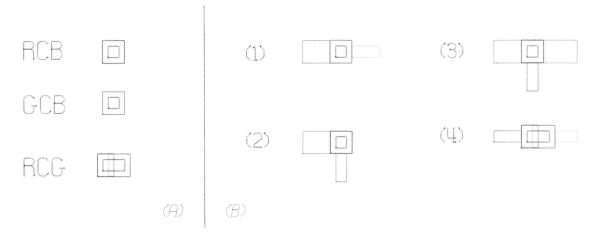

RCB

GCB

RCG

(A)

(1) (3)

(2) (4)

(B)

FIGURE 1.5

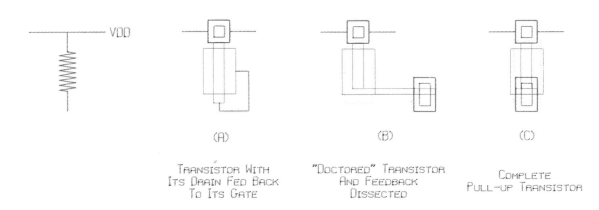

VDD

(A)

TRANSISTOR WITH
ITS DRAIN FED BACK
TO ITS GATE

(B)

"DOCTORED" TRANSISTOR
AND FEEDBACK
DISSECTED

(C)

COMPLETE
PULL-UP TRANSISTOR

FIGURE 1.10

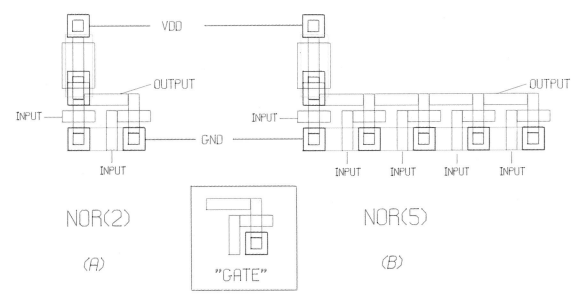

FIGURE 1.15

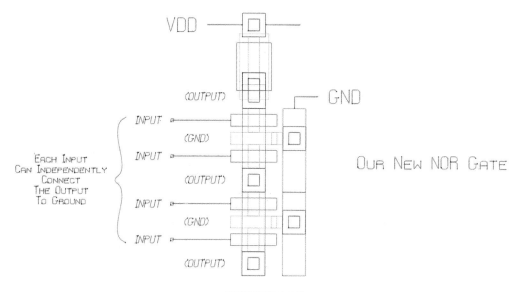

FIGURE 1.16

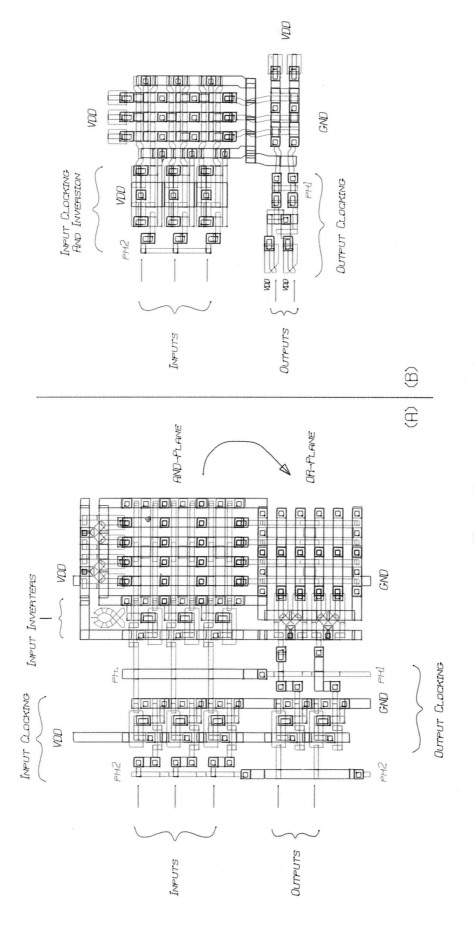

Two Functional PLAs

FIGURE 4.5

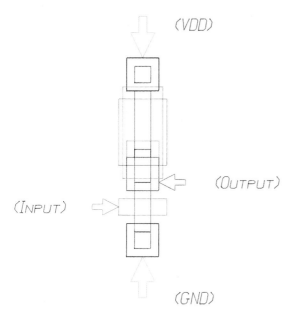

INVERTER_CELL
WITH PORTS SHOWN
VIA ARROWS   **FIGURE 6.1**

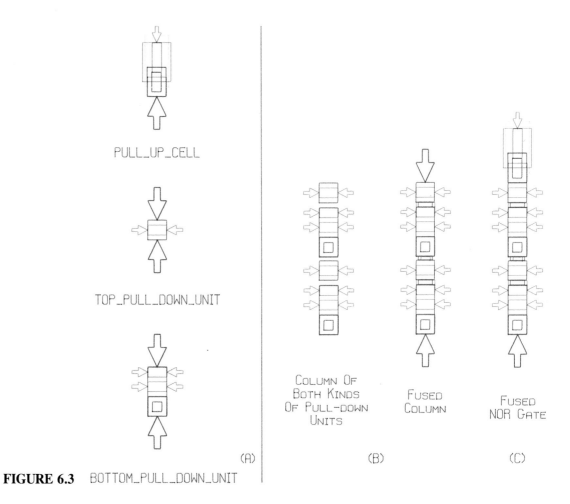

PULL_UP_CELL

TOP_PULL_DOWN_UNIT

COLUMN OF
BOTH KINDS
OF PULL-DOWN
UNITS

FUSED
COLUMN

FUSED
NOR GATE

(A)   (B)   (C)

FIGURE 6.3   BOTTOM_PULL_DOWN_UNIT

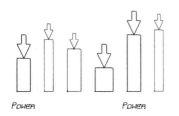

ORIGINAL CELL

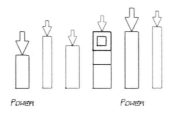

RESULT OF \NONBLUE

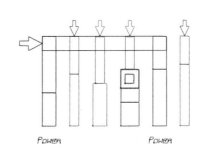

RESULT OF \SEAL_POWER

FIGURE 6.10

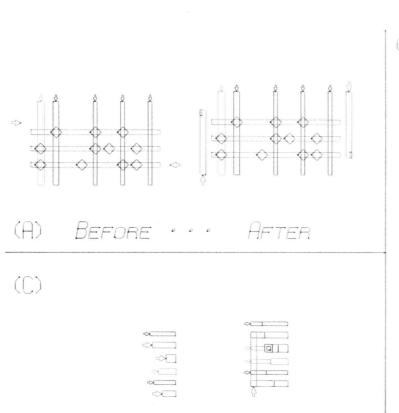

(A)   BEFORE · · · AFTER

(C)

BEFORE · · · AFTER

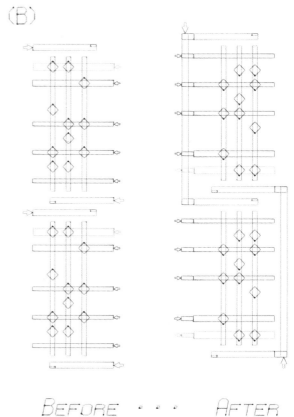

(B)

BEFORE · · · AFTER

CELL \SEAL_SIDE_POWER   ->   CELL

FIGURE 6.11

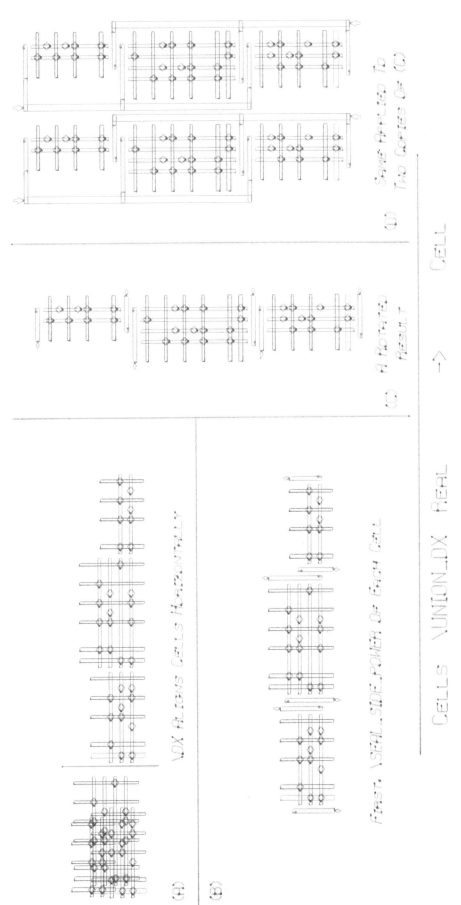

CELLS \UNION_DX REAL → CELL

FIGURE 6.12

FIGURE 6.17

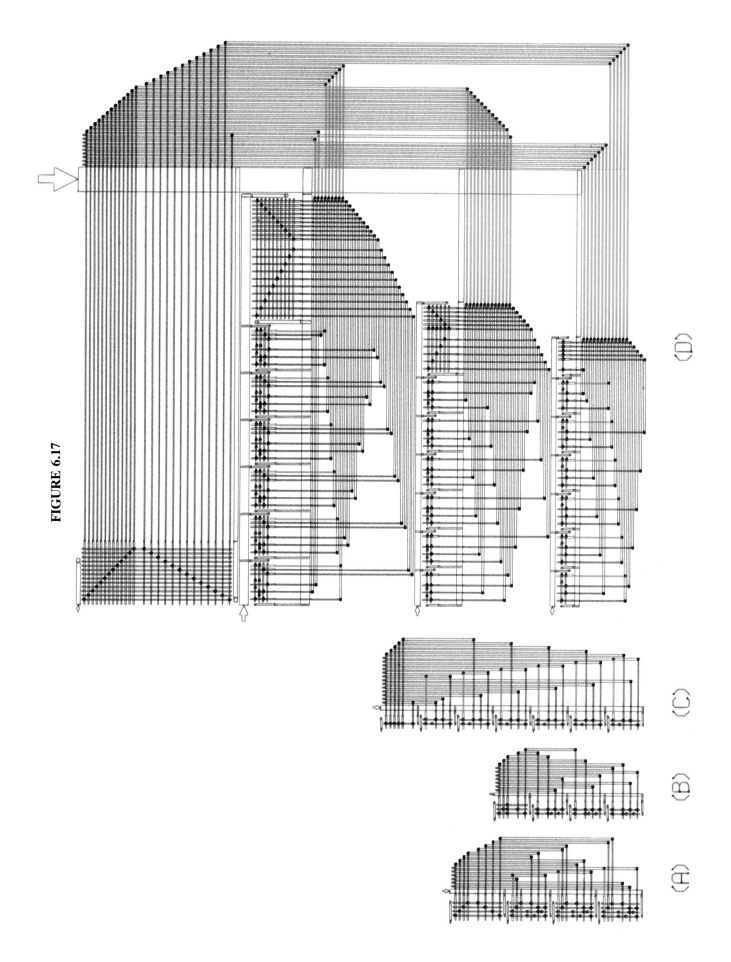

(A) (B) (C) (D)

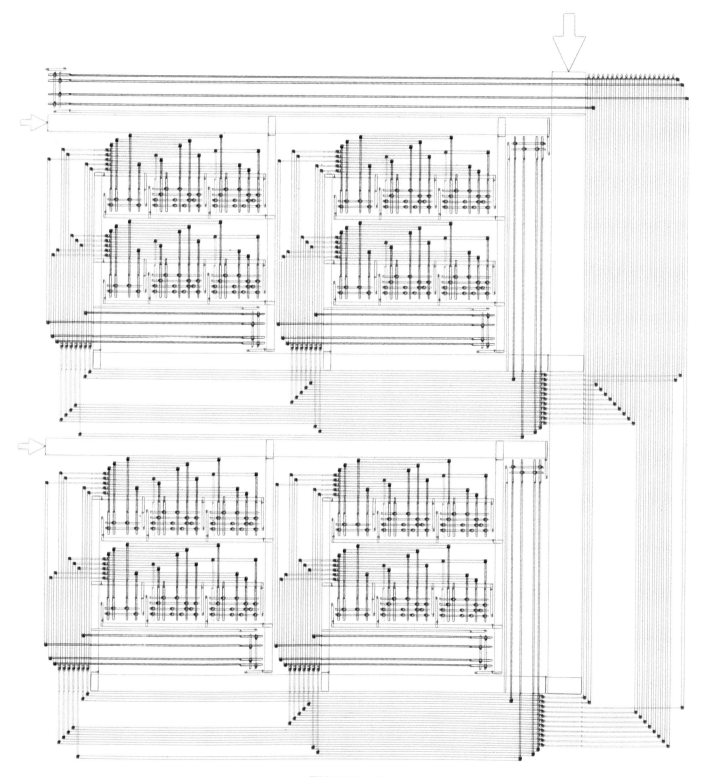

FIGURE 6.18

FIGURE 6.21

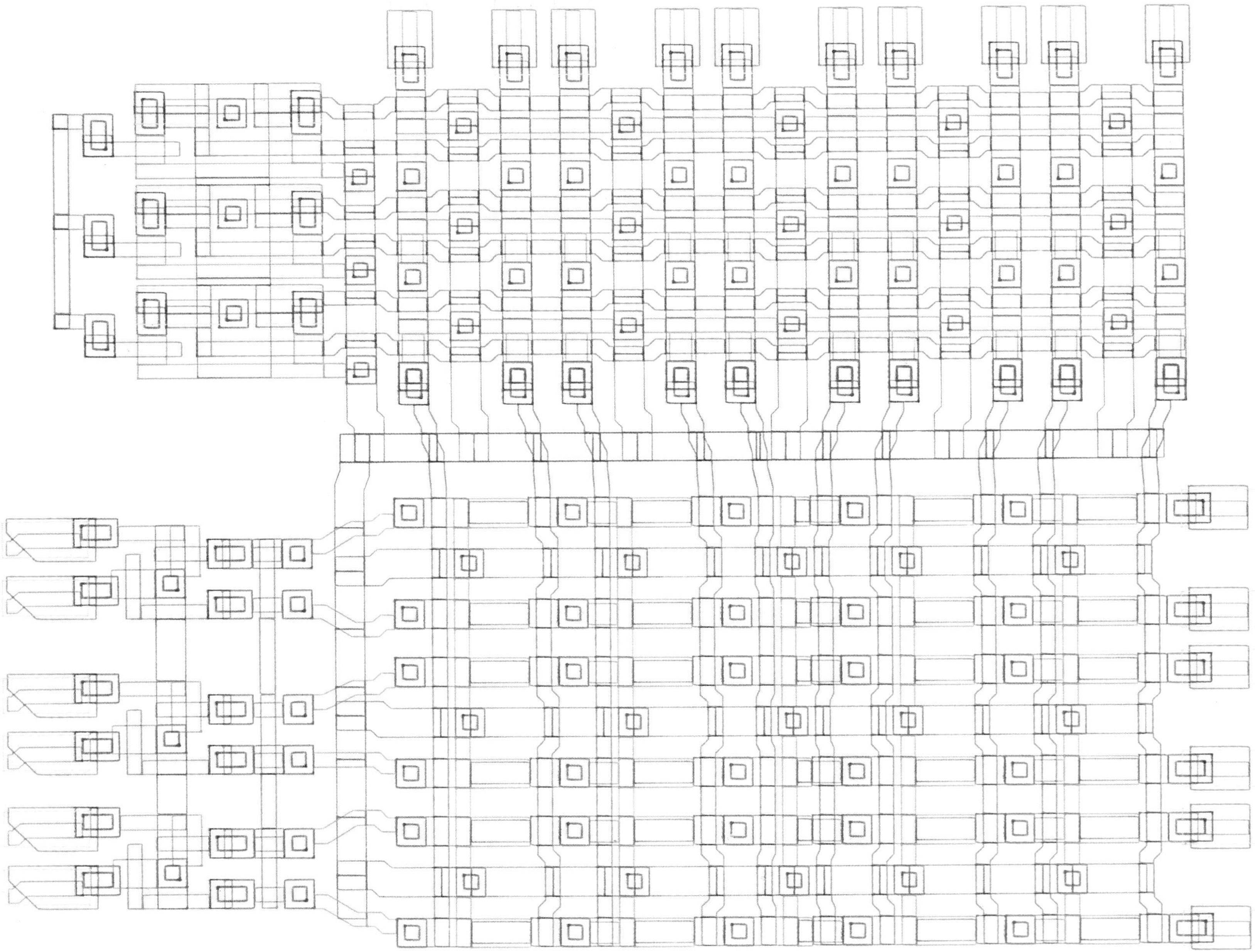

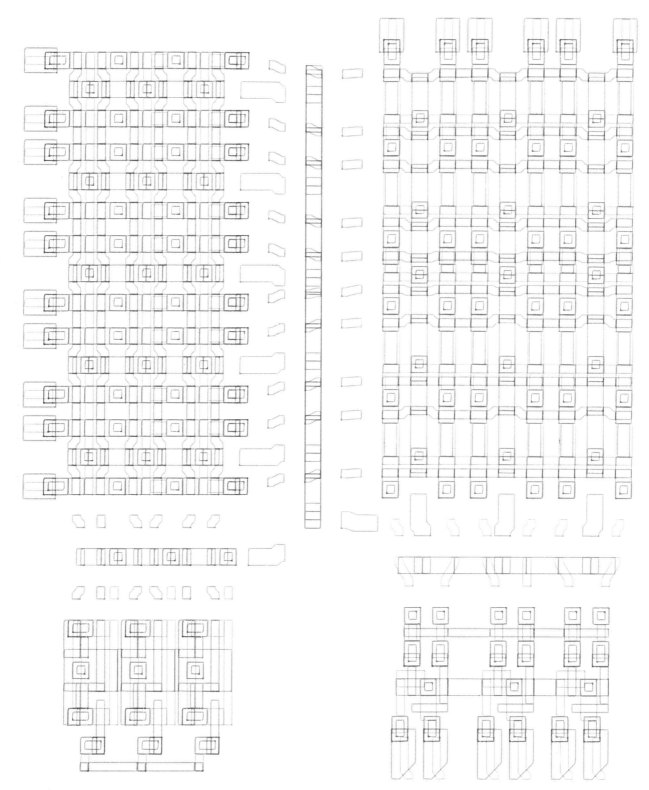

FIGURE 6.25

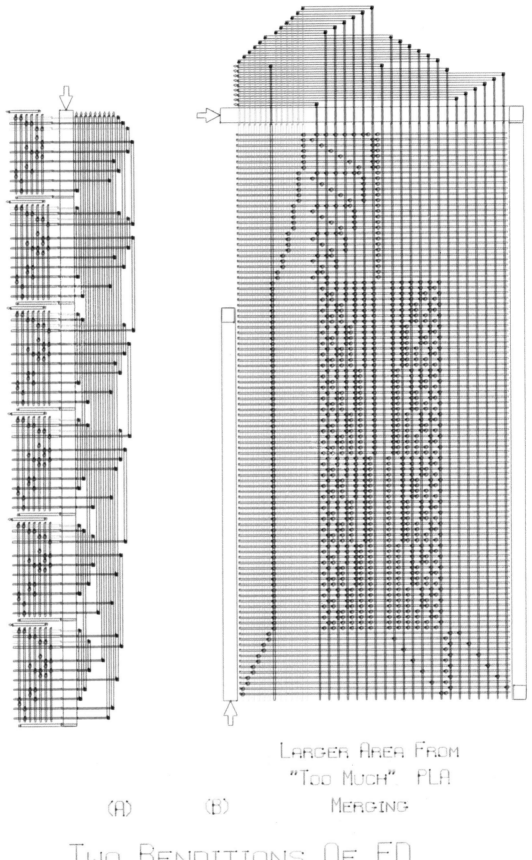

LARGER AREA FROM
"TOO MUCH" PLA
MERGING

(A)   (B)

TWO RENDITIONS OF FD

FIGURE 7.37

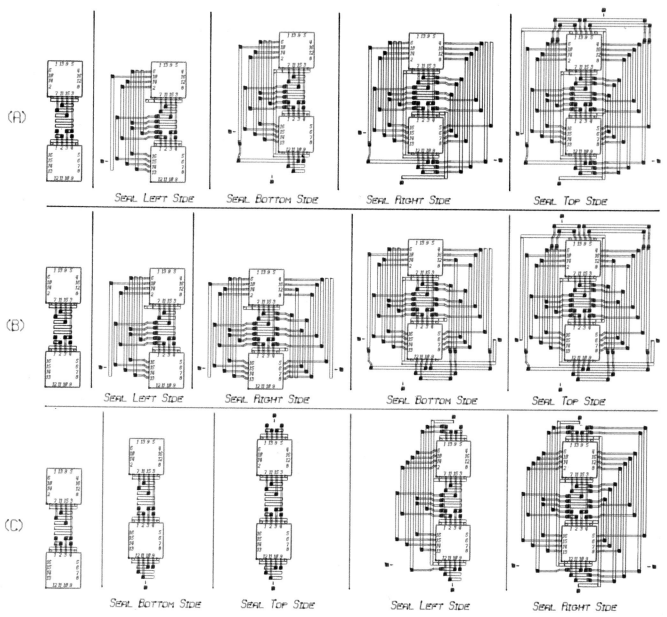

(A)

SEAL LEFT SIDE   SEAL BOTTOM SIDE   SEAL RIGHT SIDE   SEAL TOP SIDE

(B)

SEAL LEFT SIDE   SEAL RIGHT SIDE   SEAL BOTTOM SIDE   SEAL TOP SIDE

(C)

SEAL BOTTOM SIDE   SEAL TOP SIDE   SEAL LEFT SIDE   SEAL RIGHT SIDE

COMPLETION OF NEED SATISFACTION AROUND THE EDGES

FIGURE 8.30

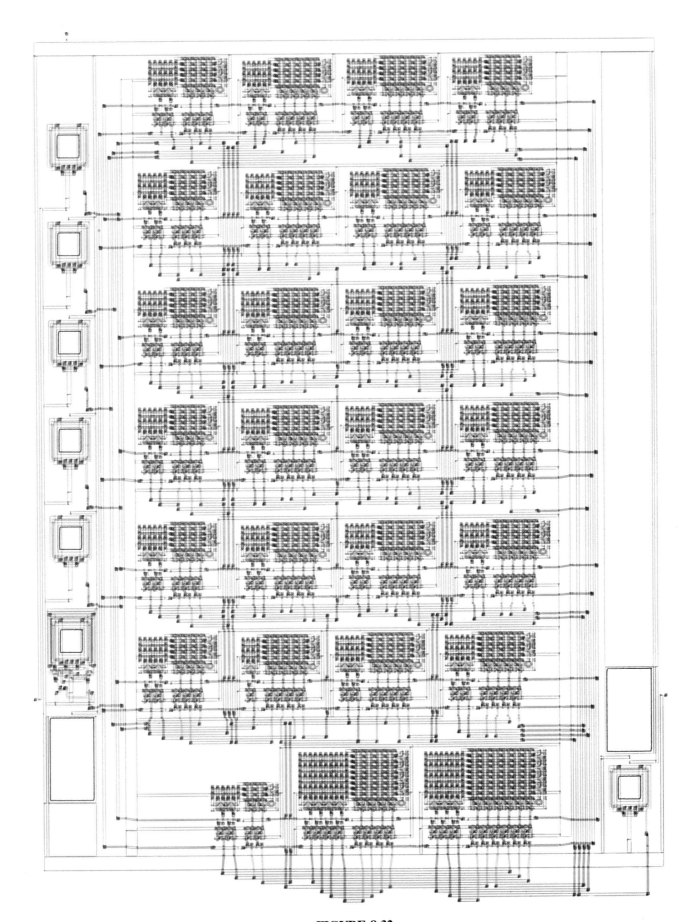

FIGURE 8.32

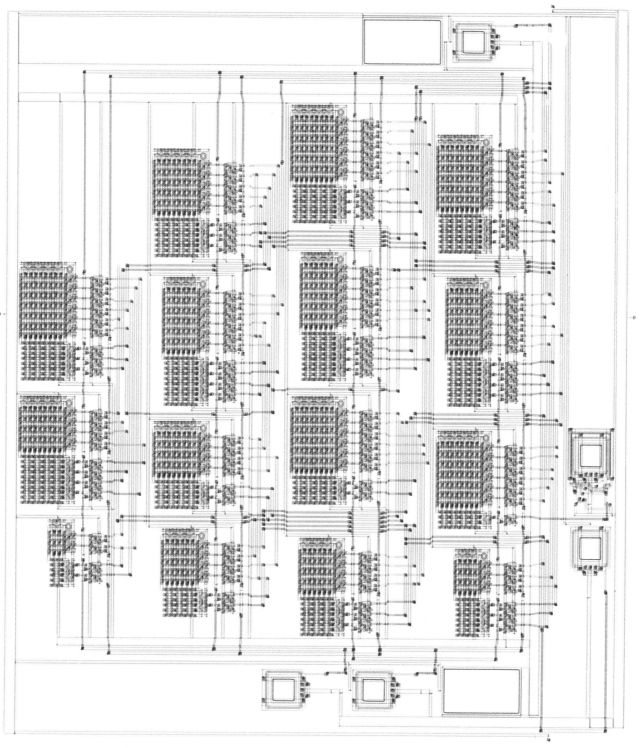

FIGURE 8.33

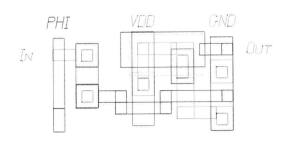

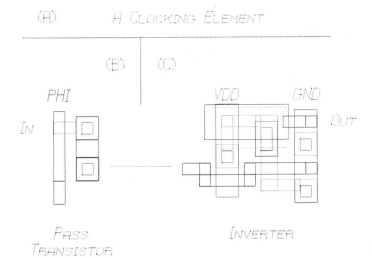

(A)   A CLOCKING ELEMENT

(B)   (C)

PASS
TRANSISTOR

INVERTER

FIGURE 9.16

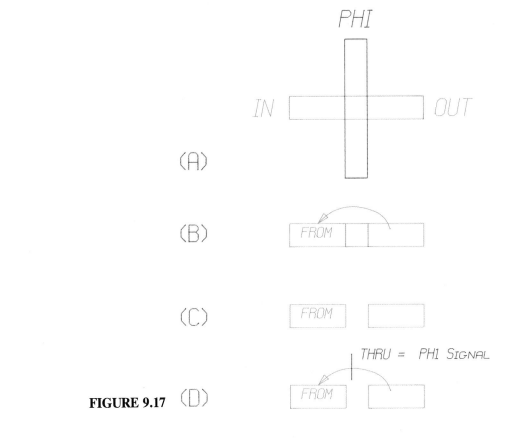

PHI

IN   OUT

(A)

(B)   FROM

(C)   FROM

THRU = PH1 SIGNAL

FIGURE 9.17   (D)   FROM

Notice how these four signals are used to define the LOAD signals for the various registers. The brightness register is loaded (from OPERAND) precisely when all of the following are true:

1	FLASH	(i.e., OP contains a valid instruction
2	ENABLE	(i.e., this chip is to respond to instructions
3	A \AND NOT(B)	(i.e., the valid op-code indicates the LOAD_BRIGHTNESS instruction.

All register LOAD signals occur only with FLASH, so that the signals A and B are known to be valid. The enable flip-flop is loaded (from the EQ comparator) upon FLASH with the appearance of the ENABLE instruction. Thus, the ENABLE instruction sets this flip-flop to TRUE if the operand matches the address register, and to FALSE otherwise.

The definition of the LD LOGIC_CELL follows:

```
DEFINE   LD  =  LOGIC_CELL:
    BEGIN    VAR  TIME,GE,BRIGHTNESS,OPERAND,OP,EQ,ENABLE_FF,ADDRESS,
                  FLASHER=  LOGIC_CELL;
                  FLASH,A,B,ENABLE,SYNC,
                  DATA_IN,OUTPUT=   SIGNAL;
    DO                " Create Inventory ... "
                  TIME:=COUNTER(6) \NAMED  'TIME';
                  GE:=GE(6) \NAMED  'GE';
                  BRIGHTNESS:=REGISTER(6) \NAMED  'BRIGHTNESS';
                  ENABLE_FF:=REG_BIT \NAMED 'ENABLE_FF';
                  OPERAND:=SHIFTER(6) \NAMED  'OPERAND';
                  OP:=SHIFTER(2) \NAMED  'OP';
                  EQ:=EQ(6) \NAMED  'EQ';
                  ADDRESS:=REGISTER(6) \NAMED  'ADDRESS';
                  FLASHER:=COUNTER(3) \NAMED  'FLASHER';
                  SYNC:=NEW;
                  DATA_IN:=NEW;
                  OUTPUT:=NEW;
                  FLASH:=NEW;
                  A:=NEW;
                  B:=NEW;
                  ENABLE:=NEW;
    GIVE                " The logic cell ... "
        [ INPUTS:    {       DATA_IN \NAMED  'DATA_IN';
                             SYNC \NAMED  'SYNC'             }
          OUTPUTS:  {       OUTPUT \NAMED  'OUTPUT'    }
          EQUATIONS:    {
            TIME \S 'RESET_IN'    \EQU SYNC ;
            TIME \S 'CARRY_IN'    \EQU TRUE ;

            FLASHER \S 'RESET_IN'    \EQU    SYNC ;
            FLASHER \S 'CARRY_IN'    \EQU    TRUE ;
            GE \SS 'A'    \EQU  ( TIME \SS 'VALUE' ) ;
            GE \SS 'B'    \EQU  ( BRIGHTNESS \SS 'OUT' ) ;

            BRIGHTNESS \SS 'IN'    \EQU   ( OPERAND \SS 'VALUE' ) ;

            BRIGHTNESS \S 'LOAD'    \EQU
                    ( FLASH \AND  ENABLE \AND  A \AND  NOT(B) ) ;
            EQ \SS 'A'    \EQU  ( OPERAND \SS 'VALUE' ) ;
            EQ \SS 'B'    \EQU  ( ADDRESS \SS 'OUT' ) ;
```

```
            ADDRESS  \SS  'IN'    \EQU    (  OPERAND  \SS  'VALUE'  )  ;
            ADDRESS  \S  'LOAD'    \EQU     FLASH  \AND
                   (  ENABLE  \AND  NOT(A)  \AND  NOT(B)    \OR
                      (  A  \AND  B  )  )  ;

            OPERAND  \S  'IN'    \EQU    DATA_IN  ;
            OPERAND  \S  'SHIFT'    \EQU    TRUE  ;

            OP  \S  'IN'    \EQU    OPERAND  \S  'SHIFT_OUT'  ;
            OP  \S  'SHIFT'    \EQU    TRUE  ;

            ENABLE_FF  \S  'LOAD'    \EQU    (  FLASH  \AND  NOT(A)  \AND  B  )  ;
            ENABLE_FF  \S  'IN'    \EQU    EQ  \S  'EQ_OUT'  ;

            A  \EQU    OP  \S  (  'VALUE'  \SUB  1  )  ;
            B  \EQU    OP  \S  (  'VALUE'  \SUB  2  )  ;

            FLASH    \EQU    (  FLASHER  \S  'CARRY_OUT'    \AND  NOT(SYNC)  )  ;
            ENABLE  \EQU    (  ENABLE_FF  \S  'OUT'  )  ;

            OUTPUT  \EQU    (  GE  \S  'GE_OUT'  )                    }
    SUBCELLS: {  TIME  ;  GE  ;  BRIGHTNESS  ;  ENABLE_FF  ;
                 OPERAND  ;  OP  ;  EQ  ;  ADDRESS  ;  FLASHER  }        ]
END      ENDDEFN
```

5.3.2 Toward Translation from LOGIC_CELLs into Layouts

We break away from LOGIC_CELLs for a moment so that we may prepare for their translation into LAYOUTs. We will first introduce the notion of a layout cell. As an example of layout cell generation, we will finally provide the translation from PLA_LOGIC (Section 4.2) to the symbolic PLA represented as a cell. From there, we will provide a simple form of automatic interconnection among layout cells so that we may translate entire LOGIC_CELLs into layouts.

We will find that a layout implementation for a LOGIC_CELL is often more efficient when rendered as an interconnected set of small PLAs as opposed to an implementation in terms of one large PLA, for example, a single large PLA generated from the entire set of equations as extracted by the \EQUATIONS operator.

In fact, the specific hierarchy, or grouping, implicit in any LOGIC_CELL affects profoundly the resulting layout. We will therefore explore operators upon LOGIC_CELLs whose sole purposes will be to modify the hierarchies, without changing the overall behavior of the LOGIC_CELLs.

Part 3

SILICON
COMPILATION

6

A Marriage
between Layout and Logic

Up to this point, we have explored separately the domain of layouts and the domain of behavioral specification. The domain of layouts has introduced geometric concepts such as shapes, positions, and colors. The domain of behavior has introduced concepts such as signals and equations.

We now begin to integrate these two domains by introducing the notion of layout cell, an entity that contains not only geometry, but also logical (behavioral) information. A layout CELL will encapsulate layout just as a LOGIC_CELL encapsulates logic.

Recall that a LOGIC_CELL consists basically of two parts:

1 Some logic (the EQUATIONS field)
2 An interface (INPUTS and OUTPUTS)

Of these two portions of a LOGIC_CELL, the interface portion is utilized by far to the greatest extent.

The interface is used each time this LOGIC_CELL is incorporated as a subcell within another LOGIC_CELL. A larger LOGIC_CELL incorporates this subcell by including equations specified in terms of this subcell's interface signals (e.g., the carry chain in Example 2 of Section 5.1.1). It is in fact the use of this subcell's interface signals which makes this subcell's presence relevant at all.

Thus, the notion of LOGIC_CELL demonstrates how the interface serves to characterize entirely the logic cell, relevant to its integration into larger LOGIC_CELLs. New LOGIC_CELLs are synthesized in the computer without regard for the logical function represented by any subcell.

In analogy, we will now synthesize new layouts via procedures so general in application that they must be oblivious to the sublayouts involved. Each sublayout will be known only in terms of its "interface," an abstraction of that sublayout which provides the most convenient handle to that sublayout's essential properties relevant to integration.

247

Perhaps you have noticed that each layout we have generated in our examples so far requires intimate familiarity with that layout in order to incorporate it into a larger layout. For example, the inverter layout shown in Figure 1.13 requires a connection to VDD at location 0#2, a connection to GND at location 0#-22, takes in its input in red at location -3#-16, and produces its output in green (or blue) at location 2#-13. The inverter layout by itself does not tell us these things. Figure 6.1, in contrast, does show this interface information.

In fact, all layouts synthesized in Chapter 1 involve detailed numbers, representing sizes and separations, all of which were derived only via great familiarity with the particular sublayouts involved. Such rigid dependencies on the concrete subcells limits any wider an application of those programs.

Each layout ever generated includes conceptually a small set of ports, locations at which the layout interfaces with the outside world. These ports are of crucial importance to the process of integrating separate layouts together to form one larger layout.

We might say that a layout without interface information is like a complex device without an instruction manual describing how to handle it.

6.1 LAYOUT CELLS: CONVENTIONS AND REPRESENTATION

Our goal in silicon compilation is to write a small set of programs that will integrate arbitrary sets of a large variety of cells. If one program is to manipulate a large variety of cells, then in at least one sense all those cells must be identical. Certainly, the layouts of a large variety of cells are not at all identical.

We render all layout cells sufficiently identical by two means. First, we extend beyond the representation of layout so to include knowledge of the layout's ports of communication. An extension of representation is necessary because generally a layout's ports cannot be deduced from the layout itself. Second, we establish a convention, or

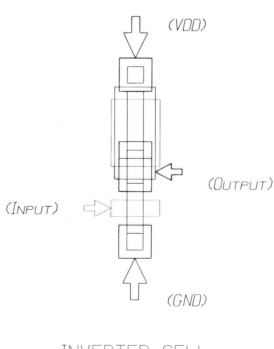

INVERTER_CELL
WITH PORTS SHOWN
VIA ARROWS

FIGURE 6.1 (*See also color plate*).

agreement among ourselves, which characterizes important properties of ports relative to the layout.

The choice of conventions is perhaps the area where the greatest innovation can take place in the field of silicon compilation. One can choose particularly simple conventions which make silicon compilers easy to write and verify, or one can choose more refined conventions that render ultimately more efficient layouts. We will consider three different sets of conventions, so to provide a wide perspective.

The need for a convention of some sort arises because processes that fuse cells together need to make assumptions about how they may add layout fragments to complete the fusion, while guaranteeing to introduce no design rule violations.

Conventions. We can give names to our three sets of conventions by applying a different adjective to the word CELLs:

1 Tiny CELLs

2 One-sided CELLs

3 Four-sided CELLs

Although these adjectives provide a clear distinction among the three sets, they are also misleading. For each adjective, one can dream up many distinct sets of conventions, and also, one can come up with very different adjectives which characterize the sets of conventions considered here.

For example, we might label the sets of conventions correspondingly as

1 Atomic cells

2 Certified cells

3 Certified "Manana" cells

The "Manana" (four-sided) cells have the peculiar property that their physical growth occurs at a time much later than the need for such growth occurs. In fact, these cells delay growth to such an extent that they will not grow to completion unless confronted ultimately with a dummy cell along each of the four sides.

For each of these three sets of conventions, we will explore to varying degrees systems that utilize such conventions.

We will show in detail a translation from the LOGIC_CELL behavioral representation to an integrated layout in the domain of one-sided cells. This will be our first silicon compiler, and it will serve to produce clear, geometric illustrations for LOGIC_CELLs. Such illustrations will be used in later chapters to illustrate dynamics of LOGIC_CELL reorganizations.

We will then sketch a "silicon assembler" which deals with tiny cells. Such a silicon assembler, like a software assembly language, provides few guarantees of overall correctness, and hence we will assign to "tiny" cells relatively few conventions. However, it is fun to play with cells in such an unrestricted manner.

Later, we will show in detail a set of conventions for four-sided cells, and we will describe programs that translate from LOGIC_CELLs into integrated layouts in the four-sided domain (Chapter 8).

Representation. We wish to avoid like the plague any situation that requires examination of layout in order to make decisions. Rather than examine layouts, we prefer to maintain at all times a scaffolding around each layout.

This scaffolding, or extra representation, will be easy to examine. In fact, we will manipulate and "grow" layout cells by examining only such scaffoldings. We will examine layouts per se only to determine layout MBBs.

Let's consider now a fundamental unit of the layout scafolding, one port of connection.

6.1.1 The PORT Datatype

Let us characterize a port, a single connection point for a layout cell, with the following type definition:

TYPE   PORT= [P: POINT   C: COLOR   S: SIGNAL   W: REAL] ;

This says that a port of connection has a position (the P field) and a color (the C field). These two fields alone specify where and with which color we can connect to that port.

The S field is a SIGNAL and it characterizes the identity of that port, for example, whether the port is meant to connect to VDD or to GND or to some logical signal. PORT signals will in large part come from our LOGIC_CELL behavioral representation. In fact, PORTs' signals will direct general interconnection (wiring) procedures, that is, the signals in cells' PORTs will alone serve as the "wire list," specifying implicitly how cells are to be interconnected.

Interconnection procedures will assure simply that all PORTs of the same signal become wired together electrically. In addition, all procedures will check to assure that two ports of different signals will never become electrically connected.

The W (width) field can be used to specify how wide the connecting wire must be. That is, the position (P) specifies the center of the connection and the W field specifies the width. However, we can utilize the W field to a greater extent by adopting a slight variation on this theme.

Note that we can deduce the minimum legal width for a port simply by considering the port's color. The minimum width for a wire of a given color is given by (Section 1.2.3)

DEFINE   WIDTH(C:COLOR)= REAL:
          IF C=RED   THEN   2
          EF C=GREEN   THEN   2
          EF C=BLUE   THEN   3
          ELSE   DO HELP; GIVE 3   FI   ENDDEFN

The following function gives us always a legal width for a port:

DEFINE   WIDTH(P:PORT)= REAL:
          WIDTH(P.C)   MAX   P.W   ENDDEFN

This function yields the W field of the port but makes sure that this width is at least minimal.

There are two reasons for accessing a port's width via this WIDTH function as opposed to merely extracting the W field. We will take the liberty to specify a PORT omitting the W specification, just for convenience. Particular to this programming language is the fact that unspecified fields in a record take on the value zero. Hence, this WIDTH function tolerates the omission of the W field by interpreting an unspecified W (zero) as the minimum width permitted by the PORT's color.

Second, we will use the W field to represent power consumption for ports that carry power. Unlike other ports, ports carrying power may need to pass relatively large amounts of current. A tolerance for greater current requires a greater width. Similarly, many devices require so little current that a minimum width port is more than wide enough. As we wish the W field to represent power consumption even for small currents, we may therefore create ports whose W fields are less than the minimum legal width. No matter, the WIDTH function overlooks such small values of W and always yields at least the minimum geometric width. (When we want to know the power consumption represented by a power port, we will examine the W field directly.)

Along with the consideration of power ports, let us invent two new signals whose sole purposes are to represent VDD (5 volts) and GND (0 volts):

VAR   THE_VDD_SIGNAL, THE_GND_SIGNAL = SIGNAL;
THE_VDD_SIGNAL:= NEW;
THE_GND_SIGNAL:= NEW;

The following function is introduced for convenience:

DEFINE   POWER(S:SIGNAL) = BOOL:
(S \EQ THE_VDD_SIGNAL) ! (S \EQ THE_GND_SIGNAL)   ENDDEFN

It tells us if a signal represents power.

Let us conclude our discussion of individual PORTs by providing a natural linguistic convenience. The following coercions provide for the fact that we very often think of a PORT as being simply a point, a color, or a signal:

LET   PORT   BECOME   POINT   BY   PORT.P;
LET   PORT   BECOME   COLOR   BY   PORT.C;
LET   PORT   BECOME   SIGNAL BY   PORT.S;

Thus, given a PORT, say Q, the following concise expressions are well defined:

Q.Y	is the Y coordinate of Q	(literally Q.P.Y)
Q=BLUE	is TRUE when Q has color BLUE	(literally Q.C=BLUE)
Q \EQ CARRY_IN	is TRUE when Q carries the signal CARRY_IN	
		(literally Q.S \EQ CARRY_IN)
POWER(Q)	is TRUE if Q carries power	(literally POWER(Q.S))

These coercions relieve us from specifying which field of a PORT we wish to look at; instead, program context specifies that for us.

6.1.2   The Layout CELL Datatype

Let us define the representation for a layout cell (or simply CELL) as follows:

TYPE   CELL= [L, R, T, B: PORTS   LAYOUT: LAYOUT];
TYPE   PORTS = { PORT } ;
TYPE   CELLS = { CELL } ;

We establish here that a layout CELL has a layout and also an interface. The interface is four sets of PORTs, one set for each of the four sides of a box: T (top), B (bottom), R (right), and L (left).

For example, we can imagine that a CELL representing an entire chip has as its ports precisely the chip's pads. (Pads are the ports of communication from the silicon of a chip out to the package containing the chip.)

This encapsulation of a layout in a cell is sufficient for the employment of general algorithms to build complete chips from a small set of cells that we will define manually. The ports in cells provide the handles necessary for placing cells relative to one another so that communicating ports among cells touch. In cases where ports do not line up precisely as desired, general algorithms may provide extra layout such as interconnection wires so to assure complete communication among sets of cells. It is the ports of cells that establish for interconnect procedures the interconnection problem to be solved.

We will use the term "fusion" to denote any process that takes in two or more cells and produces one cell as output. A cell resulting from fusion typically contains the layouts of the given cells together with any extra layout required to implement communications among the given cells. We will build complete chips simply by applying fusion algorithms repeatedly.

We will use the term "leaf" cell to denote any cell that is not the result of a fusion process. Leaf cells are precisely the cells that we specify manually.

Finally, we include a coercion from CELL to LAYOUT because we often think of a CELL simply as its LAYOUT:

    LET CELL BECOME LAYOUT BY   CELL.LAYOUT ;

6.1.3   Conventions 1 and 2: Port Ordering

Let us establish now our first two conventions about CELLs. We will agree on the following conventions about any CELL C:

1 The top and bottom ports of C (C.T and C.B) are ordered from left to right (increasing in X).

2 The left and right ports of C (C.L and C.R) are ordered from bottom to top (increasing Y).

This convention is present only for efficiency. It says nothing at all about geometry or logic. (We could always sort unordered sets of ports, but it is much nicer just to assume that they are presorted. Surprisingly perhaps, we will find that the maintenance of this convention is very inexpensive.)

6.1.4   Convention 3: Interior Ports

Convention 3, in contrast, does impose a geometric constraint.

We will say that a port P of a cell C is an interior port of C if P's position lies strictly within C.LAYOUT's MBB. Ports that lie exactly on the perimeter of this MBB are the most natural kind of ports, and will be called surface ports. It is easiest to think that all ports in a cell are surface ports, but we will nonetheless tolerate interior ports because they can sometimes afford optimizations within the result of a fusion process. Whereas the tolerance of interior ports is not essential, if they do exist, they must always obey the following assumption:

3 An interior port on a given side of a cell carries with it the assumption that running a wire from that port out to its corresponding edge, in the port's color, violates no design rules. (The directions of travel are due east for a port in C.R, due west for C.L, due north for C.T, and due south for C.B.)

Figure 6.2 shows how internal ports may arise very naturally. When we place two cells of different sizes next to one another, the top ports of the smaller cell may appear as interior ports relative to the resulting, fused cell. We could if we chose render these interior ports as surface ports immediately by adding wires as shown in Figure 6.2B. However, by tolerating those interior ports, we can transfer the generation of such wires to a later time (e.g., to a process that later places this cell below another cell). That later process can itself introduce those wires, and perhaps even use the internal space for other very limited purposes.

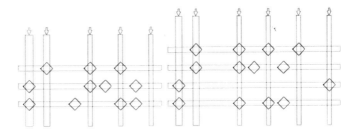

(A)

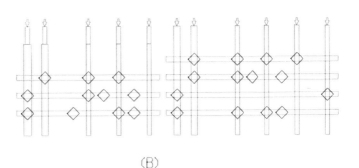

(B)

INTERIOR PORTS
ARISE NATURALLY

FIGURE 6.2

(Such "other purposes" are as yet unspecified. We will refine this convention, rendering two different versions of a "convention 4," one for our compilers and one for our assembler.)

6.1.5 Examples

Following are three examples for the specification of leaf CELLs. For these examples we suspend our special interpretation of the W field in power ports; that is, these examples use the W field of ports to represent the physicial widths of ports, even for little power ports.

Example 1: The Inverter as a CELL

Let's render our inverter from Section 1.3.3 as a CELL. Recall that the layout was assigned to the layout variable INVERTER and is shown in Figure 1.13. The following defines the variable INVERTER_CELL:

```
VAR        INVERTER_CELL   =   CELL  ;
INVERTER_CELL:=
[LAYOUT:    INVERTER
 T:      {  [  P:  0#2    C:  BLUE    S:  THE_VDD_SIGNAL  ]  }
 B:      {  [  P:  0#-22  C:  BLUE    S:  THE_GND_SIGNAL  ]  }
 L:      {  [  P:  -(3#16)  C:  RED   S:  SIGNAL1  ]    }
 R:      {  [  P:  2#-13   C:  GREEN  S:  SIGNAL2  ]  }        ]  ;
```

Figure 6.1 shows the INVERTER_CELL with the ports represented by arrows. This example includes only one port per side, but because the CELL representation accommodates many ports per side, we always include the braces to form the type PORTS for each of the T, B, L, and R fields.

This example refers to two signals, SIGNAL1 and SIGNAL2, which we have not yet declared. In contrast, the following rendition of the inverter as a CELL is a function that takes in two signals, IN and OUT, as parameters, and produces a result that does not reference SIGNAL1 and SIGNAL2:

```
DEFINE    INVERTER(  IN,  OUT  :  SIGNAL  )  =  CELL  :
          [LAYOUT:    INVERTER
          T:      {  [  P:  0#2    C:  BLUE    S:  THE_VDD_SIGNAL  ]  }
          B:      {  [  P:  0#-22  C:  BLUE    S:  THE_GND_SIGNAL  ]  }
          L:      {  [  P:  -(3#16) C:  RED    S:  IN ]    }
          R:      {  [  P:  2#-13   C:  GREEN  S:  OUT ]  }        ]
ENDDEFN
```

This function provides conveniently for the specification of the logical identities for the input and output ports. In other words, this function produces a CELL with the logical intent built in immediately.

Example 2: The NOR Gate and Its Parts as CELLs

Let us define two very small cells that can be used to form NOR gates. The sort of layout we intend to build from the following cells has already been built (Section 1.3.7). However, we can use the following cells in conjunction with a silicon assembler (Section 6.3) to build NOR gates. In fact, the advantage we will see in using general fusion algorithms on tiny cells like these will include, among other things, the automatic "stretching" of completed NOR gates so to accommodate inputs which are spaced apart by amounts other than the 8/6 lambda separations imposed by the rigid NOR gate.

We use the small set of dummy signals as declared by:

```
VAR      SIGNAL1,  SIGNAL2,  SIGNAL3,  SIGNAL4,  SIGNAL5  =  SIGNAL  ;
SIGNAL1:=  NEW;         SIGNAL2:=  NEW  ;         SIGNAL3:=  NEW  ;
SIGNAL4:=  NEW;         SIGNAL5:=  NEW  ;
```

We later map these dummy signals into real signals with an operator called \MAPPING, for example,

```
INVERTER_CELL    \MAPPING    [  FROM:  SIGNAL1    TO:  CARRY_IN  ]
                 \MAPPING    [  FROM:  SIGNAL2    TO:  NOT_CARRY_IN  ]    .
```

This renders a copy of INVERTER_CELL where SIGNAL1 is replaced by CARRY_IN and where SIGNAL2 is replaced by NOT_CARRY_IN. This CELL expression is therefore equivalent to the following use of our second, parameterized rendition of the inverter cell:

```
INVERTER(  CARRY_IN,    NOT_CARRY_IN  )
```

Figure 6.3 shows the following two cells, and how they might look when fused together at a later time.

```
VAR      BOTTOM_PULL_DOWN_UNIT,  TOP_PULL_DOWN_UNIT,  PULL_UP_CELL  =  CELL;
" In the following, SIGNAL1 is the input and
          SIGNAL2 is the output "
```

```
TOP_PULL_DOWN_UNIT:=
              [  LAYOUT:  {  -(2#2)  \BB  2#2  ;
                            -(2#1)  \RB  2#1  }
                  T:  {      [P:  0#2  W:4  C:BLUE    S:SIGNAL2]  ;
                            [P:  0#2  W:4  C:GREEN   S:SIGNAL2]  }
                  B:  {      [P:  0#-2.  W:4  C:BLUE    S:SIGNAL2]  ;
                            [P:  0#-2.  W:4  C:GREEN   S:THE_GND_SIGNAL]    }
```

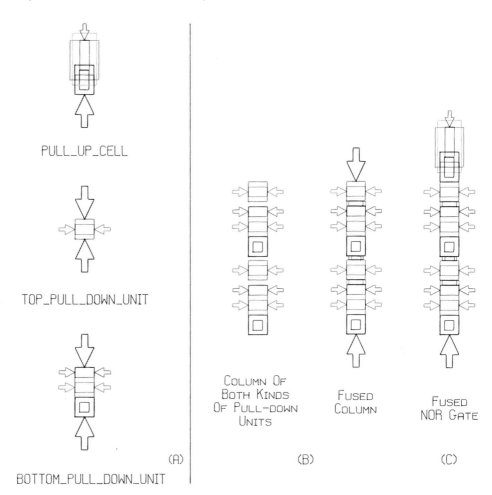

FIGURE 6.3   Cells for NOR gate construction (*see also color plate*).

```
L: {        [P:  -2.#0   W:2   C:RED   S:SIGNAL1]  }
R: {        [P:  2#0     W:2       C:RED   S:SIGNAL1]  }      ]    ;
```

Notice that we have included a comment defining the meanings of SIGNAL1 and SIGNAL2. This will serve to remind us which signals are to be mapped, so as to render a TOP_PULL_DOWN_UNIT within an appropriate logical context.

```
BOTTOM_PULL_DOWN_UNIT:=
                [  LAYOUT:  {   -2.#0  \BB   2#10;
                                -2.#8  \GB   2#10;
                                -2.#5  \RB   2#7  ;
                                GCB  \AT   0#2     }
                T: {     [P:  0#10  W:4   C:BLUE   S:SIGNAL2]  ;
                         [P:  0#10  W:4   C:GREEN  S:THE_GND_SIGNAL]  }
                B: {     [P:  0#0   W:4   C:BLUE   S:SIGNAL2]  ;
                         [P:  0#0   W:4   C:GREEN  S:SIGNAL2]      }
                R: {     [P:  2#6   W:2   C:RED   S:SIGNAL1];
                         [P:  2#9   W:2   C:GREEN   S:THE_GND_SIGNAL]  }
                L: {     [P:  -2.#6   W:2   C:RED   S:SIGNAL1];
                         [P:  -2.#9   W:2   C:GREEN   S:THE_GND_SIGNAL]  }  ];
```

The next example cell is a pull-up. Unlike our earlier renditions, this cell does not include the blue-to-green feedthrough at the top.

'' SIGNAL1 is the pull-up signal (in green and blue) ''

```
PULL_UP_CELL:=
            [  LAYOUT:  {        RCG   \ROT  -90.  \AT   0#3;
                                 -3.#3  \RB   3#11;
                                 -1.#5  \GB   1#11;
                                 -2.5#2  \YB  2.5#12.5    }          \ROT  -90.
               L:         {  [C:  GREEN  W:4  S:SIGNAL1  P:0#0];
                            [C:  BLUE   W:4  S:SIGNAL1  P:0#0]  }
               R:         {  [C:  GREEN  W:2  S:THE_VDD_SIGNAL  P:  11#0]  }  ];
PULL_UP_CELL  ::=  \ROT_CCW;
```

This pull-up cell is specified in a horizontal orientation, and the last assignment rotates the cell by 90 degrees (counterclockwise) so that the cell takes on our more familiar vertical orientation. (This \ROT_CCW operator will be defined shortly.)

Figure 6.3C shows one possible fusion of the three example cells to form a NOR gate. This rendition accepts its inputs at positions separated by more than the minimally possible separations. The connections between adjacent pairs of these cells have been supplied automatically, simply by providing short wires to connect corresponding ports. Here we begin to see the enormous payoff via automation afforded by the inclusion of ports in our specifications.

Example 3: Input and Output CELLs for a Functional PLA

Figure 6.4 shows each of the following two cells. These cells, and those introduced in Example 2, will be used in Section 6.3 as the set of leaf cells from which to build automatically a functional PLA.

```
        VAR     INPUT_CELL,  OUTPUT_CELL  =  CELL;
```

Of these two cells, we show the layout text only for the first cell:

```
        VAR     INPUT=  LAYOUT;
        INPUT:=  {
                0#4  \RB   2#6;
                0#4  \GB   4#6;
                4#0  \RB   17#2;
                11#-1.  \GB   15#3;
                11#-3.  \GB   36#-1.;
                11#4.5  \TO   36#9.5  \PAINTED   YELLOW;
                11#6  \RB   21#10;
                15#6  \GB   36#8;
                15#4  \RB   21#7;
                19#0  \RB   21#4;
                19#0  \RB   36#2;
                GCB  \AT   24#6;
                27#6  \RB   36#10;
                27#4  \RB   32#6;
                32#-1.  \GB   36#3;
                RCG      \ROT  90  \AT   6#3;
                RCG      \ROT  -90.  \AT   13#6;
                RCG      \ROT  -90.  \AT   34#6;
                19#-3.  \BB   29#10        }  ;
```

Let us assume that the layout for the other cell resides in the layout variable OUTPUT. The definitions for these two cells follow:

```
    ''   The signals are as follows:
            SIGNAL1        is input
            SIGNAL2        is output
            SIGNAL3        is NOT(output)
            SIGNAL4        is phi                        ''
```

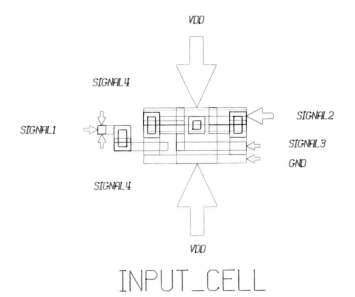

INPUT_CELL

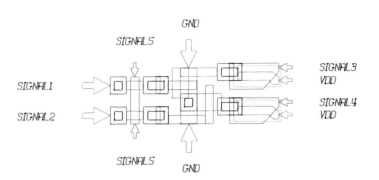

OUTPUT_CELL

FIGURE 6.4   Cells for PLA input and output.

```
INPUT_CELL:=
       [  LAYOUT:   INPUT
          L:      {  [  C:GREEN  P:0#5  S:SIGNAL1]  }
          T:      {  [  C:RED   P:1#6   S:SIGNAL4  ];
                     [  C:BLUE  P:24#10  S:THE_VDD_SIGNAL  W:10  ]  }
          B:      {  [  C:RED   P:1#4   S:SIGNAL4  ];
                     [  C:BLUE  P:24#-3.  S:THE_VDD_SIGNAL  W:10  ]  }
          R:      {  [  C:GREEN  P:36#-2.  S:THE_GND_SIGNAL  ];
                     [  C:RED   P:36#1   S:SIGNAL3  ];
                     [  C:RED   P:36#8   S:SIGNAL2  W:4  ]  }     ]  ;
and
       " The signals are as follows:
          SIGNAL1        is   input1
          SIGNAL2        is   input2
          SIGNAL3        is   output1
          SIGNAL4        is   output2
          SIGNAL5        is   phi                      "
```

```
OUTPUT_CELL:=
    [ LAYOUT:  OUTPUT
        L:    { [ C:GREEN  P:-5.#2   W:4  S:SIGNAL2 ];
                [ C:GREEN  P:-5.#9   W:4  S:SIGNAL1 ] }
        T:    { [ C:RED    P:1#11        S:SIGNAL5 ];
                [ C:BLUE   P:14#13       S:THE_GND_SIGNAL  W:4 ] }
        B:    { [ C:RED    P:1#0         S:SIGNAL5 ];
                [ C:BLUE   P:14#0        S:THE_GND_SIGNAL  W:4 ] }
        R:    { [ C:GREEN  P:36#2        S:THE_VDD_SIGNAL ];
                [ C:RED    P:36#5        S:SIGNAL4 ];
                [ C:GREEN  P:36#10       S:THE_VDD_SIGNAL ];
                [ C:RED    P:36#13       S:SIGNAL3 ]              } ];
```

These two cells implement the input and output clocking (and inversion) for one PLA input and one pair of PLA outputs, respectively.

Figure 6.5 shows how an entire input section for a PLA appears, as constructed from the INPUT_CELL. Notice once again that the ports residing between cells determine the little wires that connect these cells. This bank of input cells has been created via the same function that created the NOR gate in Figure 6.3C. Once again, that function can "stretch" the cells apart so to accommodate future neighboring contexts to the left and right.

Example 4: The Symbolic PLA Cell

The following function takes in a PLA_LOGIC (Section 4.2) and produces the symbolic PLA cell for that logic.

We choose to show the CELL definition for the symbolic PLA as opposed to a functional PLA because the symbolic PLA is considerably simpler than a functional PLA, and hence serves best to illustrate clearly a parameterized cell definition. This symbolic PLA will be used in most of the subsequent illustrations in this text. However, please keep in mind that we can at any time replace this definition of the symbolic PLA by a similar definition for a functional PLA. Such a

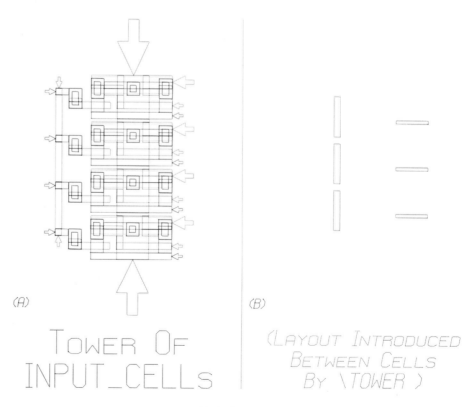

(A)   (B)

TOWER OF   (LAYOUT INTRODUCED
INPUT_CELLS   BETWEEN CELLS
                               BY \TOWER)

FIGURE 6.5

redefinition would render immediately all subsequent layout illustrations as completely functional layouts, although less clear as illustrations of principles.

Because of the symbolic nature of this cell, we will accept several REAL parameters in addition to the PLA_LOGIC. These parameters specify merely the distances between adjacent inputs, AND terms, and outputs, and overhangs:

```
DEFINE    SYMBOLIC( PLA:PLA_LOGIC  A,A1,B,B1,C,C1,Q,W,D:REAL ) = CELL:
   BEGIN   VAR  IN,  OUT = PORTS;  S = SIGNAL;  P = PORT;  CLK,GO=BOOL;
                NC= NOR_COLUMN_LOGIC;  X,Y,RIGHT,TOP,BOTTOM = REAL;
                MINS= {REAL};  DOT,GRID,LINKS=LAYOUT;  POWER = REAL ;

      DO      IN:= { FOR  S  $E  PLA.INPUTS;  FINALLY_DO  TOP:=Y;;
                    &&  FOR  Y  FROM  A  BY  A1;     COLLECT
                          [P:  0#Y  C:RED  S:S]   }  ;

              OUT:={ FOR  S  $E  PLA.OUTPUTS;  FINALLY_DO    BOTTOM:=Y;;
                    &&   FOR  Y  FROM  -B  BY  -B1;
                      &&   FOR  CLK  $E  PLA.CLOCKS;    COLLECT

                    [P:  0#Y  S:S   C:
                               IF  CLK  THEN  GREEN  ELSE  RED  FI ]   }  ;

              MINS:=  { FOR  NC  $E  PLA.AND;  FINALLY_DO  RIGHT:= X;;
                    &&  FOR  X  FROM  C  BY  C1;    COLLECT   X }  ;

              DOT:=  -(2#2)  \TO  (2#2)  \ROT  45  \PAINTED  BLACK  ;

              GRID:=  { FOR  P  $E  IN;  COLLECT  P-0#1  \RB  RIGHT+D#P.Y+1  }
                    \UNION
                    { FOR  P  $E  OUT;  &&  FOR  CLK  $E  PLA.CLOCKS;
                           EACH_DO  Y:=  IF  CLK  THEN  1.8  ELSE  1.5  FI;  ;
                           COLLECT  P-0#Y  \TO  RIGHT+D  #  P.Y+Y  \PAINTED
                                        IF  CLK  THEN  GREEN  ELSE  RED  FI  }
                    \UNION
                    { FOR  X  $E  MINS;  COLLECT
                           X-1.2#BOTTOM-Q/2  \BB  X+1.2#TOP+W/2  }  ;

              LINKS:=  { (FOR  NC  $E  PLA.AND;  &&  FOR  X  $E  MINS;)   !!
                         (FOR  GO  $E  NC;  &&
                                       (FOR  P  $E  IN;  !!  FOR  D  $E  {0;-7.};))
                           WITH  GO  ;
                           COLLECT     DOT  \AT  X  #  P.Y+D   }
                    \UNION
                    { (FOR  NC  $E  PLA.OR;  &&  FOR  P  $E  OUT;)   !!
                      (FOR  GO  $E  NC;  &&  FOR  X  $E  MINS;)
                           WITH  GO  ;
                           COLLECT     DOT  \AT  X#P.Y          }  ;

              POWER:= (      ( + 2 FOR  S  $E  PLA.INPUTS;  ) +
                             ( + 1 FOR  NC  $E  PLA.AND;  )   +
                             ( + 2 FOR  S  $E  PLA.OUTPUTS; )          )
                    *  .125  ;

   GIVE    [LAYOUT:       GRID  \UNION  LINKS
           L:      REVERSE(OUT)  $$  IN
           T:      { [P:  RIGHT#TOP+W  S:THE_VDD_SIGNAL  W:POWER  C:BLUE] }
           B:      { [P:  RIGHT/3#BOTTOM-W  S:THE_GND_SIGNAL  W:POWER
                                                           C:BLUE] }    ]

   END    ENDDEFN
```

The first two assignments define the sets of ports IN and OUT. These appear in the finished cell, concatenated in the L (left) field. (The concatenation in the L field is written so that the entire set of L ports increase in Y-coordinates.)

These two sets of ports are also used in the definitions for the layouts GRID and LINKS, contributing the Y-coordinates for the input and output lines. The third assignment, MINS, is the set of X-coordinates for the vertical AND-term lines. All three of IN, OUT, and MINS contribute all geometric positions within the definitions for layouts GRID and LINKS.

The set of ports IN takes signals from PLA.INPUTS, Y positions from the "FOR Y" quantifier, and all these ports have color RED. (RED is a natural port color for functional PLAs.) The set of ports OUT takes signals from PLA.OUTPUTS, and all these ports have color RED or GREEN; GREEN only if the output represents a \NEXT (clocked) equation. The set of positions MINS correspond one-to-one with PLA.AND the list of AND gates intended for the PLA. All of these first three assignments also define the three REAL variables TOP, BOTTOM, and RIGHT so to hold the positions of the extreme lines. (The left side of the cell is chosen to be zero, as indicated both in the X-coordinates of the IN and OUT ports and in the definition of GRID.)

The layout variable DOT contains a diamond that will be used to represent the PLA programming (the pulldown transistors that make up the layout LINKS).

The GRID layout is the \UNION of three parts: the input, output, and vertical AND-term lines. Since this layout is symbolic, we are free to choose colors as we please. These symbolic colors have no functional meaning, unlike the colors of real layouts. We have chosen to make each input line a long red box of thickness 2, which extends from 0 on the left to RIGHT+D on the right. (D is one of the REAL input parameters, representing how far beyond the rightmost vertical line we wish to extend the input lines.)

The second part of the \UNION specifies the output lines. These output lines are generated with reference not only to the output ports OUT, but also to the clocking information in PLA.CLOCKS. A clocked output has width 3.6 and color green, whereas an unclocked output has width 3 and color red. The third and final part of the \UNION forms the vertical AND lines.

The specification of LINKS forms the \UNION of two parts: a carefully placed set of dots for each of the AND and OR planes. The complex quantification used here is similar to that used in Section 1.4.3. In this case, the AND plane is slightly more complex than the OR plane because for each input there are potentially two dots, one for the input and another for the negation of that input. As explained in Section 4.2.2, the symbolic PLA shows input lines only for the actual (positive) inputs, but just below each input line there is an invisible line upon which dots may be placed in order to capture the negations of inputs.

The dots for the AND plane are placed according to the quantifier

(FOR NC $E PLA.AND; && FOR X $E MINS;)

which scans the set of AND terms, presenting together the NOR_COLUMN_LOGIC (NC) for that AND term and also the intended X-coordinate for that AND term. This quantifier in effect scans left to right in the AND plane. This quantifier participates in a Cartesian product (!!) with another quantifier. This second quantifier,

(FOR GO $E NC; && FOR P $E IN; ...)

scans from bottom to top each input accepted by the present AND gate. This quantifier sets the boolean GO and the port P for each input so that we know the Y coordinate of the dot (P.Y) and whether or not a dot should appear there at all (GO). However, the AND field of the PLA_LOGIC accommodates twice as many booleans as there are inputs; every other boolean refers to the negation of an input. Hence, we really use the quantifier

(FOR GO $E NC ; &&
                         (FOR P $E IN; !! FOR D $E {0;-7};)   )

which creates two iterations for each input port P by setting D to 0 and then to -7. (The -7 corresponds to negative inputs, and hence we use the expression

P.Y + D

to represent the Y-coordinate of the dot, which is meant to correspond with the boolean GO.) The entire quantifier for the AND plane is completed as we write the WITH clause, so that a dot will be contributed only for those iterations which find GO = TRUE.

Finally, as we look at the finished cell, we see that the layout is the union of GRID and LINKS, and that we have specified ports for L, T, and B. The ports in T and B have been chosen somewhat arbitrarily, but they are present simply to represent the fact that the PLA requires VDD on the top and GND on the bottom. The positions for these two ports were chosen to lie slightly outside the grid so that power connections to this cell will be distinguished by the appearance of a small gap.

Let us define a simpler SYMBOLIC function which supplies all the dimensions required as parameters to the flexible SYMBOLIC function just presented:

```
DEFINE    SYMBOLIC( PLA:PLA_LOGIC ) = CELL:
     IF  DEFINED(PLA)  THEN  SYMBOLIC( PLA,  10,14,10,8,15,8,10,10,10)
                                          \SWAPPABLE
     ELSE   NIL    FI                                  ENDDEFN
```

This function not only creates the symbolic PLA cell, but it also makes it \SWAPPABLE, so that the cell will consume only minimal computer memory. (The \SWAPPABLE function for cells will be defined shortly.)

Figure 6.6A shows the symbolic PLA for the equations extracted from our COUNTER_BIT LOGIC_CELL:

```
SYMBOLIC(    COUNTER_BIT  \EQUATIONS    )
```

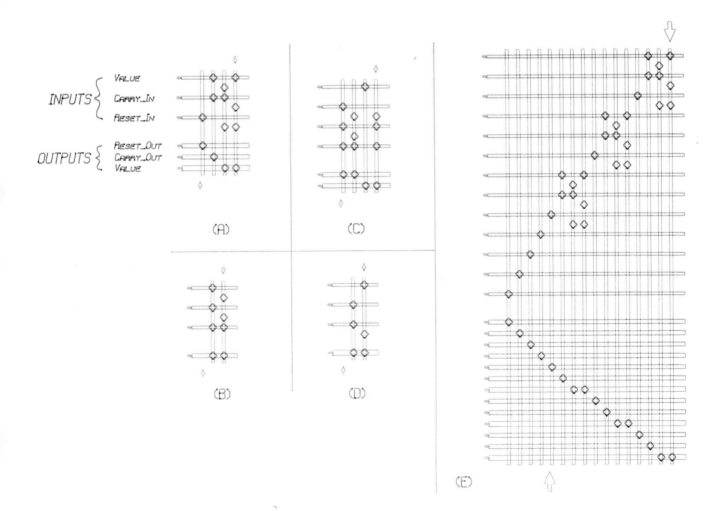

SYMBOLIC PLAs

FIGURE 6.6

The input and output ports are labeled with signal names, and you are invited to identify each of the four vertical DF_TERMs. Figure 6.6B, C, and D show

(B)   SYMBOLIC(EQ_BIT   \EQUATIONS   )
(C)   SYMBOLIC(GE_BIT   \EQUATIONS   )
(D)   SYMBOLIC(REG_BIT   \EQUATIONS   )

Figure 6.6E shows a single PLA for a 3-bit counter:

SYMBOLIC(COUNTER(3)   \EQUATIONS   )

Although these figures show only the layout of the PLA cells and not their ports, the signal names appearing on the inputs and outputs in fact match the signals represented in those ports. The PLAs in Figure 6.6A, D, and E require feedback wires to connect, for example, the input and output VALUE ports (part A), that is, so that the PLA can read the VALUE signal which it also defines.

Fortunately, all the feedback requirements are represented securely in the signals of all these ports: Ports of the same signal are, by convention, meant to be connected. In other words, we are able to omit the feedback wires now because their need to exist is represented by the existence of several different ports that carry the same signal. The contribution of actual feedback wires will occur later, when this cell becomes interconnected with other cells.

6.1.6   A Basic CELL Algebra

We now extend the familiar orientation operators of LAYOUTs into the domain of CELLs. We also define one logical operator, which affects a CELL's ports' signals.

The geometric operators are

cell	\AT point	→	cell	(move a cell)
cell	\ROT_CW	→	cell	(rotate clockwise)
cell	\ROT_CCW	→	cell	(counterclockwise)
cell	\MIRX	→	cell	(mirror about X-axis)
cell	\MIRY	→	cell	(mirror about Y-axis).

These operators for cells omit the LAYOUT orientation operators \SCALED_BY and \ROT (rotation by arbitrary angles). We can rotate a cell only by a multiple of 90 degrees simply because the four sets of ports must always be horizontal or vertical. (We have, in fact, rotated layouts only by such restricted angles.)

We reorient a cell always by reorienting the cell's layout and also reorienting the positions of each of its ports. For example, we define the cell \AT operator with

DEFINE   AT(C:CELL   P:POINT)=   CELL:
          [LAYOUT: C.LAYOUT   \AT   P   T: C.T   \AT   P   B: C.B   \AT   P
                                                   L: C.L   \AT   P   R: C.R   \AT   P   ]   ENDDEFN

This definition assumes the existence of an \AT operator for PORTS which displaces each port by a point:

DEFINE   AT(PS:PORTS   Q:POINT)   =   PORTS: BEGIN   VAR   P=PORT;
          {COLLECT   P   FOR   P $E   PS;   EACH_DO   P.P:=   P.P   +   Q;;}   END   ENDDEFN

In analogy, if we were to move a building presently under construction, we would want to move the surrounding scaffolding by exactly the same amount. For another analogy, if a company moves geographically, the company generally wants to reflect this movement in its interface with the post office by noting a change of address.

We define the other cell orientation operators in a manner similar to the definition of the \AT operator. The definitions will refer to the following orientation operators for the type PORTS:

ports	\ROT_CW boolean	$\rightarrow$	ports
ports	\MIRX	$\rightarrow$	ports
ports	\MIRY	$\rightarrow$	ports

[The boolean parameter in \ROT_CW specifies clockwise (TRUE) versus counterclockwise (FALSE).] These PORTS operators merely transform the P field in each PORT; reorientation does not affect color, width, or signal.

The remaining cell orientation operators follow:

```
DEFINE  ROT_CCW(C:CELL)  =  CELL:
      [LAYOUT:  C.LAYOUT  \ROT  90        T:  REVERSE(  C.R  \ROT_CW  FALSE  )
                                          B:  REVERSE(  C.L  \ROT_CW  FALSE  )
                                          R:  C.B  \ROT_CW  FALSE
                                          L:  C.T  \ROT_CW  FALSE  ]         ENDDEFN

DEFINE  ROT_CW(C:CELL)  =  CELL:
      [LAYOUT:  C.LAYOUT  \ROT  -90.      T:  C.L  \ROT_CW  TRUE
                                          B:  C.R  \ROT_CW  TRUE
                                          R:  REVERSE(  C.T  \ROT_CW  TRUE  )
                                          L:  REVERSE(  C.B  \ROT_CW  TRUE  )  ]
                    ENDDEFN
DEFINE  MIRX(C:CELL)  =  CELL:
      [LAYOUT:  C.LAYOUT  \MIRX           T:  C.B  \MIRX     B:  C.T  \MIRX
                                          L:  REVERSE(  C.L  \MIRX  )
                                          R:  REVERSE(  C.R  \MIRX  )  ]       ENDDEFN

DEFINE  MIRY(C:CELL)  =  CELL:
      [LAYOUT:  C.LAYOUT  \MIRY           T:  REVERSE(  C.T  \MIRY  )
                                          B:  REVERSE(  C.B  \MIRY  )
                                          L:  C.R  \MIRY    R:  C.L  \MIRY  ]  ENDDEFN
```

Notice two things in these definitions: Besides orienting the layout and the positions of all the ports, these definitions uniformly interchange the four sets of ports, and also reverse some of these sets. For example, ROT_CCW specifies that the T (top) ports of the resulting cell are precisely the R (right) ports of the unrotated cell. [The T ports of the unrotated cell become the new L (left) ports.]

In addition, each set of ports may or may not be REVERSEd. The reversal is present only to maintain the "increasing" order for ports as demanded by conventions 1 and 2. That is, we maintain these two conventions by:

1 *Gift:* Assuming that the given cell has its ports ordered correctly
2 *Constraint:* Applying such simple operators as REVERSE to restore order upon the reoriented ports

Notice that the maintenance of port order requires much less computation than a sort procedure (i.e., linear versus quadratic cost). This maintenance of order is so cheap only because we assume this order of the given cell.

We can add one more geometric operator for cells, to rotate by 180 degrees:

```
DEFINE  ROT_180(  C:CELL  )  =  CELL  :
                    C    \MIRX    \MIRY                        ENDDEFN
```

Finally, we introduce one logical (nongeometric) CELL operator which affects only the SIGNALs of a CELL:

cell \MAPPING [FROM: signal TO: signal]   →   cell

This operator replaces all occurrences of the FROM signal with the TO signal.
We define this operator by first declaring a type for the second parameter:

TYPE   SIGNAL_MAP = [FROM, TO: SIGNAL] ;

We now define \MAPPING via three steps. We define:

port \MAPPING   signal_map   →   port
ports \MAPPING   signal_map   →   ports
cell \MAPPING   signal_map   →   cell

We define \MAPPING first for a single port:

DEFINE   MAPPING(P: PORT   X: SIGNAL_MAP) = PORT:
    DO   IF P.S \EQ X.FROM THEN   P.S:= X.TO;   FI
    GIVE P   ENDDEFN

This leaves the port unchanged unless the port carries precisely the FROM signal.
We define \MAPPING for the types PORTS and CELL as follows:

DEFINE   MAPPING(PS: PORTS X: SIGNAL_MAP) = PORTS:
    BEGIN   VAR P = PORT ;
        {COLLECT   P \MAPPING X   FOR P $E PS; }
    END   ENDDEFN

DEFINE   MAPPING(C: CELL   X: SIGNAL_MAP) = CELL:
    DO   C.T::= \MAPPING X;
          C.B::= \MAPPING X;
          C.R::= \MAPPING X;
          C.L::= \MAPPING X;
    GIVE   C   ENDDEFN

[We use the abbreviated "::=" notation, e.g.,

C.T ::= \MAPPING X;

to mean

C.T. := C.T \MAPPING X;

The "::=" maps into our more familiar ":=" by copying the left side onto the right side. For example,

I ::= +1;   means   I:=I+1   ]

We conclude the basic algebra for CELLs by introducing an identity function whose only purpose is to conserve computer memory. Recall the \SWAPPABLE operator for LAYOUTs, which tells the computer that the layout may reside on disk if main memory becomes full (Section 2.6.9). We now extend \SWAPPABLE to apply to CELLs:

DEFINE   SWAPPABLE(C:CELL) = CELL:
            DO   C.LAYOUT:= C.LAYOUT \SWAPPABLE ;
                  GIVE   C   ENDDEFN

SWAPPABLE applied to a cell merely makes the cell's layout swappable. Thus, no matter how complex a cell might be, \SWAPPABLE relieves memory consumption due to its layout. (The rest of a cell, the ports, generally consume minimal memory.)

6.1.7 A Closer Look at Conventions

The term "convention" refers to an agreement among ourselves which is not represented explicitly in our formal system (the computer). This notion takes on different names in different fields. Mathematicians often call such agreements "axioms" while other scientists may use the term "invariants."

6.1.7.1 Examples of conventions in general. Let us consider a class of conventions (axioms or invariants) that arises profusely in the domain of software. When we write the following program in FORTRAN

```
I  =  5
J  =  I  +  1
```

FORTRAN establishes for us at least one convention. FORTRAN allocates a word of memory that will forever serve as the storage location for the variable "I." This word may reside at address 763 or 57431 or wherever. However, the entire essence of this convention rests precisely in the fact that a particular association between "I" and the specific memory address exists as long as the program exists. It does not change. Let us choose for purposes of discussion the address 7631 (chosen out of a hat).

Such a convention is relevant to us as FORTRAN users in that it maintains the property that the two occurrences of "I" in this sample program text are in fact the same variable.

To the FORTRAN compiler, this convention represents two things, a gift and a constraint:

1 *Gift:* The compiler can assume that the value of "I" resides at the specific memory address 7631 (e.g., FORTRAN can execute the second assignment, obtaining for the value of "I" merely the contents of location 7631. Computers can fetch from such a concrete memory address in less than one millionth of a second).

2 *Constraint:* The compiler must maintain that the value of "I" resides at the specific memory address 7631 [e.g., it is not sufficient to leave a new value for "I" (e.g., 5) resident in a register; that value must be stored back into the specific memory address 7631, even if such activity introduces overhead].

Clearly, if FORTRAN does not maintain the constraint, then FORTRAN cannot depend on the gift.

This convention about "I" is represented in the computer at compile time, when FORTRAN translates this program into machine language. However, this convention ceases entirely to be represented in the computer at run time, when this program actually executes, with FORTRAN absent from the scene. However, this convention certainly persists in spirit; the compiled machine language program always obeys it implicitly.

An "optimizing" FORTRAN compiler, which is expected to make an effort at generating particularly efficient machine language programs, may adopt a different convention about variables (e.g., "I"). Such a compiler might be written so to assume and maintain a more refined convention, for example.

The value of "I" resides at the specific memory address, except within a DO-loop which calls no subroutines, at which times the value of "I" resides instead in a specific register.

Although this convention is more complicated, it relieves some of the effort required in the maintenance of our original convention. For example, it is no longer required that FORTRAN assemble an extra STORE instruction just to transfer ''I'''s value out of the register into location 7631.

However, this savings carries with it a cost: No longer can FORTRAN assume that ''I'''s value resides in location 7631. Does this imply that the savings afforded by omitting the STORE instruction must now be spent in order to find out where ''I'''s value resides?

Fortunately, such a cost can be absorbed during compile time as opposed to runtime; that is, the FORTRAN compiler must in fact be ''smarter'' in its effort to determine the whereabouts of ''I'''s value, but run time is saved because typically access to wherever ''I'' resides (a register) requires no additional machine instructions.

Another kind of convention is apparent in human cultures. Each culture tends to have a specific language through which its members communicate. The language itself is a convention. People in that culture utilize the convention as follows:

1 *Gift:* The listener feels free to associate meaning with the utterances of the speaker.

2 *Constraint:* The speaker makes an effort to formulate his or her intended meaning into the specific language.

The convention of language is implicit during conversation. The speaker does not provide with each word uttered a complete description of the language itself.

For another software (firmware) example, consider the fragment of microcode shown in Section 1.4.1. Following the second instruction is the instruction MULTIPLY. The convention present in this piece of microcode is that the MULTIPLY instruction takes its two parameters from INPUT#1 and INPUT#2. Although this convention does not appear explicitly as part of the microcode, it is nonetheless central to the correct execution of that microcode.

6.1.7.2   *The two roles conventions play, and how to choose conventions.*   Conventions always play a dual role, as indicated in the preceding examples. Each serves both as a gift and a constraint. We say that a process ''maintains'' a convention if that process always yields a situation adhering to the convention. We say that a process ''assumes'' a convention when it takes for granted adherence to the convention and does not bother to verify its truth.

The profit gained by adopting a convention is greatest when

1 The gift (assumption) is very valuable, and its verification is expensive (or impossible), and simultaneously

2 The maintenance of the convention is relatively inexpensive.

We might wonder if a convention can ever be profitable; it appears that whatever is gained must be paid for in maintenance. However, there are many examples of profitable conventions.

The key value of a convention rests in the fact that its benefit is realized in contexts usually distinct from the contexts that must be concerned with maintenance. In other words, contexts that can affect the truth of a convention (i.e., those contexts that must be concerned with maintenance) most often have at hand the information and tools necessary for maintenance. In contrast, those contexts that benefit by assuming the convention most often do not have such information and tools.

For example, the maintenance of an automobile occurs upon a tow truck and at a garage. In contrast, the correct operation of the car is assumed only on freeways and surface streets. If these two contexts were not different, we would have to imagine that maintenance occurs right on the freeway, or that we drive cars only inside a garage. In either case, the expense of (freeway) maintenance is very high, or the car confined to a garage presents no value to us. It is the distinction between the ''gift'' and ''constraint'' contexts that makes possible the existence of profitable conventions.

For another example, FORTRAN's maintenance of the convention about ''I'' occurs in the context of compile time, when information such as the symbol table is readily available. In contrast, the benefit is realized at run time, a context that does not have the symbol table. The profit in this convention is seen clearly by noting that the cost of a few seconds for compile time often yields a run-time increase in efficiency of a factor of 100. Savings in run time are extremely valuable when we run programs that consume a half an hour as opposed to 50 hours.

It is perhaps the need for distinct contexts which lends value to compilers of any sort.

In addition, perhaps the essential value of tools in general is the distinction between the contexts of

1   Making the tool
2   Using the tool

A tool that must be remade during each moment of its use is no longer a tool, but merely part of the overall process that inspired the need for the tool in the first place.

6.1.7.3 *How conventions affect us as compiler writers.* We feel the effects of a choice of conventions in three ways:

1   We often find that the entire programming task is reduced simply to the maintenance of the chosen conventions.

This is typical when we choose conventions whose assumptions match the desired solution very closely. For example, a convention of this sort might state very simply:

''All layout cells are interconnected together correctly''

However, while this proposed convention carries with it a great gift, its maintenance may be no easier than the entire programming task conceived initially. Fortunately, we can slightly refine this convention so that it yields an equally valuable gift but requires relatively little maintenance.

The second phenomenon associated with a choice of convention concerns debugging:

2   Debugging a program is reduced to discovering the first violation of conventions.

An entire debugging scenario usually proceeds as follows:

a   The program gives a wrong answer.
b   Why?

Determining "why," in the absence of conventions, requires consideration of the entire program and all possible interactions among its parts. In contrast, the discovery of "why" in the presence of conventions requires finding only the first violation of convention. (All programmers utilize unsaid conventions of some sort; otherwise, they could not produce working programs.)

Finally, the adoption of conventions makes it possible to:

3   Verify correctness of the program (e.g., silicon compiler.)

Conventions enter the domain of program verification in exactly the same way that axioms, or inductive hypotheses, enter into mathematical proofs. They provide the framework for deciding:

a   What in fact needs to be verified

b   What can be assumed in the formulation of proofs

For example, the set of conventions that we associate with a layout cell affects profoundly how we will prove the correctness of fusion processes, processes that take in several cells and produce one integrated cell as output. We prove a fusion process by:

1   Assuming that the given cells adhere to the conventions, (the gift)

2   Proving that the fused cell generated for output also adheres to these conventions (the constraint)

A proof of this sort is often called an "inductive" proof and perhaps makes up the majority of all formal proofs.

We will very often find such proofs easy to write. The difficulty of proof is of course dependent on the choice of conventions. However, we will naturally choose conventions that will ease the programming task as much as possible, rendering typically a set of short clear procedures.

Each procedure (e.g., fusion procedure) typically does very little. It adds very little layout beyond the layouts given already with the given cells. Thus, the proof of the resulting fused cell becomes nearly trivial because the majority of layout comes from the given, certified (by assumption) cells. However, no matter how miniscule a layout we contribute beyond those layouts given, one can prove correctness only by assuming something about the given layouts.

6.1.7.4   *Examples of conventions for CELLs.* Consider some possible cell conventions. We might agree to the convention that all ports lie on the perimeter of the layout's bounding box (MBB). This would assure simply that all connections made to that layout never need penetrate that layout's MBB. (See convention 3, Section 6.1.4.)

We might agree further that all adjacent ports along any one of the four sides of a cell are separated by at least some specific distance. This would assure the ability to connect distinct wires, each of some minimal width, to the cell.

We might also agree that all cells require VDD along only the top and right edges and require GND only along the left and bottom edges. Such a separation of VDD and GND ports may assure the ability to route each of VDD and GND entirely in blue. (Note that the inverter shown in Figure 6.1 adheres to the second and third conventions, but conflicts with the first convention because the output port lies slightly within the interior of the layout's MBB.)

Although layout cells adhering to different conventions may not be interchangeable directly, it is quite plausible to imagine a single silicon compiler which operates within distinct sets of conventions during distinct subprocesses. Each of the distinct sets of conventions has advantages over the others in distinct contexts. In fact, it is profitable for a silicon compiler to make several renditions of the "same" cell within differing conventions, and maintain such multiplicity, or "ambiguity," until such a time that advantages of one choice over another become clear.

A single silicon compiler can take fullest advantage of a variety of conventions and still yield a single integrated layout as long as it provides for the translation from cells rendered within one set of conventions into the same cells rendered in terms of a different set.

6.1.8   CELL Conventions for Our Compilers

We now introduce three more conventions for cells used in our silicon compilers. A summary follows:

4   Refined convention for interior ports, and separation between adjacent ports

5   The interconnection "service" convention

6   Convention for power ports

Let us further restrict the nature of interior ports with the following refined version of convention 3:

4a   Not only is it assumed that we can draw a wire from an interior port out to its corresponding edge, but we assume further that the interior port implies an absence of layout along its exit path. In other words, an interior port provides by assumption a dent in the MBB, as shown in Figure 6.7.

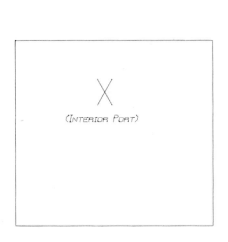
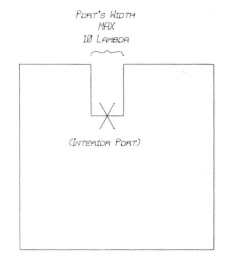

THE GIVEN   THE ASSUMPTION

CONVENTION #4
ABOUT
INTERIOR PORTS

FIGURE 6.7

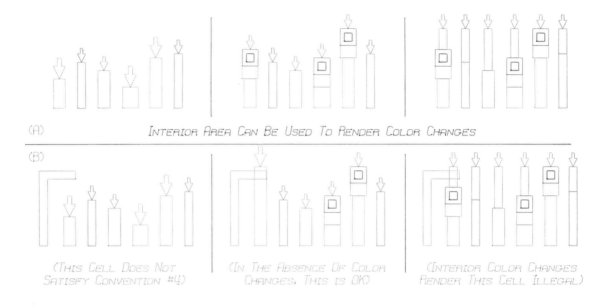

(A) INTERIOR AREA CAN BE USED TO RENDER COLOR CHANGES

(B)

(THIS CELL DOES NOT SATISFY CONVENTION #4)

(IN THE ABSENCE OF COLOR CHANGES, THIS IS OK)

(INTERIOR COLOR CHANGES RENDER THIS CELL ILLEGAL)

CONVENTION #4 ALLOWS INTERIOR COLOR CHANGES HOWEVER, IT PLACES A NEW RESTRICTION ON CELLS

FIGURE 6.8

We see in this convention that an interior port offers an advantage over a surface port: We can use the interior space between that port and its corresponding edge to change colors, and thereby avoid or minimize using area outside the layout for implementing a color change (Figure 6.8A).

This added feature does outlaw the existence of some interior ports in CELLs. For example, under condition 3 alone there could be a blue interior port which lies so far to the interior that its path outward may, in fact, intersect some green shapes (Figure 6.8B). However, under condition 4, such an interior port is illegal because condition 4 states that we may in fact blindly place a blue-to-green feedthrough at that port and then travel outward on a green wire. This green wire would intersect green shapes on the way out and hence probably violate design rules.

This convention also implies that adjacent ports of a cell must be separated by at least 7 lambda (4 lambda for the thickness of the possible feedthrough and 3 lambda blue-to-blue separation between such feedthroughs). Since we desire that cells can be integrated into any enviornment, we will extend to all ports, interior and surface, the 7 lambda minimal separation:

4b Adjacent ports along an edge are separated in position by at least 7 lambda.

Under these assumptions, we are guaranteed the ability to route from each and every port upon a straight wire of any desired color.

Finally, note that the 10-lambda clearance required for interior ports is consistent with adjacent ports separated by 7 lambda. The clearance requirement is stated relative to layout delivered with the given cell originally, and does not refer therefore to any layout we might add in the effort to route interior ports outward.

We now provide another convention for cells which profoundly affects the fusion algorithms for cells. It simultaneously relieves the builders of major cells from completing local interconnections (e.g., feedback wires for PLAs).

5 Any two ports along the same side of a cell that carry the same signal will be connected together automatically.

The fusion algorithm will maintain this convention, and in fact that is all it will do. All wires of interconnect will arise simply in the maintenance of this convention. It will be the maintenance of this convention in a recursive environment that will give rise implicitly to much more complex-looking wirings.

Finally, we impose one more convention to account for power ports. This convention serves to guarantee the ability to route VDD and GND entirely in blue. (Power must be routed entirely in blue because red and green wires introduce substantial resistence, and would hence render 0 and 5 volts as 1 and 4 volts, or worse.)

> **6** All power ports along the same side of a cell must be of the same polarity (i.e., all VDD or all GND). In addition, the top side of a cell may not include GND ports, and symmetrically, the bottom side may not include VDD ports. Finally, all power ports are blue.

All of these conventions will come into play as we explore fusion for "one-sided" and "four-sided" cells.

6.2 THE FUSION OF "ONE-SIDED" CELLS

We now explore in detail the fusion of cells that have all nonpower signals resident along exactly one side. Our symbolic PLA is an example of a one-sided cell. (All nonpower ports reside on the left side.) Functional PLAs also tend to be one-sided. (We will consider one functional PLA that is not one-sided when we consider the fusion of the fully general four-sided cells.)

We impose one more convention for one-sided cells:

> **7** The signal side of a one-sided cell is the top.

We will render our symbolic PLA consistent with this convention simply by rotating it clockwise.

We present the entire translation from the type LOGIC_CELL to a single integrated one-sided layout CELL in detail. It depends heavily on a set of programs that fuse general one-sided cells. The particular, symbolic PLA will enter the scene only at the end (Section 6.2.6).

In summary, we provide the following operators:

> **1** cell \NONBLUE   →   cell
>
> to render a cell so that its nonpower ports on top appear in a color other than blue.
>
> **2** cell \SEAL_POWER signal   →   cell
>
> to seal off all power requirements along the top edge of the cell. (The given signal distinguishes between VDD and GND.)
>
> **3** cells \DX real   →   cells
>
> to align a set of cells horizontally so that they are separated by the given distance.
>
> **4** cells \UNION_DX real   →   cell
>
> to render the result of \DX as a single integrated cell.
>
> **5** An operator called \FLY_AT which produces one horizontal scan-line of interconnect.
>
> **6** cells \PACK signals   →   cell
>
> to fuse the given cells together with all necessary interconnect. The given signals designate which signals among the given cells are to appear as ports in the resulting cell.
>
> **7** logic_cell \CELL → cell
>
> to translate an entire LOGIC_CELL into a complete layout cell.

6.2.1 Color Changes

We define the operator \NONBLUE which will add some layout to the top of a CELL so that all its nonpower ports (on top) will appear as red or green, and not blue. This operator will be a prerequisite for subsequent placement of a blue power wire horizontally atop the cell. (Any blue signal ports atop the cell could not cross the intended blue power wire without shorting to power.) This operator is the only operator that creates color changes in the domain of one-sided cells:

```
DEFINE    NONBLUE( C:CELL ) = CELL: BEGIN    VAR  P = PORT;
    DO      C.LAYOUT::=  \UNION
                {FOR  P  $E  C.T;  WITH  -POWER(P)  &  P=BLUE  ;
                        COLLECT     GCB  \AT  P  +  0#2+3  \UNION
                                        P  -  2#0  \BB  P  +  2#3           } ;
            C.T:=  {FOR  P  $E  C.T;  COLLECT
                    IF  -POWER(P)  &  P=BLUE  THEN
                            DO          P.P.Y::=   +  4+3  ;
                                        P.C:=  GREEN;
                        GIVE        P
                ELSE      P          FI            } ;
    GIVE    C                                       END      ENDDEFN
```

\NONBLUE augments the top of the cell C by placing a blue-to-green feedthrough just above each (nonpower) blue port. Each feedthrough is placed above the port so to maintain a 3 lambda separation between the port and the bottom of the feedthrough.

The first assignment appends to C's layout precisely these feedthroughs and also a short blue box to fill in the gap between each port and its feedthrough. The second assignment redefines C.T, the top ports, by moving up by 4+3 the Y-coordinates of those ports affected with the feedthroughs. (Four lambda is the height of a feedthrough). Refer to Figure 6.9A.

In general, we will modify a cell by adding new layout and by appropriately modifying ports. We will never delete or change a cell's existing layout.

This \NONBLUE function thus has added layout and compensated for this in the ports. In all cases, the result of \NONBLUE contains no blue nonpower ports.

6.2.2 Utilities for Ports

We add the operator

> ports   \S   signal   →   ports

to select the subset of ports that carry the given signal, i.e.,

```
DEFINE  S(X:PORTS  S:SIGNAL)= PORTS:    BEGIN    VAR  P=PORT;
    {COLLECT  P  FOR  P  $E  X;  WITH  P  \EQ  S;}        END      ENDDEFN
```

Similarly, we include an operator to remove from a set of ports all ports that carry a given signal:

> ports   \LESS   signal   →   ports

In addition, we will allow a set of ports to be interpreted as a set of points (a polygon) via

```
LET  PORTS  BECOME  POLYGON  BY    BEGIN  VAR  P=PORT;
        {COLLECT  P.P  FOR  P  $E  PORTS;}        END  ;
```

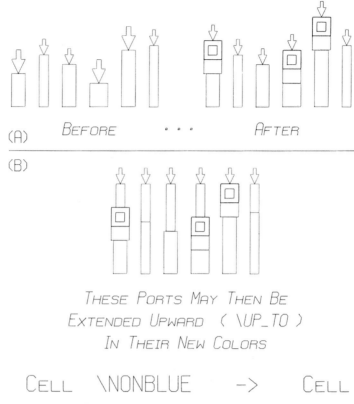

FIGURE 6.9   The \NONBLUE operator.

For example,

ports   \MBB

yields the smallest box that contains all of the given ports' positions.

The following operator produces a layout consisting of a single box:

port   \UP_TO   real   →   layout

\UP_TO takes a port (presumably a top port) and a Y value, and produces a layout that extends the port upward to Y:

```
DEFINE  UP_TO(P:PORT  Y:REAL)=  LAYOUT:              BEGIN     VAR  W  =  REAL  ;
     DO    W:=  WIDTH(P)    / 2. ;
     GIVE  IF  Y  >  P.Y  THEN     { P - W#0 ; P + W#0 ; P.X#Y }    \MBB
                                                   \PAINTED  P.C
            ELSE     NIL     FI                          END        ENDDEFN
```

The layout is a vertical box whose width and color are that of the port, and which extends up to Y. (The \MBB function used in this definition transforms the string of three points into the smallest enclosing box.) For example, refer to Figure 6.9B.

6.2.3   Sealing Power

The next function takes a cell and a signal (GND or VDD) and seals the top of the cell so that the power ports (GND or VDD) cease to exist on the top. Instead, a new power port

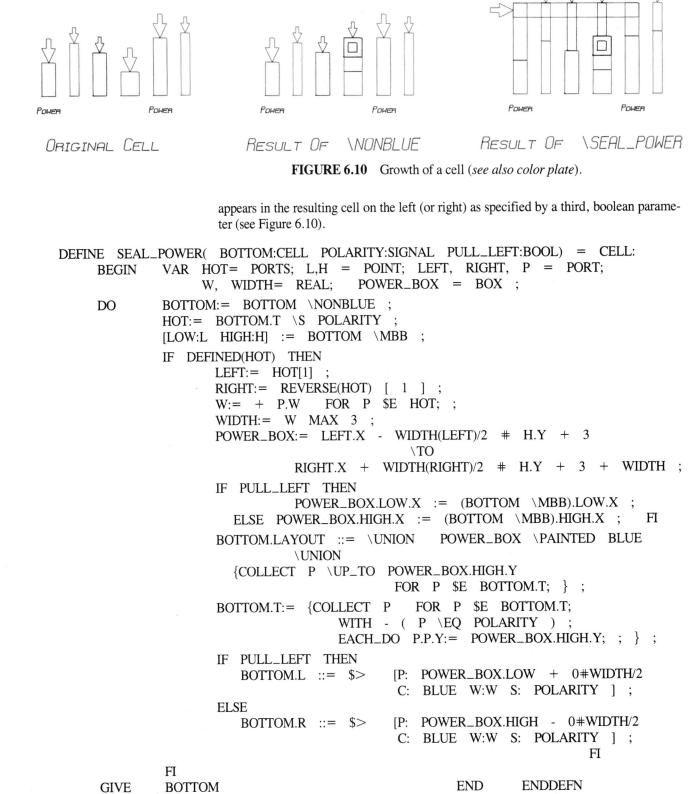

POWER   POWER   POWER   POWER   POWER   POWER

ORIGINAL CELL   *RESULT OF \NONBLUE*   *RESULT OF \SEAL_POWER*

FIGURE 6.10   Growth of a cell (*see also color plate*).

appears in the resulting cell on the left (or right) as specified by a third, boolean parameter (see Figure 6.10).

```
DEFINE  SEAL_POWER(  BOTTOM:CELL  POLARITY:SIGNAL  PULL_LEFT:BOOL)  =  CELL:
    BEGIN      VAR  HOT=  PORTS;  L,H  =  POINT;  LEFT,  RIGHT,  P  =  PORT;
               W,  WIDTH=  REAL;     POWER_BOX  =  BOX  ;

    DO         BOTTOM:=  BOTTOM \NONBLUE  ;
               HOT:=  BOTTOM.T \S  POLARITY  ;
               [LOW:L  HIGH:H]  :=  BOTTOM \MBB  ;

               IF  DEFINED(HOT)  THEN
                   LEFT:=  HOT[1]  ;
                   RIGHT:=  REVERSE(HOT)  [  1  ]  ;
                   W:=  +  P.W     FOR  P  $E  HOT;  ;
                   WIDTH:=  W  MAX  3  ;
                   POWER_BOX:=  LEFT.X  -  WIDTH(LEFT)/2  #  H.Y  +  3
                                                 \TO
                           RIGHT.X  +  WIDTH(RIGHT)/2  #  H.Y  +  3  +  WIDTH  ;

               IF  PULL_LEFT  THEN
                           POWER_BOX.LOW.X  :=  (BOTTOM \MBB).LOW.X  ;
                   ELSE  POWER_BOX.HIGH.X  :=  (BOTTOM \MBB).HIGH.X  ;     FI
               BOTTOM.LAYOUT  ::=  \UNION      POWER_BOX \PAINTED  BLUE
                               \UNION
                   {COLLECT  P  \UP_TO  POWER_BOX.HIGH.Y
                                       FOR  P  $E  BOTTOM.T;  }  ;

               BOTTOM.T:=  {COLLECT  P     FOR  P  $E  BOTTOM.T;
                               WITH  -  (  P  \EQ  POLARITY  )  ;
                               EACH_DO  P.P.Y:=  POWER_BOX.HIGH.Y;  ;  }  ;

               IF  PULL_LEFT  THEN
                   BOTTOM.L  ::=  $>     [P:  POWER_BOX.LOW  +  0#WIDTH/2
                                         C:  BLUE  W:W  S:  POLARITY  ]  ;
               ELSE
                   BOTTOM.R  ::=  $>     [P:  POWER_BOX.HIGH  -  0#WIDTH/2
                                         C:  BLUE  W:W  S:  POLARITY  ]  ;
                                                                       FI
                FI
    GIVE      BOTTOM                                    END      ENDDEFN
```

The first assignment renders all blue nonpower ports in green. The second assignment sets HOT to the set of all top ports that carry power of the specific POLARITY. These

HOT ports are precisely the set of top ports that will cease to exist. The third assignment sets L and H to the two corners of BOTTOM's MBB, so that L.X and H.X represent the horizontal span of BOTTOM.

If some power ports do exist (i.e., HOT is defined), the function sets LEFT and RIGHT so to refer to the two extreme power ports. It also computes the width W to represent the combined power consumption of all the HOT ports. The variable POWER_BOX is set to represent the blue wire to which all the HOT ports will connect. (POWER_BOX is made initially to span horizontally over all the power ports, and then either its left or right side is extended farther to an extreme edge of the cell BOTTOM, as directed by PULL_LEFT.)

The function then augments the cell's layout by including the POWER_BOX and an extension from each port up to the top of the power box. The HOT ports are then removed from the cell's "top" interface, and all remaining top ports are moved upward so to reside along the top of the power box.

Finally, a port is added on either the left or right sides, to represent the fact that the power requirement now resides on the left (or right) and no longer on the top. This port, of course, touches either the left or right edge of the blue power box. Notice that this new port has W in its W field; that is, this port "consumes" as much power as all the HOT ports consumed together.

The following version of SEAL_POWER defaults to pulling power out to the left:

```
DEFINE   SEAL_POWER(  BOTTOM:CELL   POLARITY:SIGNAL  )  =  CELL:
            SEAL_POWER(  BOTTOM,   POLARITY,   TRUE  )              ENDDEFN
```

Finally, we provide a function that seals power on both the left and right sides of a cell, so that a one-sided cell can be rendered without any (power) ports on the left or right. This facility will be useful so that we may place cells together horizontally in a row without having to consider (power) ports residing between cells.

This function, \SEAL_SIDE_POWER, first determines the power polarity of each of the left and right sides, and then seals that polarity of power on each side by calling \SEAL_POWER on the cell rotated by a quarter turn:

```
DEFINE   SEAL_SIDE_POWER(  C:CELL  )  =  CELL:
    BEGIN   VAR LP, RP  =  SIGNAL  ;   P  =  PORT  ;
    DO      " Determine the left and right polarities (LP and RP) ...  "
        LP:=   IF  FOR  P  $E  C.L;  THERE_IS  POWER(P)
               THEN   P        ELSE   NIL   FI    ;
        RP:=   IF  FOR  P  $E  C.R;  THERE_IS  POWER(P)
               THEN   P        ELSE   NIL   FI    ;
        IF  DEFINED(LP)  THEN
            " Seal left side "
            C:=  SEAL_POWER(  C \ROT_CW, LP, LP \EQ THE_GND_SIGNAL  )
                    \ROT_CCW;          FI
        IF  DEFINED(RP)  THEN
            " Seal right side "
            C:=  SEAL_POWER(  C \ROT_CCW, RP, RP \EQ THE_VDD_SIGNAL  )
                    \ROT_CW ;          FI
    GIVE        C                      END      ENDDEFN
```

Once the polarity of each side is determined, this function calls \SEAL_POWER on the cell rotated clockwise (to seal left power) and then it does the same on the cell rotated counterclockwise (to seal right power). (Each of these two assignments undoes the rotation after calling SEAL_POWER.) The second parameter to \SEAL_POWER, the polarity, is given by LP (and then RP). The PULL_LEFT boolean parameter is carefully

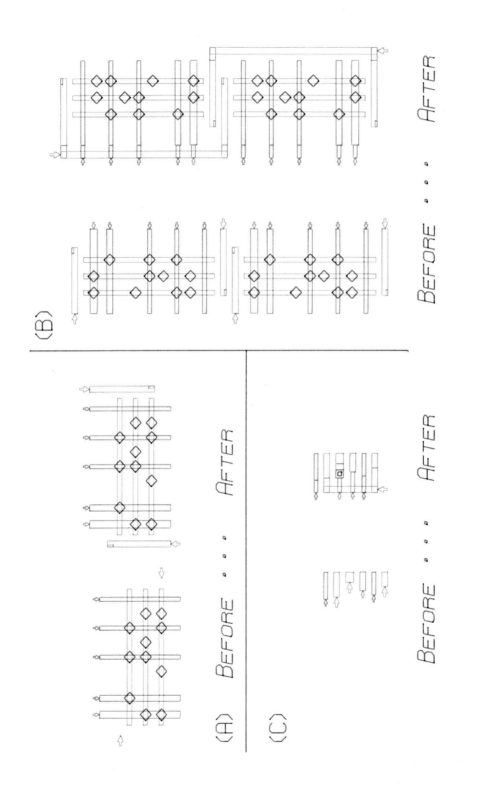

FIGURE 6.11 Examples of \SEAL_SIDE_POWER (*see also color plate*).

chosen so that after the un-rotation, a GND polarity will appear on the bottom side and a VDD polarity will appear on the top, all to satisfy convention #6 about power and ground orientation. (Refer to Figure 6.11.)

6.2.4 Placement of Sets of CELLs

The function \DX takes in a set of cells and a REAL separation, and returns the same set of cells now placed in a horizontal row where adjacent cells are separated by the specified REAL (Figure 6.12A):

```
DEFINE  DX(CS:CELLS  DX:REAL)=  CELLS:
     BEGIN     VAR  C=  CELL;  LEFT,X,Y=  REAL;
          {COLLECT  C     FOR  C  $E  CS;
               FIRST_DO          LEFT:=  0;;
               EACH_DO           C::=  \AT  -(C\MBB).LOW  +  LEFT#0  ;
                                 LEFT:=  (C\MBB).HIGH.X  +  DX;  ;     }
     END       ENDDEFN
```

The EACH_DO clause displaces each cell C in the set so that the cell's lower-left corner resides at LEFT#0. [The displacement

$$- (C \backslash MBB) . LOW + LEFT \# 0$$

represents two movements: first, C's lower left corner moves to 0#0, and then to LEFT#0.] LEFT is then set to the right-hand edge of the placed cell C, plus DX, to prepare for the next iteration.

The next function, \UNION_DX, takes in a set of cells and a separation, but returns a single cell. It aligns the given cells via \DX and then forms the \UNION of their layouts. \UNION_DX also asserts that no ports reside between cells, after having applied \SEAL_SIDE_POWER to each cell (Figure 6.12B):

```
DEFINE  UNION_DX(  HORZ:CELLS  SEP:REAL  )  =  CELL:
     BEGIN     VAR  C  =  CELL  ;
     DO        HORZ:=  {COLLECT  C  \SEAL_SIDE_POWER  FOR  C  $E  HORZ;  }
                         \DX  3  ;
               ASSUME(  NEVER  DEFINED(C.L)  !  DEFINED(C.R)  FOR  C  $E  HORZ;  ,
                         'Side  ports  exist'  );
     GIVE      [LAYOUT:          {COLLECT  C.LAYOUT  FOR  C  $E  HORZ;  }
               T:     $$   C.T   FOR  C  $E  HORZ;
               B:     $$   C.B   FOR  C  $E  HORZ;          ]  END  ENDDEFN
```

The first assignment aligns the set of cells, rendered as a set of sealed cells, via \DX. The ASSUME statement asserts that no cell in the set has any left or right ports. (ASSUME writes an error message if this assumption is violated; it should never be violated.) The resulting cell has as layout the union of the carefully placed cells' layouts. The top ports are formed simply by the concatenation of all the cells' top ports, and the same for the bottom ports.

Because this function produces a new cell, we would like to verify that this new cell satisfies all the one-sided cell conventions. First, we can see that the T and B ports are ordered left to right (conventions 1 and 2) because each C.T in this concatenation is assumed to be so ordered, and adjacent cells in HORZ appear strictly left to right due to \DX.

Second, conventions 3 and 4 are satisfied because each top port in each cell C has unhindered vertical clearance; that is, we have added no layout above any ports. We

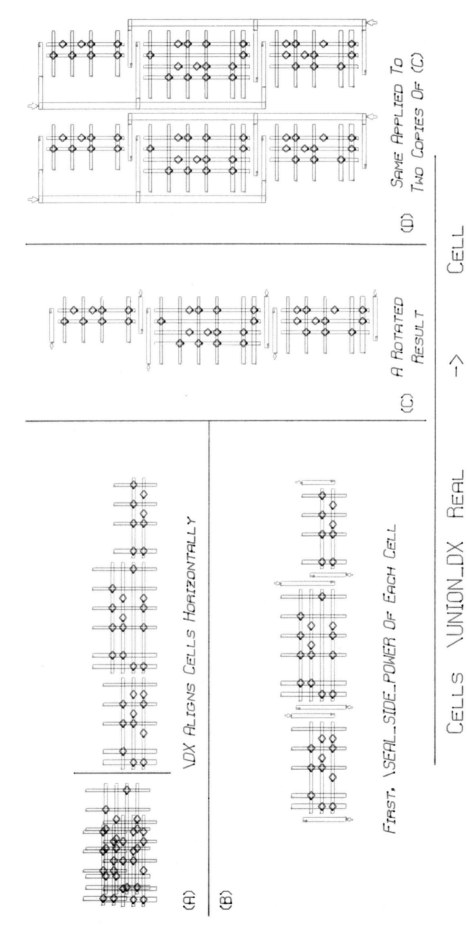

Cells \UNION_DX Real →〉 Cell

FIGURE 6.12 Examples of \UNION_DX (*see also color plate*).

278

must be careful, however, to assure the maintenance of the required 10-lambda width of clearance for interior ports, and also the 7-lambda separation between adjacent ports.

We are assured of the minimum separation between adjacent top ports within each cell C (by assumption), so we need verify only that each pair of adjacent ports that spans over two adjacent cells is separated sufficiently.

If the two extreme ports along the top edge of any cell each resides at least 2 lambda from the (left or right) edge, the 3-lambda separation between cells contributes to a total of at least 7-lambda separation between the positions of adjacent pairs of ports from distinct cells. In addition, such an assumption would guarantee the 10-lambda width of clearance required by convention 4a; that is, a 5-lambda half-width is guaranteed by the 3-lambda cell separation and the assumed 2-lambda distance between the port center and the edge of the cell.

Thus we can prove adherence to convention 4 if we assume that the positions of the two extreme ports along the top edge of any cell each lies at least 2 lambda from the edge. The latter condition would be easy to prove if we knew, for example, that all ports had half-widths of at least this 2 lambda. However, ports may have half-widths of as little as 1 lambda. Hence, to prove convention 4, we have a choice of two methods:

1 Increase the separation between an adjacent pair of cells if the adjacent pair of top ports straddling the two cells has separation less than 4 lambda.

2 Introduce a new convention which states that the extreme ports of each edge of a cell must have positions lying at least 2 lambda inward from the two endpoints of that edge.

We will adopt the second proposition simply because it is true for the PLA cell and all cells that will result from fusion in this silicon compiler.

Convention 6 is satisfied because each cell C by itself demands no GND on top nor any VDD on the bottom, and because new power ports added by \SEAL_SIDE_POWER have been chosen carefully in \SEAL_SIDE_POWER so that all new VDD ports lie on top and all new GND ports lie on the bottom.

Convention 5 is maintained in this new cell, although we prove this in a backward way. Convention 5 unlike the other convention specifies not a constraint, but instead a service. Because the ports C.T of each cell C appear as top ports in the result, the services provided by convention 5 on this resulting cell serve equally well upon each cell C individually. Not only do equal signals along the top of each cell C alone imply interconnections within C itself, but in addition, equal signals resident in distinct cells contribute new implied interconnections. This new implication by itself provides for the interconnection among the entire set of cells.

Finally, we are assured that no signals of any cell C in the set are lost. The ASSUME statement relieves the need to consider left and right ports for each C. The top and bottom ports for each cell C continue to appear on the resulting cell.

6.2.5 The Completion of Fusion for One-Sided Cells

The function \UNION_DX, in fact, fuses cells together to form one cell. However, if we used \UNION_DX to fuse all cells, the total number of ports of the finished chip (as a cell) would equal the sum of the numbers of ports taken over all subcells (i.e., no ports would drop out of the picture). In addition, the finished chip would be very long horizontally and very short vertically.

There is a principle in both hardware and software design which helps lead to efficient implementations. That principle suggests that a functional piece of layout (or software) be encapsulated so that all communications between it and its surrounding environment become well defined, and small enough in number so as to maintain understandability. This principle emerges for layouts also via a geometric argument: A large number of communications (signals) required between two cells leads to more wires connecting the two cells, and hence to more area. Wires for communication between cells often occupy the majority of the area in many designs.

In addition, when only a subset of ports on a cell carry signals that are to communicate with other cells, it is most efficient to have those ports located as closely to one another as possible, so as to accommodate, if necessary, a long cable of wires having minimal physical width.

Our LOGIC_CELL datatype conforms to this principle because of all signals involved in its equations and subcells, the LOGIC_CELL specifies explicitly in its interface (INPUTS and OUTPUTS) precisely the subset of all signals that are meant to communicate with the outside world. For example, if we used \UNION_DX exclusively to fuse subcells, the top ports of the resulting very long cell would include an abundance of noninterface ports; for example, it would include besides the interface signals, all those signals used for communication among subcells, among the subcells' subcells, and so on. This giant set of ports would, in fact, expose all signals involved in the entire LOGIC_CELL. This effect certainly conflicts with the principle of limited interface.

We will now accommodate this need to focus together ports carrying interface signals, leaving behind noninterface ports. We will provide an operator

$$\text{cells} \quad \backslash\text{PACK} \quad \text{signals} \quad \rightarrow \quad \text{cell}$$

which like our \UNION_DX operator, fuses the given cells together to form one cell, but in addition, it focuses together those ports which carry the signals specified in the second parameter, leaving behind all other nonpower ports. This operator is our official fusion algorithm for one-sided cells.

As Figure 6.13 shows, \PACK simultaneously provides complete interconnect among the given cells while bringing to the left precisely those signals specified in the second parameter. \PACK finally rotates this result simply to maintain the one-sided property that requires ports to reside along the top (and not left) edge.

This rotation also relieves the phenomenon arising from an exclusive use of \UNION_DX: the generation of very long but thin layouts. The rotation renders long thin cells into tall slim cells. These tall slim cells themselves pack together horizontally very nicely to form layouts tending toward a square shape. Thus, the rotation breaks an otherwise very linear growth.

6.2.5.1 Interconnect: flying to produce one scan line. \PACK forms the necessary interconnect by first applying \UNION_DX to transform the given set of cells into a single (wide) cell (Figure 6.13B). \PACK then produces the interconnect above this fused cell.

\PACK constructs one horizontal slab of interconnect at a time. That is, the interconnect shown in Figure 6.13C has been formed by first producing the lowest horizontal row of activity in its entirety. This lowest horizontal row of interconnect, when placed above the cell, changes slightly the appearance of the top edge of that cell; some ports disappear. Those ports that are connected together by this lowest "scan line" cease to appear on the top of this slightly augmented cell.

\PACK then paints another layer of interconnect, the second scan line, on the augmented cell, and as the result we get a doubly augmented cell that has even fewer ports remaining on the top edge. \PACK repeatedly adds scan lines until no ports appear along the top edge.

We now embark on the generation of individual scan lines. We can understand the generation of a scan line by analogy with skywriting airplanes. Imagine the set of (top) ports as the ground, and imagine that we are flying an airplane at a specific altitude above this ground. The altitude at which we fly is the Y-coordinate of the scan line we are about to generate.

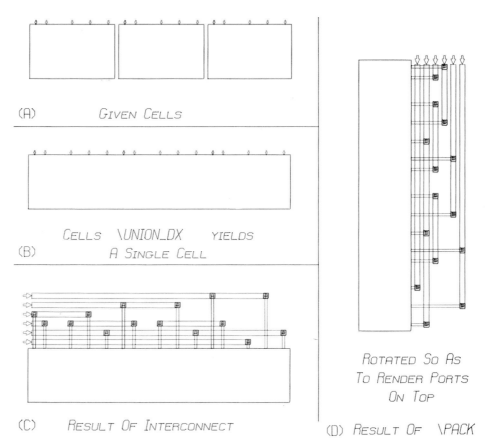

(A)   GIVEN CELLS

(B)   CELLS \UNION_DX   YIELDS A SINGLE CELL

(C)   RESULT OF INTERCONNECT

ROTATED SO AS TO RENDER PORTS ON TOP

(D) RESULT OF \PACK

FIGURE 6.13   One-sided cell fusion.

We begin our flight from the left side and end it on the right side. Starting from the left, we fly to the right until we notice a port on the ground directly beneath us. At this point, we turn on the smoke, that is, begin drawing a blue horizontal wire. We keep the smoke turned on even as we pass above other ports. We turn off the smoke only when we pass over the rightmost port which carries the same signal as that carried by our starting port. This final matching port marks the end of the new blue wire.

The flight toward the right continues with the smoke off, until we pass over the very next port, at which time we turn the smoke back on, that is, begin drawing a new blue wire. This flight continues, following the same flight plan (smoke algorithm) until we reach the right-hand edge of the cell, where there are no more ports below.

This single scan line flight is recursive, at least the way we have described it. As soon as we turn off the smoke, we in fact begin a new flight (without moving the airplane) following this identical algorithm.

Upon completion of such a flight, we have a set of nonintersecting blue wire(s) lying all at the same altitude. We augment this blue layout and connect it to the matching ports below by providing from each matching port below one new nonblue wire, reaching from the matching port below up to the blue wire. We finally "staple" that nonblue vertical wire onto the blue horizontal wire by providing a feedthrough at their intersection. It is precisely the sets of matching ports below the blue wire(s) which cease to exist as top ports after the flight is completed. Only the rest of the top ports continue to exist as top ports; these remaining ports have not yet been subject to interconnection.

Figure 6.14 illustrates this process. This process does require, of course, that all ports be nonblue, so that they may be extended upward arbitrarily high without touching any of the new (blue) layout being added.

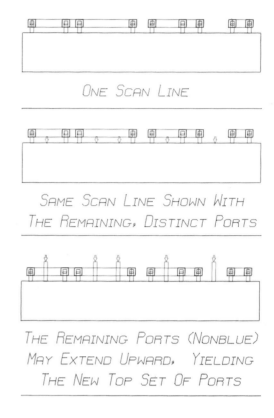

ONE SCAN LINE

SAME SCAN LINE SHOWN WITH
THE REMAINING, DISTINCT PORTS

THE REMAINING PORTS (NONBLUE)
MAY EXTEND UPWARD, YIELDING
THE NEW TOP SET OF PORTS

A "SCAN LINE" OF INTERCONNECT
AFFECTS THE TOP PORTS

FIGURE 6.14

A repeated use of this flying algorithm to form many scan lines at increasing altitudes can remove ultimately all top ports. Upon such completion, we can say that this algorithm has maintained convention 5 because each set of matching ports (ports carrying the same signal) has all its members connected to the same blue wire. In addition, our care in maintaining port visibility (by running all horizontal wires in blue and all vertical wires in nonblue) assures that no ports of distinct signals become connected.

This algorithm not only provides complete interconnection among the top set of ports, but it also can be coaxed into bringing interface signals outward to the left edge of the augmented cell. \PACK tricks the pilots into bringing signals out to the left simply by introducing one additional top port for each interface signal. These fake top ports are created so to reside to the left of the cell, as shown in Figure 6.15. As this figure suggests, we come back afterward to clip off this left appendage and then acquire the desired availability of interace signals on the left.

\PACK will, in fact, introduce these fake interface ports, and will also place them all along the same vertical axis, just to the left of the leftmost real (top) port. The vertical spacing will be chosen to match precisely the set of altitudes of the first scan lines. The vertical positions will affect the pilots so to result directly with Figure 6.15C without the need for clipping (after Figure 6.15B). That is, the first three scan lines will each start naturally with one of the three fake ports. When each scan line becomes stapled to matching ports below, the vertical placements of these three fake ports will render vertical wires of length zero. We will check for such zero-length vertical extensions in the flying algorithm so to avoid drawing such zero length vertical wires and their corresponding feedthroughs.

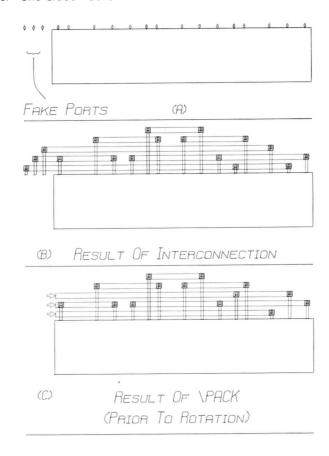

FAKE PORTS   (A)

(B)   RESULT OF INTERCONNECTION

(C)   RESULT OF \PACK
             (PRIOR TO ROTATION)

\PACK TRICKS THE \FLY_AT OPERATOR
SO AS TO BRING SOME SIGNALS
TO THE LEFT

FIGURE 6.15

6.2.5.2 The \FLY_AT operator. Inherent in the flying algorithm is the need to know at once all ports of the same signal. This need arises primarily because the airplane needs to know when to stop drawing the blue wire. That is, the pilot must be able to detect the last (rightmost) port in a set of matching ports. (It would be more difficult to have the pilot realize that the airplane has overshot the final matching port too late, when the airplane reaches the right-hand edge. The pilot in this case would have to back up and erase a portion of the now-overextended blue wire.)

We represent an entire set of matching ports with the datatype CONNECTION:

    TYPE   CONNECTION = PORTS ;

Unlike most sets of ports, a CONNECTION is a set of ports all of whose members carry the same signal. The entire set of ports atop the cell can be represented as a set of CONNECTIONs:

    TYPE   CONNECTIONS = { CONNECTION } ;

The type CONNECTIONS can represent each and every port, but it groups all ports into distinct sets of matching ports.

This type is also known as a "wire list." It represents explicitly all distinct sets of interconnecting ports; that is, all ports of each CONNECTION are meant to be connected together. In fact, the signals represented in each port cease to be required; the grouping of ports by itself is now sufficient specification.

We translate a set of ports, say, the top edge of a cell, into a CONNECTIONS via the \MATE operator:

```
DEFINE    MATE( TOP:PORTS )  =  CONNECTIONS:
     BEGIN  VAR  C  =  CONNECTION  ;
     IF  DEFINED(TOP)  THEN
              DO      C:=  TOP  \S  TOP[1].S  ;
                      IF - DEFINED( C[2-] )  THEN    C:= NIL;         FI
              GIVE    C  <$  ( TOP  \LESS  TOP[1].S    \MATE  )
     ELSE   NIL    FI                                  END       ENDDEFN
```

\MATE translates a set of ports, TOP, into a CONNECTIONS, with the aid of recursion. It sets C, a CONNECTION, to the set of ports in TOP whose signals match the signal contained in the first port in TOP. If the entire set of matching ports does not contain two or more ports, then C is set to NIL; that is, we ignore the lonely, noncommunicating port by omitting its existence from the resulting set of CONNECTIONS. (Convention 5 makes no statements about such singleton matching sets.) \MATE finally produces as the entire CONNECTIONS this first CONNECTION, C, and the result of MATing together all remaining ports (i.e., all ports carrying a different signal).

This rendition of \MATE produces a set CONNECTIONS that has a useful property. First, the equivalent ports in each CONNECTION are ordered from left to right because TOP is presumably ordered from left to right due to convention 1. In addition, each CONNECTION in the set of CONNECTIONS is ordered from left to right when we choose to look at the first port in each CONNECTION. For example, the first CONNECTION contains the very leftmost port, and the second CONNECTION contains the leftmost port whose signal differs from the signal of the very leftmost port. This particular order facilitates implicitly the production of an optimized interconnection.

The \FLY_AT operator's definition follows, and it can be considered as the heart of the entire interconnection process because it produces the individual scan lines. \FLY_AT takes in the set of top ports represented as a set CONNECTIONS, and an altitude. It produces an object of type CONN_STATUS:

```
TYPE    CONN_STATUS  =  [ DO: CONNECTIONS    LAYOUT: LAYOUT ]  ;
```

We might like to think that \FLY_AT produces merely a layout (i.e., the scan line). However, \FLY_AT not only produces a layout, but it also removes some CONNECTIONS from those it receives as input. Recall that the flying algorithm removes from the entire set of ports precisely those ports that have become interconnected by the resulting scan line. Therefore, \FLY_AT yields a CONN_STATUS, which represents both the layout and the subset of CONNECTIONS that remain untouched by this scan line.

The repeated use of \FLY_AT, which builds the complete set of scan lines, passes to each higher \FLY_AT precisely the subset of CONNECTIONS left undone by the previous scan line. Initially, the DO field of a CONN_STATUS contains all CONNECTIONS, and upon completion of producing all scan lines, the DO field becomes empty.

```
DEFINE   FLY_AT( FLOOR: CONNECTIONS Y: REAL )  =  CONN_STATUS:
     BEGIN    VAR  L,H  =  POINT;   REST  =  CONN_STATUS ; P = PORT ;
     IF  DEFINED(FLOOR)  THEN
         DO   [LOW:L  HIGH:H]  :=  FLOOR[1]  \MBB  ;
              REST:=  FLOOR[2-]  \RIGHT_OF  H.X    \FLY_AT  Y  ;
```

```
GIVE [LAYOUT:    L.X   #   Y-2     \BB    H.X   #   Y+2                    \UNION
                 REST.LAYOUT                                              \UNION
        {COLLECT    {  IF   P=RED    THEN   RCB
                       EF   P=GREEN  THEN   GCB
                       ELSE NIL    FI            \AT   P.X#Y  ;
                       P  \UP_TO  Y    }
                 FOR  P  $E  FLOOR[1];  WITH  P.Y  <   Y; }
          DO:    (  FLOOR[2-]  \LEFT_OF  H.X  )     $$    REST.DO  ]
ELSE    NIL    FI                                                    END       ENDDEFN
```

Most of the work is done in the first two lines of this function. Assuming that the FLOOR (the set of CONNECTIONS over which we fly) exists, \FLY_AT computes the MBB of the set of ports contained in the first CONNECTION. This MBB contains the X-coordinates (L.X and H.X) of the entire blue wire which will implement this first CONNECTION. Before \FLY_AT even produces this first blue wire, it first calls itself recursively so to complete the flight onward to the far right.

Since the recursive flight continues at the same altitude, we must remove from its domain all ports that lie under our blue wire, lest it produce a blue wire that intersects ours. The result of this recursive flight is a CONN_STATUS, assigned to REST. REST therefore includes both the layout produced to the right in the recursive flight and also the entire set of CONNECTIONS left undone to the right of H.X.

\FLY_AT produces a CONN_STATUS whose layout consists of three parts. The first part is the blue wire, of thickness 4, centered vertically about the altitude Y. The second part is the layout generated by the recursive flight to the right. The third part is a collection of layouts, one for each port in the CONNECTION implemented by our blue wire. Each port contributes a feedthrough of the appropriate color residing directly above the port at the altitude of the blue wire. Contributed also is a vertical wire reaching from the port up to the blue wire and feedthrough. Such contributions from (fake) ports which lie at or above the altitude Y are omitted (due to the WITH clause).

\FLY_AT yields in the DO component of the resulting CONN_STATUS precisely the subset of CONNECTIONs left undone by this flight at altitude Y. The undone CONNECTIONs include all CONNECTIONs to the left of H.X (i.e., those CONNECTIONs not even considered by the recursive flight) less the very first CONNECTION, the one we just completed. Also undone are all those CONNECTIONs left undone by the recursive flight itself (REST.DO).

The \RIGHT_OF and \LEFT_OF operators:

```
connections   \RIGHT_OF   real       →     connections
connections   \LEFT_OF    real       →     connections
```

are defined by

```
DEFINE  RIGHT_OF(  X:CONNECTIONS  LEFT:REAL  )=  CONNECTIONS:
    BEGIN    VAR  CONN  =  CONNECTION  ;
    {COLLECT CONN    FOR  CONN $E  X;  WITH  CONN[1].X  >  LEFT; }
    END       ENDDEFN
DEFINE  LEFT_OF(  X:CONNECTIONS  RIGHT:REAL  )=  CONNECTIONS:
    BEGIN    VAR  CONN  =  CONNECTION  ;
    {COLLECT CONN    FOR  CONN $E  X;  WITH  CONN[1].X  <  RIGHT; }
    END       ENDDEFN
```

Each of these operators decides the "left of" and "right of" status of a CONNECTION based entirely on the first (leftmost) port in the CONNECTION. Thus, \RIGHT_OF yields all CONNECTIONS whose ports all lie to the right of the REAL parameter.

(\FLY_AT requires this interpretation so that the result of \RIGHT_OF, the parameter for the recursive flight, will include only CONNECTIONS all of whose ports lie to the right of H.X.) The \LEFT_OF operator yields precisely all CONNECTIONS omitted by \RIGHT_OF.

6.2.5.3 *The fusion operator for one-sided cells:* \PACK. The \PACK operator is defined as follows. The first assignment by itself fuses together the given set of cells via \UNION_DX and seals off the power requirements of all the cell tops. The rest of \PACK provides the interconnect:

```
DEFINE    PACK(CS:CELLS  SS:SIGNALS)=  CELL:
    BEGIN    VAR  LEFT  =  PORTS;  BASE,INCR,Y,X=  REAL;  S=  SIGNAL;
                    C=  CELL;  POL=  PORT;  INTERCONNECT,  MEAT  =  LAYOUT;
                    TOP  =  CONNECTIONS  ;
    IF  DEFINED( CS[2-] )     THEN
      DO      C:=  CS \UNION_DX 3    \SEAL_POWER  THE_VDD_SIGNAL  ;
              BASE:=  (C\MBB).HIGH.Y  +  5  ;
              INCR:=  7;
              LEFT:=  {COLLECT  [P:  X#Y  S:S  C:BLUE  W:4]
                          FOR  S  $E  SS  \UNIQUE;  &&  FOR  Y  FROM  BASE  BY  INCR;
                              INITIALLY         X:=  C.T[1].X  -  2;  ;  }  ;
              INTERCONNECT:=
                  {  FOR  Y  FROM  BASE  BY  INCR;
                          INITIALLY      TOP:=    LEFT  $$  C.T    \MATE  ;  ;
                      &&     WHILE  DEFINED(  TOP  )  ;
                      EACH_DO  [DO:TOP    LAYOUT:MEAT]:=  TOP  \FLY_AT  Y;;
                              COLLECT            MEAT    }  ;
      GIVE  [  L:    C.L  $$  LEFT
              B:    C.B
              R:    C.R
              LAYOUT:          INTERCONNECT    \UNION  C.LAYOUT          ]
              \ROT_CW           \SWAPPABLE
    ELSE   CS[1]    FI              END      ENDDEFN
```

The overall IF-THEN-ELSE statement specifies that unless the set of cells contains at least two cells, then do not bother to provide interconnect; the one cell in the set by itself stands as the result.

\PACK, in the first assignment, sets C to represent the cell produced by \UNION_DX (Figure 6.16A). Since this cell may have power requirements along the top edge, this assignment also seals all power requirements along the top edge. (The \SEAL_POWER operator replaces the top power consumptions by one power consumption residing on the left side of C. The choice to seal of the VDD polarity of power is necessary and sufficient due to convention 6.) Figure 6.15B shows the effects of \SEAL_POWER. We have chosen to seal power first because we wish always to route power entirely in blue, and hence the interconnect produced by \FLY_AT must not route power for us; \FLY_AT uses nonblue (vertical) wires.

This \SEAL_POWER operation also renders all remaining top ports in nonblue colors. Thus, the rest of \PACK can use \FLY_AT with the assurance that no ports will contribute blue vertical wires. (Blue is used entirely for \FLY_AT's horzontal wires, which must never short accidentally with vertical wires).

\PACK produces interconnections by calling \FLY_AT repeatedly. \PACK sets BASE to the first (and lowest) altitude, chosen to be the minimum distance above the top of cell C. An altitude increment of 7 is chosen, again; this is the smallest increment

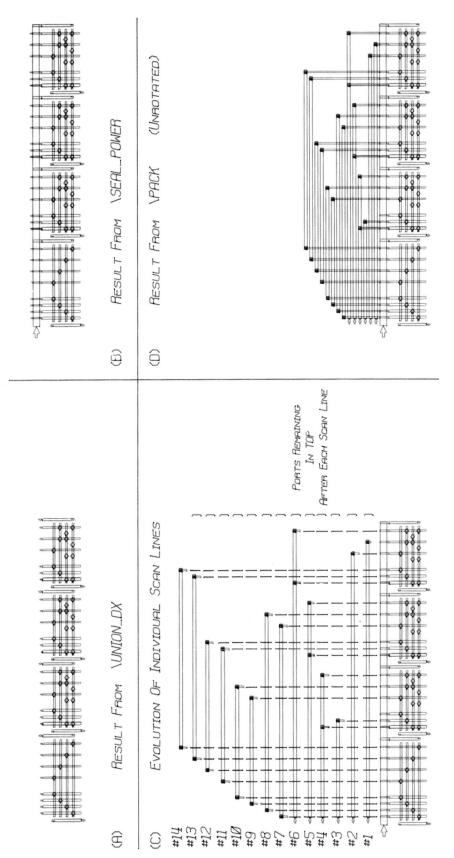

(A) RESULT FROM \UNION_DX

(B) RESULT FROM \SEAL_POWER

(C) EVOLUTION OF INDIVIDUAL SCAN LINES

(D) RESULT FROM \PACK   (UNROTATED)

PORTS REMAINING
IN TOP
AFTER EACH SCAN LINE

#14
#13
#12
#11
#10
#9
#8
#7
#6
#5
#4
#3
#2
#1

FIGURE 6.16

287

allowed by design rules between blue wires that contain feedthroughs. \PACK then defines LEFT, the vertical set of ports for interface signals. These will appear on the left side of the finished cell.

\PACK assigns to INTERCONNECT the entire set of scan-line layouts produced by repeated calls to \FLY_AT. The quantifier defines the altitude Y, for each scan line, and initially defines TOP to be the entire set of CONNECTIONS derived by \MATE for all the top ports of C together with the LEFT interface ports. (LEFT is included in the mating so to cause \FLY_AT to bring these interface signals out to the left side.) This scan-line altitude quantifier, which will by itself produce forever higher and higher altitudes, is made to iterate only as long as TOP remains nonempty.

Each iteration of this quantifier calls \FLY_AT in the EACH_DO clause. \FLY_AT produces one scan line, a CONN_STATUS, and the EACH_DO clause assigns the layout to MEAT and the undone CONNECTIONs back into TOP. Thus, this entire expression assigns to INTERCONNECT the collection of the values of MEAT, the layouts produced for each scan line.

Each iteration finds TOP modified from the previous iteration. TOP keeps shrinking on each iteration, representing the fewer and fewer undone CONNECTIONs. The loop terminates when TOP dwindles to nothing, and TOP always dwindles to nothing in finite time. Each call to \FLY_AT removes at least one CONNECTION from TOP, unless TOP is already empty. Figure 6.16C shows the evolution of scan lines.

Notice how \PACK produces interconnect without regard for whether the interconnected ports come from the same cell or different cells.

\PACK yields the complete cell whose layout consists of the interconnect together with C's layout (the layouts of all the given cells with power sealed). The L ports consist of C's left ports (e.g., VDD from \SEAL_POWER) and then the LEFT ports, the interface signals of the interconnect. The other sets of (power) ports are taken from C. There are no top ports; the interconnect has removed all top ports.

Finally, \PACK rotates the cell so that the nonpower ports come to reside on the top as opposed to the left side. This rotation thus renders a legal one-sided cell. This result is subjected to the \SWAPPABLE operator so to consume only minimal computer memory.

6.2.6   Translation from LOGIC_CELL to Layout CELL

The entire translation from a LOGIC_CELL to a CELL is specified in the operator

$$\text{logic\_cell} \quad \text{\textbackslash CELL} \qquad \rightarrow \qquad \text{cell}$$

defined by

```
DEFINE  CELL( L:LOGIC_CELL )  =  CELL:
     BEGIN    VAR  L1  =  LOGIC_CELL  ;
     IF  DEFINED(L)  THEN
          SYMBOLIC( L.EQUATIONS )  \ROT_CW      <$
               {COLLECT L1 \CELL  FOR  L1  $E  L.SUBCELLS;}
               \PACK        L.INPUTS  $$  L.OUTPUTS
ELSE    NIL    FI                                          END      ENDDEFN
```

This function calls \PACK, passing in as the set of cells to be connected the logic cell's equations rendered as a symbolic PLA CELL and also all the logic cell's subcells each rendered as a CELL (recursively). The symbolic PLA is rotated so to render its nonpower ports on the top (i.e., to render it as a legal one-sided cell). The other cells, the logic cell's subcells, are already legal simply because each is the result of this \CELL function. The second parameter to \PACK, the interface signals, is precisely the set of input and output signals making up the interface of the logic cell. The result of this \CELL operator is a legal one-sided cell because it is the result of \PACK applied to legal subcells.

If we replace the call to SYMBOLIC by a call to a functional PLA generator, this \CELL function will produce working layouts. However, since a functional PLA would require the clock signals ph1 and ph2, we would need to include these two signals in addition to L.INPUTS and L.OUTPUTS in the second parameter to \PACK. Ph1 and ph2 are implicit interface signals.

In conclusion, \CELL maps a LOGIC_CELL into a layout CELL whose nonpower ports are precisely the LOGIC_CELL's interface signals. We see finally how important a role LOGIC_CELLs' interfaces play in layout generation. These interfaces serve to keep communication paths as narrow as possible. Figure 6.17 shows the following:

(A) COUNTER(3) \CELL

(B) EQ(3) \CELL

(C) REGISTER(6) \CELL

(D) FD \CELL

6.2.7 Example: A Very Recursive Rendition for a Counter

To give a larger view for how \CELL translates a logic cell into a layout, we introduce another logic cell example:

$$\text{integer} \quad \backslash \text{CNT} \qquad \rightarrow \qquad \text{logic\_cell}$$

Unlike the COUNTER(integer) logic_cell, where the integer specifies the number of counter bits, the integer parameter to \CNT specifies the logarithm of the number of counter bits. Thus,

$$0 \quad \backslash \text{CNT} \qquad \rightarrow \qquad \text{1-bit} \quad \text{counter}$$
$$1 \quad \backslash \text{CNT} \qquad \rightarrow \qquad \text{2-bit} \quad \text{counter}$$
$$4 \quad \backslash \text{CNT} \qquad \rightarrow \qquad \text{16-bit} \quad \text{counter}$$
$$6 \quad \backslash \text{CNT} \qquad \rightarrow \qquad \text{64-bit} \quad \text{counter}$$

The definition for \CNT follows:

```
DEFINE  CNT(  N:INT  )  =  LOGIC_CELL:
    BEGIN     VAR  LEFT,RIGHT=LOGIC_CELL;
       IF  N=0  THEN            COUNTER_BIT
       ELSE    DO    LEFT:= N-1\CNT;          RIGHT:= N-1\CNT;
          GIVE    [SUBCELLS:      {LEFT;RIGHT}
                   INPUTS:        { RIGHT  \S  'CARRY_IN'  ;
                                    RIGHT  \S  'RESET_IN'      }
                   OUTPUTS:       { LEFT  \S  'CARRY_OUT'  ;
                                    LEFT  \SS  'VALUE'  $$
                                        (RIGHT  \SS  'VALUE')
                                            \NAMED  'VALUE'      }
                   EQUATIONS:     { LEFT  \S  'CARRY_IN'  \EQU
                                            RIGHT  \S  'CARRY_OUT'  ;
                                    LEFT  \S  'RESET_IN'  \EQU
                                            RIGHT  \S  'RESET_IN'  }  ]
    FI                        END    ENDDEFN
```

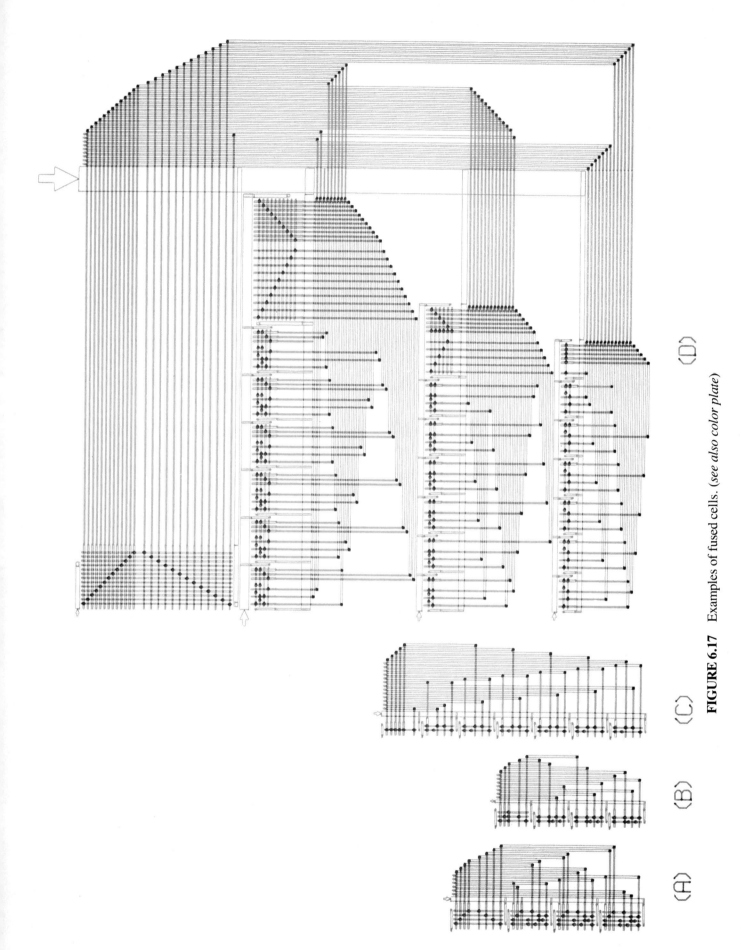

⟨A⟩ ⟨B⟩ ⟨C⟩ ⟨D⟩

FIGURE 6.17 Examples of fused cells. (*see also color plate*)

This function yields simply COUNTER_BIT, a 1-bit counter, if N=0. Otherwise, it sets LEFT and RIGHT each to a counter having half the desired number of bits. The result references LEFT and RIGHT as subcells, and feeds inputs to RIGHT and yields outputs from LEFT. In addition, the outputs include the concatenation of the 'VALUE' outputs from LEFT and RIGHT. This large set of is assigned a unique subscript (from one to the number of bits). Finally, the EQUATIONS connect the carry chain between the two halves, and feed our input (RIGHT \S 'RESET_IN') also to LEFT.

Figure 6.18 shows

    CNT(4)   \CELL

6.3 SKETCH OF A SILICON ASSEMBLER AND A FUNCTIONAL PLA

Let us introduce a few CELL operators which provide for the rapid combination of tiny cells. Each of these operators is relatively straightforward to implement, and together they constitute a silicon "assembler." We may use these operators to produce a functional PLA.

The material presented in this section is not essential for understanding other sections.

We distinguish between the CELL operators presented in this sketch and all other CELL operators presented throughout the rest of this text. The cell operators presented here have the following pair of properties.

"Assembler" properties:

1 These operators do not by themselves guarantee the absence of design rule errors in the result, but

2 These operators provide the capability to construct automatically very efficient layouts.

In contrast, all other CELL operators we have and will consider have the following corresponding pair of properties.

"Compiler" properties:

1 The operators do always guarantee that the result adheres to design rules, but

2 The result may include a slight overhead in layout area.

We use the terms "assembler" and "compiler" to denote a similar distinction found in the software domain:

1 An assembler allows people to specify arbitrary programs that may exhibit "profound" errors. In addition, these programs run extremely efficiently on the computer.

2 A compiler allows people to specify a less flexible class of programs, but ensures the absence of "profound" errors. However, these programs may run a little more slowly than assembly language programs.

A "profound" error can be understood only in terms of the actual computer on which the program runs. Other errors, in contrast, can be understood entirely independently of the host computer. For example, two profound errors follow:

1 *Illegal memory reference:* The program asks for the contents of a memory locations that does not exist anywhere.

2 *Illegal instruction:* The program tells the computer to execute a machine instruction that has no meaning whatsoever on the particular computer.

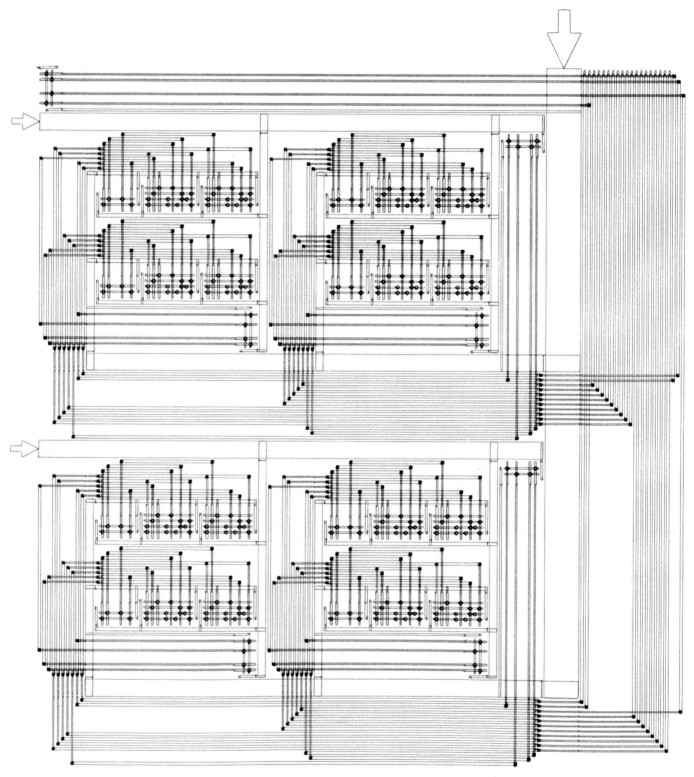

FIGURE 6.18 A counter implemented recursively. (*see also color plate*).

In contrast, other kinds of errors include:

1 The program yields the wrong answer.
2 The program enters an infinite loop (i.e., never finishes execution).

In our analogy, design rule errors in layouts, which correspond to "profound" errors, produce chips whose behaviors cannot be understood simply in terms of logical aberrations in logical function. Design rule errors produce behaviors that can be understood only in terms of the actual physical silicon.

The profit gained by utilizing a silicon assembler is a reduction in detail required for the specification of some crystalline cell structures (e.g., a PLA). Neighboring cells fused together by a silicon assembler tend to have nearly identical interfaces, although not necessarily completely identical.

Any time detail is removed from a specification, the specification becomes clearer, at least for the discovery of design errors apparent only from a higher level of abstraction.

For example, a silicon assembler does not by itself assure power routing, nor does it assure wire routing for necessary communications. However, it does relieve some of the very detailed cell placement specification, so that in fact missing power or signal routing becomes more clearly apparent, and also more easily repaired. Besides providing for the abutment of nearly identical cells, a silicon assembler provides "micro" wiring, or short-distance wiring on the order of a few micrometers.

This silicon assembler by itself does not assure design rule correctness or any kind of logical behavior. It is a geometric tool. In contrast, we have and will adopt "compiler" techniques throughout the rest of this text so as to provide guarantees for both design rule correctness and logical behavior (i.e., guarantees that the chip will perform as intended).

6.3.1 Tiny Cells

We might wonder if a silicon assembler is even useful, particularly in the face of compilers that offer much more tangible (and essential) guarantees of correctness. As noted previously, such delightful "compiler" guarantees bring with them some overhead into layout area (or run-time expense for software).

For example, we can guarantee power routing in a compiler by introducing a blue powerwire along each edge of a cell, so to focus all power requirements of the cell to just a few well-understood positions about the cell. The overhead here is extra blue wires (7-lambda expansion along each edge) and the guarantee is complete power routing.

The aversion to overhead of any kind is usually related to the percentage by which the overhead increases total cost. An overhead that increases layout area by 1% is very tolerable, whereas an overhead of 100% is less tolerable. Overhead measured as a percentage is minimal when dealing with large cells and is large when dealing with small cells. Thus, in a domain where we wish to fuse very small cells, the layout area required for a brute-force maintenance of some guarantees such as power routing may be so large as to be intolerable.

Let us use the term "tiny" cell to denote any cell designed to fit snugly next to other cells within a tightly packed mosaic. Examples of tiny cells include the cells presented in Examples 2 and 3 in Section 6.1.5. Each of those cells fits snuggly into mosaics as shown in Figures 6.5 and 6.3.

The symbolic PLA (Example 4), in contrast, is difficult to call a tiny cell, not so much because it is physically large, but because we have not imagined a larger mosaic within which it might fit snugly, without the need for lots of wire routing. Finally, the inverter cell presented in Example 1 (Figure 6.1) may or may not be a tiny cell; Can you imagine a tight mosaic structure within which it might be a member?

As the name implies, "tiny" cells tend to be small. Algorithms that fuse tiny cells must therefore introduce virtually no additional layout into the result, lest the percentage of overhead be intolerable. For example, the TOP_PULL_DOWN_UNIT cell has a size of only 4 by 4 lambdas. The addition of a 3-lambda-thick blue wire requiring also a 3-lambda separation would introduce an overhead greater than 100%.

We will therefore consider for tiny cells a class of operator very different from those considered in our silicon compiler. These operators will introduce little or no overhead, but at the same time, they will impose great constraints on the situations they can handle.

6.3.2   Conventions for Tiny Cells

Recall that for all cells we already have two conventions, which impose an ordering upon ports along each edge of a cell. We continue to adopt these conventions for tiny cells; those conventions impose no geometric constraint.

What conventions shall we choose for tiny cells? Let us make the conventions loose enough so to admit all the cells presented so far in examples. We can determine right away some conventions we must omit in this endeavor. We will not adopt the following conventions, for example:

3   All ports lie on the MBB's perimeter.

4   Adjacent ports along a side are separated by at least 1 lambda.

In fact, we will for now adopt only one other convention, convention 3 (Section 6.1.4). Recall that convention 3 states that interior ports may be brought out to the surface via straight wires of the ports' colors.

We do not adopt convention 4, which imposed a minimum separation between adjacent ports, nor do we adopt convention 5, which offered some guarantee about wire routing.

We will come back later to tighten convention 3, so to allow a little more freedom for the silicon assembler, in its effort to fuse slightly mismatching cells.

6.3.3   "Micro" Wiring: Cell Abutment and the \TOWER
           Operator

Let us define perhaps the central operator in this silicon assembler, \TOWER. \TOWER is a fusion operator; that is, it takes in two cells and produces one cell:

      cell   \TOWER   cell   →   cell

\TOWER fuses together the two given cells into one cell, where the second cell is made to appear above the first cell. Besides placing the cells relative to one another, \TOWER provides additional layout which connects together each pair of corresponding ports between the cells.

\TOWER cannot fuse any pair of cells. It requires that each pair of corresponding ports between the cells match in all respects (i.e., in color, x-coordinate, and signal). \TOWER will take the liberty to move the top cell so that at least one pair of corresponding ports matches in the x-coordinate. However, beyond this liberty, \TOWER does no more to enforce this requirement, except to complain if this requirement is not met.

The definition of this operator will show us once more that:

1 Ports may be used to direct the placement of CELLs relative to one another.
2 Ports may be used to direct the generation of additional layout.
3 Ports are generated automatically for the resulting cell.
4 An operator can detect situations it cannot handle.

We will use in the definition of \TOWER the following operator, which was presented in Section 6.2.2:

    port   \UP_TO   real   →   layout

This operator simply produces a vertical box whose width, color, and bottom are taken from the given port, and whose top is given by the second parameter, a y-coordinate. The definition for \TOWER follows:

```
DEFINE    TOWER( BOTTOM, TOP: CELL )  =  CELL:
      BEGIN  VAR DISP= POINT; P1, P2 =  PORT;
      DO
              " How far to displace TOP so that its bottom port(s) coincides
                with BOTTOM's top port(s) "
              DISP:=    - TOP.B[1]  +  BOTTOM.T[1]  ;
              " Restrict the displacement so that TOP's MBB resides above
                BOTTOM's MBB "
              DISP.Y:=  DISP.Y    MAX  MBB(BOTTOM).HIGH.Y  -  MBB(TOP).LOW.Y  ;
              " Finally, restrict the displacment so that we never move TOP
                downward "
              DISP.Y:=  DISP.Y  MAX  0  ;
              " Move TOP now. "
              TOP:=  TOP  \AT  DISP;

              " Call HELP if a pair of corresponding ports (P1 and P2)
                do not match in x-coordinate, color, or signal "
              IF  FOR  P1  $E  BOTTOM.T;  &&  FOR  P2  $E  TOP.B;  THERE_IS
                              ( P1.X  <>  P2.X )  !  ( P1.C  <>  P2.C )  !
                              - ( P1.S  \EQ  P2.S )
              THEN     HELP;                         FI
      GIVE   " The finished cell ... "
             [  LAYOUT:         { TOP.LAYOUT ;  BOTTOM.LAYOUT }  \UNION
                                {COLLECT  P1  \UP_TO  P2.Y
                                        FOR  P1  $E  TOP.B;  &&
                                        FOR  P2  $E  BOTTOM.T;  }

                      T:      TOP.T
                      L:      BOTTOM.L  $$  TOP.L
                      R:      BOTTOM.R  $$  TOP.R
                      B:      BOTTOM.B                   ]      END      ENDDEFN
```

The DO clause moves the TOP cell so that it lies above the BOTTOM cell, in such a way that the ports between the cells will line up in x-coordinate, if this is at all possible. The DISPlacement slides the TOP cell horizontally without restriction, and pushes it upward if the TOP cell presently lies below or upon the BOTTOM cell. The DISPlacement, however, is restricted from moving the TOP cell downward at all.

This policy about displacement assures not only that the two cells will be separated sufficiently so not to overlap, as dictated by the cells' MBBs, but also that if the two cells reside presently farther apart than necessary, this extra separation will remain. This maintenance of extra separation provides the ability for other processes, those that employ \TOWER, to separate the cells as dictated by concerns other than port positions, for example by concerns like:

1 Separation required by design rules
2 Separation required simply because other, surrounding context demands an even greater separation

We will see examples of both of these "external" concerns. Thus, \TOWER by itself provides no design rule guarantees.

\TOWER yields a cell whose layout is the union of the two cells' layouts and also a set of wires that connect the cells (e.g., Figure 6.3). (Recall that since the TOP cell has been moved, its layout has been moved also.) The ports for the resulting cell are derived easily from the two given cells. Of all eight edges of the two given cells, ports along the two inner edges disappear (and become additional layout instead), while ports along the six exposed edges appear on the result. The left and right edges of the result have as ports the concatenation of the two cells' left and right edges, respectively.

We can utilize \TOWER to fuse together a vertical list of cells by defining a convenient operator

cells \FIX   →   cell

We render the given list of cells as a single (tall) cell by defining:

DEFINE   FIX(CS: CELLS) = CELL: BEGIN VAR C = CELL ;
          \TOWER   C   FOR C $E CS;   END   ENDDEFN

This forms a cumulative tower of the given cells. Because \TOWER never moves cells closer together vertically, the vertical separations between adjacent cells in the list will at most increase.

6.3.4 Policy about Vertical Lists of Cells

Throughout this silicon assembler, we will maintain a property that applies not to individual cells, but instead to columns of cells. We will use the term "column" to refer to any list of cells intended to be arrayed vertically:

Convention A: The vertical separation between adjacent cells in a column of cells will never be decreased by any operator.

We can think of this nondecreasing restriction as a statement of entropy. A column, as it passes through various operators, only stretches; it never shrinks.

6.3.5 A Powerful Fusion Operator That Affects SIGNALs

\TOWER's and \FIX's maintenance of extra cell separation is utilized by another, more complex operator, \TIMES:

ports \TIMES cells   →   cell

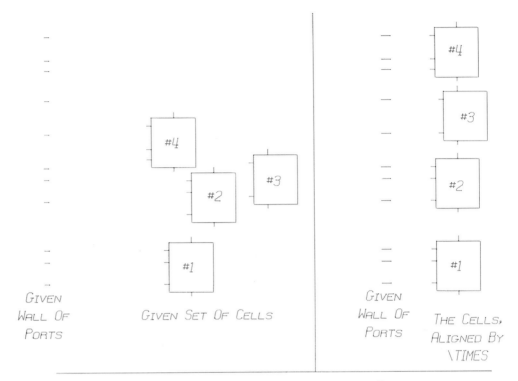

\TIMES ALIGNS A SET OF CELLS
AGAINST A WALL OF PORTS

FIGURE 6.19

The ports parameter represents a context against which the given list of cells, arrayed vertically, will reside. As Figure 6.19 indicates, the ports act like a wall which attracts the given cells. \TIMES moves each of the given cells vertically so to render each cell next to corresponding ports on the wall. \TIMES scans the wall of ports from bottom to top, and scans the list of cells similarly, consuming enough wall ports so to match the number of left ports on each cell. (\TIMES ignores power ports entirely in this consideration.) This action is analogous to zipping up a zipper, and to perhaps the synthesis of proteins from genetic DNA and RNA.

The ports parameter to \TIMES provides not only geometric context, but also logical context. As each cell binds itself somewhere along the wall of ports, \TOWER maps the cells' ports' signals so that the port correspondence matches logically as well as geometrically.

More specifically, \TIMES first modifies the given list of cells and finally applies \FIX on the new list so to produce the single resulting cell. \TIMES modifies each cell in the list in two ways:

1   \TIMES moves the cell vertically so to match as closely as possible ''corresponding'' ports along the left wall. However, \TOWER will not decrease separation between adjacent cells in the list (convention A).

2   \TIMES applies the \MAPPING operator on each cell so that the cells' left ports' signals come to match the signals in the corresponding wall ports.

Finally, \TIMES will take the liberty to recycle through the list of cells in case \TIMES runs out of cells in the list before it runs out of wall ports.

For example, Figure 6.5A is the result of

        ports   \TIMES   {   INPUT_CELL   }

where ports is

{   COLLECT   [P: 0#Y   ]   FOR   Y   FROM   0   BY   14;   &&   REPEAT   4;   }

This example causes \TIMES to cycle through the singleton list a total of four times.

In this example it is the positions of the given ports that actually determine the vertical placements of the set of INPUT_CELLs (a 14-lambda increment). (The horizontal placement of each cell is always determined in \TOWER itself, in \TOWER's effort to make top and bottom ports correspond in x-coordinate.)

In contrast, this figure may be specified in a different manner, where the vertical placements are determined not by the left ports, but instead by the MBB of the INPUT_CELL itself. We write

        ports   \TIMES   {   INPUT_CELL   \SEP   0#1   }

where ports is simply

        { COLLECT [P: 0#0] REPEAT 4; }

In this example, if vertical displacements were determined only by the given list of ports itself, all four INPUT_CELLs would lie directly on one another. This time, however, the cells are placed with regard to MBBs.

The 1-lambda separation between the cells apparent in the figure is due to our use of the \SEP operator,

        cell   \SEP   point   →   cell

which actually enlarges the MBB of the given cell (by 0 in X and 1 in Y, per this example). This operator cheats to gain this effect. It enlarges the MBB not by making the layout larger, but instead by affecting directly the MBB stored with the LAYOUT itself (Section 2.6.8.3).

6.3.5.1   Uses and limitations of \TIMES.   The logical service provided by \TIMES is substantial in that we may specify tiny cells using dummy signals, as we have done in Examples 1, 2, and 3 in Section 6.1.5. At the time we specify a tiny cell, we do not know the logical context(s) into which it will be integrated. \TIMES therefore "infects" each cell with the logical context found in the wall of ports.

Note, however, that \TIMES cannot guarantee a perfect match between the given wall of ports and the resulting cell, neither geometrically nor logically. For example, imagine that the wall of ports has a 20-lambda separation between each adjacent pair of ports. No perfect match is possible if at least one of the given cells has two left ports which reside only 10 lambda apart. In addition, a logical match is impossible if all the wall ports carry distinct signals but a given cell has two left ports which carry the same signal. (No application of \MAPPING can ever destroy signal equality.)

6.3.6   A High-Level Specification for Flexible NOR-Gate Cells

Let us now utilize \TIMES to form a NOR gate in a manner which is much less dependent on the character of the constituent subcells than the rendition given in Section 1.4.3.

The following function produces a NOR gate by forming merely a list of the constituent cells, and by then applying \TIMES to fuse them into a single cell.

This function accepts the logic specification for the NOR gate in terms of a parameter of type NOR_COLUMN_LOGIC, as before (Section 1.4.3). In addition, this function accepts a parameter of type PORTS which serves as a left neighboring context. This context is used for two purposes, both of which are implemented by a single call to \TIMES: The positions of the PORTS determine how the NOR gate will stretch, so to accommodate input separations other than the rigid 6/8-lambda separations imposed by earlier renditions. In addition, the PORTS' signals define the input signals to be adopted by the finished NOR gate.

```
DEFINE NOR_GATE( LEFT: PORTS    LOGIC: NOR_COLUMN_LOGIC ) = CELL :
    BEGIN    VAR YES, TOP = BOOL ;    COLUMN = CELLS ;
    DO      COLUMN := LEFT \TIMES
                    { FOR YES $E LOGIC;
                                    FIRST_DO        TOP:=  FALSE  ; ;
                                    OTHER_DO        TOP:=  - TOP  ; ;
                    COLLECT
                        IF  YES  THEN
                        IF  TOP  THEN  ACTIVE_TOP_PULL_DOWN_UNIT
                        ELSE   ACTIVE_BOTTOM_PULL_DOWN_UNIT  FI
                        ELSE
                        IF  TOP  THEN  TOP_PULL_DOWN_UNIT
                        ELSE  BOTTOM_PULL_DOWN_UNIT  FI  FI   } ;
    GIVE    COLUMN $> PULL_UP_CELL    \FIX          END         ENDDEFN
```

This function sets COLUMN to a list of cells that is aligned ultimately to the given set of LEFT ports, via \TIMES, both geometrically and logically. The list of cells contains occurrences of four cells, chosen by two independent considerations.

For each input (represented in NOR_COLUMN_LOGIC):

1 YES: The input participates in the NOR gate, and
2 TOP: Alternate iterations switch between the "TOP" and "BOTTOM" versions of the cells.

The two cells

ACTIVE_TOP_PULL_DOWN_UNIT and ACTIVE_BOTTOM_PULL_DOWN_UNIT

are identical to the "inactive" versions that we defined earlier, except that each of these "active" cells includes the green "link," which completes the pull-down transistor. Finally, this function appends onto the end of this COLUMN list the PULL_UP_CELL.

This specification per se is entirely oblivious of the sizes of the four basic cells. None of this specification expresses cell placement or wiring.

6.3.7 A Power Sealant

We can define another operator, similar to \NOR_GATE, which produces a slab of power sealent:

ports \SEAL_POWER signal   →   cell

This operator produces a cell that is meant to abut leftward to the given vertical list of ports. The ports represent the right-hand ports of another, left neighboring cell. The

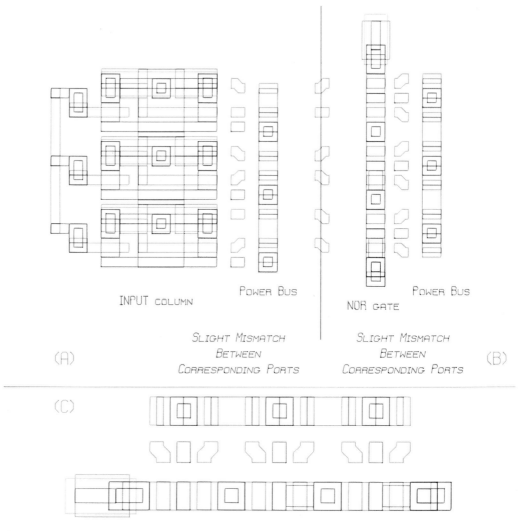

FIGURE 6.20   Absorption of small misalignments.

resulting cell provides a power bus which interconnects all power ports, and which provides passage across the power bus for all nonpower ports (e.g., Figure 6.20A and B). The signal parameter distinguishes between VDD and GND.

The nature of the cell generated by \SEAL_POWER is defined almost entirely from the given set of ports. \SEAL_POWER, like \NOR_GATE, forms a list of all the tiny cells it wishes to include, one per port, and calls \TIMES finally to produce a single cell.

As Figures 6.20A and B show, both the given ports and the tiny cells' MBBs in the power list participate naturally in cell placement. We see here that MBB separation dominates, rendering a power bus whose ports do not align exactly with those ports given as the first parameter, the NOR gate's right-hand ports.

6.3.8   "Silicon Quakes," Stress, and Fault Lines

Figure 6.20C shows how we might use \TOWER to fuse the power bus onto the NOR gate. We can apply \TOWER simply by first rotating the two cells.

Unfortunately, \TOWER will complain at such a task (Figure 6.20C) because the ports do not align exactly. The power bus really does require this different spacing because the connection from each of the NOR gate's green power ports requires a green-to-blue feedthrough, which is 4 lambda wide.

We can imagine resolving this problem simply by stretching the NOR gate so that the separations between its red signal and green power ports increases so to match the geometric constraint imposed by the power bus. However, a glance at Figure 6.21 would indicate that the NOR gate's height is, in fact, the major area consumer.

Let us resolve this slight port mismatch instead by modifying \TOWER itself to provide slanted interconnection as shown in Figure 6.20. Figure 6.22 shows how such slants are restricted by design rules. Each wire travels straight outward for a short distance, then embarks on a slant that may continue for an arbitrary distance. Finally, we terminate the wire by straightenning out for a short distance, equal to the distance of original straight travel.

The new \TOWER takes the liberty to produce such slanted routes for all ports, including interior ports. To reflect this liberty, we modify convention 3 about interior ports for tiny cells so as to read:

3′   We will take the liberty of introducing a wire stretching from an interior port directly outward to that port's edge, employing at most a 45-degree slant en route, buffered at start and finish by straight travel of 1 lambda for red, and 1.5 lambda for each of green and blue.

Again, this convention merely forewarns the user; it does not state anything about design rules.

The new \TOWER does guarantee to introduce no design rule violations for surface ports between any slanted wire and the given layout (Figure 6.22). \TOWER also guarantees design rule correctness among the slanted wires themselves at least to the extent that \TOWER will note any violations.

In summary, this silicon assembler as a whole guarantees design rule correctness at least to the extent of notifying the user of design rule violations, except for the following responsibilities left entirely up to the user:

1   The user is responsible for employing the \SEP operator (as in our input buffer example) so to assure sufficient separation around a cell.

2   The user must verify design rule correctness manually for cells that include interior ports.

These requirements are simple enough for the user to satisfy. The user most often has on the tip of his or her tongue just the information needed for the first requirement. Often the user may define tiny cells, employing right in their original definitions the \SEP operator, thus relieving this concern for those tiny cells. However, employment of \SEP upon specific appearances of a tiny cell can take advantage of smaller separations in some cases, ultimately rendering more efficient layouts.

The user can avoid possible design rule violations due to interior ports by rendering all interior ports as surface ports. In fact, a silicon assembler can provide 100% design rule guarantee if it performs these services for the user. To play it this safe, however, an assembler might have to compromise layout efficiency by separating all cells by 3 lambda, and rendering all ports as surface ports. This surrenders the possibility of gaining some horizontal routing within a cell's MBB by starting the route within the MBB. For example, the slanted routing between a NOR_GATE and a power pole occurs partly within the NOR_GATE's MBB (Figures 6.20C and 6.21).

6.3.8.1   New alignment for \TOWER.   Once we allow \TOWER to absorb position mismatches by introducing slanted wires, we need to reconsider how \TOWER places

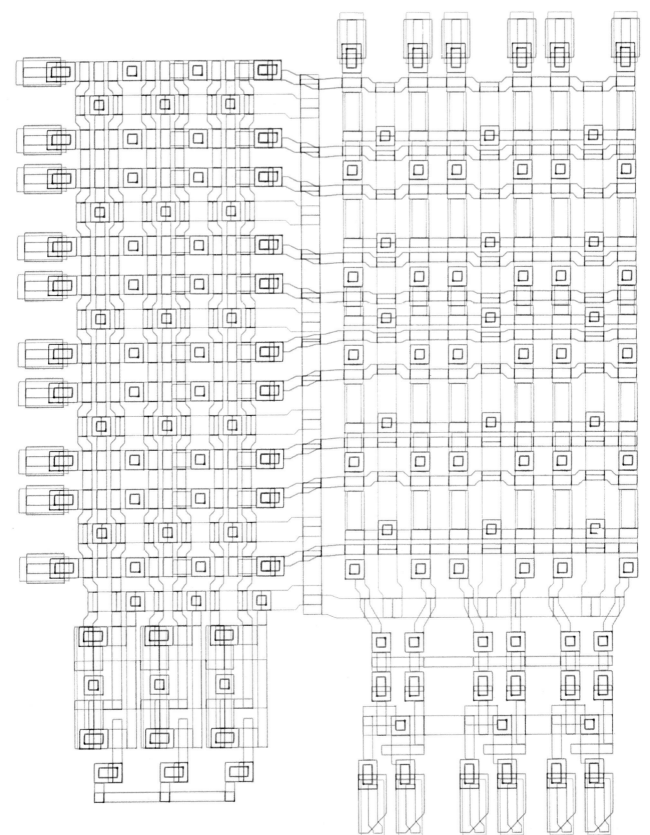

FIGURE 6.21 A functional PLA. *(see also color plate)*

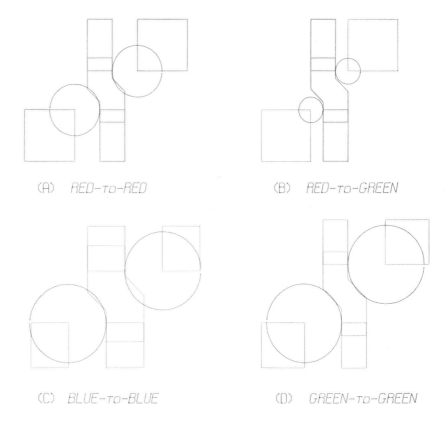

(A) RED-to-RED   (B) RED-to-GREEN

(C) BLUE-to-BLUE   (D) GREEN-to-GREEN

RESTRICTIONS ON SLANTED WIRES

FIGURE 6.22

the top cell relative to the bottom cell. First, \TOWER must increase the cell separation vertically if port position mismatches are large. Since slants are restricted to 45 degrees, a greater horizontal distance requires an increase in vertical distance. Thus, \TOWER will increase cell separation as required to implement the slanted routing.

The increase in vertical separation required to accommodate horizontal routing presents a new cost. We wish, therefore, to have \TOWER align the cells horizontally so to minimize horizontal mismatch. Back when we required corresponding ports to align exactly, \TOWER could determine horizontal displacement simply by examining exactly one pair of corresponding ports.

Now that we have dropped this requirement of zero misalignment between corresponding ports, \TOWER must examine all pairs of corresponding ports in order to determine how far to displace the top cell horizontally. \TOWER minimizes vertical separation by minimizing a number n, which is the maximum horizontal misalignment between any pair of corresponding ports.

For example, we can imagine another horizontal alignment procedure which computes for each of the two abuting sets of ports a center of gravity, or average port position. Taking the average over a set of ports does reduce the set to one representative port position. We can imagine then that \TOWER moves the top cell so that its "average bottom port" aligns directly above the bottom cell's "average top port."

Whereas alignment via port averages does result in an average port misalignment equal to zero, this does not in general minimize individual port misalignments, or more important, it does not minimize the greatest of all port misalignments. It is, however, the greatest of misalignments which imposes the magnitude of necessary vertical displacement.

Let us introduce a notion of "stress" which will aid in \TOWER's alignment effort. This notion will also provide the basis for a more advanced silicon assembler which will resolve some problems barely mentioned as yet.

6.3.8.2 Stress. Let us introduce a notion of stress by defining the following datatype:

TYPE   STRESS = [LEFT: REAL   RIGHT: REAL] ;

For consistency, let us imagine always that a stress is felt only by the top cell. Thus, the two components of STRESS represent how far LEFT to move the top cell in order to achieve alignment and how far RIGHT to move the top cell to achieve the same.

Figure 6.23A shows an example of this interpretation. We see the desire to move the top cell LEFT by 5 lambda. Figure 6.22B shows the numbers for both LEFT and RIGHT which we will adopt officially. LEFT and RIGHT will always be negatives of one another if we consider stresses arising from exactly one pair of ports.

In contrast, Figure 6.23C shows a STRESS arising from two pairs of corresponding ports. Due to the choice of port positions, it is clear that no matter how we might displace the top cell, a misalignment will persist. This persistence is reflected in the STRESS in that LEFT and RIGHT are no longer negatives of one another. Figure 6.23D shows a similar situation.

Considering each of Figure 6.23B, C, and D, we can figure how far to displace the top cell:

(B) left by 5   (right by −5)
(C) left by 2.5   (right by −2.5)
(D) left by 0   (right by 0)

In general, we can transform a STRESS into a single number representing the horizontal displacement which will render a minimal misalignment:

DEFINE   TOP_DISP(S: STRESS) = REAL :
          (S.RIGHT - S.LEFT) / 2   ENDDEFN

This function yields the following (right) displacements:

(B) −5   (C) −2.5   (D) 0

To measure the misalignment presented by a given stress, let us introduce the operator

stress \COST   →   real

This operator makes no attempt to minimize the stress prior to rendering a cost; it measures merely the cost of the stress as is:

DEFINE   COST(S: STRESS) = REAL :
          S.RIGHT MAX S.LEFT   ENDDEFN

This yields

(B) 5   (C) 5   (D) 5

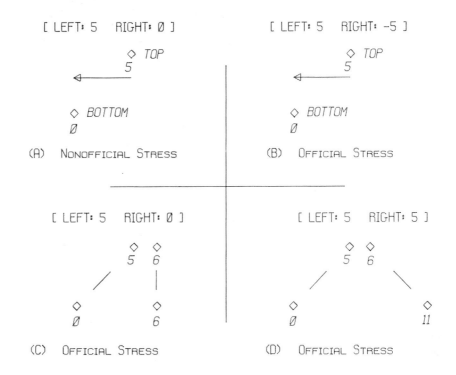

[LEFT: 5   RIGHT: 0]   [LEFT: 5   RIGHT: -5]

◇ TOP   ◇ TOP
5   5

◇ BOTTOM   ◇ BOTTOM
0   0

(A) Nonofficial Stress   (B) Official Stress

[LEFT: 5   RIGHT: 0]   [LEFT: 5   RIGHT: 5]

◇   ◇   ◇   ◇
5   6   5   6

◇   ◇   ◇   ◇
0   6   0   11

(C) Official Stress   (D) Official Stress

STRESS And Its Representation

FIGURE 6.23

Let us define an operator that "moves" a stress:

stress \AT real   →   stress

This yields the stress that would be felt after moving the top cell to the right by the indicated amount:

DEFINE   AT(S: STRESS   DX: REAL) = STRESS :
[LEFT: S.LEFT + DX   RIGHT: S.RIGHT - DX]   ENDDEFN

That is, moving the top cell to the right increases the LEFT pull and decreases the RIGHT pull.

We can now know the following about any stress S:

(S \AT X)   \COST   is minimized when
X = S \TOP_DISP

That is, if

S = [LEFT: L RIGHT: R],   and
X = S \TOP_DISP   (= (R - L) / 2)

then

S \AT X =   [LEFT: L+X   RIGHT: R-X]
        =   [LEFT: L + (R-L)/2 RIGHT: R - (R-L)/2]
        =   [LEFT: (R+L)/2   RIGHT: (R+L)/2]

In other words, \TOP_DISP yields a displacement which moves the stress so that LEFT = RIGHT. This stress's cost is minimal because a movement (\AT) by any amount will increase one of LEFT and RIGHT, therefore rendering a greater cost.

We conclude our discussion of the STRESS datatype by including two operators which form STRESSes from the information we have at hand when considering cells:

$$\text{real} \quad \backslash\text{ABOVE} \quad \text{real} \quad\quad \rightarrow \quad \text{stress}$$
$$\text{stress} \quad \backslash\text{MAX} \quad \text{stress} \quad\quad \rightarrow \quad \text{stress}$$

The first operator yields the stress introduced by one pair of ports, or more precisely, one pair of x-coordinates:

```
DEFINE    ABOVE( TOP, BOTTOM : REAL ) = STRESS:
          [LEFT: TOP - BOTTOM    RIGHT: BOTTOM - TOP ]       ENDDEFN
```

The second operator combines two stresses to form one stress. The result represents the overall stress implied by the presence of both stresses, with each anchored on the same pair of rigid bodies:

```
DEFINE    MAX( A, B: STRESS ) = STRESS:
          [LEFT:    A.LEFT  MAX  B.LEFT
           RIGHT:   A.RIGHT  MAX  B.RIGHT  ]                 ENDDEFN
```

For example, looking at Figure 6.23C, we specify the overall stress with

```
( 5 \ABOVE 0 )    \MAX    ( 6 \ABOVE 6 )
```

We compute the entire stress between two cells, say TOP and BOTTOM, by forming the commulative \MAX of the stress introduced by each pair of corresponding ports:

```
DEFINE ABOVE( TOP, BOTTOM: CELL ) = STRESS:
       BEGIN      VAR P1, P2 = PORT ;
          \MAX    ( P1.X \ABOVE P2.X )    FOR P1 $E TOP.B; &&
                                          FOR P2 $E BOTTOM.T;
       END                                              ENDDEFN
```

\TOWER may now use the following point to align the TOP cell horizontally relative to the BOTTOM cell:

```
( TOP \ABOVE BOTTOM )    \TOP_DISP    #    0
```

This displacement renders port alignments that present the smallest maximum horizontal misalignment, and hence allows \TOWER to separate the two cells vertically by a minimal amount.

Notice that the misalignment of ports between the NOR gate and the power bus in Figure 6.20C is at most 1 lambda in magnitude. This gives rise to slanted wires whose heights are at most 3 lambda (1 lambda for each of the vertical portions, and then 1 lambda to absorb the 1-lambda horizontal mismatch). Thus, the vertical separation between corresponding ports must be 3 lambda. Notice finally that this 3-lambda separation introduces absolutely no overhead simply because the blue-to-blue design rule separation between the two cells imposes by itself the requirement for a 3-lambda separation.

6.3.8.3   Stress in the \TIMES operator. Recall that the \TIMES operator aligns vertically a set of cells along a left wall of ports. \TIMES adjusts each cell vertically so that the cell's left ports align as closely as possible to the corresponding wall ports. There are no guarantees that perfect alignment is always possible.

\TIMES aligns each cell against the wall so to minimize stress between the cell and the wall. It is possible that this endeavor may render two vertically adjacent cells so to overlap. By itself this phenomenon is harmless. \TIMES's ultimate call to \FIX (\TOWER) will cause these overlapping cells to separate so to render no overlap. However, \TOWER implements this separation by moving the top cell upward, and may hence render substantial misalignment between the top cell and the left wall of ports. In fact, we might prefer instead to have the bottom cell moved down a little, as a compromise, so to minimize the overall misalignment of the two cells relative to the wall of ports (Figure 6.24).

\TIMES does consider such a phenomenon. \TIMES recognizes when it places two cells so that they overlap. Such an occurrence implies obviously that the two cells need to be as close to one another as possible (e.g., abutting one another). Thus, \TIMES recomputes a stress now based on the two abutting cells taken as a whole (i.e., as a single rigid body). This new stress directs \TIMES how to place the rigid pair as a whole relative to the wall. \TIMES applies this single movement then to each cell independently prior to calling \FIX.

In fact, \TIMES will coalesce adjacent cells into single rigid bodies as long as overlaps persist. It is possible, for example, that the entire list of cells will be coalesced into a single rigid body if the wall of ports is very short, therefore forcing abutment between all the cells.

Note, however, that as stated earlier, \TIMES will never decrease separations between cells. Specifically, \TIMES "abuts" cells in its effort to compute combined stresses by:

1 Separating the cells if they overlap
2 Considering the two cells as a single rigid body even if they are separated presently beyond tight abutment (convention A)

Generally, we apply \TIMES to a list of cells whose elements are separated presently by nothing, or whose elements are all overlapping. Both specifications presented earlier for the column of INPUT_CELLs shown in Figure 6.5 gave to \TIMES a list

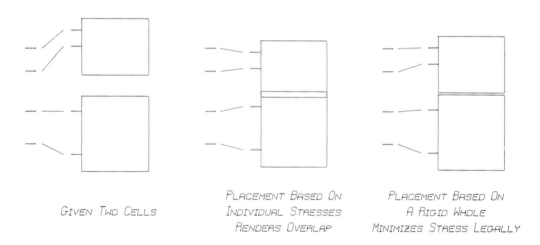

GIVEN TWO CELLS

PLACEMENT BASED ON
INDIVIDUAL STRESSES
RENDERS OVERLAP

PLACEMENT BASED ON
A RIGID WHOLE
MINIMIZES STRESS LEGALLY

TREATMENT OF STRESS IN \TIMES

FIGURE 6.24

all of whose elements were overlapping (i.e., coincident). Thus, \TIMES by itself generally determines all cell placements, based on stress computations, satisfying simultaneously the desires to:

1   Render a legal column (no overlap)
2   Render a column that fits as closely as possible against the given wall of ports

Finally, we introduce one more tendency into \TIMES:

3   \TIMES renders as short a column as possible, even by tolerating new stresses not to exceed 1 lambda.

That is, even if \TIMES can render a column with zero stress, \TIMES will actually pull all cells toward the center of the column as far as possible, as long as

1   The present stress is not increased, or
2   The stress grows to a maximum of 1 lambda.

This choice to tolerate stresses of 1 lambda is taken because the slanted wires required to absorb this stress impose only a 3-lambda separation between cells. A 3-lambda separation is generally required for other reasons (e.g., blue-to-blue separation).

6.3.9   Construction of a PLA

Figure 6.25 illustrates how a functional PLA can be built from these operators. This figure shows the PLA blasted apart.

We start from the upper-left corner, the input buffer. We have already seen several ways to create this part (e.g., Figure 6.5). Notice in Figure 6.4 that each INPUT_CELL in this column produces not only a signal and its inverse along the right-hand edge, but it also requires GND in green. We therefore utilize a \SEAL_POWER operator along the input column's right-hand ports. (The GND requirements are thus focused to the bottom of the GND pole, connecting ultimately to the horizontal GND bar residing between the top and bottom halves of the entire PLA.)

Notice in this blasted figure little slanted wires, provided ultimately by \TOWER to fuse the input column and the GND pole. (The GND pole appears shorter than necessary relative to the input column. This phenomenon is due to \TIMES's attempt to shrink as much as possible within 1 lambda of stress.)

Following to the right of the input column and its GND pole, we see the AND-plane. This particular AND plane was constructed via the following steps:

1   Each NOR_GATE is constructed relative to the wall of ports presented by the input column, and hence all NOR_GATEs appear identical in height.
2   One GND pole is constructed relative to the wall of ports presented by the NOR_GATE.
3   Finally, a horizontal list of NOR_GATEs and GND poles is formed, with GND poles included so that each NOR_GATE is next to one GND pole.

(Generally, GND poles are needed much less frequently; for example, 12 NOR_GATEs or more can reside between two GND poles. The GND poles are present so to supply GND to the horizontal green GND lines in the NOR_GATEs. Recall that long green

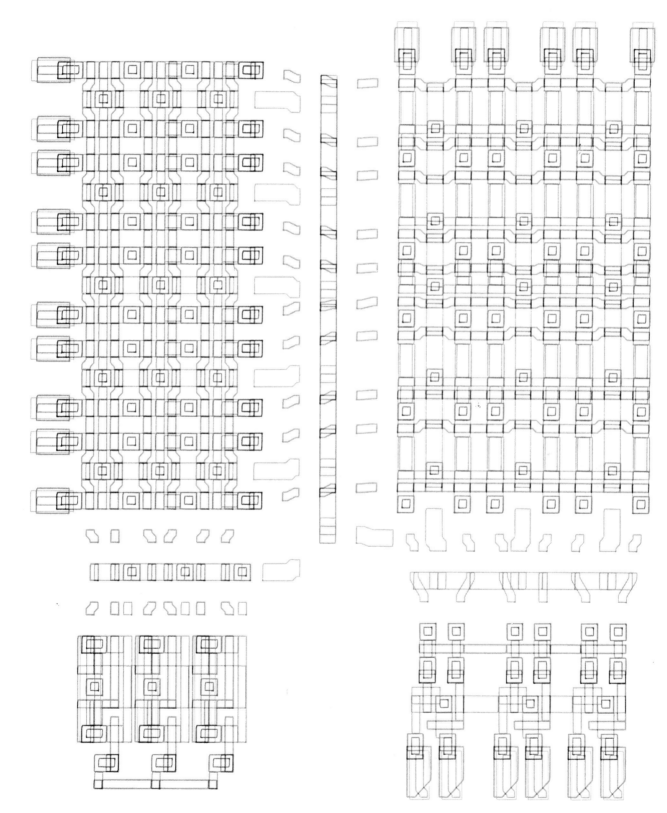

FIGURE 6.25 The glue between PLA sections. (*see also color plate*).

wires impose too great a resistance to maintain GND at 0 volts. We have chosen such a high density of GND poles to illustrate stretching in the subsequent OR plane.)

The AND plane is completed by applying \FIX to this list, rotated temporarily so to be vertical. Similarly, the parts of the entire top half of the PLA are fused together by another application of \FIX.

The bottom half of the PLA is generated in a similar manner. However, we start by constructing the OR plane, not the output buffers. If we rotate Figure 6.25 counterclockwise, we see the AND plane's output presenting a vertical wall of ports. The NOR gates of the OR plane are constructed in this rotated orientation, so to take their inputs from the AND-plane's outputs.

We see in the OR plane that each NOR gate is stretched to accommodate the erratic spacing presented by the AND plane's output ports, due in part to the AND plane's GND poles. It is here, in the construction of the OR plane, where we really have to abandon the old 6/8-lambda separation between NOR gate inputs.

The bottom half of the PLA is completed by attaching a column of OUTPUT_CELLs to the left side of the OR plane. If we turn Figure 6.25 upside down (180 degrees), we see that the OR plane presents a vertical wall of ports against which \TIMES places the OUTPUT_CELLs. (In fact, we first apply a \SEAL_POWER operator against this wall of ports so to seal off the GND requirements of the OR plane).

The two halves of the PLA fuse to form the entire PLA as a whole, but first we seal off the GND requirements of the top half, introducing the horizontal GND bar between the halves. Figure 6.21 shows the completed PLA. It takes GND along the bottom edge, and VDD along all three of the other edges. (VDD is required on the top and right to feed the NOR gate's pull-up cells. VDD is needed also along the left edge to feed the output cells' pull-ups.)

We have ignored a thorn in this mechanism: The horizontal GND bar between the halves connects not simply to the top half only. It has one connection to the bottom half in addition. The thorn is that our \SEAL_POWER operator seals power along only one wall of ports. However, we desire the horizontal GND bar to connect to the lower half, so as to focus all GND requirements of the entire PLA to the bottom edge.

This two-sided GND bar is, in fact, the superposition of two GND bars, one created for the top half, and the other for the bottom half. These two GND bars appear coincident because of a "cheat." The \SEP operator was applied to the bottom half, supplying a negative value for separation.

6.3.10   Two-Dimensional Hardening

We were careful with the PLA example to choose an ordering for cell composition so that each wall of ports imposed only a requirement to stretch the new column of cells. Never did we encounter a wall of ports that requried cells to shrink so far as to overlap.

We built the OR plane after building the AND plane, and we fused the output cells onto the finished OR plane rather than vice versa.

That is, looking between the top and bottom halves of the PLA, it is the output of the AND plane which imposes the widest port separations, so we built it first. In contrast, had we built the OR plane first, the OR-plane would yield the minimum 6/8-lambda separation between its inputs. Then building the AND-plane on the OR-plane's input ports would create a situation where the column of cells (the AND-gates) could not shrink together closely enough to accommodate the wall of ports. The final fusion between the two halves of the PLA would cause \TOWER to issue an error message.

Similarly, had we built the output column without knowledge of the OR-plane's constraint, we would get a much more tightly packed output column. Once again, an attempt to build the OR-plane along the wall of ports presented by the output column would require the impossible shrinking of the OR-gates into a situation of overlap.

Figure 6.26A shows a given column of cells, how they stretch to accommodate a tall wall, and how they cannot accommodate a short wall without overlapping. Figure 6.26B shows that the short wall itself comes from another, previously constructed column of cells. Figure 6.26B shows also that by reversing the situation, we can in effect cause the wall to stretch.

Thus, we must always generate first the cell that imposes the widest of port separations. Given a parameterized problem, however (e.g., the generation of PLAs), can we always determine, for all possible parameter values, which subcell will impose the greatest constraint? Perhaps the parameter values themselves can cause variation in the order required for subcell composition.

It is even conceivable that between two cells, part of the common interface is constrained to the greatest extent by one cell, whereas along a different portion of that same interface, the other cell imposes the dominant constraint. In this sort of situation, neither cell can be constructed first.

We are troubled by concrete walls, walls that cannot be rebuilt later, in the face of more imposing constraints. What makes a wall concrete is simply that the cell whose right-hand ports make up the wall is itself a single cell. Usually, however, as in all our examples, the wall is made up of a column of cells hardened previously via an application of \FIX.

If we delay the application of \FIX, we then delay the hardening of a column of cells into a single cell. Let us, in fact, remove from \TIMES its application of \FIX, and

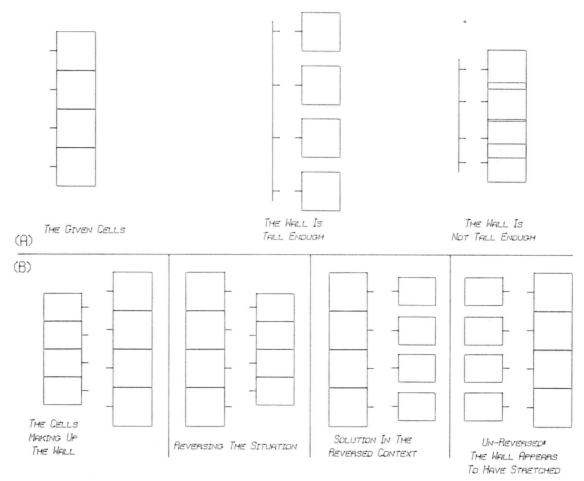

FIGURE 6.26 Environmental constraints on cell alignment.

have \TIMES therefore return not a single hardened cell, but instead another column of cells:

    ports   \TIMES   cells   →   cells

Where we use to take the resulting cell's right ports by writing

    cell.R

we now introduce an operator to perform the same when given not a cell but a column of cells:

    cells   \RIGHT_PORTS   →   ports

Briefly, we increase by one the dimension of memory so that where we use to deal with one cell, we now deal with a column of cells, and where we use to deal with a horizontal row of cells, we now deal with a horizontal row of columns of cells.

Figure 6.27 shows how a horizontal row of columns can be hardened with no bias introduced by the choice of hardening order. Each column of cells presents its \RIGHT _ PORTS as the left wall for the next column. Since each column is not hardened immediately, each column may be subjected to stretching a second time, this time from a wall appearing on the right. That is, stress is propagated first from left to right, and then bouncing back, from right to left.

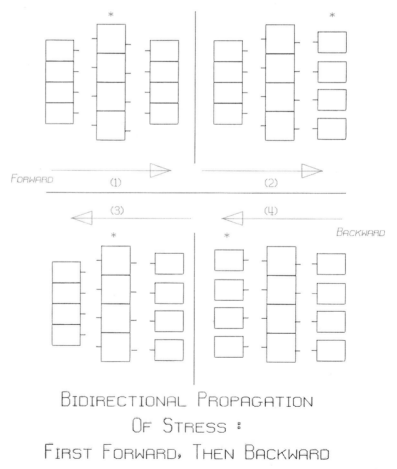

BIDIRECTIONAL PROPAGATION
OF STRESS :
FIRST FORWARD, THEN BACKWARD

FIGURE 6.27

This bidirectional propagation of stress removes the ordering problem, as follows. There is a most constraining column among the row of columns. In Figure 6.27, this is the middle column. The first pass from left to right renders all columns to the right of the major column stretched so to accommodate the major column. Columns to the left of the major column are at this time still too small. However, the second, right-to-left pass, stretches the remaining columns, those to the left of the major column, as necessary.

The illustrations in this sketch of a silicon assembler utilize this two dimensional system.

EXERCISES

Section 6.1.5

1. Consider Figure 6.6. Label the PLA inputs and outputs by consulting the logic specification (Sections 6.1.5 and 5.2.5 examples) and looking at the logic represented by the dots in the PLA.

Section 6.1.8

2. Render the inverter (Figure 6.1) consistent with a convention that all ports reside on the perimeter of the layout's MBB.

3. Consider three possible cell conventions.

   1 All ports of a cell reside on the perimeter of the cell's MBB.

   2 Adjacent ports are separated by at least 2 lambda.

   3 Ports along each edge of a cell are separated by a distance sufficiently great that we can route outward from that edge a distinct blue wire from each port.

   To which subset of these three conventions, does each of the following cells adhere?

   (a) INVERTER_CELL

   (b) TOP_PULL_DOWN_UNIT

   (c) BOTTOM_PULL_DOWN_UNIT

   (d) INPUT_CELL

   (e) OUTPUT_CELL

   (f) PULL_UP_CELL

4. Suggest a refined version of convention 2 (Problem 3) which involves the same separation but which also takes ports' signals into account. Choose this convention so that at least the PULL_UP_CELL adheres to it.

5. Geometric And Logical Invariance Of Our Conventions:
   Indicate for each of the following cells which subset of conventions 1 through 6 remains true. Assume that cell C obeys all conventions.
   (a) Displacement: The cell   C \AT point
   (b) Mirroring about the Y-axis: C \MIRY
   (c) Mirroring about the X-axis: C \MIRX
   (d) Arbitrary application of the cell reorientation operators.
   (e) Cell C, where all occurrences of one signal (S, say) are replaced by occurrences of another signal (T, say)
   (f) Same as part e, where signal S is known not to be THE_GND_SIGNAL or THE_VDD_SIGNAL

6. Show that the \MAPPING operator has the following very important property:

   If C is a cell, and C1   =   C   \MAPPING any SIGNAL_MAP,
   then logical port equality in C is preserved in C1.

That is, if P1 and P2 are any two ports in C, and Q1 and Q2 are the corresponding ports in C2, then

if P1 and P2 carry the same signal   (i.e., P1.S \EQ P2.S)
then Q1 and Q2 carry the same signal   (i.e., Q1.S \EQ Q2.S)

Describe an example in which the converse if false: that is, where P1 and P2 carry distinct signals, whereas Q1 and Q2 carry the same signal

Section 6.2.1

7. Consider the \NONBLUE operator. Why is it important to maintain the 3-lambda separation between each feedthrough and the blue port below it?

8. Consider the \NONBLUE operator. Why is it OK to fill the 3-lambda gap between a blue port and the blue-to-green port feedthrough with a blue box of width 4?

Section 6.2.3

9. Why in \SEAL_POWER do we extend the horizontal power box so that its left (or right) endpoint extends to the left (or right) edge of the cell, and not merely to the leftmost (or rightmost) power port (LEFT.X or RIGHT.X)?

Section 6.2.4

10. Why have we had to verify adherence to conventions for the result of UNION_DX but not for \DX?

Section 6.2.5.3

11. Consider the \PACK operator. Why is BASE, the lowest altitude of flight, chosen to be 5 lambda above the top of the cell? How does this relate to convention 4 in case the scan lines' left ports become interior ports?

12. Consider the \PACK operator. Notice that LEFT, the set of ports representing the left edges of the scan lines, has X-coordinate equal to

C.T[1]X - 2   (due to the INITIALLY clause)

The interface scan lines thus extend leftward beyond the leftmost port (C.T[1]) by 2 lambda

Why is this 2 and not simply 0?

Might 2 be larger than needed in some cases?

Might 2 be smaller than needed in other cases (i.e., perhaps we have here a program bug)?

Suggest another expression to replace "2" which will always yield a legal and minimal extension beyond the leftmost port.

13. In \PACK, why does the application of \SEAL_POWER with THE_VDD_SIGNAL always render no power ports on the top edge, not even GND power ports?

Section 6.2.7

14. Trace the carry chain in Figure 6.18.

Section 6.3.3

15. Verify conventions 1 and 2 upon the result of \TOWER.

Section 6.3.8

16. \TIMES attempts to minimize column height by pulling cells toward the center, tolerating at most a 1-lambda stress. We have suggested that a red wire which undergoes 1-lambda stress (slant) imposes only a vertical separation of 3 lambda. Suppose that such 1-lambda stress is felt by a blue wire. Do we still impose only a 3-lambda vertical separation? If not, find a counterexample in Figure 6.21.

7

Reorganized Logic and its Effects on Layout

We consider in this section a set of operators that modify and optimize LOGIC_CELLs. All of these operators have in common:

1 They leave unchanged the logical behavior of LOGIC_CELLs.
2 They have dramatic and global affects on the layouts generated from the resulting LOGIC_CELLs.

That is, although these operators fall strictly within the domain of LOGIC_CELLs and neither consider nor touch any objects of type LAYOUT, they nonetheless provide major variations in the layouts derived (via \CELL) from the modified LOGIC_CELLs.

We consider two categories of LOGIC_CELL modifiers. The first category of operators actually modify equations so to accommodate the removal of some equations, all under the constraint that behavior remain unchanged. The second category of operators modify logic cells by reshaping the hierarchy. We use the term "hierarchy" to refer to the grouping of logical function implied in the nesting of logic cells within one another.

7.1 LOGIC_CELL OPTIMIZATIONS: REMOVING "TRIVIAL" EQUATIONS

We see in Figure 6.17 a few PLAs that implement equations of the form

A \EQU B

This kind of equation specifies no logical computation whatsoever; that is, it contains no ANDs, ORs, or NOTs. This equation is characterized simply by the fact that its RHS, a SIGNAL_EXPR, is merely a signal; that is, the RHS resides directly in the SIMPLE state.

We will refer to such equations as "trivial" equations. These equations arise primarily from equations that connect together subcells in a LOGIC_CELL (e.g., the carry

315

chain in a counter). [The entire set of equations in the EQUATIONS field of COUNTER(N),

L \S 'CARRY_IN'   \EQU   R \S 'CARRY_OUT'

represent pure interconnection.]

    These trivial equations are both appropriate and necessary within LOGIC_CELLs because the bulletproof interface surrounding each subcell requires that each subcell not specify directly a connection to another subcell. Each subcell is written to be a single entity onto itself. Such interconnections among subcells belong to the logic cell in which these subcells first appear together. This enclosing logic cell is precisely the place where the interactions among subcells are specified.

    However, these trivial equations cause overhead in generated layouts, for example, in the generation of PLAs devoid of logic, or in other words, PLAs that implement merely interconnect.

    We can remove trivial equations, e.g.,

A \EQU B

and maintain the specified behavior by performing variable (signal) substitutions. For example, we can remove this equation if we simultaneously look through all equations and replace each appearance of the signal A with the signal B instead. In other words, we may interpret a trivial equation as a specification of signal equivalence, that is, as a linguistic convenience which specifies merely name interchangeability.

7.1.1 Manipulation of Logic Variables: INDIRECT and \FRESH

In Section 3.2.2 we declared the type SIGNAL, and included in the signal record two fields, named INDIRECT and EXPR. We suggested how each of these fields might be used to implement several mathematical transformations on logic. We now make use of these fields: for example, to render equivalent certain pairs of signals.

    Even though we have so far not used these fields, we now introduce a set of operators that nonetheless refer to these fields. The operator

```
DEFINE    FRESH( S:SIGNAL ) = SIGNAL:
     IF  DEFINED(S.INDIRECT)  THEN  S.INDIRECT  \FRESH
                              ELSE  S        FI           ENDDEFN
```

maps a signal to a signal. Notice that if the INDIRECT field is not defined, this \FRESH operator returns the same signal it takes in (the ELSE clause). Thus, in the domains we have considered so far, \FRESH is an identity.

    However, if the INDIRECT field of S somehow were defined, then \FRESH would return this other signal, the contents of the INDIRECT field. (\FRESH even applies \FRESH to this result, so that if this other signal itself had its INDIRECT defined, that "doubly indirected" signal would then be the result.)

    How might a signal come to have its INDIRECT field defined? We can see a motivation to create such indirection: If we desire to remove the trivial equation

A \EQU B

we would have to render the signals A and B equivalent. By setting A's INDIRECT field to reference signal B, we would have the following phenomenon:

A \FRESH   →   B
B \FRESH   →   B

(B remains unchanged via \FRESH because we have defined the INDIRECT field of A and not B.) This phenomenon provides the signal equivalence between A and B. Through the eyes of \FRESH, both A and B appear to be the same signal.

Thus, we may remove trivial equations and still maintain their intentions by indirecting the first signal so to reference the second signal. This action alone does not render these two signals equivalent. However, if we simply apply \FRESH to each and every signal accessible throughout a set of equations, the result will accurately represent this signal equivalence (e.g., all appearances of signal A will now appear as signal B).

We manage to apply \FRESH to each and every signal in a set of equations via the following operators. We first provide a \FRESH operator that affects all signals in a SIGNAL_EXPR:

```
DEFINE    FRESH( E:SIGNAL_EXPR  )  =  SIGNAL_EXPR:
     BEGIN    VAR  E1  =  SIGNAL_EXPR  ;
     CASE  E  OF
          SIMPLE:  E  \FRESH
          AND:     AND::  {COLLECT  E1  \FRESH  FOR  E1  $E  E;}
          OR:      OR::   {COLLECT  E1  \FRESH  FOR  E1  $E  E;}
          NOT:     NOT::  FRESH(E)
     ENDCASE                                        END      ENDDEFN
```

This operator examines the SIGNAL_EXPR and reconstructs a nearly identical copy. The \FRESH applied in the SIMPLE case maps the SIGNAL_EXPR E, which here is known absolutely to be a SIGNAL E, into the appropriate signal, via the \FRESH operator defined for signals. In contrast, the \FRESH operator appearing in all the other cases denotes a recursive application of this \FRESH operator on SIGNAL_EXPRs. (Refer to Section 3.2.5.1 for a review of the CASE construct and the examination of SIGNAL_EXPRs.) Thus, the resulting SIGNAL_EXPR is a copy of the given SIGNAL_EXPR where each signal contained therein has been replaced by its \FRESH rendition.

For example, the SIGNAL_EXPR

```
A  \AND  B   \OR   NOT(  A  )  \AND  C
```

becomes

```
B  \AND  B   \OR   NOT(  B  )  \AND  C
```

after applying \FRESH, assuming that A has previously been indirected to signal B.

We can now define \FRESH upon equations:

```
DEFINE   FRESH( E:EQUATION  )  =  EQUATION:
   [LHS:  E.LHS  \FRESH    RHS:  E.RHS  \FRESH    DELAY:  E.DELAY  ]      ENDDEFN
```

This operator applies \FRESH to all signals referenced in the equations (i.e., to E.LHS and to all signals in the SIGNAL_EXPR E.RHS). (The DELAY of E needs no \FRESH simply because it references no signals; it is merely a boolean.)

We define \FRESH for a set of equations:

```
DEFINE   FRESH( ES:EQUATIONS  )  =  EQUATIONS:  BEGIN    VAR  E  =  EQUATION;
   {COLLECT   E  \FRESH   FOR  E  $E  ES;}                      END      ENDDEFN
```

We also define \FRESH for the type NAMED_SIGNALS:

```
DEFINE    FRESH( NS:NAMED_SIGNALS  )  =  NAMED_SIGNALS:
     BEGIN    VAR  X  =  NAMED_SIGNAL;
     {COLLECT  X  FOR  X  $E  NS;    EACH_DO  X.SIGNAL::=  \FRESH;  ;}
     END      ENDDEFN
```

In all cases, \FRESH is written so to touch all accessible signals.

Now that we have \FRESH for NAMED_SIGNALS and for EQUATIONS, we can define \FRESH for LOGIC_CELLs:

```
DEFINE    FRESH( L:LOGIC_CELL ) = LOGIC_CELL:
     BEGIN VAR  L1 = LOGIC_CELL;
        [ INPUTS:        L.INPUTS  \FRESH
          OUTPUTS:       L.OUTPUTS  \FRESH
          EQUATIONS:     L.EQUATIONS  \FRESH
          SUBCELLS:      {COLLECT L1 \FRESH FOR L1 $E L.SUBCELLS;}
          NAME:          L.NAME      ]
                     \STANDARDIZE
END          ENDDEFN
```

[The \FRESH applied to the INPUTS and OUTPUTS is the \FRESH that applies to the type NAMED_SIGNALS. The \FRESH applied to the EQUATIONS is the \FRESH that applies to a set of equations. Finally, the \FRESH applied to each subcell, L1, is the \FRESH defined (recursively) for LOGIC_CELLs.]

The resulting LOGIC_CELL is a copy of the original with all signal cquivalcnccs accounted for. This logic cell is finally subjected to an operator named \STANDARD-IZE. We will define \STANDARDIZE shortly and explain why we need it here. In the meantime, think of \STANDARDIZE as an identity.

7.1.2   Setting the INDIRECT Field of a SIGNAL

So far, in the absense of a mechanism by which to set a signal's indirect field, the \FRESH operators all yield no changes. We now present an official way to set indirect fields.

We desire the effect of indirection to be apparent from all points of view. That is, if we indirect a signal, we wish that indirection to be apparent at all references to that signal. For example, if we indirect signal A to signal B, we desire all occurrences of A to sense this indirection so that \FRESH will render all occurrences of A as the signal B.

This kind of modification for the indirect field is the same kind of modification used in Section 3.2.4.3. This ''objective'' modification was used to set the VALUE field of a signal during simulation. We desire that the effecting of setting the INDIRECT field be globally apparent in just the way that setting the VALUE field was during simulation. We use the ''@'' operator to implant an objective modification.

The following procedure is our official indirect operator:

```
DEFINE  INDIRECT( FROM,TO: SIGNAL ):
     FROM::=  \FRESH;
     INDIRECTS::=  FROM  <$  ;
     @(FROM).INDIRECT:=  TO;           ENDDEFN
VAR    INDIRECTS  =  SIGNALS  ;
```

It indirects signal FROM to signal TO.

INDIRECT first \FRESHens FROM so that if FROM itself has previously been indirected to another signal, say A, then INDIRECT implants the modification to signal A. (This \FRESHening maintains the meaning of such a previous indirection, that is, that FROM is really the signal A.)

INDIRECT then puts FROM on the list INDIRECTS, simply to remember the fact that FROM has now been modified. INDIRECT finally sets FROM's indirect field to reference TO. The ''@'' operator used in this assignment specifies simply that this modification is to become apparent not merely from the point of view of the program variable FROM, but actually from the point of view of the signal itself. (Implanting the modification within the signal itself makes this modification apparent from all structures that reference this signal.)

We now have the capability to render pairs of signals equivalent in a LOGIC_CELL. We proceed in three steps:

1   INDIRECT: For each pair of signals desired to be equivalent, say A and B, do

INDIRECT(A,   B   );

2   FRESH: Render a copy of the LOGIC_CELL,

LOGIC_CELL   \FRESH

which has replaced all occurrences of the first signal of each pair (signal A) by the second signal in that pair (signal B).

3   END_INDIRECT: Clean up the original LOGIC_CELL (i.e., undo the indirection implanted in the first signal of each pair).

The second step yields the desired LOGIC_CELL. The third step undoes all the objective modifications implemented by the first step. This third step cleans the slate, so to speak, so that subsequent INDIRECT/FRESH cycles do not incorporate accidentally indirection implanted only for previous INDIRECT/FRESH cycles.

We have assumed that \FRESH yields no change initially, when no signals are indirected. The END_INDIRECT procedure in step 3 reestablishes this initial assumption:

```
DEFINE  END_INDIRECT:        BEGIN     VAR  S  =  SIGNAL  ;
        FOR  S  $E  INDIRECTS;  DO     @(S).INDIRECT:=  NIL;               END
        INDIRECTS:=  NIL;                                    END     ENDDEFN
```

7.1.3   Removing Trivial Equations from a LOGIC_CELL

We now define the operator

logic_cell   \NONTRIVIAL   →   logic_cell

which will yield a logic cell devoid of trivial equations. We define this operator as follows. It implements the three steps just shown, and refers to another operator, \NONTRIVIAL1, which does most of the work:

```
DEFINE   NONTRIVIAL(   L:  LOGIC_CELL   )   =   LOGIC_CELL:
        DO     L:=  L  \NONTRIVIAL1  ;
               L:=  L  \FRESH  ;
               END_INDIRECT;
        GIVE     L                                            ENDDEFN
```

The first assignment calls \NONTRIVIAL1 to implant the indirections (step 1) and also to yield the LOGIC_CELL with trivial equations removed. The second assignment renders the LOGIC_CELL with all signal equivalences incorporated. The third statement cleans up the effects of the first step, so that no signals persist in having indirections.

The operator \NONTRIVIAL1 removes trivial equations and simultaneously implants indirects in order to maintain the intent of the now-absent equations. \NON-

TRIVIAL1 is meant to be called only from \NONTRIVIAL because \NONTRIVIAL1 does not clean up the indirections it creates:

```
DEFINE    NONTRIVIAL1( L: LOGIC_CELL ) = LOGIC_CELL:
    BEGIN   VAR E= EQUATION; RHS = SIGNAL_EXPR; L1 = LOGIC_CELL ;
    DO      L.EQUATIONS:= {COLLECT    E    FOR  E  $E  L.EQUATIONS;
                EACH_DO      RHS:=  E.RHS;
                             CASE RHS OF
                                 SIMPLE: IF - E.DELAY THEN
                                              INDIRECT(E.LHS,  RHS);
                                         E:=  NIL;              FI
                       ENDCASE ; } ;
            L.SUBCELLS:={COLLECT  L1  \NONTRIVIAL1  FOR  L1  $E  L.SUBCELLS;};
    GIVE    L                                      END      ENDDEFN
```

The first assignment redefines L.EQUATIONS. The new set of equations looks like a collection of the original set of equations:

```
{COLLECT    E    FOR E $E L.EQUATIONS;    ... }
```

However, the EACH_DO clause takes the liberty to set E to NIL if it finds E to be a trivial equation. Setting E to NIL effectively deletes the equation E from the resulting list. (Recall that NIL values are always dropped from strings.)

The EACH_DO clause determines if an equation E is trivial by examining its RHS. If the RHS resides in the SIMPLE state (i.e., the RHS is simply a signal), the equation E is deemed to be trivial. Actually, E must also be an \EQU equation. (\NEXT equations always express a lack of equivalence simply because the LHS resides in a future time zone.) Thus, if E is not DELAYed, the trivial equation is removed, having first indirected the LHS signal to the RHS signal. Thus, the entire assignment to L.EQUATIONS both removes trivial equations and preserves their intentions via the creation of indirections.

The second assignment renders each subcell nontrivial. Thus, \NONTRIVIAL1 removes trivial equations from all subcells of the LOGIC_CELL and replaces them by indirections. The original operator \NONTRIVIAL thus produces a LOGIC_CELL with all trivial equations removed and with the implied signal equivalences implemented by the fact that all LHS signals of trivial equations have been replaced by their corresponding RHS signals.

Examples. Figure 7.1 shows

(A)	COUNTER_BIT	\CELL
(B)	COUNTER_BIT \NONTRIVIAL	\CELL
(C)	COUNTER(3)	\CELL
(D)	COUNTER(3) \NONTRIVIAL	\CELL

Figure 7.2 shows

(A)	FD	\CELL
(B)	FD \NONTRIVIAL	\CELL

Figure 7.3 shows

CNT(4) \NONTRIVIAL

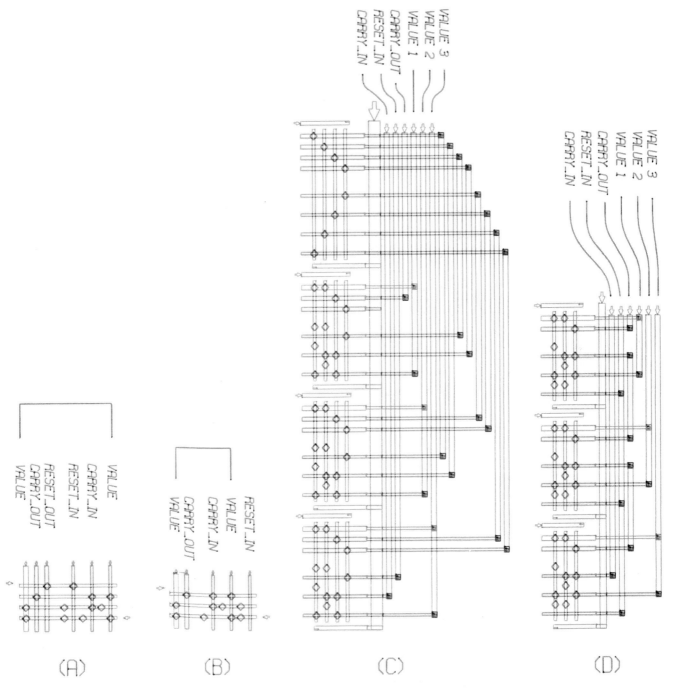

FIGURE 7.1   Effects of the \NONTRIVIAL operator.

[Figure 6.18 shows CNT(4) without the aid of \NONTRIVIAL.] Figure 7.4 shows the light dimmer logic cell.

LD   \NONTRIVIAL

Notice that \NONTRIVIAL reduces layout complexity and area. In fact, this is the first time that we can see interconnections arising directly between subcells. In the absense of \NONTRIVIAL, all subcells communicate only with the EQUATIONS PLA. The EQUATIONS PLA in these examples has served as unneeded overhead through which all intersubcell communications had to pass (much like an oversized bureaucracy).

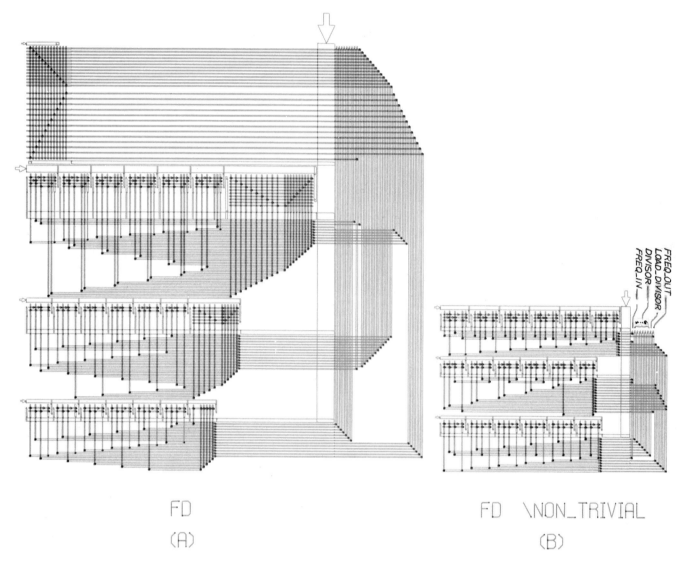

FD   FD \NON_TRIVIAL

(A)   (B)

FIGURE 7.2

Observation. We have rendered dramatic improvements in layouts without even considering the domain of layouts. These improvements were implemented entirely within the domain of LOGIC_CELLs.

We see here for the first time a fundamental nature of silicon compilation:

1 We may work in a domain other than that of layouts, a domain unencumbered by the details of layout and enhanced by the fact that the essential information is presented clearly and simply.

2 The effects of working in such abstract domains manifest themselves globally in the resulting layout.

That is, where most conventional methods of layout design involve only localized changes to layouts, these nonlayout domains provide for modifications specified from a new perspective, a perspective that maps directly into the global structure of layouts. We will see in this section more kinds of LOGIC_CELL manipulations which serve to reform layouts in their entireties.

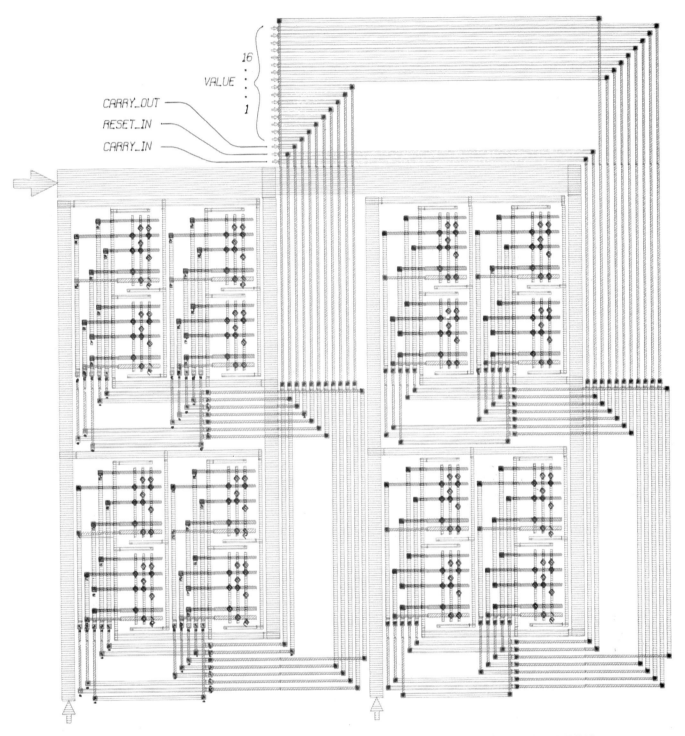

CARRY_OUT

RESET_IN

CARRY_IN

16

VALUE

1

FIGURE 7.3   The recursive counter rendered \NONTRIVIAL.

7.2   INTERFACE CONSIDERATIONS: THE OPERATOR \STANDARDIZE IN \FRESH

Compare Figures 7.1A and B. What happened to the RESET_OUT output from the PLA? RESET_OUT still appears on the interface of this logic cell, yet there is no PLA output that defines this signal. Perhaps removing that RESET_OUT equations renders an illegal logic cell, i.e., a logic cell that ceases to be \STRUCTURALLY_OK because it claims to supply an output that it does not even generate.

The removal of trivial equations is mathematically sound. Trivial equations do, in fact, merely specify signal equivalences. Thus, even though we removed an equation

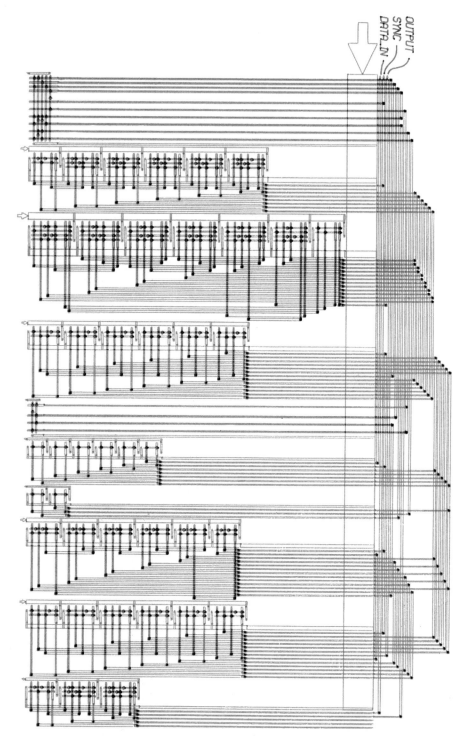

FIGURE 7.4   LD rendered \NONTRIVIAL.

that defines an interface output, the resulting logic cell still maintains that RESET_OUT is available to the outside world.

    The interface input signal RESET_IN comes into this logic cell from the outside. The removal of the RESET_OUT equation has rendered RESET_OUT and RESET_IN as the same signal. Therefore, since RESET_IN is available from the outside, that same RESET_IN (RESET_OUT) is therefore already available in the outside world. Thus,

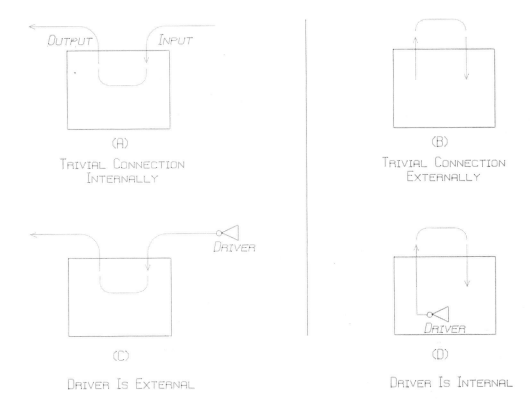

FIGURE 7.5   Interface consideration: Who drives whom?

the removal of that trivial equation has, in fact, cut off no communication paths, and hence the communications as advertised in the interface still remain intact.

The indirection from RESET_OUT to RESET_IN has rendered an unusual change within the interface itself. This one signal now appears as both an input (RESET_IN) and an output (RESET_OUT). Previous to the application of \NONTRIVIAL, RESET_IN and RESET_OUT were distinct signals. The indirection has thus introduced a phenomenon that deserves some attention: What does it mean when a signal is both an input and an output?

Figure 7.5A and B show two interpretations that can arise when a signal appears as both an input and an output. Figure 7.5C and D are more explicit; they include the fact that the signal is driven by some source (i.e., is the output of some PLA). These two interpretations differ simply on whether the signal is driven by an external source or from an internal source. Under the first interpretation, the signal is really an input, and under the second interpretation, the signal is really an output.

Can we tolerate the appearance of a signal as both an input and an output? Unfortunately we cannot, because as Figure 7.5 shows, such a duplicate appearance renders uncertain whether or not the signal is driven from within. If the signal is not driven from within (parts A and C), the interpretation of that signal as an output is misleading. For example, \STRUCTURALLY_OK (Section 5.3) would conclude that the LOGIC_CELL

COUNTER(3)   \NONTRIVIAL

is illegal because one signal (RESET_OUT) appears as the output of more than one subcell (Figure 7.6A). \STRUCTURALLY_OK believes that RESET_OUT is multiply defined. However, we can see that these three outputs are bogus; they do not drive the signal, they merely form a daisy chain which follows the one input given to the right-most subcell.

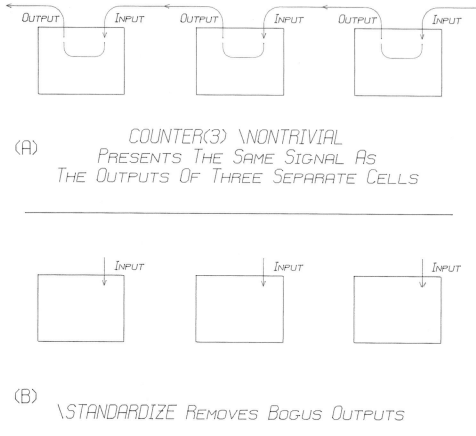

(A) COUNTER(3) \NONTRIVIAL
PRESENTS THE SAME SIGNAL AS
THE OUTPUTS OF THREE SEPARATE CELLS

(B)
\STANDARDIZE REMOVES BOGUS OUTPUTS

FIGURE 7.6

Let us therefore refine our interpretation of the input and output interfaces of logic cells. We now assert

1 A signal appearing on the output interface is in fact driven from within the logic cell.

2 A signal appearing on the input interface is in fact not driven from within (i.e., it is driven from outside this logic cell.

This is entirely consistent with our previous interpretations of logic cell interfaces. It does, however, forbid the appearance of a signal as both an input and an output. (The occurrence of such a phenomenon has arisen only due to the \NONTRIVIAL operator, which renders previously distinct signals as identical signals.)

We now introduce the \STANDARDIZE operator, which was referenced in the \FRESH operator for logic cells. At the time we introduced that \FRESH operator, we ignored the call to \STANDARDIZE. However, it is the \STANDARDIZE operator in \FRESH which automatically avoids duplicate appearances of signals in both the inputs and outputs. Thus, once we define \STANDARDIZE, the operators \FRESH and hence \NONTRIVIAL yield legal interfaces (e.g., Figure 7.6B).

\STANDARDIZE merely examines the logic cell so to distinguish between the two interpretations shown in Figure 7.5, and subsequently removes unnecessary inputs and nondriven outputs.

We introduce two operators:

logic_cell \STANDARD_INTERFACE   →   logic_cell
logic_cell \STANDARDIZE   →   logic_cell

\STANDARDIZE will utilize \STANDARD_INTERFACE. In addition, the operator \STANDARD_INTERFACE will be used for other purposes. It deduces a sufficient interface for the given logic cell, ignoring whatever interface might already be represented in the given logic cell. \STANDARDIZE will use this computed interface to modify and render legal the interface of its given logic cell.

We define \STANDARD_INTERFACE, which deduces and then defines the INPUTS and OUTPUTS of a logic cell:

```
DEFINE     STANDARD_INTERFACE(  L:LOGIC_CELL  )  =  LOGIC_CELL:
     BEGIN     VAR  E  =  EQUATION;  L1  =  LOGIC_CELL;  INPUTS,OUTPUTS=  SIGNALS  ;
     DO        INPUTS:=  (   $$    E.RHS  \INPUTS   FOR  E  $E  L.EQUATIONS;)   $$
                         (  $$  L1.INPUTS  FOR  L1  $E  L.SUBCELLS;  )
                         \LESS  {  THE_TRUE_SIGNAL  }    ;
               OUTPUTS:=  {COLLECT    E.LHS    FOR  E  $E  L.EQUATIONS;}     $$
                         (  $$   L1.OUTPUTS    FOR  L1  $E  L.SUBCELLS;  )
                         \LESS  {  THE_TRUE_SIGNAL  }    ;
               L.INPUTS:=  INPUTS  \LESS  OUTPUTS  \UNIQUE    \NAMED  'IN'  ;
               L.OUTPUTS:=  OUTPUTS  \UNIQUE    \NAMED  'OUT'  ;
     GIVE      L                                      END        ENDDEFN
```

The first assignment determines all inputs as required by the equations and subcells. We assume that all subcells already have legal interfaces; that is, all their inputs are real inputs and not bogus inputs of the kind shown in Figure 7.5D. Thus, the first assignment sets INPUTS to the set of all signals actually read by the subcells and equations.

The second assignment sets OUTPUTS to all signals that are driven, that is, all signals defined by existing equations and the outputs of all subcells. Once again, we assume that all the subcells have legal interfaces so that their outputs are, in fact, driven.

\STANDARD_INTERFACE finally sets the INPUTS and OUTPUTS fields of the logic cell. The inputs required by this logic cell are precisely all of INPUTS less all of OUTPUTS. That is, although all of INPUTS are required within this logic cell, those INPUTS that are also OUTPUTS (generated internally) cease to be inputs to the overall logic cell. (This omitted intersection of INPUTS and OUTPUTS is precisely the set of bogus inputs of the kind shown in Figure 7.5D.)

All of OUTPUTS is established as the official set of outputs for this logic cell; they are all driven. Note that bogus outputs of the kind shown in Figure 7.5C never even show up on the variable OUTPUTS because such bogus outputs are not the outputs of equations or of subcells. They do not appear on OUTPUTS because this operator does not even consider the existing interface (INPUTS) of this logic cell as potential outputs.

The \UNIQUE operator used in the assignments to L.INPUTS and L.OUTPUTS is not necessary; it merely removes duplicates independently within each part of the interface. Also, since L.INPUTS and L.OUTPUTS are of type NAMED_SIGNALS, the computed interface signals are assigned names via \NAMED.

Although \STANDARD_INTERFACE computes a legal and sufficient interface, this interface may be larger than necessary. That is, of all available outputs, only a subset may in fact be required from the logic cell. For example, \STANDARD_INTERFACE presents as outputs the LHSs of all equations and the outputs from all subcells. In contrast, logic cells that we specified by hand [e.g., COUNTER(N)] purposefully did not include all possible outputs. We included only the subset of all available outputs that we felt were appropriate interface signals, for example, the specification of COUNTER(N) does not include the CARRY_OUT signals of all subcells (COUNTER_BITs).

The functional interfaces we defined for our logic cells maintain the limited interface principle (Section 6.2.5). They specify precisely which subset of available outputs are really relevant to the intended function captured by the logic cell. Thus, we can see that \STANDARD_INTERFACE by itself destroys the conciseness of such functional interfaces. (This operator does not even read the interface given initially in L.)

The \STANDARDIZE operator utilizes \STANDARD_INTERFACE together with the existing concise interface to produce an interface that is both legal and concise:

```
DEFINE     STANDARDIZE( L:LOGIC_CELL  ) =  LOGIC_CELL:
      BEGIN    VAR  L1  =  LOGIC_CELL  ;
      DO       L1:=  L \STANDARD_INTERFACE  ;
               L.INPUTS:=  L1.INPUTS  \KEEP  L.INPUTS  ;
               L.OUTPUTS:=  L1.OUTPUTS  \KEEP  L.OUTPUTS  ;
      GIVE     L                                         END      ENDDEFN
```

It computes the legal interface and then yields the intersection (\KEEP) of the legal interface with the existing, concise interface. The result is therefore no less concise than the original interface and it contains no bogus inputs or outputs. \KEEP is defined by

```
DEFINE  KEEP( NS:NAMED_SIGNALS  SS:SIGNALS  ) =  NAMED_SIGNALS:
      BEGIN    VAR  N  =  NAMED_SIGNAL  ;
{COLLECT  N  FOR  N  $E  NS;  WITH  N.SIGNAL  \IN  SS  ;}     END      ENDDEFN
```

Finally, let us consider in its entirety how \STANDARDIZE is used within the recursive \FRESH operator. Since \FRESH always yields a logic cell that has been subjected to \STANDARDIZE, we can conclude that all the subcells computed within \FRESH, (L1 \FRESH), are legal. Thus, \FRESH's call to \STANDARDIZE passes in a logic cell all of whose subcells are legal. When \STANDARDIZE calls the \STANDARD_INTERFACE operator, it is passing in a logic cell all of whose subcells are legal. Thus, we can now see the justification for our assumption that all subcells are already legal when inside the operator \STANDARD_INTERFACE.

Figure 7.7 shows

```
FD     \NONTRIVIAL
```

if \STANDARDIZE did not perform the intersection (i.e., if \STAND-ARD_INTERFACE alone provided the interface).

7.2.1 Another Optimization: \MINIMIZE_OUTPUTS

Notice in Figure 7.2B that a wire is routed out from the counter component and is then left unconnected to anything. Apparently, that wire carries a signal which is in the interface of the counter and yet which is not read by any other cells (the register or comparator). We can, in fact, deduce that this wire is an output of the counter, not an input. (An unfed input would be illegal, whereas an unused output is entirely legal. The legality of FD has been guaranteed by \STRUCTURALLY_OK.)

That unused output is the CARRY_OUT of the counter. Whereas the CARRY_OUT is well defined and is often a desired output of a counter, the particular use of the counter within FD does not require this signal. Figure 7.8 shows the result of applying a new operator

```
logic_cell  \MINIMIZE_OUTPUTS        →      logic_cell
```

to FD; that is, this figure shows

```
FD  \NONTRIVIAL  \MINIMIZE_OUTPUTS
```

We see now that there are no unused outputs; that is, CARRY_OUT is no longer routed out from the counter, and in fact, the high order bit (PLA) of the counter has shrunk because that CARRY_OUT is not required as an output. (The CARRY_OUTs from other bits in the counter remain simply because other counter bits require these as inputs.)

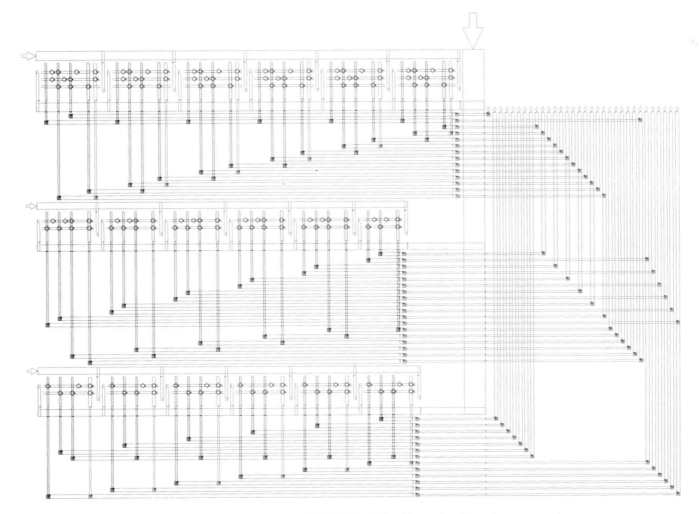

FIGURE 7.7   FD with maximal interfaces everywhere.

The optimizations apparent in Figure 7.8 are due entirely to the reduction of some interfaces, and the removal of equations whose outputs cease to be read because of the smaller interfaces:

```
DEFINE    MINIMIZE_OUTPUTS(  L:LOGIC_CELL  )  =  LOGIC_CELL:
       BEGIN    VAR  L1  =  LOGIC_CELL;  E  =  EQUATION ;  WE_NEED  =  SIGNALS  ;
       DO       WE_NEED:=  L.OUTPUTS      $$
                       (  $$    L1.INPUTS   FOR  L1  $E  L.SUBCELLS;)      $$
                       (  $$    E.RHS  \INPUTS    FOR  E  $E  L.EQUATIONS; )  ;
                L.EQUATIONS:=  {COLLECT  E  FOR  E  $E  L.EQUATIONS;
                                     WITH  E.LHS  \IN  WE_NEED; }  ;
                L.SUBCELLS:=  {COLLECT    L1  \MINIMIZE_OUTPUTS
                        FOR  L1  $E  L.SUBCELLS;
                             EACH_DO  L1.OUTPUTS::=  \KEEP  WE_NEED;; }  ;
       GIVE    L                                          END    ENDDEFN
```

This function first determines which signals are needed. (We need to define our own outputs, the inputs to all subcells, and the inputs to our equations.) Signals not in WE_NEED are simply not needed. The second assignment keeps only those equations that define signals in WE_NEED. (This is where the equation defining the final CARRY_OUT ceases to exist.) Finally, the third assignment applies \MINI-

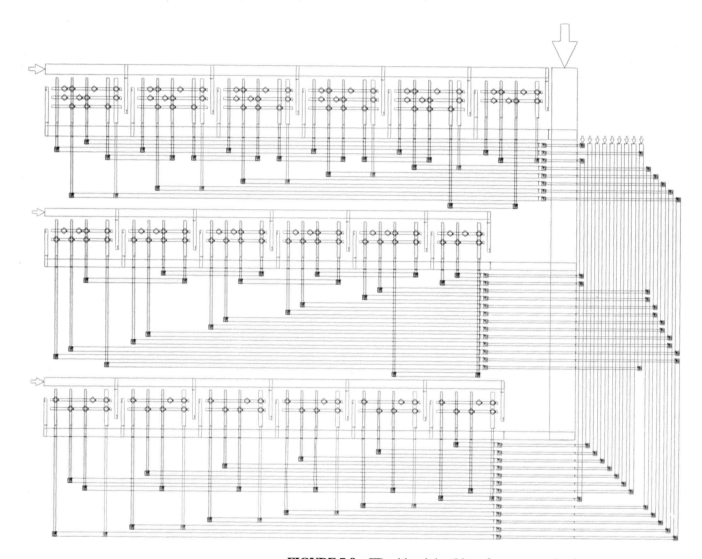

FIGURE 7.8   FD with minimal interfaces everywhere.

MIZE_OUTPUTS to each subcell. However, each subcell is first trimmed so that its interface (OUTPUTS) includes only those signals that we really need.

It is crucial to the success of this operator that each subcell's OUTPUTS be trimmed before that subcell is subjected to \MINIMIZE_OUTPUTS. For example, the application of \MINIMIZE_OUTPUTS to the logic cell FD determines initially that the CARRY_OUT presented by the counter subcell is consumed by no entity. Therefore, prior to applying \MINIMIZE_OUTPUTS to this counter, the counter is affected by removing CARRY_OUT from its interface. This removal in effect relieves the counter itself from having to produce this output.

\MINIMIZE_OUTPUTS applied to the counter thus finds CARRY_OUT absent from WE_NEED: It is absent from the counter's OUTPUTS. Thus, when \MINIMIZE_OUTPUTS is applied to the high-order counter bit, the CARRY_OUT from that counter bit is removed from its interface simply because CARRY_OUT is not in WE_NEED. Finally, \MINIMIZE_OUTPUTS applied to the high order counter bit can remove the equation that defines CARRY_OUT.

The relief from having to produce certain outputs is thus passed downward in the nested calls to \MINIMIZE_OUTPUTS. It is passed downward because a subcell's interface is trimmed before, and not after, calling \MINIMIZE_OUTPUTS. This downward passage of information is precisely the character of this computation, which customizes a subcell to take advantage of its surrounding context. (In contrast, if the interface trimming were done after calling \MINIMIZE_OUTPUTS, no information would be passed downward. We could then deduce that each subcell would be oblivious to the reduced needs of its surrounding context.)

Figure 7.9 shows

LD   \NONTRIVIAL   \MINIMIZE_OUTPUTS

Notice, for example, that compared to Figure 7.4, the three VALUE signals from the 3-bit counter (FLASHER) no longer leave that subcell.

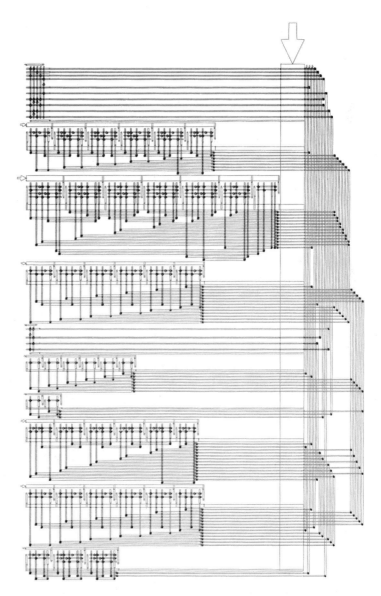

FIGURE 7.9   LD with minimal interfaces.

7.2.2 Another Optimization: Removing Unclocked Equations

We have provided for the removal of one class of equations, the trivial equations. We can remove another class of equations, (nearly) all \EQU equations. For example, the equations

A   \NEXT   (B \AND C   \OR NOT(B))
B   \EQU   D \OR F

may be reduced by removing the B equation and replacing all appearances of the signal B by appearances instead of the signal expression

D \OR F

[Recall that \EQU equations are exactly like the equations used by mathematicians (Section 3.1.1).] Thus, this pair of equations can be replaced by the single equation

A   \NEXT   ((D \OR F) \AND C   \OR   NOT(D \OR F))

We implement such substitutions automatically by a means nearly identical to that used to remove trivial equations. For example, if we write something like

INDIRECT(B,   D \OR F) ;

and simultaneously remove the B equation, the \FRESH operator applied to the first equation, the A equation, could yield the single A equation with (D \OR F) incorporated in place of B.

We now define such an INDIRECT operator, which can take a SIGNAL_EXPR instead of a mere SIGNAL:

DEFINE   INDIRECT(FROM:SIGNAL TO:SIGNAL_EXPR) :
    FROM::= \FRESH;
    INDIRECTS::= FROM <$;
    @(FROM).EXPR:= TO;   ENDDEFN

This new INDIRECT is identical to the old INDIRECT except that it stores the TO parameter into the EXPR, and not INDIRECT, field of the FROM signal. Since none of our programs yet refer to a signal's EXPR field, the INDIRECT operator does not yet affect anything.

We make use of a signal's EXPR field in a slightly new rendition of one of the \FRESH operators. We know that in order to remove the B equation, we must preserve its intentions so to affect in no way the overall behavior. We must therefore replace all appearances of B by the SIGNAL_EXPR (D \OR F).

This poses a problem unencountered in our effort to indirect one signal to another signal. We can always tolerate any signal-to-signal indirection because the substitute entity is of type SIGNAL, the same type embraced by the substituted entity. Thus, in any context whatsoever, we could replace the FROM signal by the TO signal (e.g., whether the signal appears in the RHS of an equation or in the interface of a logic cell).

In contrast, our new INDIRECT associates the FROM signal not with a SIGNAL, but with a SIGNAL_EXPR. This reduces considerably the interchangeability in various contexts. Fortunately, we can tolerate within a SIGNAL_EXPR (e.g., the RHS of any equation) the substitution of a SIGNAL by a SIGNAL_EXPR. However, we cannot tolerate such a substitution within a logic cell's interface because the interface datatype, NAMED_SIGNALS, can refer only to SIGNALs, not to SIGNAL_EXPRs.

Fortunately, these two contexts are the only contexts we need to consider. In the domain of logic cells, signals appear only in

1 Equations' RHSs   (SIGNAL_EXPRs)

2 Equations' LHSs   (SIGNALs)

3 Logic cell interfaces   (NAMED_SIGNALs)

We may ignore the second context listed here because any signal appears as the LHS of at most one equation, and, in fact, it appears precisely in the one equation we desire to remove. Thus, the only inhibition to removing a nontrivial \EQU equation is the appearance of its LHS signal in the interface of the surrounding logic cell.

We will therefore remove only those \EQU equations whose LHSs do not appear in the logic cell's interface. This restriction also arises from another argument: We can never remove an equation that defines an interface signal because this would render the logic cell not \STRUCTURALLY_OK. For example, consider the following \EQU equation from the COUNTER_BIT logic cell:

CARRY_OUT   \EQU   VALUE \AND   CARRY_IN

Any attempt to remove this equation would render undefined the CARRY_OUT in COUNTER_BIT's interface. In other words, where \EQU equations generally represent intermmediate computations, required on the way into \NEXT equations, such intermediate values must continue to exist if they are referenced from the outside world.

Consider also a small chip whose sole function is to implement a single AND gate. It cannot tolerate the removal of its one \EQU equation. Such a removal would render the chip with no function at all. Fortunately, that equation will not be removed simply because its LHS appears on the output interface.

Having decided to remove only those \EQU equations not referenced from the logic cell's interface, we need consider SIGNAL-to-SIGNAL_EXPR substitutions only in the context of SIGNAL_EXPRs. Thus, of all \FRESH operators, only the \FRESH operator

signal_expr   \FRESH $\rightarrow$ signal_expr

need consider such indirections. We implement any SIGNAL-to-SIGNAL_EXPR substitution when a SIGNAL is examined in this \FRESH operator (i.e., in the SIMPLE case). We therefore substitute the old SIMPLE case,

```
...
SIMPLE:     E   \FRESH
...
```

by

```
...
SIMPLE:     DO    E:=   E   \FRESH   ;
            GIVE  IF  DEFINED(E.EXPR)  THEN      E.EXPR  \FRESH
                                       ELSE      E                       FI
...
```

Recall that in the SIMPLE case, the variable E is of type SIGNAL. This new rendition first \FRESHens the signal E, so that E now holds the signal yielded by the old SIMPLE case. The new SIMPLE case, however, sees if E has been indirected to a SIGNAL_EXPR, and if it has, it yields this SIGNAL_EXPR (E.EXPR). This E.EXPR is itself \FRESHened (recursively) so to assure that all accessible signals have been \FRESHened.

Besides this modification to the SIGNAL_EXPR \FRESH operator, and the introduction of our new INDIRECT procedure, we need affect only one more operator, the cleanup procedure END_INDIRECT. Where END_INDIRECT specified

    @(S) . INDIRECT := NIL ;

we now write instead

    @(S) . INDIRECT := NIL ;
    @(S) . EXPR   := NIL ;

At this point, the entire \FRESH mechanism accommodates both INDIRECT operators, for indirections to SIGNALs and to SIGNAL_EXPRs.

We now introduce an operator that removes all removable \EQU equations from logic cells:

    logic_cell \PURE_CLOCK   →   logic_cell

The definition of \PURE_CLOCK mirrors identically the definition of \NONTRIVIAL (the other user of our \FRESH mechanism). \PURE_CLOCK is defined in two parts, where the second part, \PURE_CLOCK1, does most of the work. The first part is identical to the definition of \NONTRIVIAL, except that the call to \NONTRIVIAL1 is now replaced by a call to \PURE_CLOCK1:

    DEFINE   PURE_CLOCK(L: LOGIC_CELL) = LOGIC_CELL:
         DO   L:= L \PURE_CLOCK1 ;
                  L:= L \FRESH ;
                  END_INDIRECT;
         GIVE   L   ENDDEFN

\PURE_CLOCK1 is defined by

DEFINE   PURE_CLOCK1(L: LOGIC_CELL) = LOGIC_CELL:
    BEGIN   VAR E= EQUATION; L1 = LOGIC_CELL ; WE_NEED = SIGNALS ;
    DO   WE_NEED:= L.OUTPUTS $$
                        ($$ L1.INPUTS FOR L1 $E L.SUBCELLS;) ;
             L.EQUATIONS:= {COLLECT E FOR E $E L.EQUATIONS;
                        EACH_DO   IF - E.DELAY &
                                      - (E.LHS \IN WE_NEED) THEN
                                      INDIRECT(E.LHS, E.RHS);
                                      E;= NIL;   FI ; } ;
             L.SUBCELLS:={COLLECT L1 \PURE_CLOCK1 FOR L1 $E L.SUBCELLS;};
    GIVE   L   END   ENDDEFN

Unlike \NONTRIVIAL1, this definition first determines the set of interface signals, WE_NEED, which contains precisely those signals whose equations may not be removed. Notice that the second assignment, to L.EQUATIONS, INDIRECTs (and removes) and equation E only if it is both

    1 An \EQU equation   (- E.DELAY)
    2 Not defining an interface signal
                                 (- (E.LHS \IN   WE_NEED))

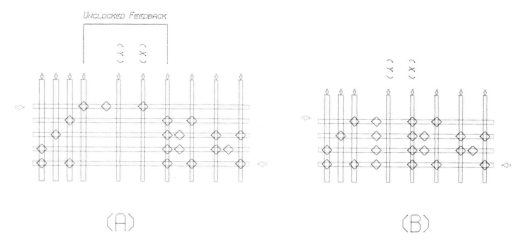

FIGURE 7.10 Example of removing unclocked feedback.

Finally, like \NONTRIVIAL1, \PURE_CLOCK1 applies itself recursively to all sub-cells.

Because \PURE_CLOCK examines interfaces of logic cells (unlike \NONTRIVI-AL), the \MINIMIZE_OUTPUTS operator presented earlier can have an effect on \PURE_CLOCK. \MINIMIZE_OUTPUTS reduces interfaces, so that following an application of \MINIMIZE_OUTPUTS, \PURE_CLOCK may find WE_NEED reduced and hence may remove more equations.

Examples of \PURE_CLOCK's effects on logic cells will be presented in following sections, after we introduce hierarchy edit operators. For all logic cells we can present at this time, \PURE_CLOCK will show no change. All our examples, except for LD, contain no removable \EQU equations. However, Figure 7.10A shows in isolation the EQUATIONS PLA of LD, and Figure 7.10B shows this same PLA after LD has been subjected to \PURE_CLOCK.

7.3 HIERARCHY EDIT OPERATIONS

The operators \NONTRIVIAL and \MINIMIZE_OUTPUTS never increase the area of derived layouts. They usually decrease the chip area substantially. All illustrations of logic cells will from now on be subjected to these two operators.

We now present another class of operators. These operators can also yield substantial decreases in area consumption. They can also increase area, and therefore they are best suited for interactive use. Their application could be rendered automatic if we were to introduce programs whose entire jobs would be to examine logic cells and determine which operators, if any, would yield improvements. The LOGIC_CELL structure, with its explicit inclusion of interface information, lends itself to efficient, recursive examination for the resolution of such questions.

We present here only the edit operators, not any operators that decide automatically where and when to apply such edit operators. We call these operators "edit" operators because

> **1** They modify only the hierarchy (organization or grouping) of subcells in a logic cell.

These operators have the property that:

> **2** They do not modify equations, nor do they add or delete equations.

Like \NONTRIVIAL and \MINIMIZE_OUTPUTS:

3   They are guaranteed to preserve the behavior of logic cells.

They also maintain, of course, acceptance by the \STRUCTURALLY_OK predicate.

In other words, these edit operators are entirely safe and may be used even recklessly. Their only effect is to change logic cell and hence layout organization. They can be used to reduce layout area and increase performance. These operators cause changes analogous to corporate reorganizations of management hierarchies. Their benefits depend on particular circumstances.

The edit operations will refer to two operators

equations   \AS_ONE   →   logic_cell

logic_cells \AS_ONE   →   logic_cell

These operators form a legal logic cell from either a set of equations or a set of logic cells:

```
DEFINE  AS_ONE( LS:LOGIC_CELLS  )  =  LOGIC_CELL:
    [SUBCELLS:  LS  ]          \STANDARD_INTERFACE              ENDDEFN
DEFINE  AS_ONE( ES:EQUATIONS  )  =  LOGIC_CELL:
    [EQUATIONS:  ES  ]          \STANDARD_INTERFACE              ENDDEFN
```

They utilize \STANDARD_INTERFACE to define completely the logic cell whose bare bones appear in these definitions. The generous, perhaps oversized interfaces generated by \STANDARD_INTERFACE will be trimmed by \MINIMIZE_OUTPUTS, which we will always apply before generating layouts.

7.3.1   Basic Edit Operators

The simplest edit operator, EXPLODE, destroys all organization, that is, it breaks all membranes of all subcells:

```
DEFINE  EXPLODE( L:LOGIC_CELL  )  =  LOGIC_CELL:
    [    INPUTS:          L.INPUTS
         OUTPUTS:         L.OUTPUTS
         EQUATIONS:       L  \EQUATIONS
         NAME:            L.NAME              ]              ENDDEFN
```

All edit operations leave unchanged the INPUTS and OUTPUTS fields. This operator extracts all at once the entire set of equations represented throughout the entire logic cell L. The result refers to no subcells because their behaviors now reside in the equations themselves. (The \EQUATIONS operator is defined in Section 5.3.1.1.) Figure 7.11 shows

(A)   COUNTER(3)   \EXPLODE

(B)   FD   \EXPLODE

These, as well as all subsequent illustrations, are subjected to the following:

...   \NONTRIVIAL \MINIMIZE_OUTPUTS   \CELL

We see that EXPLODE renders a single PLA implementation for any logic cell.

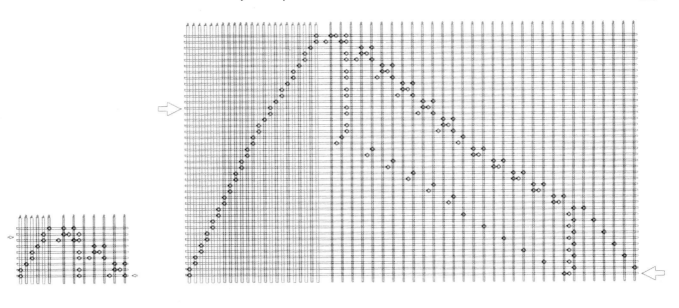

COUNTER(3) \EXPLODE

FD   \EXPLODE

(A)

(B)

EXAMPLES OF \EXPLODE

FIGURE 7.11

The following operator is a tamed and refined version of EXPLODE. It removes the membranes of only its immediate subcells (Figure 7.12A). This is analogous to a manager promoting everybody who works for him/her exactly one step up on the latter. This operator also has the effect of fusing together its immediate subcells:

```
DEFINE    FUSE(  L:LOGIC_CELL  )  =  LOGIC_CELL:  BEGIN    VAR  L1  =  LOGIC_CELL  ;
    [INPUTS:        L.INPUTS
     OUTPUTS:       L.OUTPUTS
     EQUATIONS:     L.EQUATIONS       $$
                    (  $$    L1.EQUATIONS    FOR  L1  $E  L.SUBCELLS;  )
     SUBCELLS:      $$   L1.SUBCELLS    FOR  L1  $E  L.SUBCELLS;
     NAME:          L.NAME     ]
    END       ENDDEFN
```

Upon disolving the membranes of its immediate subcells, the EQUATIONS of these immediate subcells leak out and join the EQUATIONS field of this logic cell. Also, the subcells of the immediate subcells (grandchildren) leak out and come together as the new immediate subcells (children) of this logic cell. Figure 7.13 shows

   (A)   COUNTER(3) \FUSE

   (B)   FD \FUSE

The next operator considers not only immediate subcells, but it peers one level deeper. It sees two levels of management all at once. Because of the rotations implemented by the \CELL operator, this view down through two generations corresponds to a

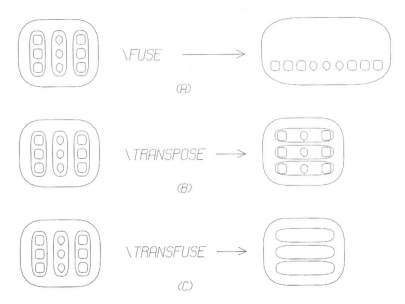

FIGURE 7.12　Hierarchy edit operations.

two-dimensional array of cells. As Figure 7.12B shows, \TRANSPOSE regroups the sub-subcells along the opposite dimension. In the result, the first subcell consists of the first sub-subcell of each original subcell, and the second subcell groups together all second sub-subcells, and so on.

```
DEFINE    TRANSPOSE(  L:LOGIC_CELL  )  =  LOGIC_CELL:
    BEGIN     VAR  L1  =  LOGIC_CELL;  I  =  INT;  HOT  =  LOGIC_CELLS  ;
    [INPUTS:              L.INPUTS
     OUTPUTS:             L.OUTPUTS
     EQUATIONS:           L.EQUATIONS      $$
                          (  $$    L1.EQUATIONS    FOR  L1  $E  L.SUBCELLS;  )
     SUBCELLS:            {  FOR  I  FROM  1  BY  1;
                                EACH_DO  HOT:=  {COLLECT  L1.SUBCELLS[I]
                                                    FOR  L1  $E  L.SUBCELLS;  }  ;  ;
                             &&  WHILE  DEFINED(HOT);
                                COLLECT          HOT  \AS_ONE    }  \NAMED  'BIT'
     NAME:                L.NAME              ]
    END     ENDDEFN
```

As in the \FUSE operator, \TRANSPOSE breaks the membranes of its immediate sub-cells and hence includes their equations in the EQUATIONS field of the result. These membranes have to be broken conceptually in order to deal freely with the sub-subcells. Finally, \TRANSPOSE forms its SUBCELLS field by setting HOT to a list consisting of the Ith sub-subcell from each subcell, and by grouping this Ith category of sub-subcells into a single subcell via the \AS_ONE operator. Figure 7.14 shows

```
        FD  \TRANSPOSE
```

The next operator combines \TRANSPOSE and \FUSE:

```
DEFINE    TRANSFUSE(  L:LOGIC_CELL  )  =  LOGIC_CELL:
    BEGIN     VAR  L1  =  LOGIC_CELL  ;
    DO        L::=  \TRANSPOSE  ;
              L.SUBCELLS:=  {COLLECT    L1  \FUSE    FOR  L1  $E  L.SUBCELLS;}  ;
    GIVE      L                                        END     ENDDEFN
```

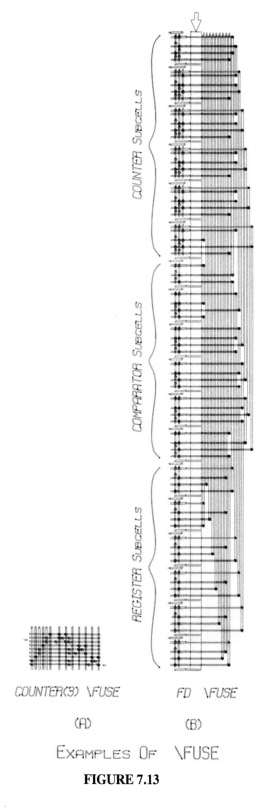

COUNTER(3) \FUSE

FD \FUSE

(A)

(B)

EXAMPLES OF \FUSE

FIGURE 7.13

Figure 7.12C shows the effect. \TRANSFUSE forms the \TRANSPOSE and then applies \FUSE upon each of the new subcells. Figure 7.15 shows

FD   \TRANSFUSE

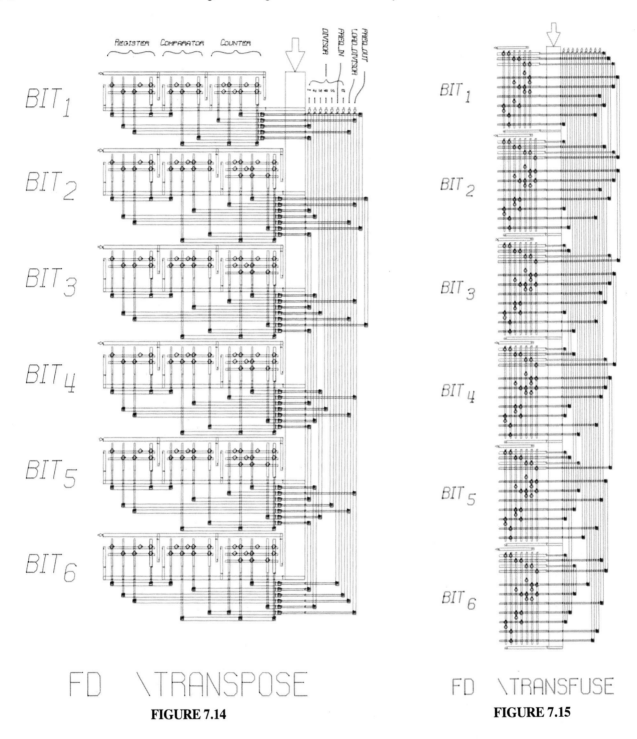

FD \TRANSPOSE

FIGURE 7.14

FD \TRANSFUSE

FIGURE 7.15

7.3.2 Effects of the \PURE_CLOCK Operator

These edit operators have produced logic cells whose EQUATIONS fields hold larger sets of equations, that is, sets of equations formed from previously separate sets. These larger sets of equations might now contain \EQU equations which define signals absent from the old interfaces. For example,

COUNTER(3) \EXPLODE

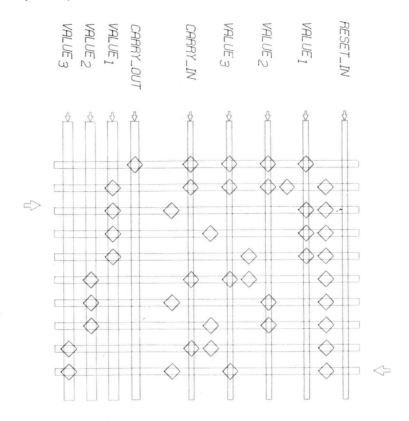

COUNTER(3)   \EXPLODE   . . .   \PURE_CLOCK

FIGURE 7.16   Three-bit counter without unclocked feedback.

contains all the carry-chain \EQU equations in one set. Intermediate CARRY_OUT signals are no longer referenced in logic cell interfaces.

Intermediate CARRY_OUT signals were referenced in the individual COUNTER_BITs within COUNTER(3). But now that all the COUNTER_BIT membranes have been broken, because of \EXPLODE, the intermediate CARRY_OUTs appear only as internal signals, not resident in the top level interface of COUNTER(3).

Figure 7.16 shows

```
COUNTER(3)   \EXPLODE
                \NONTRIVIAL   \MINIMIZE_OUTPUTS
                                    \PURE_CLOCK
                                                  \CELL
```

We will write this more simply as

```
COUNTER(3)   \EXPLODE      ...      \PURE_CLOCK
```

Implicit in other illustrations are the \NONTRIVIAL, \MINIMIZE_OUTPUTS, and \CELL operators. However, we wish to place the call to \PURE_CLOCK after \MINIMIZE_OUTPUTS and before \CELL, so to render \PURE_CLOCK most effective, after \MINIMIZE_OUTPUTS. In other words, Figure 7.16 shows

```
COUNTER(3)   \EXPLODE      ...      \PURE_CLOCK
```

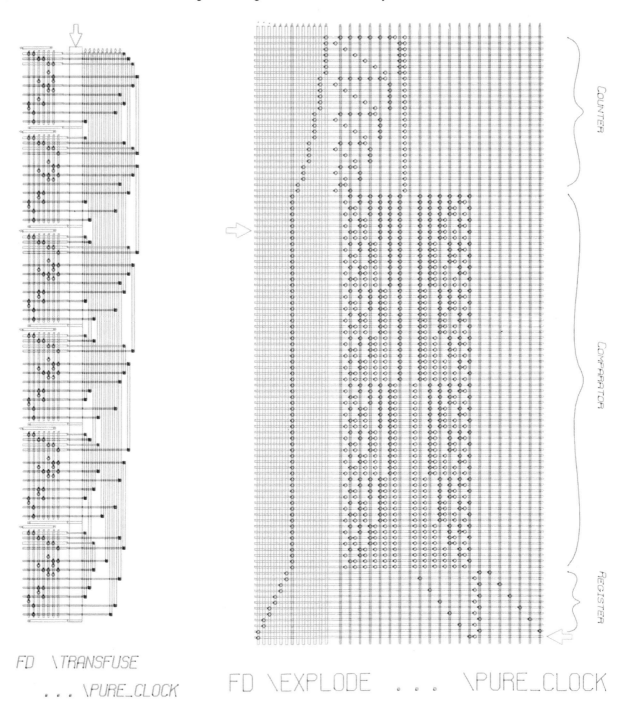

FD \TRANSFUSE
. . . \PURE_CLOCK

FD \EXPLODE . . . \PURE_CLOCK

FIGURE 7.17   **FIGURE 7.18**

Compare this to Figure 7.11A.
Figure 7.17 shows

  FD   \TRANSFUSE   ...   \PURE_CLOCK

Compare this to Figure 7.15. Figure 7.18 shows

  FD   \EXPLODE   ...   \PURE_CLOCK

Compare this to Figure 7.11B.

\PURE_CLOCK reduces the number of PLA inputs and outputs because the removed equations no longer contribute their LHS signals as outputs. These signals are simultaneously not read by the PLA; all dependencies on these removed signals have been transferred to dependencies instead on other signals, due to \PURE_CLOCK.

\PURE_CLOCK has also increased the number of PLA AND terms. The removal of equations has rendered many of the remaining equations more complex. This extra complexity manifests itself in the extra AND terms. In fact, this manifestation can be quite extreme.

Consider the equations

```
A    \EQU    (  B  \AND  C  )
B    \EQU    (  U  \OR  V  \OR  W  )
C    \EQU    (  J  \OR  K  \OR  L  )
```

Removing all but the first equation yields

```
A    \EQU    (  U  \OR  V  \OR  W  )    \AND    (  J  \OR  K  \OR  L  )
```

However, a PLA implements equations only in disjunctive form (i.e., a DF_EQUATIONS). In disjunctive form, this equation appears as

```
A    \EQU        (  U  \AND  J  )    \OR
                 (  U  \AND  K  )    \OR
                 (  U  \AND  L  )    \OR
                 (  V  \AND  J  )    \OR
                 (  V  \AND  K  )    \OR
                 (  V  \AND  L  )
```

Thus, a dramatic increase in AND-terms can result from the removal of intermediate \EQU equations.

A PLA offers exactly two levels of logic, an OR of ANDs. However, an output feeding back into the PLA can participate in a total of two trips through the PLA, and hence four levels of logic (i.e., an OR of ANDs, of ORs of ANDs). This increased number of logic levels reduces the potentially drastic expansions imposed by renditions in terms of only two levels of logic (disjunctive form).

It is possible to have even more than two trips through the PLA. For example,

```
COUNTER(3)  \EXPLODE
```

renders the two intermediate CARRY_OUT signals as unclocked feedback. In fact, from the first CARRY_IN to the last CARRY_OUT, there are a total of three trips through the PLA. This has the potential, therefore, of utilizing six levels of logic.

Compare Figure 7.19A and B:

```
(A)  EQ(3)    \EXPLODE
(B)  EQ(3)    \EXPLODE    ...    \PURE_CLOCK
```

The effects of removing the unclocked feedbacks (b) is more drastic than the similar operation on COUNTER(3). The EQ chain in EQ(3) utilizes most completely the six levels of logic. [Figures 7.20 and 7.21 compare the same for EQ(4) and EQ(5).]

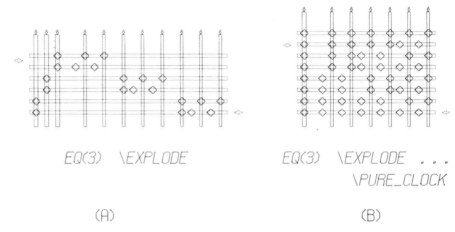

FIGURE 7.19   \PURE_CLOCK increases number of terms.

7.3.3   Electrical Performance and the \PURE_CLOCK Operator

We have seen how \PURE_CLOCK can have a drastic effect on PLA area by introducing a profusion of AND-terms. Let us consider for a moment various trade-offs in the domain of electrical performance, namely the effects imposed on the maximum operating frequency.

As discussed in Section 3.1.5, the fastest rate at which we can clock a chip is bounded above by the fact that each time unit requires nonzero time to allow unsteadiness to settle. That is, all equations must settle during the life of a single time unit.

The PLA that implements equations determines the time required for signals to settle into a steady state. Section 1.3.6 shows what keeps such resolutions from happening infinitely fast. Each wire in silicon contributes a resistance and a capacitance proportional to the wire's length, and it is in fact the product of these two numbers that dictates the slowness of signal propagations. That is, slowness increases as the square of the distance spanned by a wire. We conclude, therefore, that the delay from PLA input to PLA outputs grows linearly with the area taken by the PLA.

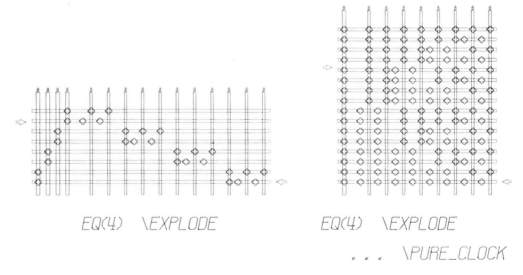

FIGURE 7.20   A more dramatic increase.

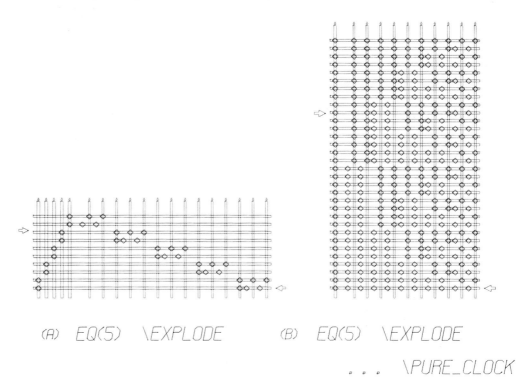

(A) EQ(5) \EXPLODE   (B) EQ(5) \EXPLODE

                                        . . . \PURE_CLOCK

FIGURE 7.21 Exponential growth of terms.

Consider now the propagation time required for the carry chain in COUNTER(3). The entire propagation must occur all within one time unit. Compare the propagation times for

1 COUNTER(3)

2 COUNTER(3) \EXPLODE

In COUNTER(3), the carry chain must propagate through three small PLAs. In contrast, the latter rendition implements the carry chain via three trips through one large PLA, or equivalently, as one trip through three separate large PLAs. Both renditions require three (unclocked) PLA trips, but the first rendition routes through small PLAs whereas the latter rendition routes through large PLAs. We expect, therefore, that the first, unEXPLODEd rendition offers a substantially faster propagation.

Consider now that \PURE_CLOCK removes unclocked feedbacks, and hence

3 COUNTER(3) \EXPLODE   ...   \PURE_CLOCK

requires only one trip through one large PLA. We expect, therefore, that this rendition will run faster than rendition 2. However, it is less clear which rendition, 1 or 3, will run faster. In fact, \PURE_CLOCK can backfire and reduce performance if it enlarges the one PLA substantially, as in the EQ(3) example. There, one trip through the very large PLA may exceed the cost of three trips through a medium-large PLA, particularly due to the quadratic delay dependence on PLA dimensions.

We will present a method for providing automatic electrical performance estimates in Chapter 9. At that point, we will compare the electrical performances computed for several renditions.

7.4 LOCALIZING THE APPLICATION OF EDIT OPERATIONS

Sometimes we wish to apply an edit operator to only a portion of a logic cell. Specifying which portion is to be subjected to an edit is called selection. In Section 2.7.4 we considered a form of selection, splitting layouts, in conjunction with an interactive graphics editor.

Let us call the results of splitting a set of logic cells a SPLIT_LOGIC:

TYPE   SPLIT_LOGIC = [SEL: LOGIC_CELLS   REST: LOGIC_CELLS] ;

The following operator,

logic_cell \SELECT   names   →   split_logic

splits a logic cell's set of subcells by rendering those with the specified names in the SEL field and all the rest in the REST field:

```
DEFINE    SELECT( L:LOGIC_CELL    NS:NAMES  )  =  SPLIT_LOGIC:
   BEGIN    VAR  L1  =  LOGIC_CELL  ;
   [ SEL: {COLLECT  L1  FOR  L1  $E  L.SUBCELLS ;  WITH  L1.NAME  \IN  NS;}
     REST: {COLLECT  L1  FOR  L1  $E  L.SUBCELLS ;  WITH  -(L1.NAME  \IN  NS);}]
   END    ENDDEFN
```

```
DEFINE  IN(  N:NAME  NS:NAMES  )  =  BOOL:         BEGIN    VAR  N1= NAME  ;
   THERE_IS    N  \EQ  N1    FOR  N1  $E  NS;              END    ENDDEFN
```

For example,

FD \SELECT { 'COUNTER' }

is a SPLIT_LOGIC in which FD's subcell named 'COUNTER' is selected (in the SEL field) and FD's other subcells, COMPARATOR and REGISTER, remain unselected (in REST).

The following operator utilizes \SELECT:

logic_cell \POP names   →   logic_cell

\POP destroys (pops) the membranes of those immediate subcells with the specified names. In contrast, \FUSE pops the membranes of all immediate subcells. For example,

FD \FUSE   is equivalent to
FD \POP   { 'COUNTER' ; 'COMPARATOR' ; 'REGISTER' }

because \POP here specifies the names of all subcells. Figure 7.22 shows

(A) FD \POP   { 'COUNTER' }
(B) FD \POP   { 'COMPARATOR' ; 'REGISTER' }

\POP is defined by

```
DEFINE    POP( L:LOGIC_CELL  VICTIMS:NAMES  )  =  LOGIC_CELL:
   BEGIN    VAR  SEL,  REST  =  LOGIC_CELLS;
   DO       [SEL:SEL  REST:REST]  :=  L  \SELECT  VICTIMS  ;
            L.SUBCELLS:=  SEL  $>  (  REST  \AS_ONE  )  ;
   GIVE    L  \FUSE                          END    ENDDEFN
```

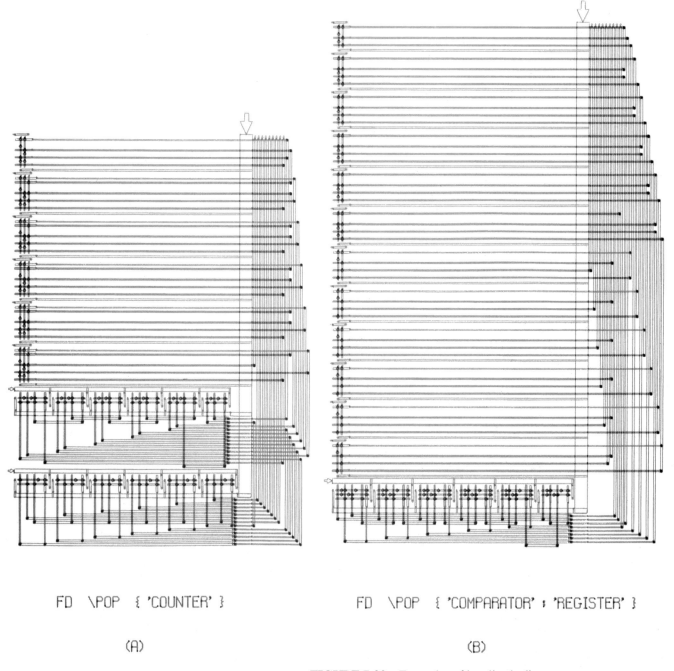

FD \POP { 'COUNTER' }

FD \POP { 'COMPARATOR' ; 'REGISTER' }

(A)

(B)

FIGURE 7.22   Examples of localized edits.

This definition pops the selected subset of subcells (SEL) by applying \FUSE to a new logic cell whose subcells are

SEL $>   (REST \AS_ONE)

\FUSE applied on this set of subcells removes the membrane from each subcell; that is, the membrane is removed from each cell in SEL and from the final subcell in this list

REST   \AS_ONE

[Recall that \AS_ONE forms a single logic cell from a set of logic cells (REST).] The loss of membrane from this final subcell results in the set of subcells

REST

In other words, to keep \FUSE from popping the membranes of those subcells in REST, \POP first puts an extra membrane around this set of subcells. \FUSE then pops this new membrane (together with the membranes of each cell in SEL) and thereby leaves the set REST unchanged.

We see that \POP is a refined version of \FUSE; \POP implements the effects of \FUSE but only on a selected subset of subcells. Let us now supply another, general form of refinement which can be used to refine all the basic edit operators. For example, where

FD   \TRANSFUSE

applies \TRANSFUSE to the entire set of subcells (Figure 7.15), we would now like to say (Figure 7.23)

FD   \TAKE   {   'COUNTER'   ;   'COMPARATOR'   }   \TRANSFUSE_TO   'MATCHER'

This notation is meant to specify an application of \TRANSFUSE on only two of the three subcells. The result of this partial \TRANSFUSE is a single cell named 'MATCH-ER', and it replaces the two given subcells.

We may characterize each of our basic edit operators by the datatype (Section 2.5)

TYPE   OPERATOR   =   //   LOGIC_CELL   (LOGIC_CELL   )   \\   ;

Each takes in a LOGIC_CELL and produces a new LOGIC_CELL in its place. For example, each of the following is an instance of type OPERATOR:

1   //(L:LOGIC_CELL)   FUSE(L)   \\
2   //(L:LOGIC_CELL)   TRANSPOSE(L)   \\
3   //(L:LOGIC_CELL)   TRANSFUSE(L)   \\

The first OPERATOR takes in a logic cell and yields the result of \FUSE applied to that logic cell (L). The second and third operators represent TRANSPOSE and TRANSFUSE, respectively.

We may characterize the association of subcell names with a logic cell via the type SELECTION:

TYPE   SELECTION   =   [FROM: LOGIC_CELL   TAKE: NAMES   ] ;

DEFINE   TAKE(L:LOGIC_CELL NS:NAMES)   =   SELECTION:
[FROM: L   TAKE: NS   ]   ENDDEFN

The \TAKE operator forms a SELECTION and we include it only to support the notation used earlier.

We now supply a general-purpose operator, APPLY, which will implement the heart of all the refined edit operations. APPLY takes in three parameters:

APPLY(operator, selection, name)   →   logic_cell

For example, the notation introduced earlier,

FD \TAKE { 'COUNTER' ; 'COMPARATOR' }   \TRANSFUSE_TO 'MATCHER'

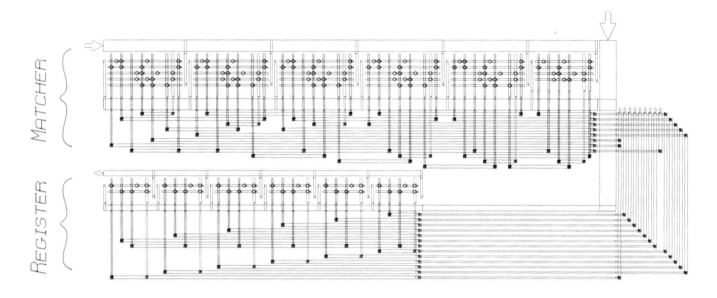

FD \TAKE { 'COUNTER' ; 'COMPARATOR' }

\TRANSFUSE_TO 'MATCHER'

FIGURE 7.23

will call upon APPLY as follows:

> APPLY(//(L:LOGIC_CELL)   TRANSFUSE(L) \\ ,
> FD \TAKE { 'COUNTER' ; 'COMPARATOR' }
> 'MATCHER'

APPLY thus knows

1. The operator, which is to be applied in a refined manner
2. The logic_cell and the names of a subset of its subcells
3. The name of the resulting subcell

We define APPLY with:

```
DEFINE    APPLY( OP:OPERATOR  S:SELECTION  TO:NAME ) = LOGIC_CELL:
   BEGIN    VAR  SEL,REST = LOGIC_CELLS ;    NEW = LOGIC_CELL ;
   DO       [SEL: SEL    REST: REST]:= S.FROM \SELECT  S.TAKE ;
            NEW:= <*OP*> ( SEL \AS_ONE ) ;
            S.FROM.SUBCELLS:= ( NEW \NAMED TO ) <$ REST ;
   GIVE     S.FROM                          END        ENDDEFN
```

The first assignment splits the given logic cell (S.FROM) according to the subcell names (S.TAKE). Thus, SEL represents the specified subcells themselves. The second assignment sets NEW to the new subcell formed from the selected subcells. NEW is formed by applying the operator, OP, on the selected set of subcells rendered as a single subcell (\AS_ONE). That is, \AS_ONE groups the selected subcells into one subcell by surrounding these subcells with a new membrane, and this "selected logic cell" becomes the input for the operator.

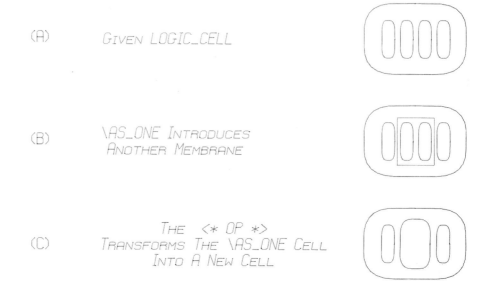

(A)   GIVEN LOGIC_CELL

(B)   \AS_ONE INTRODUCES
       ANOTHER MEMBRANE

(C)   THE <* OP *>
       TRANSFORMS THE \AS_ONE CELL
       INTO A NEW CELL

FIGURE 7.24   Implementation for local edits.

For example, Figure 7.24 shows that \AS_ONE effectively draws a circle around the subset of selected subcells. This one cell then goes through the operator (Figure 7.24C) and this result becomes the replacement for the subcells selected. The third assignment in APPLY redefines the SUBCELLS field of the original logic cell (S.FROM) so to include the NEW subcell named TO (e.g., 'MATCHER') in addition to all the unselected subcells, REST.

We define, for abbreviation, the operators

selection	\FUSE_TO	name	$\rightarrow$	logic_cell
selection	\TRANSFUSE_TO	name	$\rightarrow$	logic_cell
selection	\TRANSPOSE_TO	name	$\rightarrow$	logic_cell

These abbreviations support the notation used earlier:

```
DEFINE    FUSE_TO( S:SELECTION TO:NAME ) = LOGIC_CELL:
    APPLY(    //(L:LOGIC_CELL)    FUSE(L)    \\ ,    S,  TO )
DEFINE    TRANSFUSE_TO( S:SELECTION TO:NAME ) = LOGIC_CELL:
    APPLY(    //(L:LOGIC_CELL)    TRANSFUSE(L)    \\ ,    S,  TO )    ENDDEFN
DEFINE    TRANSPOSE_TO( S:SELECTION TO:NAME ) = LOGIC_CELL:
    APPLY(    //(L:LOGIC_CELL)    TRANSPOSE(L)    \\ ,    S,  TO )    ENDDEFN
```

These abbreviations merely supply the appropriate parameters to APPLY. We add one more operator,

selection	\TO	name	$\rightarrow$	logic_cell

which merely adds the membrane around the selected subcells. This is equivalent to demoting the selected subcells so to add a new manager above them:

```
DEFINE    TO( S:SELECTION TO:NAME ) = LOGIC_CELL:
    APPLY(    //(L:LOGIC_CELL)    L    \\ ,    S,  TO )    ENDDEFN
```

This supplies to APPLY the identity OPERATOR. Figure 7.25 illustrates how all four of these refined operators work.

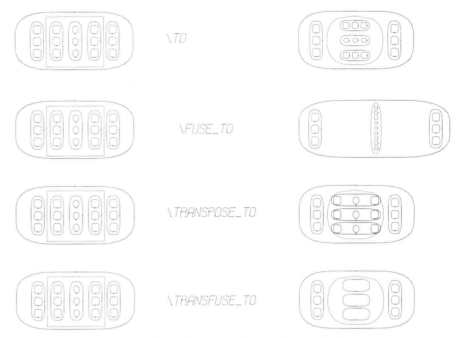

FIGURE 7.25   Abbreviations for local edits.

Figure 7.26 shows the intentions of the following operator:

logic_cell   \SUBMERGE_AS   name   →   logic_cell

This operator submerges the EQUATIONS of the logic cell so now to appear as a new subcell, which has the specified name. The resulting logic_cell ceases to have any EQUATIONS, now that they are represented securely as an extra subcell:

```
DEFINE   SUBMERGE_AS( L:LOGIC_CELL  TO:NAME ) = LOGIC_CELL:
   DO       L.SUBCELLS:= ( L.EQUATIONS \AS_ONE \NAMED TO ) <$
                                                   L.SUBCELLS ;
            L.EQUATIONS:= NIL ;
   GIVE     L                                                ENDDEFN
```

In fact, this operator in no way effects the derived layout. Notice that \CELL always puts the EQUATIONS PLA on the front of the subcells passed to \PACK. \SUBMERGE_AS effectively removes this EQUATIONS PLA and instead introduces this same cell as the first cell in the list of cells derived from the logic subcells. \SUBMERGE_AS, therefore, is used primarily in preparation for the use of other edit operators. It renders the EQUATIONS field as just another subcell, which may then participate in operators such as \FUSE_TO and \TRANSFUSE_TO.

For example, Figure 7.27A shows

GE(6)

We see the 6 GE_BIT subcells and then a seventh cell, the EQUATIONS PLA, which in this example has not disappeared entirely (\NONTRIVIAL) because it does implement some nontrivial logic. The EQUATIONS produces the GE_OUT of this entire logic cell by ORing together the GT_OUT and EQ_OUT signals from the low-order GE_BIT (named 'BIT' \SUB 6).

Figure 7.27b shows

GE(6) \POP { 'BIT' \SUB 6 }

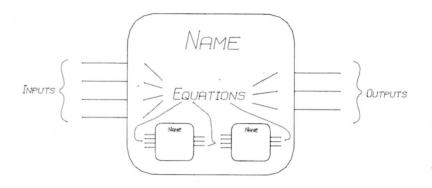

The \SUBMERGE Operator
Takes This LOGIC_CELL . . .

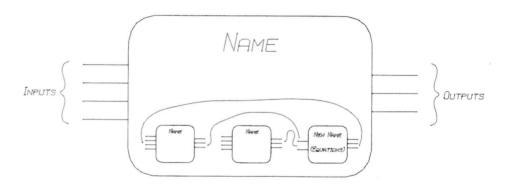

. . . And Renders The Equations
As A New Subcell

FIGURE 7.26

This removes the low-order GE_BIT and instead throws its equations up into the EQUA-
TIONS of the entire logic cell. We therefore see only six subcells, one of which is the
EQUATIONS PLA. The EQUATIONS PLA impliments both the low-order GE_BIT
and the final logical OR. Notice that this combination takes no more area than that taken
by the low-order GE_BIT in isolation.

Figure 7.27C shows

$$\text{GE(6)} \qquad \text{\POP} \quad \{ \text{ 'BIT' } \text{\SUB} \quad 6 \quad \}$$
$$\text{\SUBMERGE\_AS} \qquad (\text{ 'BIT' } \text{\SUB} \quad 6 \quad)$$

\SUBMERGE_AS is used here to reestablish the EQUATIONS logic as a subcell, reac-
quiring the name 'BIT' \SUB 6. The result therefore has no EQUATIONS field and, in
fact, the original EQUATIONS that performed the final OR have been moved effectively
into the low order GE_BIT ('BIT' \SUB 6). In general, this combination of \POP and
\SUBMERGE_AS used on the same name merges the EQUATIONS into the specified
subcell.

This example shows one unwanted side effect: The order of subcells has been
changed. \SUBMERGE_AS has put ('BIT' \SUB 6) at the "wrong" end of the list. We
can respecify any desired order for subcells via the operator

$$\text{logic\_cell} \quad \text{\ORDER} \quad \text{names} \qquad \rightarrow \qquad \text{logic\_cell}$$

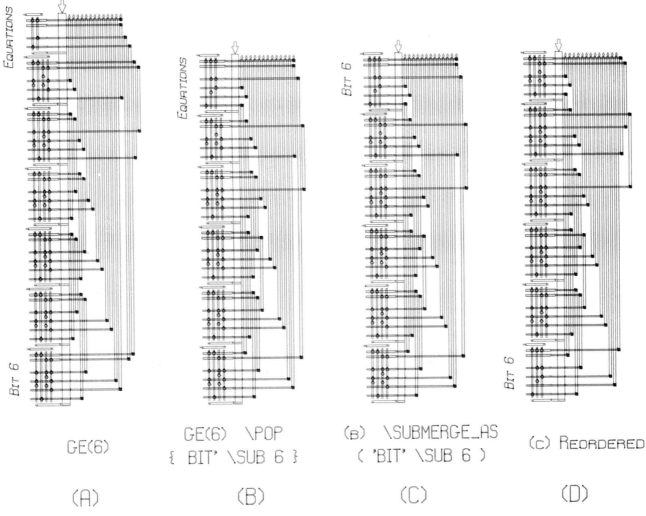

FIGURE 7.27 A sequence of edits.

This operator merely changes the order of subcells in the SUBCELLS field:

```
DEFINE  ORDER( L:LOGIC_CELL NS:NAMES ) = LOGIC_CELL :
   BEGIN    VAR SEL, REST = LOGIC_CELLS; N = NAME ;
   DO       [SEL:SEL REST:REST] := L \SELECT NS ;
            SEL:= {COLLECT    SEL \S N    FOR N $E NS; } ;
            L.SUBCELLS:= SEL $$ REST ;
   GIVE     L                                          END      ENDDEFN
```

Figure 7.27D shows

```
        GE(6)    \POP   { 'BIT' \SUB 6 }
                 \SUBMERGE_AS    ( 'BIT' \SUB 6 )
                 \ORDER {COLLECT 'BIT' \SUB I    FOR I FROM 1 TO
```

This reorders the cell back to the original ordering.

We supply one more general-purpose APPLY operator, which supports the repeated application of an OPERATOR independently over each of a selected subset of subcells. In contrast, our other APPLY has been defined to

1 Apply an OPERATOR once to a selected set of subcells rendered as a single cell (via \AS_ONE).

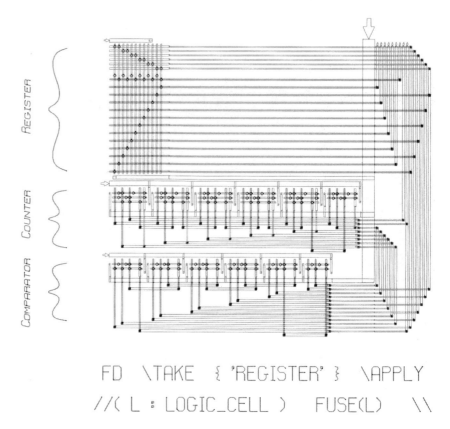

FIGURE 7.28   Localized edit using \APPLY.

The new APPLY is defined to

> **2**   Apply an OPERATOR several times, once to each selected subcell.

The new APPLY,

> selection   \APPLY   operator   →   logic_cell

can be used to form Figure 7.28, via

FD   \TAKE   {   'REGISTER'   }   \APPLY   //(L:LOGIC_CELL)   FUSE(L) \\

This applies \FUSE to the register subcell without introducing an extra membrane. In fact, the contrasting

> FD   \TAKE   {   'REGISTER'   }   \FUSE_TO   'JUNK'

is an identity; it renders no change besides that of changing from the name 'REGISTER' to the name 'JUNK'. In general, the old APPLY, (e.g., \FUSE_TO, \TRANSFUSE_TO, etc.) act as identities when given a selection consisting of only one subcell. (This \FUSE_TO example does remove a membrane, but that membrane is precisely the one created in APPLY by \AS_ONE, in its effort to group together as one cell the set of ''more than one'' selected subcells.)

The original three-parameter APPLY operator will never appear in our edit specifications, that is, it will appear only in the definitions of \FUSE_TO, \TRANSFUSE_TO, and so on. In contrast, the new two-parameter APPLY will be visible in our edit specifications, as in the example shown in Figure 7.28. The new \APPLY is defined by

```
DEFINE    APPLY( S:SELECTION OP:OPERATOR )  =  LOGIC_CELL:
   BEGIN    VAR SEL, REST  =  LOGIC_CELLS; L1  =  LOGIC_CELL ;
   DO       [SEL:SEL REST:REST]:=  S.FROM \SELECT S.TAKE ;
            SEL:=  {COLLECT    <*OP*>( L1 )    FOR L1 $E SEL; } ;
            S.FROM.SUBCELLS:=  SEL $$ REST ;
   GIVE     S.FROM                                                    END    ENDDEFN
```

The first assignment performs the selection and the second assignment applies the operator OP to each subcell of SEL independently.

7.4.1 Example: Editing the Light-Dimmer LOGIC_CELL

We now apply edit operations on the LD logic cell. Figure 7.9 shows LD as it stands unedited, except for the customary \NONTRIVIAL and \MINIMIZE_OUTPUTS procedure. First, let us order the subcells explicitly:

```
L:=  LD \ORDER {  'TIME' ;  'GE' ;  'BRIGHTNESS' ;  'ENABLE_FF' ;  'OP' ;
                  'OPERAND' ;  'EQ' ;  'ADDRESS' ;  'FLASHER'        };
```

Figure 7.29 shows the result. This order has been chosen manually so to render close together those groups of subcells that communicate the most with one another.

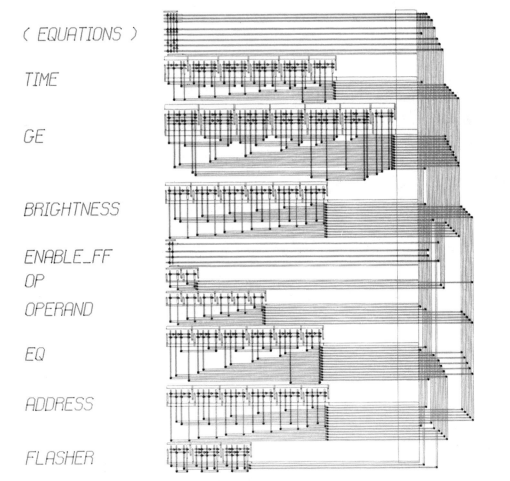

FIGURE 7.29 LD before edits.

Figure 7.29 and the remaining figures in this section are all subjected to the \PURE_CLOCK operator, described in Section 7.3.2.

Let us now perform the tiny modification to the GE component as shown in Figure 7.27:

```
A:=  L  \TAKE  {'GE'}      \APPLY
         //(L:LOGIC_CELL)
         L     \POP  {'BIT'  \SUB  6}       \SUBMERGE_AS     ('BIT'  \SUB  6)
               \ORDER  {COLLECT  'BIT'  \SUB  I  FOR  I  FROM  1  TO  6;}          \\;
A::=      \ORDER    {  'TIME'  ;  'GE'  ;  'BRIGHTNESS'  ;  'ENABLE_FF'  ;  'OP'  ;
                       'OPERAND'  ;  'EQ'  ;  'ADDRESS'  ;  'FLASHER'          };
```

Figure 7.30 shows this result. In this example, the modification to GE has been done within L, via the \APPLY operator.

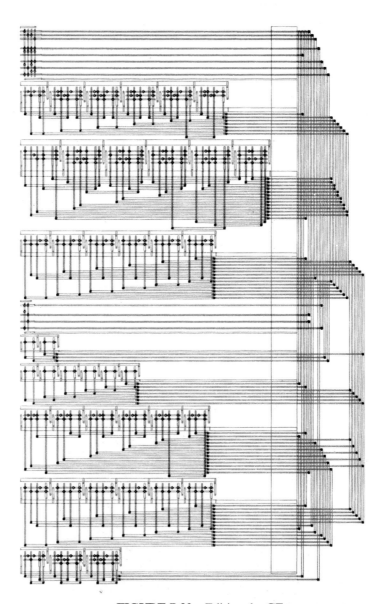

FIGURE 7.30   Editing the GE component.

Among the subcells, we see one tiny single-PLA subcell, ENABLE_FF, which resides approximately halfway up the set of subcells. Let us POP this tiniest of subcells, via

B:= A \POP { 'ENABLE_FF' } ;

Figure 7.31 shows this result. Notice that the EQUATIONS PLA (upper left) has grown slightly, so to include the now absent ENABLE_FF subcell.

We see six 6-bit subcells:

TIME, GE, BRIGHTNESS, OPERAND, EQ, and ADDRESS

We notice that each of ADDRESS and EQ consists of very small PLAs (having only two AND-terms each). We note also that ADDRESS and EQ communicate heavily with one another; that is, ADDRESS is one of the two 6-bit inputs to EQ. We can remove the interconnect required for this particular communication and also merge bitwise the tiny PLAs by applying \TRANSFUSE to each of these subcells. The following performs this, and it also transfuses two other small 6-bit subcells:

C:= B   \TAKE   { 'ADDRESS' ; 'EQ' }   \TRANSFUSE_TO 'PART1'
          \TAKE   { 'BRIGHTNESS' ; 'OPERAND' } \TRANSFUSE_TO 'PART2'
          \ORDER   { 'TIME' ; 'GE' ; 'PART2' ; 'PART1' ;
                      'OP' ; 'FLASHER'   } ;

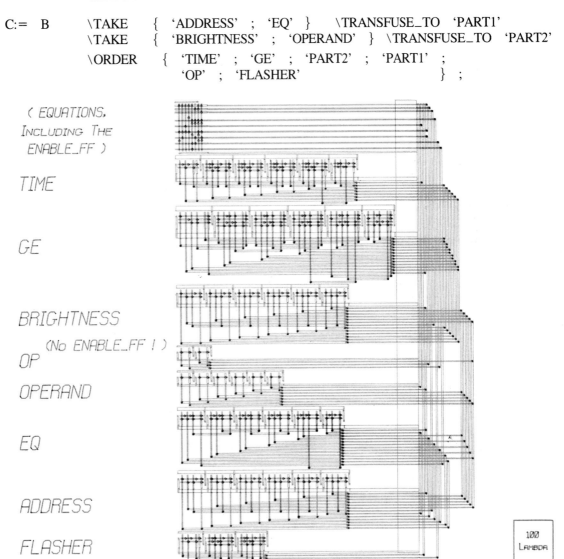

FIGURE 7.31 Removing ENABLE_FF.

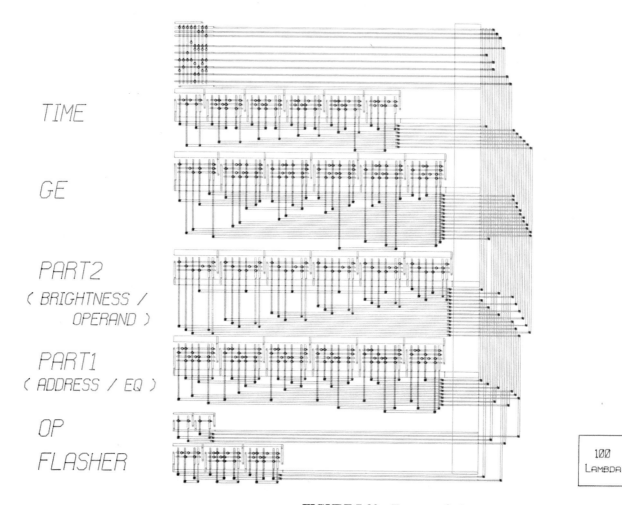

TIME

GE

PART2
(BRIGHTNESS /
   OPERAND)

PART1
(ADDRESS / EQ)

OP

FLASHER

100
LAMBDA

FIGURE 7.32   Two transfusions.

Figure 7.32 shows that the two subcells ADDRESS and EQ have become one subcell (PART1), and also that BRIGHTNESS and OPERAND have become one subcell (PART2). Thus, we have now the following 6-bit subcells:

> TIME,   GE,   PART1,   and   PART2

We now take the four 6-bit subcells and apply \TRANSPOSE to them. Figure 7.33 shows the result of

D:=   C   \TAKE   { 'TIME' ; 'GE' ; 'PART2' ; 'PART1' }
                                              \TRANSPOSE_TO 'BODY'
\POP {'BODY'} ;

We apply \POP in this expression because \TRANSPOSE_TO introduces a new membrane around these four subcells; \POP removes this artificial membrane. Thus, the four 6-bit subcells appear now to be replaced by six 4-bit subcells. Each of the original 6-bit subcells can still be seen, however, by scanning vertically the new six subcells.

\TRANSPOSE has introduced two new properties to the new logic cell. First, we can see a greater degree of regularity in Figure 7.33. There are now six nearly identical subcells as opposed to the earlier version, which had four quite different subcells. We

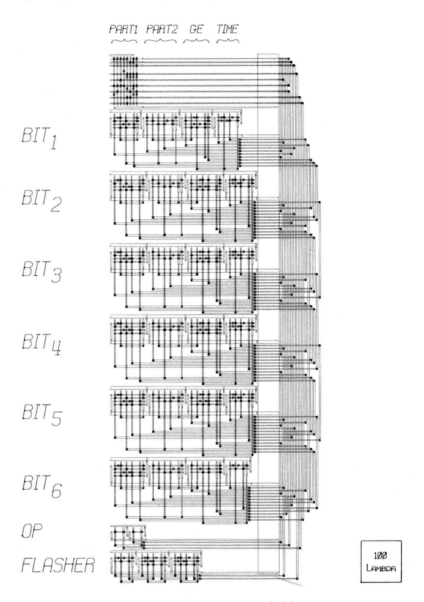

FIGURE 7.33   Transposing the six-bit parts.

see immediately a more efficient cell packing; the similarity in cell size has removed many "blank" regions. However, this particular example shows an increase in interconnect area. (Notice the wider horizontal channels.) As a result, the overall area is very nearly unchanged.

Second, this new rendition appears in a "bit-slice" format; that is, each of the six new subcells contains one bit from each of the four original subcells. As a result, the local horizontal wiring channels now serve to interconnect the dissimilar (4) bits, and the top-level vertical channel now forms the carry chain and the EQ- and GE-chains. Thus, the bit-slice effect has reversed the roles of the vertical channel and the local horizontal channels.

We consider in Chapter 8 the fusion of four-sided cells, and we will then find a substantial reduction in the area consumed by the local horizontal channels (Figure 7.34). In that more efficient context, the regularity introduced by \TRANSPOSE will show the greatest benefit.

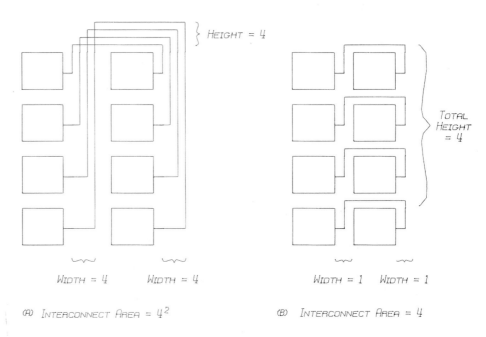

(A) INTERCONNECT AREA = 4^2 (B) INTERCONNECT AREA = 4

ROUTING SIGNALS BETWEEN CELLS
REDUCES INTERCONNECT AREA
FROM QUADRATIC TO LINEAR

FIGURE 7.34   Motivation for four-sided cells.

We can still benefit from the new regularity within our present one-sided mechanism. However, let us first clear up the irregularities introduced by the smaller, non-6-bit subcells, namely OP, FLASHER, and the equations PLA:

E:= D \TAKE   { 'OP' ; 'FLASHER' }   \APPLY //(L:LOGIC_CELL) FUSE(L) \\
      \SUBMERGE_AS   'EQUATIONS'
      \TAKE { 'FLASHER' ; 'EQUATIONS' ; 'OP' }   \TO   'RANDOM' ,

The first line renders each of OP and FLASHER as a single PLA. The second line renders the light dimmer's top-level equations themselves as a subcell, whose name is EQUATIONS. The third line groups these three entities into one subcell, so that all together these small entities will appear as one subcell (Figure 7.35). This one new subcell is named RANDOM.

We have now even a greater degree of regularity overall. However, the RANDOM subcell has thicker PLAs than those of the other six subcells. Let us therefore transfuse adjacent pairs of these other six subcells so to obtain fewer, but larger PLAs, and also to reduce interconnect:

F:= E \TAKE   { 'BIT' \SUB 1 ; 'BIT' \SUB 2 }   \TRANSFUSE_TO   'P1'
        \TAKE   { 'BIT' \SUB 3 ; 'BIT' \SUB 4 }   \TRANSFUSE_TO   'P2'
        \TAKE   { 'BIT' \SUB 5 ; 'BIT' \SUB 6 }   \TRANSFUSE_TO   'P3'
      \ORDER { 'RANDOM' ; 'P1' ; 'P2' ; 'P3' } ,

(Recall that the \TRANSPOSE operator named its resulting subcells 'BIT' \SUB I, for I from 1 to the number of subcells.) Figure 7.36 shows this result.

All the edit operators serve to affect cell placement or to merge separate PLAs into smaller numbers of larger PLAs. In contrast, none of these operators transforms one PLA into several smaller PLAs. In other words, we can imagine that these edit operators only increase entropy, removing previously refined divisions (membranes).

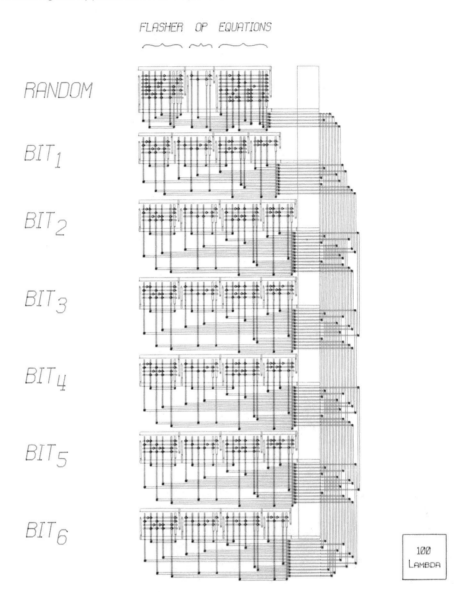

FIGURE 7.35 Collecting random pieces together.

We have so far generally benefitted from this effect. In fact, we can spell out the benefits gained by merging (two) separate PLAs into one:

1. The single PLA can often share inputs. It may be that both of the two PLAs require a common subset of inputs. Each common input is implemented twice in the separate rendition, in contrast to a single implementation in the merged rendition. For example, the RESET_IN signal in a 6-bit counter feeds six PLAs, and hence takes six implementations. In contrast, the same counter implemented in terms of three (2-bit) PLAs requires only three implementations of that input.

2. The single PLA can often share AND-terms. It may be that each of the two separate PLAs computes the same AND-term.

3. A PLA introduces area overhead independent of its logical function. Thus, a merged, although larger PLA, amortizes this overhead.

In contrast, PLA fusion sometimes backfires, increasing overall area consumption. There is a tendency toward loss in merging two PLAs if the PLAs share little or nothing

RANDOM

P1

(BIT1 / BIT2)

P2

(BIT3 / BIT4)

P3

(BIT5 / BIT6)

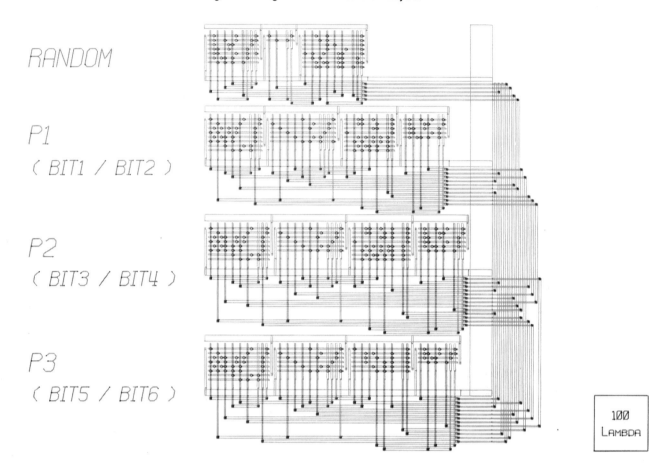

100
LAMBDA

FIGURE 7.36   Three more transfusions.

in common. Figure 7.37B shows a single PLA which implements our frequency-divider (FD) example. We see in this example great regions within the PLA which contain no diamonds (pulldown transistors). One can say that these blank regions are a PLA's way of implementing interconnect. Figure 7.38 illustrates simply how such a loss occurs.

Figure 7.37B (and Figure 7.18) shows another interesting phenomenon. We can see that the middle half serves as the comparator, and that the top and bottom quarters serve as the counter and register. Thus, even in this merged PLA, the independent components remain separated naturally.

Figure 7.37 shows two renditions of the frequency divider side by side. These two renditions differ in area by a factor of more than 2.7. Just by area consideration alone, we can deduce that the single-PLA rendition will run more slowly, in fact dramatically more slowly because the smaller version has many amplifiers (PLA inputs) (e.g., in the path of the carry chain).

We show a similar loss due to too much merging in the light-dimmer example via:

G:=   F   \TAKE { 'P1' ; 'P2' ; 'P3' ; 'RANDOM' }   \APPLY
                                    //(L:LOGIC_CELL)   FUSE(L) \\ ;

Figure 7.39 shows the result; each subcell is fused into a single PLA. The area of this rendition exceeds that of the previous rendition.

In conclusion, we see many trade-offs that arise in hierarchy editing. We see, for example, that the hierarchy is useful, because single-PLA implementations for complex behaviors often far exceed the cost of a hierarchical or organized implementation done in terms of an interconnect set of more specialized PLAs, or ''organs.''

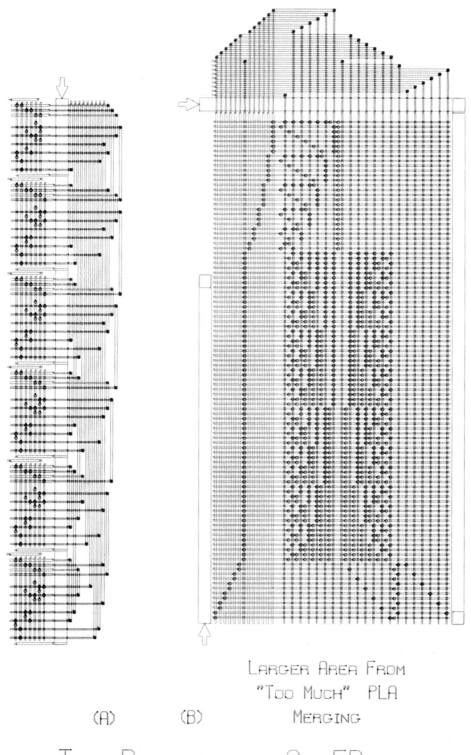

LARGER AREA FROM
"TOO MUCH" PLA
MERGING

(A)   (B)

TWO RENDITIONS OF FD

FIGURE 7.37 (*See also color plate*).

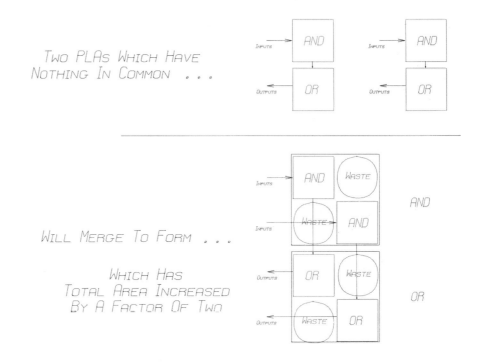

WASTE ARISING FROM "TOO MUCH" PLA MERGING

FIGURE 7.38

In analogy, our bodies are organized in terms of organs (e.g., heart, lungs, etc.) so that each may perform most efficiently a very specialized and relatively independent function. Each of our bodies is not a homogeneous entity. Such organization very often makes the difference between practical and impractical.

Even with the various overhead introduced by small PLAs and the overhead introduced by our simple one-sided fusion mechanism, we see nonetheless a savings afforded by organized logic and its modification. We have suggested a few rules of thumb for deciding which edit operators to apply, but we have shown no automatic methods for making such decisions. Some simple decision operators do exist and work. They, and undoubtedly others rely heavily on the examination of logic cell interfaces (the INPUTS and OUTPUTS fields).

The general goal in such algorithms is simply to minimize the numbers of signals on interfaces at all levels in the hierarchy. Minimial interfaces render layouts with the fewest wires. For example, we may desire operators such as the following:

1   Sprinkle some of the EQUATIONS of a logic cell over that logic cell's subcells. This is useful because an equation might deal exclusively, or primarily, with one subcell in particular. The attraction between an equation and a particular subcell can be measured by noting the change in size of that subcell's interface (number of signals) as the equation moves from outside to inside that subcell.

2   Submerge one subcell entirely within another subcell.

3   Pull a sub-subcell out from within another subcell.

The benefits of all these operators are measured by noting changes in interface size.

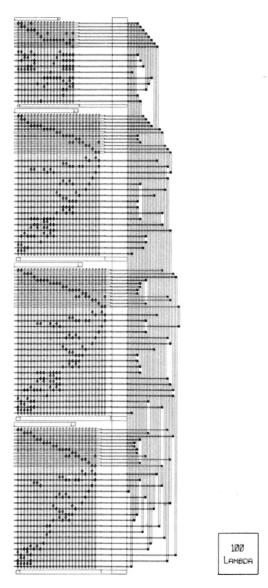

FIGURE 7.39   Too much fusion for LD.

Another class of decision-making operators would affect the order of subcells within a logic cell. Such an ordering decision is independent of the interface minimization considerations. It affects only wire lengths and the thickness of the interconnect channel required to interconnect the subcells. The interconnect channel thickness is affected because subcell order can affect how many communications can occur on one scan line of interconnect. A subcell ordering can be obtained by comparing how much each pair of subcells attract each other, where attraction is measured by the number of signals that appear in both interfaces.

We see now that many layout decisions can be made entirely within the nonlayout domain of LOGIC_CELLs, or some other abstract representations. If a new kind of optimization requires some geometric information, decisions can be made in terms of gross estimates of layout sizes derived from logic cells, or by actually generating finished layouts from intermediate logic cells under consideration.

The edit operators presented here have consumed at most a few seconds of CPU time (on a DEC-2060 processor). The generation of the layout cells shown in the illustrations each has taken generally under 20 seconds. There are a few notable exceptions, which involve only the \PURE_CLOCK operator. This operator by itself consumes insignificant time, but the subsequent translation from equations into disjunctive form has consumed more than a minute of CPU to generate the EQ(5) example (Figure 7.21), and consumed a whopping 20 minutes of CPU to generate Figures 7.18 and 7.37B, the single PLA frequency divider. However, the programs presented in this text have been rendered primarily for clarity.

EXERCISES

Section 7.1.3

1. Trace the carry chain in Figure 7.3, starting at the labeled CARRY_IN, traveling through the maze.

8

More Intimate Cell Fusion: Four-Sided Cells

We have provided for complete integration among nested sets of one-sided cells, producing as output a single one-sided cell. The heart of that algorithm, \PACK, took in a list of one-sided cells and produced a single, integrated one-sided cell.

We now sketch a mechanism by which nested sets of four-sided cells may be integrated into a single four-sided cell. A four-sided cell, unlike the one-sided variety, may have ports on all four sides which carry information (nonpower).

The only place where the one-sided mechanism actually forbids four-sided cells is in the operator \UNION_DX. Recall that \UNION_DX takes in a set of cells and produces one cell simply by placing the given cells in a row. \UNION_DX complains if any of the cells includes ports on its left or right edges. \UNION_DX simply does not provide wire routing between adjacent sides of adjacent cells (see Figure 8.1).

The interconnection provided by the one-sided mechanism interconnects only along the top of one cell, never between two cells. \UNION_DX's refusal to route between cells reflects this strict character of the one-sided mechanism. The interconnection required for four-sided integration must satisfy the need to route between two cells.

8.1 WHY EVEN CONSIDER FOUR-SIDED CELLS: DYNAMICS OF INTERCONNECT

We have gotten by just fine within the domain of one-sided cells. Even our leaf cells, the PLAs, are one-sided cells. Besides, if we desired to accommodate four-sided leaf cells, we could render them always as one-sided cells, using the existing \PACK operator (Figure 8.2).

However, the one-sided mechanism takes advantage of only one of the two physical dimensions at a time. This imposes a great topological insulation between adjacent cells. Consider, for example, the FD logic cell rendered via the one-sided mechanism in Figure 7.2B. The three subcells, the register, comparator, and counter, communicate considerably with one another. Presently, signals going from one cell to another must all travel together to one edge of the cell, and then enter the destination cell similarly from one extreme edge. However, many communications span logically only between corre-

FOUR-SIDED CELL

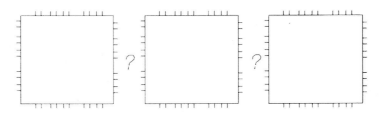

\UNION_DX DOES NOT TOLERATE
PORTS IN BETWEEN CELLS

FIGURE 8.1

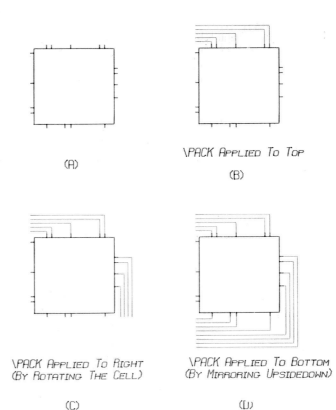

(A)

\PACK APPLIED TO TOP

(B)

\PACK APPLIED TO RIGHT
(BY ROTATING THE CELL)

(C)

\PACK APPLIED TO BOTTOM
(BY MIRRORING UPSIDEDOWN)

(D)

RENDERING A FOUR-SIDED CELL
AS A ONE-SIDED CELL

FIGURE 8.2

sponding bit positions in the source and destination cells (Figure 7.34A). Such communications would prefer a more direct route, as shown in Figure 7.34b.

Figure 7.34A shows that the crowding of signals required in the one-sided regiment contributes a width proportional to the number of signals, or in other words, the interconnect consumes a quadratic area. In contrast, Figure 7.34B shows a more direct routing, which contributes only a constant width, and hence only linear total area. (The vertical space taken by the n horizontal wires is n units in either case. With the cells as shown, no better can be done. The n signals simply must cross the second column of cells, and to keep them separate, the vertical span of n is mandatory.)

Most of our one-sided renditions of logic cells suffer devasting area penalties due to the large width of interconnect resident between adjacent cells. In fact, these widths are often greater than the widths of the PLA columns themselves. These wide channels thus contribute approximately half of the entire area, therefore rendering a functional density of at most one half. These widths disappear for the most part by accommodating the more direct wiring shown in Figure 7.34B.

Figure 8.3 shows that we must go beyond one-sided cells in order to accommodate the improved interconnections, particularly if we wish to build cells hierarchically as we are accustomed to doing. We can see that even if all leaf cells are one-sided, intermediate cells constructed during the fusion processes may become two-sided (and generally four-sided).

Figure 8.4A shows another way in which cells may become two-sided. The middle column contains wires entirely irrelevant to its own operation. These extra wires are present simply to provide the direct interconnection between the first and third columns. If those extra wires were omitted, the communications between the first and third columns would have to dodge the second column entirely, thus rendering a quadratic interconnect once again like that imposed by the one-sided regiment (Figure 8.4B).

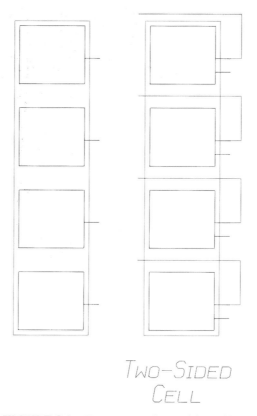

Two-Sided Cell

FIGURE 8.3 Emergence of two-sided cells.

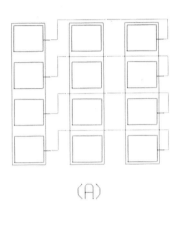

(A)

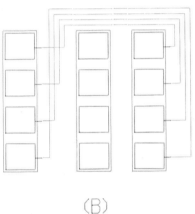

(B)

FIGURE 8.4   Foreign wires cause two-sidedness.

8.2 FOUR-SIDED CELL CONVENTIONS AND THE INTRODUCTION OF "CORNERS"

We adopt for four-sided cells the same conventions as those adopted for one-sided cells, except of course, for convention 7, which limited information signals to reside all on one side (Section 6.1.8).

Recall that convention 5 states that for each one of the four sides, ports along that side which carry the same signal will be connected together automatically. This still holds, but we emphasize that this applies only to each side independently. For example, two ports carrying the same signal but which reside on distinct edges will not by default be connected together automatically.

However, we will on occasion desire to connect ports resident on distinct edges. Of course, we could go right ahead and introduce the desired interconnection via a wire that turns a corner or two (Figure 8.5). However, such a single-minded addition would increase the size of the cell's MBB. Any increase in a cell's MBB is to be avoided because our cell conventions forbid the use of any (unused) area within the MBB, except for the trivial routing of internal ports out to the edges (conventions 3 and 4).

8.2.1 General Policy about Fusion for All Cells

We have adopted a policy concerning the fusion, or augmentation of cells, which is almost demanded by our very simple cell conventions.

We avoid like the plague any cause to increase the MBB of a cell.

The MBB of a cell plays a fundamental role in our cell conventions. The MBB divides ports into two classes, internal and surface ports. The MBB also directs the placement of cells, that is, cells are placed so that their MBBs are separated by at least 3

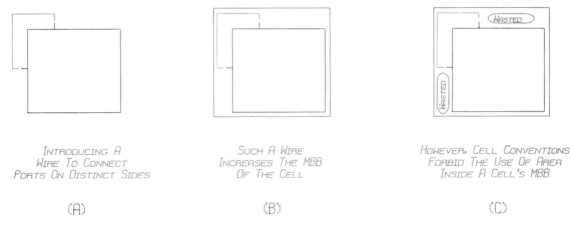

INTRODUCING A
WIRE TO CONNECT
PORTS ON DISTINCT SIDES

(A)

SUCH A WIRE
INCREASES THE MBB
OF THE CELL

(B)

HOWEVER, CELL CONVENTIONS
FORBID THE USE OF AREA
INSIDE A CELL'S MBB

(C)

FIGURE 8.5

lambda, so to guarantee the introduction of no design rule violations. Finally, the MBB defines a boundary inside which we may add no layout whatsoever, except to bring internal ports to the surface (conventions 3 and 4).

Therefore, if we need to increase a cell's MBB, we had best put everything we can inside the new MBB now, because after we augment the MBB, there will never be a chance to utilize that lost area.

For example, we have already adopted this philosophy within one-sided cells. We did not include with each PLA the wires necessary to complete the feedback. Those wires would increase the MBB of the resulting PLA cell. Instead, we omitted the wires but simultaneously represented their need to exist. Convention 5, in fact, was introduced to provide for the representation of such needs.

Figure 8.6A shows what would happen if we did introduce the feedback wires immediately with each PLA. The carry chain which ultimately connects these finished PLAs together in this example would be added after the PLA MBBs had been enlarged. Thus, Figure 8.6A shows two scan lines consumed for the interconnect. In contrast, Figure 8.6B shows the benefit of waiting until all interconnect requirements become known; both the feedback wires and the carry chain wires can be implemented at once on the same scan line.

Our policy can be stated in general:

1 Do not augment a cell. Instead, provide a means to represent the need for such augmentation.

2 Accumulate all these needs as time progresses, but do not act upon them.

3 Only at the last moment, implement the accumulated needs all at once.

For one-sided cells, this "last moment" occurs in \PACK, just before the cell is rotated.

For four-sided cells, the "last moment" occurs when two cells become fused together (Figure 8.7A); the area between the two cells by definition becomes internal to the MBB of the resulting cell. This mandates that the subset of all needs that occur between cells be satisfied at this time, before the new MBB becomes official. However, in keeping with this policy, those needs external to the now inaccessible interior remain unsatisfied (Figure 8.7B).

These external needs will become satisfied later, when they become internal, for example, when another cell begins to fuse with this result (Figure 8.7C, D, and E).

Notice how in Figure 8.7D the needs of each of the two cells divide into those which are becoming internal, and all the rest. Figure 8.7E, like part B, shows in the

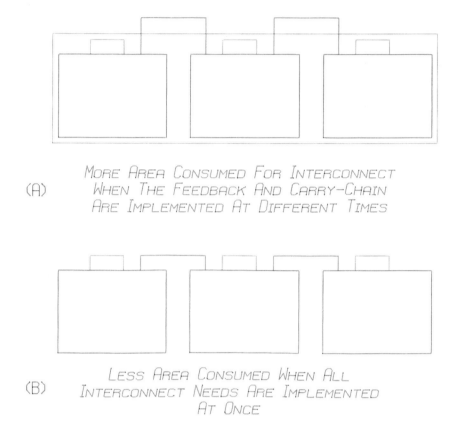

(A)   MORE AREA CONSUMED FOR INTERCONNECT
      WHEN THE FEEDBACK AND CARRY-CHAIN
      ARE IMPLEMENTED AT DIFFERENT TIMES

(B)   LESS AREA CONSUMED WHEN ALL
      INTERCONNECT NEEDS ARE IMPLEMENTED
      AT ONCE

FIGURE 8.6

result that the interior needs become satisfied, whereas all external needs remain unsatisfied.

Our choice to leave unsatisfied all external needs (Figure 8.7B) propagates these needs to a later time (Figure 8.7D), when these and other unsatisfied needs can be known all at once. In fact, all needs resident between cells can be known only at this last moment prior to fusion. The satisfaction of the accumulated, now internal needs (Figure 8.7E) occurs all at once, so the internal area between the cells can now be shared most wisely among this large and complete set of needs.

The fact that we accumulate needs and act on them all at once implies that we are satisfying interconnection needs in parallel. This contrasts with other techniques, where each wire (need) is routed (satisfied) in its entirety independent of all other needs. Although it might feel most natural to satisfy each need in isolation, such a technique imposes a blindness. The ultimate use of and constraints on the area consumed are simply not known now. They will not become known until all the other needs become satisfied. Wire routers that treat each signal one at a time often cannot guarantee complete success. The blindness to other needs can render routes prematurely which ultimately block all possible routes available to other needs.

8.2.2   Corners: A Representation for Communication Needs

Communication needs along any one side are represented securely in the ports' signals along that side, by convention 5. Communication needs between distinct sides can be satisfied by routing around corners. We can represent the desire to wrap a signal around a given corner by associating with that corner the desired signal.

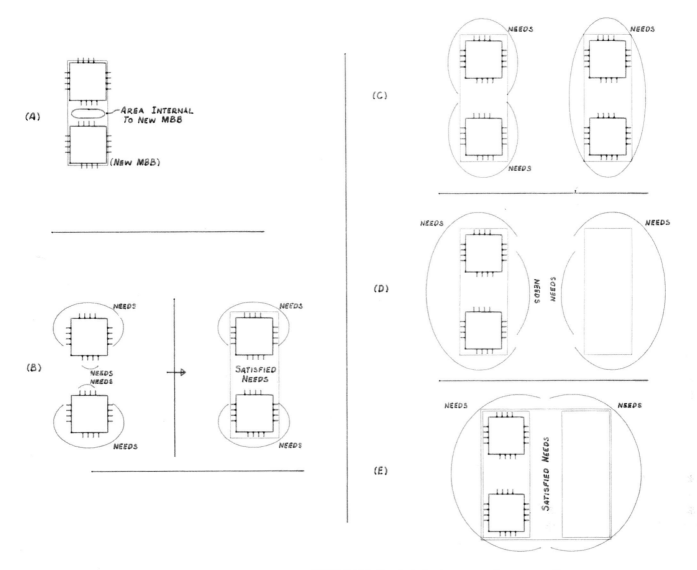

FIGURE 8.7   Satisfaction occurs between cells.

Let us in fact modify the layout CELL datatype so to represent the four corners:

```
TYPE  CELL  =    [  TL,  TR,  BL,  BR:  SIGNALS          T,  R,  B,  L:  PORTS
                                                          LAYOUT:  LAYOUT      ]  ;
```

Each of these corners, TL (top left), TR (top right), BL (bottom left), and BR (bottom right), refers to that set of signals which need routing around that particular corner.

We can imagine by analogy that each corner represents a set of mirrors placed at that corner. Each signal represented at that corner contributes one mirror which reflects around that corner only those needs which involve that signal.

For example, suppose that the top right corner, TR, includes all signals, and that the other three corners (TL, BR, and BL) each contain no signals (Figure 8.8A). TR thus represents a fully reflective mirror, which reflects all signals. It gives each of the top and right sides sight to each other. The top edge sees the right edge now as an extension of itself, and the right edge sees the top edge similarly (Figure 8.8B). This illusion is intended to coax convention 5 to take as a single edge the concatenation of the top and right edges, and thus connect all matching signals between the two edges.

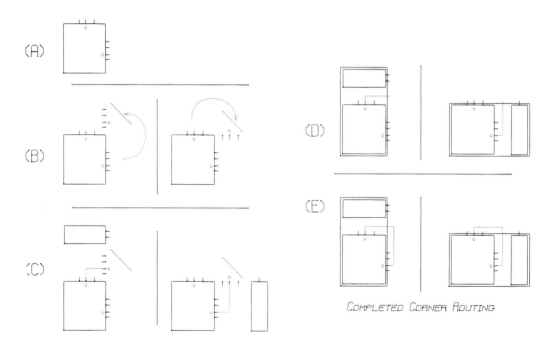

"CORNERS" ON CELLS REFLECT INTERCONNECT NEEDS
AROUND CELL CORNERS, LIKE MIRRORS

FIGURE 8.8

Figure 8.8C shows how this TR, fully reflective mirror manifests itself to implement corner routing. To see such effects, we must render such needs as internal needs so that they will begin to become satisfied. Thus, Figure 8.8C shows another cell being placed next to either edge. The mirror in effect pulls the matching signal out from between the two cells.

Figure 8.8D shows the result in each case on the completion of fusion. Even though the TR corner represents the need to wrap around that corner, we see that only part of this corner need has been satisfied. In fact, we see that of this corner need, only that part which became internal has been satisfied.

Figure 8.8E shows, however, that convention 5 by itself ultimately assures the completion of the corner need. Thus, we see that a corner need becomes satisfied by means of two steps:

1 The corner pulls the signal out from between this cell and any other cell that becomes fused to this cell.

2 Convention 5 by itself completes the entire corner route.

For another example, suppose that all corners each references all signals. This renders four fully reflective mirrors, and hence in effect extends convention 5 so to consider all four sides together. Such a situation will connect together all ports carrying matching signals regardless of their edges of residence. In contrast, a complete absence of all mirrors renders no communication between distinct edges.

We have at this point formalized only the representation for corners. We have provided an informal model for how this representation of needs manifests itself. We have yet to formalize algorithms that read and write (examine and create) corners. This will come shortly.

Let us utilize the informal model for one more example. Figure 8.9a shows two cells about to be fused vertically together with the positions of each of their four corners. Figure 8.9B shows an intended wiring between the two cells, with numbers written in to represent the five signals involved. Figure 8.9C shows these same needs but with the corners of wires emphasized. Figure 8.9D shows the corners alone. In other words, this example shows how we may specify routing (Figure 8.9B) entirely in terms of corners (Figure 8.9D).

Figure 8.9E continues this example by completing this cell fusion. As this figure indicates in general, of all eight corners presented by the two cells, only the four outer corners remain on the finished cell. In contrast, the four inner corners dissolve and transform instead into two requirements upon the internal area. The two left internal corners combine to express the need to pull signals out and leftward from between the two cells. Similarly, the two right internal corners together express the need to pull signals out to the right edge of the finished cell.

Figure 8.9F shows the result of fusion. Notice that at this point the entire routing desired (Figure 8.9B) has been implemented between the two cells. Finally, Figure 8.9G shows how convention 5 almost assures the completion of the desired wiring. Signal 1 will not be completed at this time by convention 5.

Fortunately, Figure 8.9D shows that signal 1 appears in the BL (bottom left) corner of the lower cell. Figure 8.9F and G show that signal 1 remains in this outer corner. Thus, even though Figure 8.9G does not show the signal 1 need satisfied, it does show that this need is still represented in the BL corner of the result.

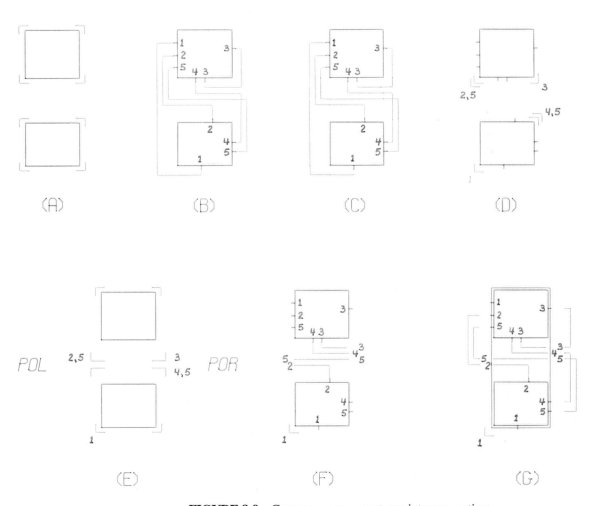

FIGURE 8.9 Corners can represent any interconnection.

The following convention, 7a, replaces convention 7 for one-sided cells, and takes corners into account:

7a   A pair of ports that carry the same signal and which reside on distinct edges will be connected automatically if that signal appears on each corner resident on a path from one port's edge to the other port's edge.

8.3 OVERALL PROGRAM STRUCTURE FOR THE FUSION OF FOUR-SIDED CELLS

There are basically four operators which together translate a logic cell into a layout cell. They are:

1   ABUT   (operates on a pair of cells)
2   ROUTE   (operates on the area between a pair of cells)
3   CONS   (operates on a pair of cells)
4   CELL4   (operates on an entire logic cell).

ABUT and ROUTE together perform essentially the same services provided by our one-sided \PACK operator. CONS assures that all communication needs between two cells become satisfied (i.e., CONS deals with corners). Finally, CELL4, like our one-sided \CELL operator, directs the complete fusion of an entire logic cell.

One general difference between our one-sided and four-sided fusion mechanisms is that the four-sided mechanism will tend to combine cells pairwise whereas the one-sided version combined at once an entire list of cells. These two approaches are interchangeable; that is, a list of cells can be fused by repeated pairwise combination. However, the extra complexity inherent in the fusion of four-sided cells becomes most understandable in an implementation that considers only two cells at a time.

8.3.1 The ABUT Operator: The Lowest-Level Fusion Operator

The ABUT operator performs primarily the same function provided by our one-sided \UNION_DX operator. ABUT differs from \UNION_DX in that

1   ABUT takes in only two cells (i.e., not a list of cells).
2   ABUT accommodates ports between cells.

Recall that \UNION_DX complains if any of its given cells contain (nonpower) ports on the left or right sides. ABUT, in contrast, tolerates such ports between cells, but ABUT imposes the following very rigid constraints on the ports residing between the two cells. Let us call the two cells LEFT and RIGHT.

ABUT requires that there be a way to align the cells LEFT and RIGHT so to render their inner ports, LEFT.R and RIGHT.L, flush with one another. Thus, ABUT complains if:

1   LEFT.R and RIGHT.L contain unequal numbers of (nonpower) ports, or if
2   Corresponding (nonpower) ports in LEFT.R and RIGHT.L do not carry the same signals, or if
3   The separations between adjacent (nonpower) ports in each of LEFT.R and RIGHT.L do not match.

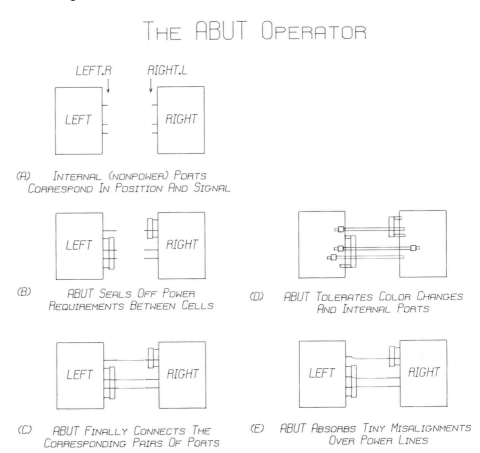

FIGURE 8.10

ABUT, like \UNION_DX's call to \SEAL_SIDE_POWER, first seals off the power requirements between the cells, and hence considers subsequently only nonpower ports between cells.

These constraints exist so to relieve ABUT from having to perform any wire routing between the cells. These constraints assure that ABUT can place the cells so that all nonpower ports between them line up exactly and carry matching signals (Figure 8.10A).

Figure 8.10B shows that ABUT seals off power requirements only between the cells, unlike \UNION_DX, which seals power also along the two extreme edges. (The extreme power requirements thus remain unsatisfied, but nonetheless well represented.)

ABUT separates the two cells horizontally by 3 lambda, like our uses of \UNION_DX, and then adds tiny bridges to connect each corresponding pair of ports (Figure 8.10C).

ABUT tolerates color differences between corresponding ports. If necessary, ABUT affects the color of one of two corresponding ports so to match the color of the other port. ABUT does this before sealing power between the cells.

In fact, ABUT takes advantage of internal ports (conventions 3 and 4) so to bury feedthroughs within one or the other cell, as does our one-sided \NON_BLUE operator. ABUT chooses to change colors at the port that lies deepest within its cell (Figure 8.10D). On occasion, however, there may be insufficient depth in which to bury completely a feedthrough, and in these cases, the MBB of one or the other cell may grow naturally so to enclose the new feedthrough(s). (This growth has occurred similarly with our one-sided \NON_BLUE operator).

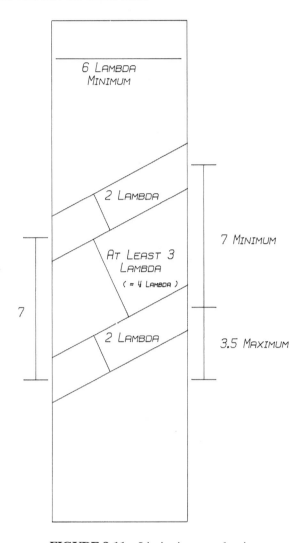

FIGURE 8.11   Limitations on slanting.

Finally, ABUT will actually tolerate corresponding ports which are misaligned very slightly. The maximum allowed misalignment is 3.5 lambda (lest ABUT complain). ABUT absorbs such misalignments by providing a slight bend in the bridge between corresponding ports. This bend occurs directly over either of the power lines (Figure 8.10E). The need for such misalignments arises from a situation particular to four-sided cells, and will be described with the operator ROUTE.

The 3.5 lambda maximum has been chosen for two reasons. First, the sole source of misalignment will produce no greater misalignments. Second, 3.5 lambda is sufficiently small as to require no verification against possible design rule violations (Figure 8.11). There is always a horizontal distance of 6 during which to implement the 3.5-lambda vertical slippage. The horizontal distance traveled is always 3 lambda across the power line and then 3 lambda more, strictly between the cells.

ABUT, like \UNION_DX, renders on the finished cell all the appropriate ports (Figure 8.12A). ABUT also renders the appropriate corners, discarding without regard the four internal corners (Figure 8.12B).

In summary, ABUT fuses two cells into one cell, providing between the cells for:

1   All color changes

2   All power routing

3   Absorbtion of up to 3.5 lambda misalignment between corresponding ports

4   The necessary access to nonsurface ports

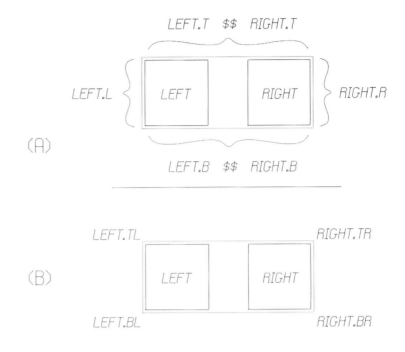

THE PORTS AND CORNERS
RESULTING FROM ABUT

FIGURE 8.12

Thus, ABUT transforms completely any arbitrary pair of cells into one legal cell when

> All ports between the two cells correspond in position and signal.

We will utilize ABUT to implement all fusions after preparing each of the two cells so to comply with this rigid condition.

Note that although ABUT produces a legal cell (i.e., a cell which by itself satisfies all conventions), ABUT does not guarantee that all required communications become implemented either between the two cells or within each cell independently. In other words, ABUT by itself does not maintain conventions 5 and 7a.

ABUT does, however, relieve us from all concerns except for the maintenance of these ''service'' conventions 5 and 7a.

8.3.2   Using ABUT Together with ROUTE to Gain the Effect of \PACK

The one-sided \PACK operator performs all at once the services supplied now by ABUT and ROUTE. \PACK both produces interconnect scan lines and also connects these scan lines to the large cell below. For four-sided cells, ROUTE will provide the scan lines, and ABUT will connect them to the cell below and to the cell above (Figure 8.13).

We use ABUT to perform vertical fusion simply by rotating each cell, calling ABUT, and finally unrotating the result. We have chosen to present the ROUTE algorithm in this vertical orientation so to clarify its similarity with the one-sided \PACK operator. In both cases, the scan lines appear horizontally, and grow upward.

The need to separate the duties of \PACK into two distinct operations arises because the interconnect produced by ROUTE will reside between two cells instead of residing above one cell. We have seen in \PACK that the number of scan lines (i.e., the

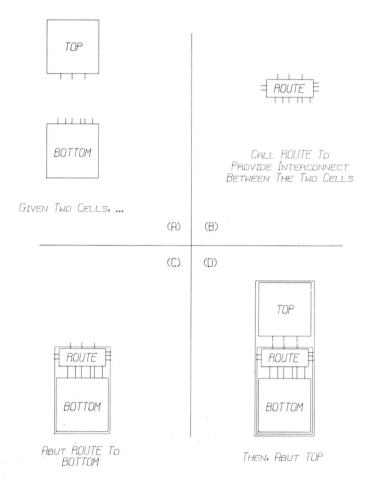

FIGURE 8.13   Pairwise four-sided cell fusion.

height of ROUTE) is unknown until after all the scan lines are produced. Thus, although ROUTE could grow scan lines directly on top of the bottom cell, it cannot build them simultaneously below the top cell. We simply do not know how far above the bottom cell to place the top cell until after ROUTE complete its job.

We will build the ROUTE cell in a context where the top and bottom cells are separated vertically by infinite distance. The ROUTE cell will thus grow freely to whatever size it must. However, the ROUTE cell will not include direct connections to the top and bottom cells. Instead, the finished ROUTE cell will be connected to each of the top and bottom cells via two applications of ABUT.

8.4 THE ROUTE OPERATOR

ROUTE provides interconnect between two cells. ROUTE takes in four parameters:

1	TOP	(PORTS)	the bottom set of ports from the top cell
2	BOTTOM	(PORTS)	the top set of ports from the bottom cell
3	POL	(SIGNALS)	signals to be pulled out to the left
4	POR	(SIGNALS)	signals to be pulled out to the right.

Figure 8.14 shows these four parameters.

The TOP and BOTTOM parameters are each of type PORTS and these dictate precisely the top and bottom interfaces required of the ROUTE cell. The parameters POL

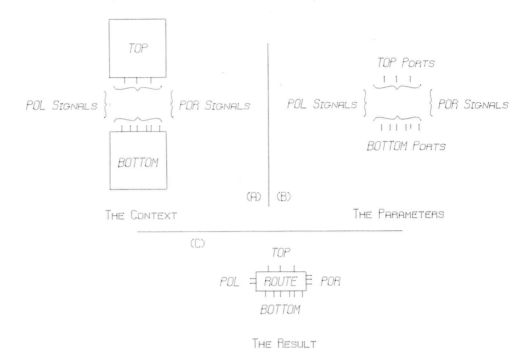

PARAMETERS FOR ROUTE

FIGURE 8.14

and POR are each of type SIGNALS, and these represent which signals are to be pulled out from between the two cells, that is, which signals are to appear on the left and right edges, respectively, of the finished ROUTE cell.

Since POL and POR are of type SIGNALS and not of type PORTS, they impose a much gentler requirement on the ROUTE cell. They do not dictate the positions of the left and right ports; they merely dictate the existence of such ports.

It is clear where the TOP and BOTTOM parameters come from; They come directly from the two cells being interconnected. In contrast, POL and POR come from less obvious sources. POL and POR will certainly include the signals resident in the four inner corners of the two cells (Figure 8.9E). POL and POR may also include signals derived from another source, the operator CELL4.

The need for the parameters POL and POR can be seen from a more basic standpoint. In their absence, no signals would appear on the left or right edges of the ROUTE cell. This would therefore render all ports between the two cells entirely inaccessible after fusion. If any of these ports carried signals absent from all the other six accessible edges, such signals would forever be inaccessible. The loss of any signals resident on a LOGIC_CELL's interface would render an incomplete implementation for that LOGIC_CELL.

The four parameters of ROUTE correspond to the two parameters of the one-sided \PACK operator:

1 TOP and BOTTOM together correspond to the top edges of the list of cells given to \PACK. They are all of type PORTS.

2 POL and POR together correspond to \PACK's second parameter, the interface signals that must be pulled out to the side so to remain accessible in the finished cell.

ROUTE guarantees the following:

1 ROUTE maintains convention 5 on each of the two inner edges, TOP and BOTTOM.

2 ROUTE also connects together ports of the same signal which reside on the distinct sides, TOP and BOTTOM.

3 ROUTE brings to the left and to the right the signals in POL and POR which reside in ports on TOP or BOTTOM.

4 ROUTE introduces an isolated wire spanning from left to right for signals resident in both POL and POR but which nonetheless appear in no port of TOP nor BOTTOM.

The first guarantee is obviously required to maintain convention 5. The second guarantee assures complete interconnect between the two inner edges TOP and BOTTOM. This guarantee can be seen as a natural extension to convention 5 by imagining the cells placed side by side as shown in Figure 8.15, where the TOP cell has rolled off from above BOTTOM, landing to its right rotated 180 degrees.

The third and fourth guarantees maintain the intended meaning of POL and POR. Guarantee 4, in particular, indicates that POL and POR have meaning even when their signals match no ports. It is this fourth guarantee which implements foreign travel between cells as shown in the second column of cells in Figure 8.4A.

ROUTE maintains these guarantees no matter how tall or wide the ROUTE cell may need to grow. ROUTE maintains these guarantees always in finite area. Such finite uncertainty in size is always accommodated in subsequent applications of ABUT, which nestle this ROUTE cell between the top and bottom cells (Figure 8.13).

8.4.1   Scan-Line Implementation for ROUTE

Suppose for the moment that all the ports in TOP and BOTTOM together have distinct X-coordinates (Figure 8.16A). We produce the two-sided interconnect by merging TOP and BOTTOM together into one set of ports, and by applying the same technique used in \PACK (Figure 8.16B). We then take this result and push the TOP ports straight upwards so to restore their top status (Figure 8.16C). POL and POR can be incorporated during the middle step (part B) just as \PACK's LEFT parameter was accommodated.

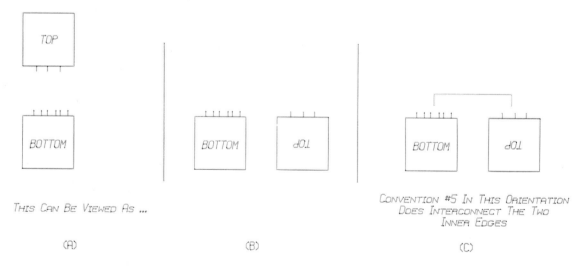

FIGURE 8.15   Analogy to one-sided interconnection.

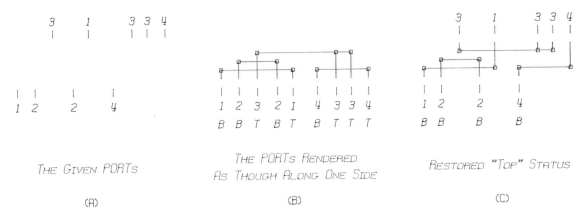

INTERCONNECT BETWEEN TWO CELLS
IMPLEMENTED VIA ONE-SIDED TECHNIQUES

FIGURE 8.16

However, the two-sided routing problem introduces a phenomenon entirely absent from the one-sided \PACK operator. If a port in TOP does lie directly above a port in BOTTOM, we cannot reduce the problem into the one-sided problem by merging the two sets of ports; two ports would become coincident (Figure 8.17B). As Figure 8.17C shows, the interconnect required for this situation requires that one vertical channel actually service two distinct signals. This result could never be derived from the one-sided reduction (Figure 8.17D) because the coincident ports short together distinct signals.

Figure 8.18 shows just how much conflict can arise. Each of Figures 8.18A and B shows a situation where the two top ports appear directly on top of the two bottom ports, and require routing that exchanges their positions. Unlike the milder conflict shown in Figure 8.17C, this exchange situation mandates the creation of an extra vertical channel, a vertical channel that lies neither beneath nor above any of the given ports. Figure 8.18C and D show a similar situation for four ports. Parts A and C claim the extra vertical channels en route between source and destination. Parts B and D show the most pathetic of all possible situations. The extra vertical channels cannot be claimed en route because adjacent ports are minimally separated, and thus provide no space for new vertical channels except as shown, at the extreme right (or left).

The need to create extra vertical channels is new with the two-sided interconnect problem. This imposes two new considerations. First, we may wish to maximize the

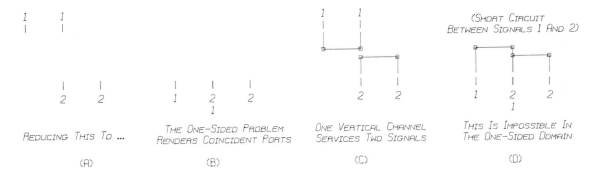

ONE-SIDED REDUCTION DOESN'T ALWAYS WORK

FIGURE 8.17

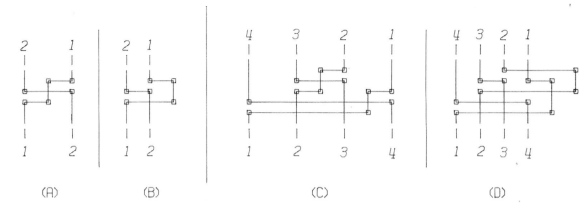

FIGURE 8.18   Difficult wiring situations.

number of available vertical channels by forcing all ports in TOP and BOTTOM to reside horizontally on a 7-lambda (minimum separation) grid. Second, our \FLY_AT operator will have to tolerate flights which do not land directly at their destinations.

8.4.1.1   Maximizing available vertical channels via gridding. Figure 8.19A shows a lack of extra vertical channels due to a lack of gridding. Even though there is 10 lambda between adjacent vertical channels, 3 lambda more than minimal spacing, no vertical channel may be created between any of the existing vertical channels. (Such creation requires a separation of 14 lambda between an adjacent pair of existing channels.) Figure 8.19B shows that by imposing a 7-lambda grid on the given ports, a new vertical channel becomes available.

The 7-lambda grid guarantees that all separations between adjacent pairs of vertical channels are multiples of 7 lambda. Hence, after gridding, adjacent vertical channels are either minimally separated or they definitely accommodate a spare vertical channel between them. ROUTE therefore always takes the liberty to slide horizontally all TOP and BOTTOM ports so to lie on a 7-lambda grid. The maximum slide is one half the grid

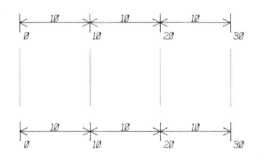

WITHOUT GRIDDING:

NO SPARE VERTICAL CHANNELS
BETWEEN PORTS

(A)

WITH GRIDDING:

PORTS LIE ON 7-LAMBDA GRID,
AND A SPARE CHANNEL EMERGES

(B)

FIGURE 8.19   Gridding for more channels.

unit, 3.5 lambda. ABUT, which must ultimately fuse the ROUTE cell into its surrounding context, has been designed to absorb such deviations.

8.4.1.2 *The two-sided \FLY_AT operator.*

The second new consideration accompanying two-sided interconnect concerns the \FLY_AT operator, which actually produces the scan lines. We discovered in Figures 8.17 and 8.18 that collapsing the two sets of ports into one set, a la one-sided interconnect (Figure 8.16), creates intractable situations on occasion. Thus, let us consider a slight change in our perception of \FLY_AT.

Even for those situations that may reduce into legal one-sided situations, let us look at \FLY_AT slightly differently. Recall that for one-sided interconnect, \FLY_AT produces a scan line and removes simultaneously those ports from the top of the cell below which are now interconnected by the new scan line. Thus, repeated applications of \FLY_AT render ultimately no ports on the top of the finished cell. In contrast, we do in fact expect the finished ROUTE cell to include top ports.

A blue wire of a scan line may now provide interconnect among ports resident both below and above the scan line, simply because with two-sided interconnect there do exist ports above (Figure 8.20A). We can see that such a scan line not only removes ports from below, as occurs with one-sided interconnect, but it also introduces new ports facing upward. Figure 8.20B shows an initial set of bottom ports, and Figure 8.20C shows the scan line, which leaves in Figure 8.20D a different set of bottom ports.

Thus, where \FLY_AT used to serve to remove bottom ports, we see for two-sided interconnect that \FLY_AT serves also to move bottom ports which communicate upward. That is, \FLY_AT seals together matching bottom ports as before, but now \FLY_AT contributes a new upward facing port so to transmit upward the signal to

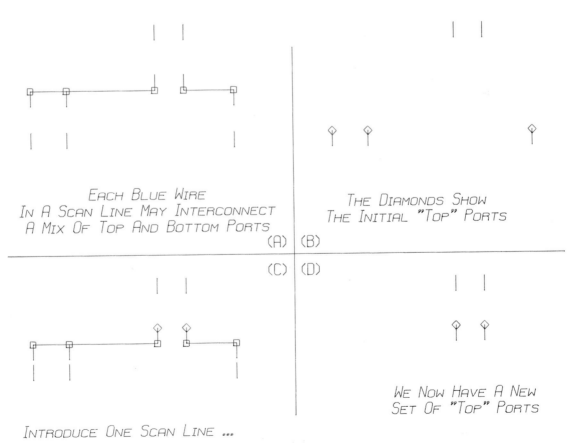

FIGURE 8.20 Scan lines affect "top" ports.

matching top port(s) if any. (It there are no matching ports above, no new upward port need be contributed.)

We now view \FLY_AT as an operator that performs the following:

1   \FLY_AT removes bottom ports which communicate with no top ports.
2   \FLY_AT moves the other bottom ports so as to reside directly beneath their corresponding top ports.
3   After multiple applications, \FLY_AT yields on top a set of ports identical to the given TOP ports.

The new \FLY_AT operator can still view each set of matching ports (from TOP and BOTTOM) all as bottom resident. However, the distinction between TOP and BOTTOM manifests itself in whether a port is removed (from BOTTOM) or introduced (to match with TOP).

Figure 8.21 shows the situation shown in Figure 8.16A, with an equivalent solution rendered now via our new way of perceiving \FLY_AT. Figure 8.21 A, B, and C show the sequence derived by adding each scan line one at a time. Notice that the ports atop the new scan lines move closer and closer to the TOP placements. Each scan line changes the appearance of BOTTOM, and the subsequent scan line is introduced only with reference to the new (latest) BOTTOM.

\FLY_AT still considers the top and bottom ports as one set, as with our one-sided rendition. However, it now checks a new condition, presented next.

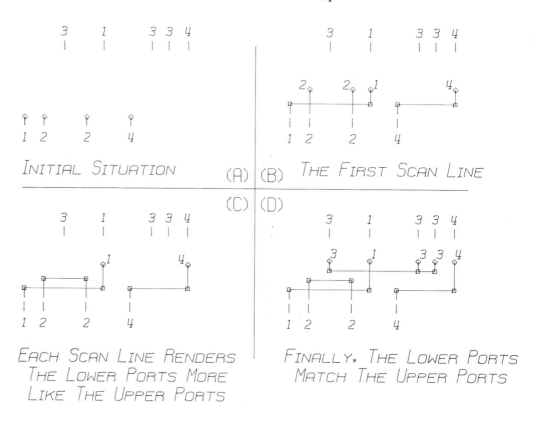

INITIAL SITUATION   (A) | (B)   THE FIRST SCAN LINE

(C) | (D)

EACH SCAN LINE RENDERS
THE LOWER PORTS MORE
LIKE THE UPPER PORTS

FINALLY, THE LOWER PORTS
MATCH THE UPPER PORTS

GROWTH OF INTERCONNECT BY SCAN LINES

FIGURE 8.21

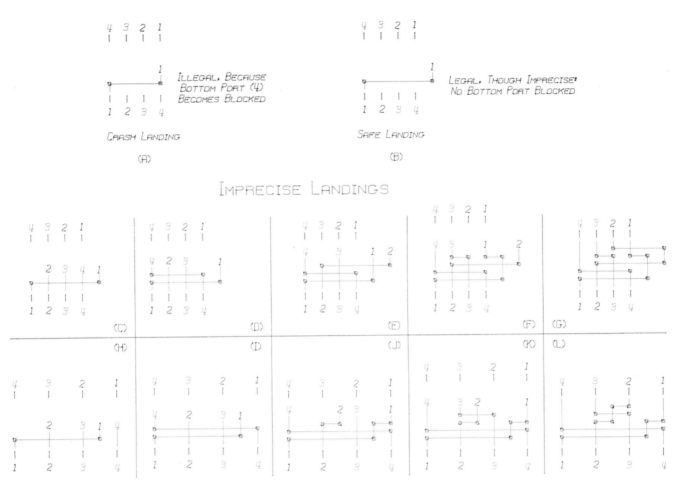

FIGURE 8.22

8.4.1.3 *The creation of new vertical channels: imprecise landings.* The creation of a new vertical channel occurs when \FLY_AT desires to introduce a new upward-facing port at a horizontal position which lies directly above an existing BOTTOM port. Figure 8.22A shows such an unsatisfiable desire. Such a move would occlude the port below (port 4 in BOTTOM) and hence render permanently incomplete any interconnect derived from this point on. Thus, \FLY_AT will introduce upward-facing ports only at positions directly over no existing BOTTOM ports (Figure 8.22B). \FLY_AT in these cases can land only close to the desired position. We call such landings "imprecise landings."

Figure 8.22C through G show the sequence of scan lines which complete the routing. Similarly, Figure 8.22H through L show the same sequence for the situation that has ports separated by 14 lambda, thus providing for more convenient imprecise landings. In studying these figures, please imagine still that each scan line is built strictly left to right (as they are). (It is tempting to imagine a dominant bottom-to-top force, which will unfortunately lead one to believe that some scan lines are generated right to left.)

If imprecise landings could be avoided entirely, the two-sided \FLY_AT operator would always complete an entire connection with only one blue wire. In fact, imprecise landings never occur when the TOP and BOTTOM ports occupy distinct horizontal positions, as shown in Figure 8.16.

However, imprecise landings must be tolerated for two-sided interconnect in general. Notice that an imprecise landing is required only when the destination (top) port resides in a vertical channel which also has a port below. We will call such a vertical channel "double-ported"; it has a port both directly below and directly above. It is precisely the existence of double-ported vertical channels that renders impossible a complete solution by means of one-sided techniques alone.

We always maintain that an imprecise landing will occur only in a vertical channel that has no port above or below (i.e., in a "zero-ported" vertical channel). This policy is evident in Figure 8.22. This poicy assures that an imprecise landing will never create a new double-ported vertical channel. (Landing in a zero-ported channel renders at most a one-ported channel.) Note also that a vertical channel never acquires a TOP port; only BOTTOM ports move from one channel to another. Thus, an imprecise landing creates a forever one-ported channel.

This zero-ported restriction on imprecise landings assures that an imprecise landing will never introduce the need for an additional imprecise landing by a subsequent flight. In other words, this policy supresses any propagation of the need for imprecise landings.

An imprecise landing is always possible because there is never a lack of available zero-ported vertical channels. An imprecise landing will choose a channel closest to its destination. However, there are always infinitely many zero-ported vertical channels available to the left or right of all BOTTOM and TOP ports.

Finally, \FLY_AT marks each new upward-facing port it creates as the result of an imprecise landing. This mark indicates to subsequent scan lines that the marked port is forbidden from participating in subsequent flights which themselves make imprecise landings. In other words, this marking removes the possibility for a port to participate in two or more imprecise landings. Thus, a port resulting from an imprecise landing may from now on participate only in a single nonstop flight which will land the port directly beneath its destination (top) port.

Perhaps it appears that such a restriction on multiple imprecise landings may inhibit the completion of interconnect. However, we will now guarantee that by waiting long enough (i.e., by seeping directly upward through subsequent scan lines), each imprecise port can always fly directly to its destination.

8.4.2 Assurance of Complete Interconnect

We refer to the type CONNECTION introduced in Section 6.2.5.2 in conjunction with the one-sided \FLY_AT operator. A CONNECTION represents a complete set of matching ports. However, a CONNECTION in the two-sided context provides for the distinction between its top and bottom ports.

As long as CONNECTIONs remain to be done, a call to \FLY_AT can always either

1 Complete a CONNECTION, or
2 Perform an imprecise landing.

We know this by the following argument. (This argument does not by itself show that \FLY_AT will perform one or the other action. It merely shows that \FLY_AT could perform one or the other action.)

> If no CONNECTION can be completed, we conclude that the destination vertical channels of each and every pending CONNECTION are double-ported. However, we also know that the bottom port in each and every double-ported channel is not the result of an imprecise landing. (Imprecise landings never occur in channels that lie beneath TOP ports.) Thus, \FLY_AT is free to take any one of these bottom ports on a flight that lands imprecisely.

Not only is \FLY_AT able to perform at least one of these two actions, but \FLY_AT, in fact, will always perform one of these actions. \FLY_AT always inspects at least one CONNECTION, and either completes it or tries to resolve it in part by making an imprecise landing (Figure 8.22B). It is conceivable that neither of these two actions can be performed on the first chosen CONNECTION (e.g., if all the bottom ports of the CONNECTION are imprecise ports and hence unavailable to participate in new imprecise landings). However, \FLY_AT then tries the next pending CONNECTION, and in fact, ultimately attempts all pending CONNECTIONs.

The one-sided \FLY_AT also skips over CONNECTIONs so to concentrate on one it can complete. We know that such skips occur in the one-sided \FLY_AT program because it uses the \RIGHT_OF operator (Section 6.2.5.2).

Finally, we conclude that the ROUTE cell can be generated completely by calling the two-sided \FLY_AT repeatedly, in a finite number of calls: As noted above, each call to \FLY_AT either

1 Completes a CONNECTION, or

2 Performs an imprecise landing.

There are only a finite number of CONNECTIONs to be completed, and there are only a finite number of possible imprecise landings. [Each imprecise landing removes at least one bottom port, the source port(s) of the flight, and renders in its place only a marked port. The marked port by definition can never again participate in imprecise landings. Thus, the number of imprecise landings is bounded above by the number of ports given initially in BOTTOM.] Since each of the two options can be taken only a finite number of times, all the connections will be implemented in finite time, and hence the ROUTE cell will be completed.

The introduction of imprecise landings has been necessary to guarantee that no (bottom) ports become occluded. This has guaranteed that all pending CONNECTIONs remain securely represented.

8.5 CONS: THE COMPLETE FUSION OF PAIRS OF CELLS

CONS takes in two cells and produces one cell as output. The one cell contains each of the two cells and implements all communication requirements between them. CONS guarantees that any signal resident in both cells will be connected together.

CONS is to four-sided cells what \PACK is to one-sided cells. \PACK combines one-sided cells and assures that matching signals resident on distinct cells become connected. CONS guarantees precisely the same. However, when \PACK is given a pair of cells, it has only to consider communications between one pair of edges, the two top edges. In contrast, CONS accommodates intercell communication between any side of one cell and any side of the other cell (i.e., between 16 pairs of sides) (Figure 8.23).

CONS uses ROUTE and ABUT together to fuse ultimately the two cells. ROUTE by itself guarantees to complete the communication needs between the two inner edges, and hence ROUTE by itself resolves one of the 16 pairs of sides (Figure 8.23C).

CONS implements communications between the other 15 pairs of edges simply by augmenting the corners of each of the two cells. CONS by itself generates no new wires; it generates merely their need to exist.

As shown in Figure 8.9, interconnection between any pair of sides can be represented very naturally by placing the signal to be connected in the appropriate subset of corners. The choice of this appropriate subset arises directly by imagining the entire route for the wire, and noting merely which corners it wraps around.

8.5.1 CONS Has Choices

CONS guarantees to connect each and every signal which appears somewhere on both cells. Such a shared signal may actually appear more than once on each cell. It may even appear on distinct edges of one or the other cells. Such multiple appearances of that signal on either cell present choices to CONS.

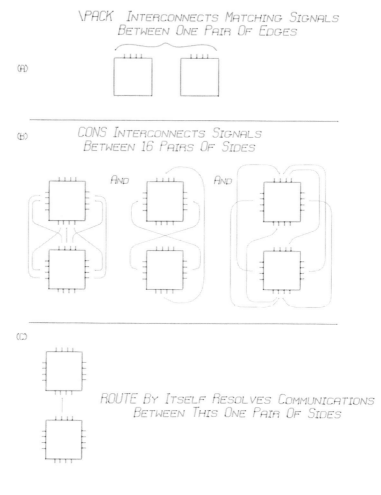

SIGNAL COMMUNICATIONS AMONG SIDES

FIGURE 8.23

CONS is free to connect any one of these possible pairs of ports (Figure 8.24). CONS is not required to provide interconnection between all such pairs of ports. Convention 7a establishes that each cell independently already includes in its corners all interconnect needed among its own four sides. Thus, CONS never introduces connections among ports of the same cell.

CONS therefore augments corners of the two cells, and hence represents a new interconnect via the following:

For each signal apparent on both cells:
   1   Choose one of that signal's ports from the top cell.
   2   Choose one of that signal's ports from the bottom cell.
   3   Augment the corners of the two cells so to represent a route
       between these two chosen ports.

CONS chooses one pair from among the possible pairs of ports by considering for each pair the corresponding pair of edges on which the two ports reside. There are 16 possible edge pairs, and of the given edge pairs, CONS chooses the "most efficient" pair (i.e.,

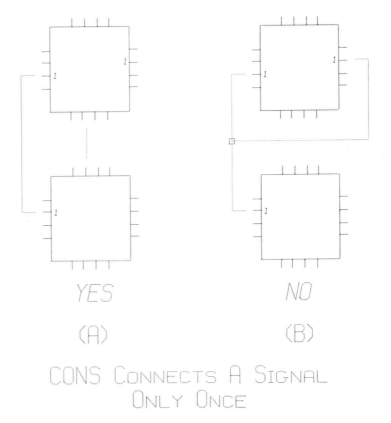

YES   NO

(A)   (B)

CONS CONNECTS A SIGNAL
ONLY ONCE

FIGURE 8.24

the pair that requires the shortest wire length). Figure 8.25 shows an efficiency ordering for the 16 edge pairs.

Together with these choices, CONS considers the corners already in existence on the two cells. Such existing corners participate in resolving otherwise arbitrary choices. For example, the route shown in Figure 8.25F can be implemented equally well along the left or right sides.

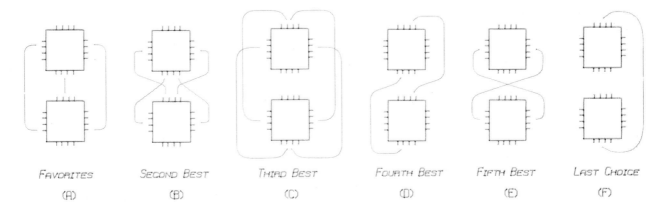

FAVORITES   SECOND BEST   THIRD BEST   FOURTH BEST   FIFTH BEST   LAST CHOICE

(A)   (B)   (C)   (D)   (E)   (F)

CONS CHOOSES AMONG THESE 16 PAIRS OF SIDES
FOR EACH SIGNAL RESIDENT ON BOTH CELLS

FIGURE 8.25

When CONS finishes the "routing" of all matching signals between the two cells, CONS calls ROUTE, passing as parameters

1	TOP ports:	(the top cell) . B		
2	BOTTOM ports:	(the bottom cell) . T		
3	POL signals:	(the top cell).BL	$$	(the bottom cell).TL
4	POR signals:	(the top cell).BR	$$	(the bottom cell).TR

This conforms to Figure 8.9E. Finally, CONS stuffs the resulting ROUTE cell between the two given cells, calling ABUT twice.

8.5.2   The Two Roles of CONS

We see that CONS plays two major roles:

1   CONS augments all eight corners of the two cells to implement intercell communication.
2   CONS translates the four inner corners directly into requests to ROUTE.

These roles are significant independently. The first role of course implements intercell communications and relies heavily on convention 7a to justify its means. The second role, in contrast, actually implements convention 7a, independent of intercell communications. It is precisely CONS's definitions of the parameters POL and POR for ROUTE which translate corner needs into actual layout (via ROUTE).

8.5.3   CONS Takes in Four Parameters

Although we imagine that CONS takes in only two parameters, the two cells to be fused, CONS actually accepts two additional parameters. These two parameters are called POL and POR, and like ROUTE's parameters by the same names, POL and POR specify signals that are to appear on the left and right sides of the finished cell (Figure 8.26A).

CONS uses these POL and POR parameters in part simply to augment the POL and POR computed for the call to ROUTE. These parameters thus provide a means by which to communicate through CONS directly to ROUTE (Figure 8.26B and C).

The ability to specify POL and POR in a call to CONS makes it possible to guarantee that these signals (POL and POR) remain accessible on the finished cell. This pair of parameters will be used to:

1   Assure that LOGIC_CELL interface signals remain accessible
2   Introduce nonstop horizontal wires between the cells which carry foreign signals

The first capability is clearly needed; the parameters POL and POR together correspond directly to \PACK's second parameter. As with one-sided cells, we can never tolerate the loss of interface signals. It is possible that some interface signals reside only between the cells. Thus, POL and POR may guard against the otherwise certain extinction of such endangered interface signals.

The second capability facilitates the phenomenon shown in Figure 8.4A. Here we wish to route between two cells a signal that might appear nowhere on either cell. Such a foreign wire is created simply by including the foreign signal in both POL and POR simultaneously.

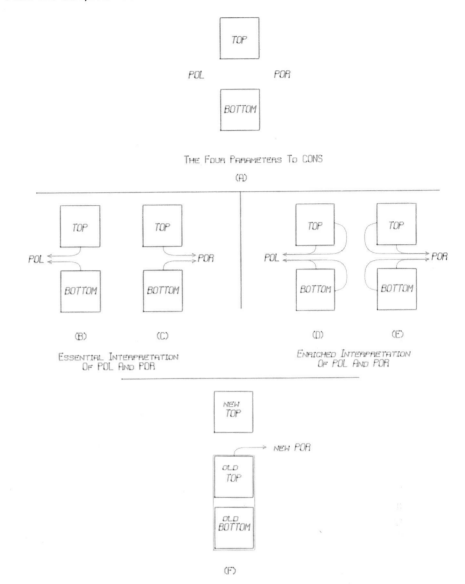

FIGURE 8.26 The parameters POL and POR.

CONS actually supports a richer interpretation for POL and POR. Figure 8.26D and E show that CONS will bring to either side signals specified in POL and POR which nonetheless do not reside strictly between the cells.

This richer interpretation supports more than the rescue of endangered signals residing between the cells. It provides for externally specified topological desires. In other words, POL and POR may represent the demands of external context.

For example, Figure 8.3 shows wires routing from the right sides of cells in the second column between adjacent cells to the left edge of the column. This routing occurs because these signals were specified in POL during construction of the second column (Figure 8.26D).

CONS supports this richer interpretation of POL and POR by:

1 Augmenting corners to accommodate these new routes (as usual)

2 Passing to ROUTE a POL and POR which contain the signals originally given to CONS in POL and POR, in addition to the signals from the four internal corners

CONS does not use POL and POR to pull signals residing on the top or bottom edges of the final fused cell. Such routing will occur at a later time, when this finished cell itself becomes a parameter to CONS (Figure 8.26F). At that time, a new POL and POR will be supplied, and then if the topological desire still persists, POL and POR will again include such signals.

In summary, CONS takes in the following parameters:

1   TOP and BOTTOM, each of type CELL

2   POL and POR, each of type SIGNALS, which express topological placements for sets of signals.

The highest fusion operator, CELL4, is presented next. CELL4 calls on CONS repeatedly to do most of the work. CELL4 is the process that considers LOGIC_CELLs, and directs "long distance" routing (Figures 8.4A and 8.3). Thus, CELL4 is the sole process that defines POL and POR for all calls to CONS.

8.6 CELL4: IMPLEMENTATION OF A LOGIC_CELL IN FOUR-SIDED CELLS

CELL4 translates a LOGIC_CELL into a four-sided layout cell, just as \CELL translates a LOGIC_CELL into a one-sided layout cell.

The simplest rendition of CELL4 could look exactly like the one-sided \CELL operator. Where \CELL fuses together a list of cells by calling \PACK, the simple CELL4 would apply CONS repeatedly to fuse together the same list. The interface signals passed to \PACK would now be passed to CONS repeatedly, in either POL or POR.

However, such a simple rendition of CELL4 would result with Figure 8.4B instead of Figure 8.4A. In fact, it would not even produce Figure 8.3. It would yield little or no improvement over the one-sided mechanism. We would see some improvement only if our leaf cells (PLAs) were themselves four-sided cells.

The interconnect savings apparent in Figure 8.3 are due entirely to the fact that the interface signals of the second column have been brought out to the left. The savings apparent in Figure 8.4A are due to the introduction of foreign wires which cross the second column at convenient heights.

Figure 8.27A shows how we have viewed a LOGIC_CELL in terms of its immediate subcells. Figure 8.27B shows a view two levels deep (i.e., a view in terms of sub-subcells). We need to view LOGIC_CELLs two levels at a time so that we can see simultaneously the sub-subcells in a column and the context to the left and to the right (Figure 8.27C). Figure 8.27D shows how the LEFT and RIGHT contexts contain the desired information which leads toward the efficient routing shown in Figures 8.4A and 8.3

We define therefore CELL4 to take in such contextual information; that is, CELL4 takes in

1   LEFT: the set of ports that will ultimately lie to the left of the logic cell

2   BODY: the logic cell itself

3   RIGHT: the set of all signals that might ever be desired on the right.

LEFT and RIGHT thus represent the context residing to either side of the BODY logic cell. CELL4 translates BODY, the given logic cell, into a single cell that will ultimately reside between the two contexts.

The asymmetry in representation between the LEFT and RIGHT contexts (i.e., the fact that LEFT is of type PORTS and RIGHT is of type SIGNALS) arises as a practical matter. We assume that LEFT represents the ports of a left resident cell which is already built. In contrast, we cannot expect also to have a finished cell on the right; the right cell

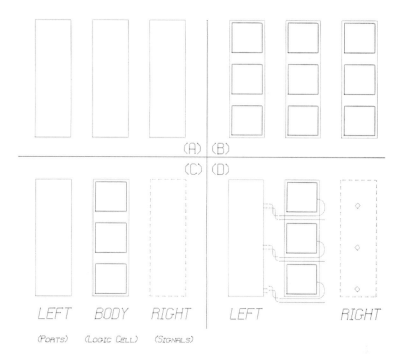

FIGURE 8.27 Context developed for logic cell fusion.

cannot be built until our cell, BODY, is complete. Our BODY cell will supply its finished right ports as the LEFT context for the subsequent formation of the right cell. In analogy, LEFT represents a certain past, whereas RIGHT represents an uncertain future.

CELL4's entire job is to call CONS repeatedly, passing in appropriate signals in CONS's parameters POL and POR. Figure 8.28A shows the repeated calls to CONS which integrate the subcells of this logic cell into a single, tall cell. Figure 8.28B, C, and D begin to show the considerations involved in defining the POL and POR for each call to CONS.

Let us assume for the moment that all of BODY's subcells are already built. We will consider their construction shortly.

We wish to guarantee the following of the resulting cell, referred here to as "the column":

1 LEFT signals appear on the left side of the column.
2 The positions of these left signals match the corresponding positions in LEFT as closely as possible.
3 RIGHT signals resident in any subcell, or resident on LEFT, appear on the right side of the column.
4 All interface signals remain accessible.

In support of guarantee 2, Figure 8.28B shows how the LEFT ports are translated into the parameter POL for each call to CONS. POL includes those LEFT signals that reside in ports up against the upper half of the lower subcell and the lower half of the upper subcell. (The extreme top and bottom ports may become corners on the resulting cell.)

However, it is possible that a signal in LEFT resides only in a subcell far away vertically from the LEFT port. The division of LEFT ports shown in Figure 8.28B does not account for these nonlocal LEFT ports. Hence, we support guarantee 1 by including in POL for a given CONS any LEFT ports that appear in no closer a subcell. Figure 8.28C shows this global interpretation, which renders LEFT merely as a set of signals, like RIGHT.

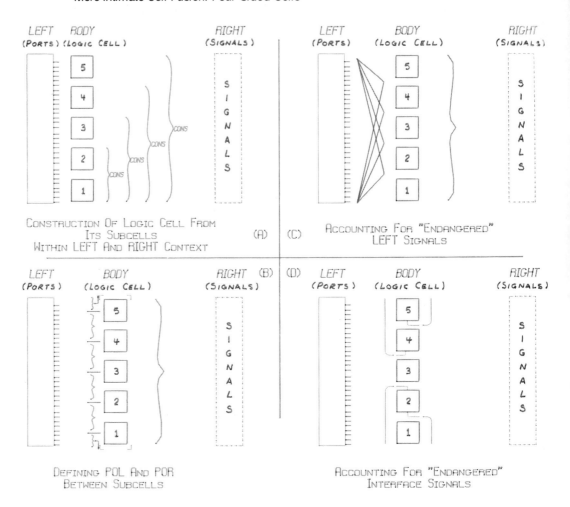

FIGURE 8.28   Considerations for parameters POL and POR.

In support of guarantee 3, we include in POR all of RIGHT, except for those signals that already reside on the right edge of some subcell.

Notice that a signal in RIGHT which also resides in a locally close LEFT port will show up naturally on both POL and POR. Such LEFT/RIGHT signals might even be foreign to the subcells. This phenomenon gives rise to the bridges crossing the second column in Figure 8.4A.

Finally, it is possible that some interface signals of the BODY logic cell appear in neither LEFT nor RIGHT. (LEFT and RIGHT can in fact be NIL.) The fourth guarantee guards against the loss of any interace signals. We rescue endangered signals potentially trapped between cells by including in POL (or POR) all of BODY's interface signals which are absent from LEFT and RIGHT (Figure 8.28D).

We have now seen how the LEFT and RIGHT contexts participate in CONSing together BODY's subcells to form the column. We have assumed that each of BODY's subcells already exists as a layout cell. However, BODY's subcells are logic cells (not layout cells), and they need to be rendered as layout cells before we can CONS them together. Thus, CELL4, like the one-sided \CELL operator, first transforms the logic subcells into layout cells (recursively).

We may also wonder where LEFT and RIGHT contexts come from in the first place. They arise precisely in this translation from logic subcells into layout subcells.

Initially, when given an entire logic cell to translate, CELL4 takes NIL as the LEFT and RIGHT contexts. CELL4 then transforms subcells into layout cells within contexts which CELL4 itself defines. CELL4 defines such contexts and passes them into CELL4's recursive calls upon itself.

Figure 8.29A shows the situation upon entry into CELL4. The subcells are shown here as circles, indicating that each is a logic cell and not a layout cell. As with the one-

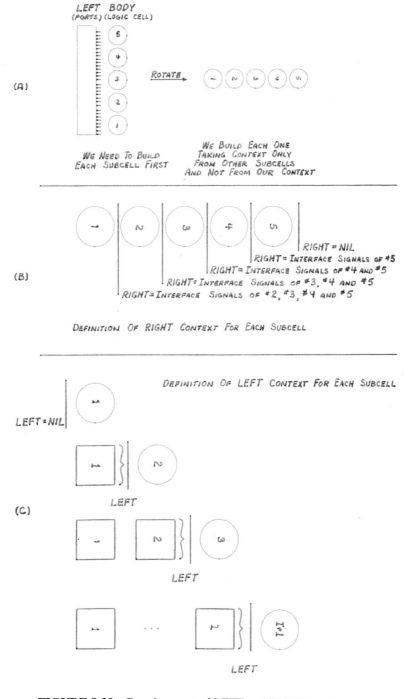

FIGURE 8.29 Development of LEFT and RIGHT context.

sided \PACK operator, CELL4 constructs subcells in an environment rotated by 90 degrees.

Figure 8.29B shows how RIGHT context is defined between each of the logic subcells, now aligned horizontally. The RIGHT context of each subcell includes all interface signals resident in all subcells farther to the right. Thus RIGHT represents all signals that will ever be required to the right.

We are able to define all RIGHT contexts even before we begin translating any logic subcell into a layout cell. This is possible because each logic subcell characterizes its ultimate layout cell sufficiently, simply in terms of the logic subcell's interface signals. Because RIGHT context is of type SIGNALS and not of type PORTS, the positions of signals need not be represented in this context. Hence, interface signals by themselves, in the absence of layout cells, serve to characterize RIGHT.

Figure 8.29C shows how LEFT context is developed. LEFT context, unlike RIGHT, is of type PORTS and hence requires a finished layout cell for its definition. Thus, the logic subcells are translated into layout cells sequentially from left to right. The completion of one subcell provides the LEFT context for the next subcell. Of course, each logic subcell is translated into a layout cell by calling CELL4 (recursively) with the developed LEFT and RIGHT contexts.

8.7 SATISFYING THE FINAL SET OF EXTERNAL NEEDS

We have seen with our four-sided cell conventions that of all interconnection needs, only those needs resident between cells become satisfied. This policy was chosen to optimize interconnect, implementing each region of interconnect only at such time that all needs which involve that region become known.

As a by-product, we are left ultimately with a grand cell that has all internal interconnections completed, but which has none of its surface interconnects implemented. That is, the four sides of the final cell have interconnection needs represented (via conventions 5 and 7a), but none of these four sides has ever become an internal edge, and hence these surface needs remain unimplemented.

We complete the final cell, in fact, by rendering each of its four edges as an internal edge, one at a time. We actually CONS the final cell against a dummy cell four times. To affect all four sides, we rotate the result prior to each CONS, e.g.,

```
final_cell   \CONS   dummy_cell
   \ROT_CW        \CONS      dummy_cell
   \ROT_CW        \CONS      dummy_cell
   \ROT_CW        \CONS      dummy_cell
```

The dummy cell used in this compiler is simply a blue-to-green feedthrough (devoid of ports).

Figure 8.30 shows three different orders by which a "final cell" might be sealed up. The leftmost frames in each of parts A, B, and C are identical; each shows the "final cell." This final cell was chosen especially to illustrate a pair of cells that require all of the 16 possible edge-to-edge communications.

The initial frame shows the internal needs satisfied between the two cells. Although relatively little interconnection is apparent at this stage, the needs for the entire interconnection are represented securely in the four corners of this final cell.

In fact, we can see between the two cells two horizontal wires which as yet connect to nothing. These were created naturally within the ROUTE operator, due to the appearance of two "foreign" signals in each of the parameters POL and POR. These two signals (6 and 16) were introduced into POL and POR by CONS in its effort to route from the top cell's left edge to the bottom cell's right edge (6), and vice versa for signal 16.

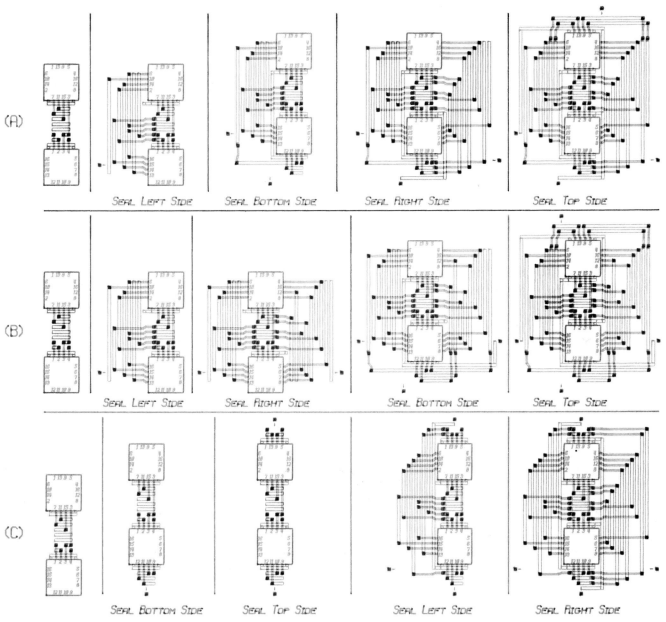

COMPLETION OF NEED SATISFACTION AROUND THE EDGES

FIGURE 8.30 *(See also color plate.)*

Each of the nonfirst frames in Figure 8.30 shows the result of CONSing one dummy cell onto the result presented by the previous frame. Parts A, B, and C differ only in which order we seal off the four sides. All the frames have been rendered "unrotated" so that the progress between frames can be seen most clearly.

Although the completed wiring shown in the three final frames looks very complex, the entire specification for this wiring has been present since the initial frames, represented in the cell's ports and corners.

Figure 8.30 shows three different orders of sealing off edges, one at a time, so to accentuate the order independence of cell fusion in general. Our conventions, particularly convention 7a about corners, were derived carefully to maintain such order independence. Figure 8.8 shows how a corner need is satisfied no matter which of its two adjacent edges become internal (satisfied) first. As Figure 8.30 shows, different orderings may give rise to slightly different wirings, but in each case the wiring is complete.

Figure 8.30 was generated automatically, but the orginal pair of cells was created manually. In addition, the algorithm was cut short in that it has not introduced pads around the final cell. As a result, there appear in this figure some unsatified power wires, which come outward only to stop next to two of the four dummy cells.

8.8 COMPLETION VIA THE INTRODUCTION OF PADS

Any chip intended for use must include a large layout called a pad for each of its interface signals. Pads are introduced to provide a practical interface to the outside world, for example, to the package that will contain the chip. Pads are large so to provide a reasonable target for the start of a gold wire that connects the pad out to the package.

We know from the given LOGIC_CELL which signals need pads. We need one pad for each of the LOGIC_CELL's interface signals (INPUTS and OUTPUTS). In fact, we can choose between two kinds of pads based on whether the signal appears in INPUTS or in OUTPUTS.

Pads for output signals are different from pads for input signals. Output pads must amplify the output signal so to provide a substantial force on the outside world. Input pads, in contrast, merely read signals coming in from the outside world.

There are pad types for signals other than input and output signals. Although our LOGIC_CELL representation does not provide for the use of any other kind of pad, pads do exist which act both as input and output pads. Pads may vary also in the force they deliver to the outside world. Such force affects the maximum fan out, or number of devices, which can be connected to the output simultaneously.

Figures 8.31 through 8.34 show each of the logic cells shown in Figures 7.29, 7.35, 7.36, and 7.39, now rendered as complete, functional chips within the four-sided domain. Each of these has pads included.

We complete a chip via the following steps:

1 Obtain the "final cell" as derived from the given LOGIC_CELL.
2 Determine from the LOGIC_CELL's interface those signals that require pads.
3 Create one pad for each signal, and also one pad for each of GND, VDD, and the two clocks. (These pads come from a set of three predefined layout cells).
4 Divide the pads into four sets, one set for each of the four edges of the "final cell." CONS each set into a single cell by itself.
5 CONS the four rows of pads along the four edges.
6 Finally, apply the four dummy cells to the four sides of the result, so to complete all interconnect.

The fourth step, the CONSing of each set of pads, maintains in the parameter POR (or POL) the interface signals serviced by those pads, so as to assure that each solidified row of pads presents all its signals, losing none to burial within the row itself.

(It is curious to note that although all four of these figures implement the same function, they have different numbers of pads! Some have nine pads, and others have seven pads. The light dimmer itself has three interface signals, therefore accounting for three pads. In addition, four pads exist for GND, VDD, and the two clocks, accounting now for a total of seven pads. Why do some of these figures contain two extra pads? What signals do they represent?

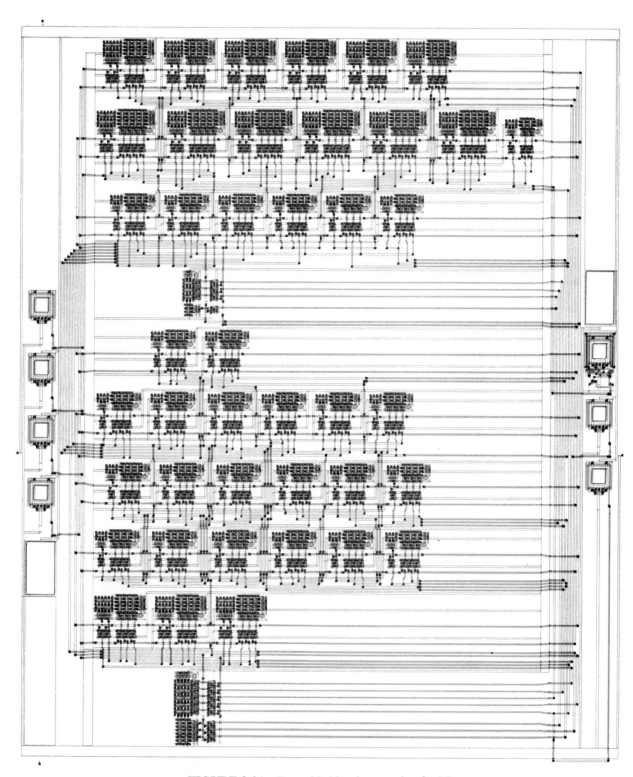

FIGURE 8.31 Four-sided implementation for LD.

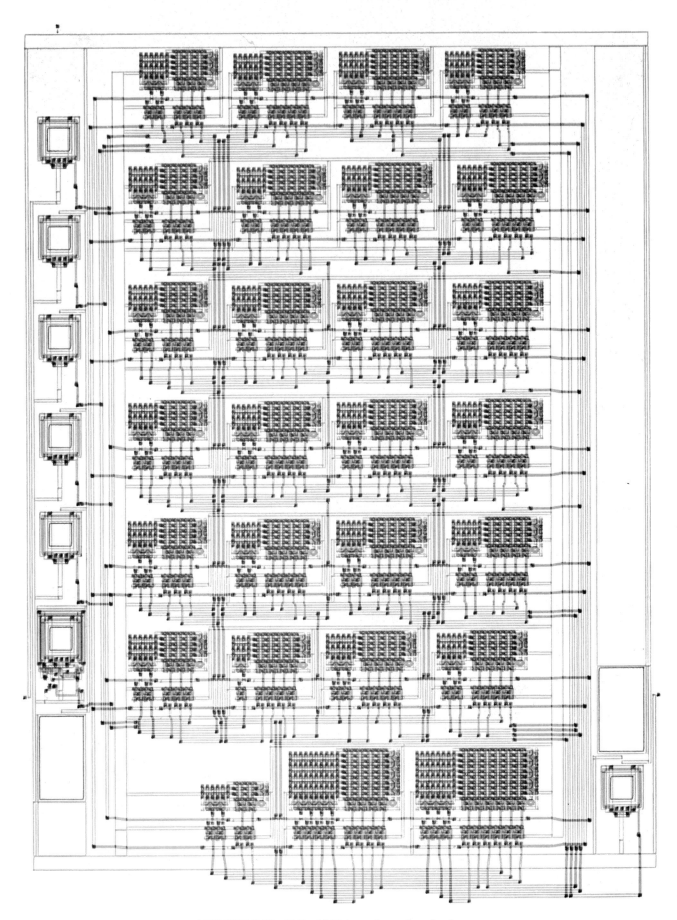

FIGURE 8.32 Edited LD (*see also color plate*).

402

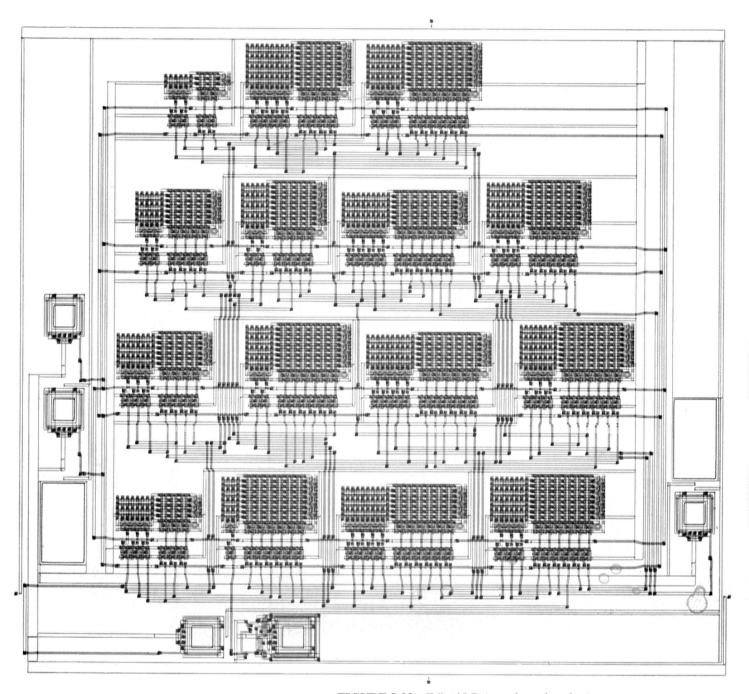

FIGURE 8.33 Edited LD (*see also color plate*).

(The two extra pads, input pads, actually represent the signals TRUE and FALSE. Some of the figures include these two extra pads, and others do not, because the differing logic organizations have subjected various parts of the chip to differing degrees of logic optimization.

The logic optimizer used in the four-sided compiler differs slightly from the one presented in this text. Neither optimizer is particularly better than the other, but they do differ in how they treat the constant signals TRUE and FALSE. This slight difference also manifests itself in the PLAs generated. For example, there is in Figure 7.35 one PLA that generates FALSE and another PLA that reads this constant FALSE. This phenomenon is absent in Figure 8.32.

403

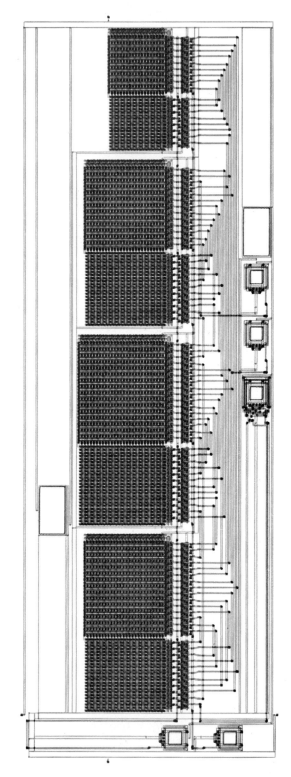

FIGURE 8.34 Edited LD.

EXERCISES

Section 8.8

1. We have suggested that all surface needs become satisfied in the "final cell" simply by CONSing a dummy cell against each side. However, once this is done, the resulting cell still has four surface edges. Can there remain along the four surface edges still more surface needs as yet unsatisfied? Why?

2. In Figure 8.25, why would we include as "favorites" (part A) interconnection between the two left edges and between the two right edges?

3. Is there any place in any of Figures 8.31 through 8.34 where convention 5 provides redundant interconnection. [*Hint:* Look at the clock lines.]

4 Consider Figure 8.30B, the second frame. There is a wire coming down which, as yet, connects to nothing. Why is that wire there? [*Hint:*

1 What signal is carried by that wire?
2 In the first frame we see a cell. Of its four corners, which one contains this wire's signal?
3 How did that corner come to include that signal?
4 Did one of the two subcells contain that corner prior to fusion? If so, which one? If not, which operator created that corner?

9

Electrical Modelling

We now present a strategy for automatically computing the maximum clock rate at which a chip can be run. This strategy applies not only for cells constructed from PLAs, but also for cells constructed from arbitrary cells, where the lowest-level "leaf" cells include appropriate electrical information.

Two major problems face us. First, what is a concise representation for the essential electrical properties? Second, how can we render an abstraction of these electrical properties so that a cell can be represented without reference to every detailed circuit contained within? A solution to the latter question will imply that we can deal successfully with cells of arbitrary nesting depth, and hence arbitrary complexity.

As we hunt for an appropriate electrical abstration, keep in mind that this abstraction will be delivered with the top-level cell representing the entire chip. What information do we want at this highest level? We will need to know the maximum acceptable clock rate, and if the chip includes an output dependent on an input without clocking (e.g., our chip is a single AND gate), we will need to know how long we must wait for the output to settle after we have changed the input.

STRATEGY We first choose a concise and abstract model for an electrically connected region called an electrical island. We then introduce the notion of electrical islands related by means of logical dependencies. We complete this model by incorporating the notion of clock elements.

We incorporate this electrical model into the layout CELL representation by means of a slight modification of the CELL and PORT datatypes. We then extend the cell abutment operation so as to maintain this model for cells constructed from sets of smaller cells. This will render complete electrical modelling for arbitrary cells constructed from a small set of leaf cells whose electrical behavior has been specified manually. Finally, we provide a recursive electrical simplification and provide a means of interpreting this model so to report the performance of the cell (chip).

9.1 RESISTANCE, CAPACITANCE, AND TIME

Let us represent each of resistance and capacitance as a REAL. If we declare

TYPE   RESISTANCE   =   REAL ;

TYPE   CAPACITANCE   =   REAL ;

then the types RESISTANCE and CAPACITANCE are rendered identical; both are REALs. This would render legal the following assignments:

resistance   :=   capacitance ;   or

resistance   :=   capacitance   +   resistance ;

However, such assignments (i.e., the mixing of resistance and capacitance) are generally not sensible physically. These assignments are "dimensionally" inconsistent; that is, resistance and capacitance have incompatible physical units: ohms and farads.

An assignment such as the first assignment implies that there really is a general answer to the question

"How many ohms are in a farad?"

However, any sensible answer to this question would have to reference a particular circuit which renders some kind of relationship locally between these otherwise unrelated units.

In analogy, if someone asked

"How many apples are in an orange?"

we could provide the answer

"Two"

in a context where one apple costs 50 cents and one orange costs 1 dollar, but such an answer has meaning only with reference to the particular marketplace. Such a local answer requires an abstraction that compares apples and oranges by rendering each as the same type of object: in this case, prices. That is, the marketplace defines the coercions

apple $\rightarrow$ price

orange $\rightarrow$ price

and we answer the question

"How many apples are in an orange?"

only by applying the coercions and instead answering the question

"How many 50 cents are in 1 dollar?"

We see therefore a necessary distinction arising between RESISTANCE, CAPACITANCE, and REALs (e.g., apples, oranges, and prices). They are really not at all interchangeable generally.

The need to distinguish between RESISTANCE and REAL is made clearer in the following examples. If RESISTANCE is a REAL, as declared earlier, then whether we like it or not, we get among others the following rules defined for all REALs, now applied to the synonymous type RESISTANCE:

resistance	+	real	$\rightarrow$	resistance	(undefined units)
resistance	/	resistance	$\rightarrow$	resistance	(absence of units)
resistance	*	resistance	$\rightarrow$	resistance	(ohms squared)

For example, we may write

    resistance :=   resistance + 5 ;

which adds 5 to a resistance. Engineers and physicists will write this sort of thing only when the units are understood by convention; that is, it is understood that

    5   really means   5 ohms, or 5 kilohms

However, such an implicit assumption can only be made locally, by the group of people who read and write the particular document. A different group of people, for example, those working at power generating stations, might render a different implicit assumption on this assignment. They might assume that

    5   really means   5 micro-ohms

The type declaration given above for RESISTANCE introduces conceptually the coercions

    real $\rightarrow$ resistance
    resistance $\rightarrow$ real

because the types REAL and RESISTANCE are one and the same type. We would prefer instead to have the rules

    real \OHMS $\rightarrow$ resistance   and
    resistance $\rightarrow$ real

A RESISTANCE includes units, whereas a REAL does not include units. The first rule requires the specification of units together with the REAL to produce a RESISTANCE. The latter coercion merely abandons units.

9.1.1 A Linguistic Type Distinction: The PRIVATE Type Construction

Let us now declare the types RESISTANCE and CAPACITANCE with

    TYPE   RESISTANCE =   PRIVATE REAL ;   " ohms "
    TYPE   CAPACITANCE=   PRIVATE REAL ;   " pfs "

This renders each of the types RESISTANCE and CAPACITANCE and REAL entirely unrelated linguistically. Each is still represented by REAL, but the types RESISTANCE and CAPACITANCE share no other properties with REAL, or with each other. For example, none of the following rules exist now:

    resistance + resistance $\rightarrow$ resistance
    resistance + real $\rightarrow$ resistance
    resistance * real $\rightarrow$ resistance

In fact, absolutely no rules exist which involve either RESISTANCE or CAPACITANCE, except for the following tiny set of rules, generated entirely by the PRIVATE type constructor:

    PUBLICIZE:::(resistance) $\rightarrow$ real
    RESISTANCE:::(real) $\rightarrow$ resistance

    PUBLICIZE:::(capacitance) $\rightarrow$ real
    CAPACITANCE:::(real) $\rightarrow$ capacitance

(These two pairs of rules must exist in order to create or examine the two new types.) The triple colons used in these rules make it very clumsy to use these rules.

The types RESISTANCE and CAPACITANCE are so private that we must introduce explicitly each and every rule we wish ever to involve these types. We introduce the rules

real	\OHMS	$\rightarrow$	resistance
real	\KOHMS	$\rightarrow$	resistance
real	\PFS	$\rightarrow$	capacitance

by writing

DEFINE   OHMS(R: REAL) = RESISTANCE: RESISTANCE:::(R)   ENDDEFN
DEFINE   KOHMS(R: REAL) = RESISTANCE: R * 1000 \OHMS ENDDEFN
DEFINE   PFS(R: REAL) = CAPACITANCE: CAPACITANCE:::(R)   ENDDEFN

Each of these creates its result by using the clumsy rules generated by the PRIVATE type constructor. (The unit specification \PFS stands for picofarads.)

We introduce the following rules:

resistance	$\rightarrow$	real
capacitance	$\rightarrow$	real

so that a RESISTANCE (or CAPACITANCE) can be interpreted as a REAL, stripping off its units. Although these rules strip off units, their resulting REALs cannot be reinterpreted as RESISTANCEs or CAPACITANCEs except by utilizing the rules given earlier which (re)specify units. We introduce these two new rules by writing

LET RESISTANCE   BECOME REAL BY   PUBLICIZE:::(RESISTANCE) ;
LET CAPACITANCE BECOME REAL BY   PUBLICIZE:::(CAPACITANCE) ;

Again, we use clumsy notations to get from each of these private types back into REALs.

The privacy shrowding the types RESISTANCE renders nonexistent the rule

resistance	+	resistance	$\rightarrow$	resistance

We now instead combine resistances by means of the following two rules:

resistance	\SERIES	resistance	$\rightarrow$	resistance
resistance	\PARALLEL	resistance	$\rightarrow$	resistance

We introduce each of these rules with

DEFINE   SERIES(A,B:RESISTANCE)= RESISTANCE:
    RESISTANCE:::(
        IF A>= INFINITY ! B>= INFINITY THEN INFINITY
                                                ELSE   A+B FI   )   ENDDEFN
DEFINE   PARALLEL(A,B:RESISTANCE)= RESISTANCE:
    RESISTANCE:::(
        IF A>= INFINITY THEN B
        EF B>= INFINITY THEN A
                                ELSE   A*B/(A+B)   FI   )   ENDDEFN

Each of these two definitions is very careful to check for infinite resistances. The variable INFINITY is of type REAL and has presumably been set to a very large number. (Computer arithmetic generally cannot be trusted to assure that infinities behave as they do in mathematics.)

Each of these two definitions makes implicit use of the rule

$$resistance \quad \rightarrow \quad real$$

so to involve resistances within arithmetic expressions, and within the comparisons against the REAL variable INFINITY. In addition, the arithmetic expressions each yields type REAL and not type RESISTANCE. Thus, each of these functions encloses its arithmetic result within

$$RESISTANCE:::(\quad the \quad REAL \quad expression \quad)$$

so to render the REAL values as RESISTANCEs. We will use this construction very rarely (and only in this section). Whenever we use this construction, we are in effect putting our stamp of approval on the interpretation of the REAL as a RESISTANCE. In other words, the use of this construction implies that we have verified the validity of units (e.g., via dimensional analysis).

We introduce scalar multiplication on RESISTANCEs, i.e.,

$$resistance \quad \backslash TIMES \quad real \quad \rightarrow \quad resistance$$

by writing

> DEFINE   TIMES(R:RESISTANCE X:REAL)= RESISTANCE:
>   RESISTANCE:::(R*X)   ENDDEFN

We also introduce the rule

$$INFINITY \quad \rightarrow \quad resistance$$

by writing

DEFINE   INFINITY= RESISTANCE: RESISTANCE:::(INFINITY)   ENDDEFN

(The INFINITY referenced within this definition is the REAL variable by that name.) The latter definition facilitates a convenient specification for infinite resistance (i.e., complete insulation).

In summary, we have precisely the following rules for RESISTANCEs:

real \OHMS	$\rightarrow$	resistance
real \KOHMS	$\rightarrow$	resistance
resistance \SERIES resistance	$\rightarrow$	resistance
resistance \PARALLEL resistance	$\rightarrow$	resistance
resistance \TIMES real	$\rightarrow$	resistance
INFINITY	$\rightarrow$	resistance
resistance	$\rightarrow$	real

We have for CAPACITANCEs the following rules (by writing similar function definitions):

real \PFS	$\rightarrow$	capacitance
capacitance \PLUS capacitance	$\rightarrow$	capacitance
capacitance \TIMES real	$\rightarrow$	capacitance
capacitance	$\rightarrow$	real

9.1.2 The Type TIME

We declare the type TIME to be a PRIVATE REAL, as we did for the types RESIST-
ANCE and CAPACITANCE:

TYPE   TIME=   PRIVATE   REAL;   '' Microseconds ''

In addition, we introduce the following rules:

real	\MS	$\rightarrow$	time	(microseconds)
real	\NS	$\rightarrow$	time	(nanoseconds)
time	\SERIES time	$\rightarrow$	time	(sequential time)
time	\PARALLEL time	$\rightarrow$	time	(concurrent time)
time	\TIMES real	$\rightarrow$	time	(scalar multiplication)
time		$\rightarrow$	real	

These rules are defined via

```
DEFINE    MS(N:REAL)=  TIME:  TIME:::( N )            ENDDEFN
DEFINE    NS(N:REAL)=  TIME:  N/1000. \MS             ENDDEFN
DEFINE    SERIES(A,B:TIME)=  TIME:    TIME:::( A+B )           ENDDEFN
DEFINE    PARALLEL(A,B:TIME)=  TIME: TIME:::( A  MAX  B ) ENDDEFN
DEFINE    TIMES(T:TIME  X:REAL)=  TIME:       TIME:::( T*X )       ENDDEFN
LET   TIME   BECOME   REAL   BY     PUBLICIZE:::( TIME ) ;
```

Finally, we introduce a rule for deriving the delay time imposed by a resistor in
series with a capacitor (Figure 1.9):

resistance \TIMES   capacitance $\rightarrow$ time

This is defined by

```
DEFINE    TIMES(R:RESISTANCE  C:CAPACITANCE)=  TIME:
    TIME:::( R*C / 1000000. )                         ENDDEFN
```

Notice that we divide the R*C by 1 million. This has to be considered now because we
are putting our stamp of approval (TIME:::) on the result. The factor of 1 million arises
because we are given ohms and picofarads and we yield microseconds.

We have gone to the trouble to incorporate units into the type-checking mechanism
(via PRIVATE) because many programming (and conceptual) errors arise out of
mismatched units. From here on, we can ignore units entirely and still maintain confidence in our specifications. Our specifications will include units only for literal values,
for example,

5 \OHMS

6.1 \PFS

3.2 \NS

Fortunately, the specification of literals is the one place where unit specification is very
natural. (In fact, many people feel awkward omitting units from literal specifications.)

Example: A capacitance and a resistance. We define now the resistance per square for the polysilicon layer (the RED layer) and the capacitance per 2×2 lambda area for diffusion (the GREEN layer):

```
VAR        DIFF_CAPACITANCE= CAPACITANCE;  POLY_RESISTANCE= RESISTANCE;
DIFF_CAPACITANCE:=      0.001   \PF  ;
POLY_RESISTANCE:=       15.  \OHMS  ;
```

These values have been somewhat typical of what silicon foundries can offer. (The polysilicon resistance is optimistically on the low side.)

9.2 MODEL FOR ELECTRICAL ISLANDS: THE TYPE LOAD

We use the term "electrical island" to refer to any portion of a layout that is electrically connected. A layout is made up of many electrical islands. Each electrical island is characterized by the fact that charge injected at any point on the island flows to all other points on the island.

Figure 9.1 shows several examples of electrical islands. Parts A and B show obvious examples, physically connected (and hence electrically connected) wires. Part C shows that the input red wire of an inverter is itself an island. Part C shows also that the rest of the inverter is definitely not part of this input island. (Charge does not flow from red to green. Refer to Section 1.2.2.) Part D shows that the rest of the inverter, the output portion, is itself an electrical island.

Electrical islands affect chip performance because each island takes time to charge from a 1 (5 volts) to a 0 (0 volts), and vice versa.

Figure 9.2 shows a model for electrical islands represented in terms of resistances and capacitances. The capacitances are shown relative to GND, even though there may be no GND signals anywhere nearby. However, the capacity to hold charge arises because the substrate underneath the layout is grounded (presumably).

Figure 9.2A shows the model for a wire. The wire presents capacitance to GND at each and every point on the wire. The wire also presents a resistance from one end to the

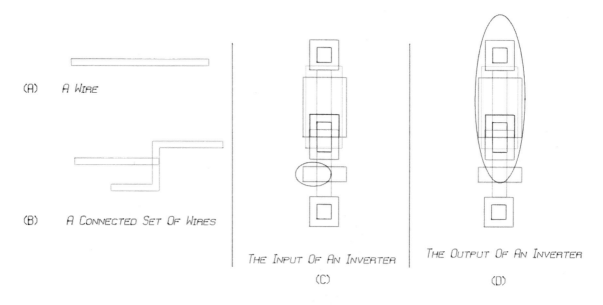

(A)   A WIRE

(B)   A CONNECTED SET OF WIRES

THE INPUT OF AN INVERTER
(C)

THE OUTPUT OF AN INVERTER
(D)

EXAMPLES OF ELECTRICAL ISLANDS

FIGURE 9.1

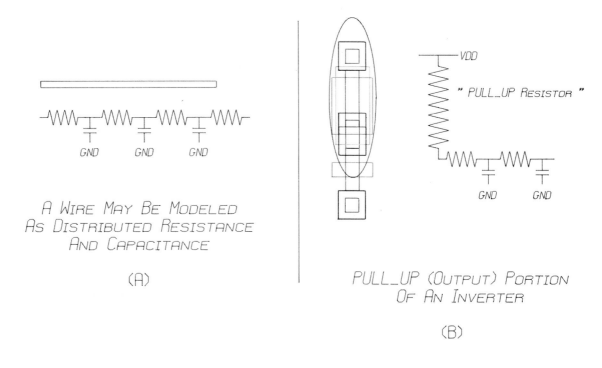

A WIRE MAY BE MODELED
AS DISTRIBUTED RESISTANCE
AND CAPACITANCE

(A)

PULL_UP (OUTPUT) PORTION
OF AN INVERTER

(B)

MODEL FOR ELECTRICAL ISLANDS

FIGURE 9.2

other. This model shows resistance and capacitance distributed (continuously) across the wire. The (infinitely many) resistors are shown in series, broken by (infinitely many) capacitors at each point along the wire.

Figure 9.2B shows the model for a circuit involving a pullup resistance toward VDD (e.g., the output island of an inverter). Besides the pullup resistor itself, we see the output wire modeled as shown in Figure 9.2A.

9.2.1 Simplified Model for Electrical Islands

Figure 9.3A shows a simplified model for a wire. We see here only one resistor and one capacitor. The one resistor represents at once all the little resistors from the previous model, and similarly the capacitor represents at once all the tiny capacitors. Figure 9.3B shows this simplification rendered on the output island of the inverter.

This simplification introduces small inaccuracies. The accurate model (Figure 9.2) and this simplified model behave slightly differently. These two models would be equivalent if the combination of resistance and capacitance were commutative, for example, if we could exchange adjacent elements and thereby render all the resistances on one side and all the capacitors on the other side. Figure 9.4 shows the variation of behavior that renders the commutative law invalid. We thus adopt the following approximation:

Approximation 1: We embrace the commutative law between resistors and capacitors connected in series, to justify the simple model. However, we bias the inaccuracy toward the worst (slowest) case by rendering the resistances in front of the capacitors.

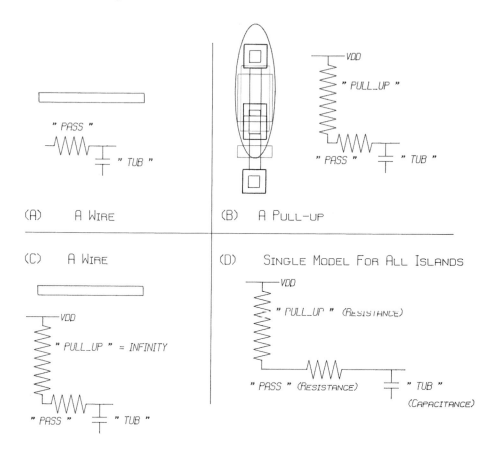

SIMPLIFIED ELECTRICAL MODEL
FOR ISLANDS

FIGURE 9.3

Figure 9.3C again shows the wire model, but now it includes an infinite pullup resistance. Figures 9.3A and C are, in fact, equivalent because an infinite resistance represents total insulation. Thus, the infinite resistance may or may not be written at all.

Figure 9.3D shows the simple model we will adopt for all islands. It represents a capacitance and two resistances. The ''PASS'' resistor represents the resistance encountered in traveling from one side of the island to the other. In contrast, the ''PULL_UP'' resistance represents the resistance between the island and VDD.

We declare the type LOAD to represent the electrical character of an island:

TYPE   LOAD=   [TUB: CAPACITANCE   PULL_UP, PASS: RESISTANCE] ;

Notice that this representation includes no information relating to geometry. It represents the island only as a homogeneous entity, showing no variation dependent on physical position within the island:

Approximation 2: We abstract away the geometric shape of an island, and disregard the possibility that the resistance between pairs of points along the island's border may vary with the choice of the two points. Again, we will bias this variation to the worst (slowest) possibility.

Figure 9.5A shows an inverter in terms of its two (input and output) islands. The inverter, like an amplifier, necessarily involves two islands. The two islands represent

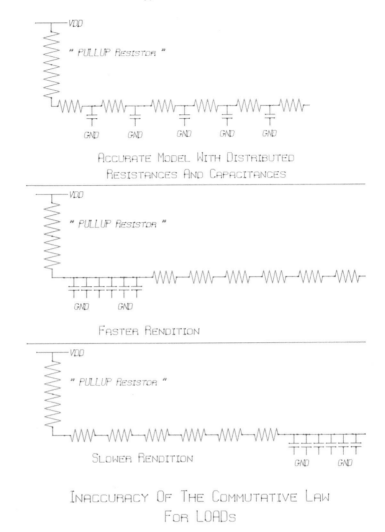

ACCURATE MODEL WITH DISTRIBUTED
RESISTANCES AND CAPACITANCES

FASTER RENDITION

SLOWER RENDITION

INACCURACY OF THE COMMUTATIVE LAW
FOR LOADS

FIGURE 9.4

the electrical isolation provided between the input and the output. Clearly, such an isolation must exist between the two islands because the two islands of the inverter are always supposed to represent opposite voltages. Section 3.1.5 discusses such electrical insulation in the implementation of unit memories.

The dependence of the output on the input is not an electrical dependence; rather, it is a logical dependence (Section 1.2.2). We will consider logical dependencies shortly.

Example: LOADs for colored wires. We define three functions, one for each of the three signal-carrying layout colors. Each function yields the LOAD imposed by a box of dimensions L by W. We assume that L is the length of the wire and that W is its width:

```
DEFINE    BLUE( L,W:  REAL  )=  LOAD:
   [ TUB:  (L/2.*W/2.)  *  0.001  \PF
        PASS:  0\OHMS           PULL_UP:  INFINITY  ]           ENDDEFN
DEFINE  RED( L,W:  REAL  )=  LOAD:
   [ TUB:         (L/2.*W/2.)  *  0.001  \PF
        PASS:         POLY_RESISTANCE  \TIMES  L/W
        PULL_UP:    INFINITY                       ]           ENDDEFN
DEFINE  GREEN( L,W:  REAL  )=  LOAD:
   [ TUB:  DIFF_CAPACITANCE  \TIMES  (L/2.  *  W/2.)
        PASS:  L/W  *  10.  \OHMS          PULL_UP:  INFINITY  ]          ENDDEFN
```

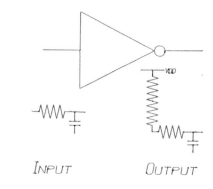

INPUT   OUTPUT

(A)   INVERTER'S INPUT AND OUTPUT ISLANDS

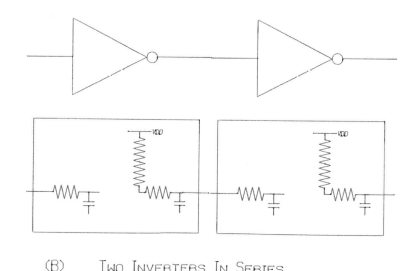

(B)   TWO INVERTERS IN SERIES

FIGURE 9.5   Connected islands.

These functions expose the electrical parameters assumed for performances quoted in this text. These parameters are somewhat typical of what chip fabricators have offered.

9.2.2   Each LOAD Imposes a Delay Time

Electrical islands affect chip performance in that they impose delays. It takes time to charge up an island from 0 volts to 5 volts, and vice versa. If such voltage changes could occur infinitely fast, chips would run infinitely fast. Islands therefore impose an "inertia" (i.e., an apparent reluctance to change voltage).

We transform a LOAD into a delay TIME via the coercion

```
LET    LOAD  BECOME  TIME  BY
    IF  LOAD.PULL_UP  >=  INFINITY  THEN         LOAD.PASS  \TIMES  LOAD.TUB
    ELSE    LOAD.PULL_UP  \SERIES  LOAD.PASS     \TIMES  LOAD.TUB          FI  ;
```

Let us consider only the ELSE clause in this coercion. We see that the delay time imposed by the LOAD is the product of the total resistance and capacitance. (Refer to Sections 1.3.2 and 1.3.6 and Figure 1.9.) The THEN clause is never taken in practice because an island insulated entirely from VDD does not experience voltage changes.

This clause was introduced so to measure such incomplete LOADs as though they were connected directly to VDD with zero pullup resistance.

We will render a LOAD as a delay TIME only when the LOAD is complete. Although we can (and will) represent LOADs insulated from VDD (e.g., wires), such a LOAD is incomplete at least until it is connected to a driver, for example, when the wire is connected to the output of an inverter, which does involve VDD.

9.2.3 Connecting LOADs Together

LOADs become connected together when we abut cells together. Figure 9.5B shows two inverters connected together. The two inverters independently represent a total of four islands. In contrast, the two inverters connected together represent only three islands. The output island of the first inverter has become electrically connected to the input island of the second inverter. Any time two islands become electrically connected, they cease to be islands and instead, by definition, become one (fused) electrical island.

Now for the first time, the input island of the second inverter involves VDD due to this fusion with the first inverter's output island. In general, LOADs are subject to fusion with other LOADs as long as they remain accessible on the ports of a cell.

Figure 9.6 shows how two LOADs become connected together to form one fused LOAD. This is represented by the rule

load \CONNECT load   →   load

For example, the middle island between the two inverters (Figure 9.5B) has a LOAD equal to

first inverter's output load

\CONNECT

second inverter's input load

The input island of the first inverter and the output island of the second inverter remain unchanged.

The \CONNECT operator is defined by

```
DEFINE     CONNECT( A,B:  LOAD )=  LOAD:
   IF  -DEFINED(A)  THEN     B
   EF  -DEFINED(B)  THEN     A
   ELSE    [TUB:             A.TUB \PLUS B.TUB
           PULL_UP:          A.PULL_UP \PARALLEL  B.PULL_UP
           PASS:             A.PASS \SERIES  B.PASS ]              FI
   ENDDEFN
```

The PULL_UP resistors combine in parallel, the PASS resistors combine in series, and the capacitors sum together.

Since the LOAD types represent no geometric information, we cannot know from the two LOADs themselves how they connect up physically. The \CONNECT function therefore chooses the worst possible mode of interconnection (approximation 1). The pass resistors are placed together in series, and in front of the entire capacitance. This renders the slowest of all possible arrangements; charge has to pass through both resistors before entering any of the capacitors. (The PULL_UPs are connected in parallel because they each connect to VDD at one end.)

The approximate nature of this model rests in this definition of CONNECT. The approximation has been chosen to bias toward the worst case so that the performance

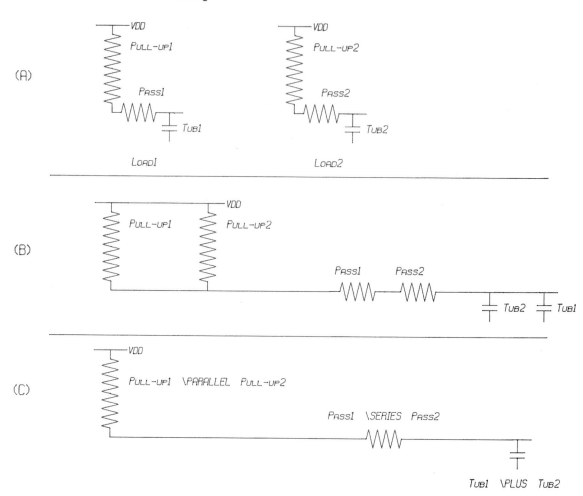

CONNECTING TWO LOADS TOGETHER
TO FORM ONE LOAD

FIGURE 9.6

derived for a chip is known to be maximally pessimistic. Such derived performance therefore represents a lower bound on what can be expected of the real chip.

This approximation is of particular computational benefit. It provides for a consistently simple model for arbitrary islands, no matter how such islands may have been formed.

Finally, there is another, mathematically abstract motivation for this definition of CONNECT and the type LOAD. Suppose that we start over by assuming that whatever a LOAD might be, we wish that it includes the notion of resistance and capacitance. We note that there is one operator that combines capacitances (\PLUS), and that there are two operators that combine resistances (\SERIES and \PARALLEL). To accommodate all three operators, we define LOAD so to represent one capacitor and two resistances. We then define CONNECT so to apply \PLUS between the capacitances, to apply \SERIES between one pair of resistors, and to apply \PARALLEL between the other pair of resistors.

9.3 LOGICAL DEPENDENCIES: THE TYPE NODE

The type LOAD allows us to represent electrical islands and to derive the delay times they impose. We have seen that an inverter contains two distinct LOADs (islands), an input and an output island. We have not yet provided for the fact that the output island depends logically on the input island.

This logical dependence is necessary in order to represent the fact that there is a delay between the arrival of a signal on the input and the stabilization of a well defined signal on the output. We begin to model this delay by imagining the following sequence:

1   A signal arrives at the input.

2   The input island stabilizes to the given voltage.

3   After the input island stabilizes, the output island begins to stabilize.

4   The output island finally stabilizes to the appropriate voltage and renders the transmission complete.

Steps 2 and 4 represent the entire delay imposed by the inverter. In other words, a logical dependency renders a total delay equal to the island delays taken in series.

Let us replace our association between islands and LOADs now with an association between islands and NODEs. A NODE represents a LOAD together with a set of logical dependencies. Each logical dependence refers to another island. Such a reference represents the fact that the other island must stablize before this island can begin to stablize.

We represent a single logical dependence via the type DEPENDENCE:

TYPE   DEPENDENCE = [FROM: NODE   DELAY: TIME   THRU: SIGNAL] ;

Let us ignore for now the THRU field; it will be used only in conjunction with clocks. A DEPENDENCE represents the dependence on an island (FROM) and a further delay imposed after the stabilization of the island (the DELAY field). We will always specify zero for the DELAY field. The DELAY field will become nonzero only by automatic means.

Figure 9.7A illustrates a DEPENDENCE. The total delay represented by the DEPENDENCE is the delay imposed by the FROM node followed by the time in the DELAY field. Figure 9.7B shows the DEPENDENCE of an inverter's output island on its input island. Figure 9.7C shows the dependencies of a NOR gate's output island upon all its input islands. The plural form,

TYPE   DEPENDENCIES = { DEPENDENCE } ;

represents the maximum delay imposed by any of its elements. That is, multiple dependencies represent that all the dependencies must stabilize before proceeding onward.

We have referred to the type NODE in the type DEPENDENCE, assuming that it represents an island. We now define this type as follows:

TYPE   NODE =   [LOAD: LOAD
                         WAIT: DEPENDENCIES
                         ISOLATED: BOOL
                         BEEN_HERE_BEFORE: BOOL
                         INDIRECT: NODE   ] ;

If we ignore the final three fields, we see that an island has a LOAD and a set of logical dependencies (the WAIT field). We will never specify values for the final three fields; these fields will be defined and used only by automatic means.

Example: The two NODEs of an inverter. We define the two NODEs of the inverter shown in Figure 9.16C as follows. We declare two variables to hold the two NODEs:

VAR   IN_NODE, OUT_NODE = NODE ;

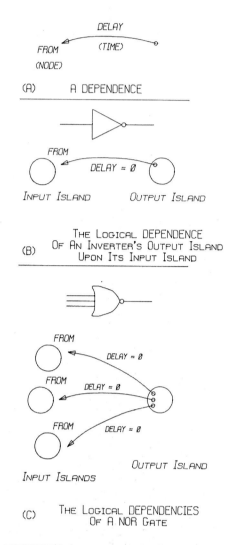

FIGURE 9.7 Logical dependencies.

We define IN_NODE with

```
IN_NODE:=  [  LOAD:        [  PULL_UP:  INFINITY
                              PASS:     POLY_RESISTANCE  \TIMES  11
                              TUB:      .001*11  +  .01*1.5  \PFS          ]      ] ;
```

The LOAD in this NODE characterizes the input red wire. These numbers are derived by looking closely at the layout, accounting for the resistance of the input red wire and the capacitance contributed by the red wire and the intersection of the red and green wires.
We define OUT_NODE with

```
OUT_NODE:=  [  LOAD:        [  PULL_UP:  40  \KOHMS
                              PASS:     30  \OHMS
                              TUB:      0.001*3.5*2.7  +  0.01*4  +  0.01*1.5  \PFS  ]
               WAIT:         { [ DELAY:  0\NS    FROM:  IN_NODE ] }        ] ;
```

We see here that the OUT_NODE depends logically on the IN_NODE. (The DELAY field is zero, as always.)

9.3.1 Incorporating the Electrical Model into the Layout CELL Type

Let us incorporate the electrical model into the CELL representation. The ports on a CELL provide the entire interface to the cell. When we wish to measure performance of a CELL, we will ask questions like

"How long does it take for an output port to stabilize after we stabilize each input port?"

Of all islands contained in a CELL's layout, only those islands that contain the physical positions of ports are visible from outside the cell. All other islands are inaccessible, that is, isolated electrically from the outside world. Because we augment a cell only by connecting to ports, only the port islands can ever be affected. In other words, the ports of a cell present precisely the set of accessible islands.

For example, Figure 9.8A shows two inverters about to be connected. Figure 9.8B shows the fused inverters, and Figure 9.8C shows a more abstract view, showing only the logical dependencies. We see here that of the three islands, only two are accessible from the outside. The middle island is forever isolated from the outside precisely because it has access to no port.

In contrast, Figure 9.8D shows again the two inverters fused, but this time the island between the inverters appears as a port on the finished cell. Figure 9.8E shows the abstraction of Figure 9.8D. In this example, all three islands remain accessible.

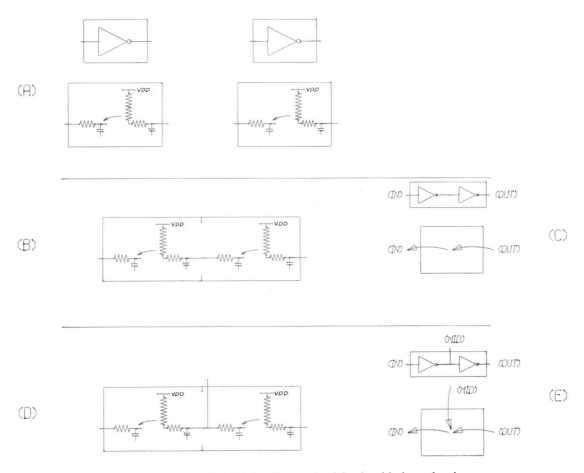

FIGURE 9.8 Connecting islands with dependencies.

Let us augment the datatype PORT so to now represent the island at that port. We introduce a new field, called E (Electronics), which refers to the island (NODE) resident at the port:

```
TYPE    PORT  =  [ E:  NODE        P:  POINT    S:  SIGNAL
                                    W:  REAL     C:  COLOR      ]  ;
```

We may now find all accessible islands (NODEs) of a CELL simply by examining the CELL's ports.

Because we have included in each port a NODE, and not merely a LOAD, each port refers not only to a LOAD, but also to all other NODEs in the cell on which the port depends logically. For example, Figure 9.8C shows that the output of the inverter pair depends logically on the middle, isolated NODE, which itself depends on the input NODE of the inverter pair. Figure 9.8E shows that the ports labeled MID and OUT each depend on the middle NODE, and that this middle NODE depends on the input NODE.

Example: A NOR-gate CELL.

The following renders the NOR-gate discussed in Section 1.4.3 (Figure 1.20) as a CELL. This rendition is complete as far as the electrical model is concerned. The parameter, of type NOR_COLUMN_LOGIC, affects the model in that the output NODE depends logically only on the appropriate subset of input NODEs. This parameter also affects the LOAD of the output NODE because the presence of a transistor contributes a significant additional capacitance. The following rendition, however, is not complete in the definition of the positions of the ports; we will consider a much easier way to form this cell after this rendition.

```
DEFINE   NOR_UNIT(  LOGIC:  NOR_COLUMN_LOGIC  )  =  CELL:
  BEGIN    VAR IN_NODES  =  NODES ;    OUT_NODE,  IN  =  NODE  ;
           N  =  INT;  B  =  BOOL;  Y  =  REAL  ;
  DO       IN_NODES:=    {  FOR  B  $E  LOGIC;  COLLECT
                            [LOAD:  RED(  8,  2  )     " Red input wire "
                                        \CONNECT       " Possible transistor "
                            [PULL_UP:  INFINITY
                             PASS:    0 \OHMS
                             TUB:        IF  B  THEN  .01
                                             ELSE  0  FI  \PFS  ]
                                        ]    }  ;
           N:=  +  1  FOR  B  $E  LOGIC;  ;
           OUT_NODE:=    [LOAD:
                             [PULL_UP:  40  \KOHMS     " pull-up resistor "
                              PASS:     4  \OHMS
                              TUB:      0.01*4  \PFS  ]            \CONNECT
                              BLUE(  14  *  N/2,  4  )      " Entire blue column "
                                                              \CONNECT
                              GREEN(  4  *  N/2,  4  )       " Green on feedthroughs "
                                                              \CONNECT
                              (  \CONNECT
                                  GREEN(  3,  2  )     " The green LINK "
                                                          \CONNECT
                              [PULL_UP:  INFINITY
                               PASS:  0  \OHMS       " Capacitance added "
                               TUB:  .01  \PFS  ]  " by the transitor "
                              FOR  B  $E  LOGIC;  WITH  B;  )
```

```
                        WAIT:     {COLLECT  [DELAY:  0  \NS  FROM:  IN  ]
                                   (  FOR  IN  $E  IN_NODES;   &&
                                      FOR  B  $E  LOGIC;    )  WITH  B;  }  ]  ;
GIVE     [  LAYOUT:         NOR_UNIT(  LOGIC  )
           L:    {COLLECT  [  P:  -4#Y   C:  RED   E:  IN  ]
                             FOR  IN  $E  IN_NODES;  &&  FOR  Y  ...  ;  }
           R:    {COLLECT  [  P:  4#Y   C:  RED   E:  IN  ]
                             FOR  IN  $E  IN_NODES;  &&  FOR  Y  ...  ;  }
           B:    {  [  P:  0  #  -14  *  N/2    C:  BLUE    E:  OUT_NODE  ]  }  ]
END      ENDDEFN
```

The important things to look at here are the definitions of the input NODEs list and the single output NODE, and also their incorporation into the ports of the resulting cell.

This function produces one NODE per input in the list IN_NODES. Each of these input NODEs includes the LOAD introduced by the red wire, i.e.,

RED(8 , 2)

which reflects the 8 by 2 lambda red layout. In addition, some of these LOADs include a 0.01 pF capacitance contributed by a pulldown transistor (called LINK in Section 1.4.3). This transistor contribution occurs precisely for those inputs that participate in the NOR gate, as dictated by the parameter LOGIC. Finally, each input NODE depends on no other NODE.

The single output NODE, assigned to the variable OUT_NODE, includes both a LOAD and a set of logical dependencies. The various contributions to this LOAD are indicated in the program text. These are derived by looking at the layout. The final part of the LOAD expression again contributes 0.01 pF for each pulldown transistor. The capacitance contributed by each pulldown transistor thus affects both the corresponding input NODE and the single output NODE.

Finally, the output NODE includes in its WAIT field a logical DEPENDENCE for each input NODE which can affect the output NODE. The FROM field for each dependence is taken from the set of input NODEs (IN_NODES). Each input NODE that contributes a pulldown transistor, as dictated by the LOGIC parameter, contributes one logical dependence.

The resulting CELL has its layout defined by the layout NOR_UNIT function from Section 1.4.3. The L and R sets of ports refer to the input NODEs, and the one port in B, the output port, references OUT_NODE. Notice that each corresponding pair of ports in L and R refers to the very same input node (IN). Each of these pairs of ports is electrically connected.

We could construct this NOR gate much more easily if we were to adopt the partitioning of effort used in Section 1.4.3 to form the NOR-gate layout in the first place. That NOR_UNIT layout function produces its layout not all at once, but instead by combining repetitively the two simply layouts PULL_UP and PULL_DOWN_UNIT.

Figure 6.3 shows a similar set of three cells, and how these three cells may be combined to form a NOR-gate. This NOR gate does not include any pulldown transistors; they were meant to be introduced subsequently. However, we can form a complete NOR-gate from a set of five cells:

1	PULL_UP_CELL	(as before)
2	TOP_PULL_DOWN_UNIT	(as before)
3	BOTTOM_PULL_DOWN_UNIT	(as before)
4	ACTIVE_TOP_PULL_DOWN_UNIT	(new)
5	ACTIVE_BOTTOM_PULL_DOWN_UNIT	(new)

The latter two cells correspond to the second and third cells; they differ only in that the latter two cells include the pulldown transistor. The entire NOR gate can be formed from these five cells by the NOR_GATE function presented in Section 6.3.6. Hence, if we

1 Provide the electrical definition for each of these five tiny subcells
2 Provide for the maintenance of the electrical model for cells resulting from fusion

we can easily render a NOR_GATE complete with electrical model.

We will consider shortly the maintenance, or "growth," of the electrical model that will occur as the result of cell fusions. First, however, let us introduce electrical information for a representative subset of these five tiny cells.

We now redefine three of these five tiny cells with the electrical information included. Refer to Example 2 in Section 6.1.5 for their original definitions devoid of electrical information. Here we affect only the ports, by including now the E fields.

Let us first declare three variables of type NODE to aid in the new definitions:

```
VAR       RED_NODE, BLUE_NODE, GREEN_NODE  =  NODE  ;

RED_NODE:=  [  LOAD:  RED(4,2)  ]  ;
BLUE_NODE:=  [  LOAD:  BLUE(4,4)  ]  ;
```

The RED_NODE represents the LOAD imposed by the 4×2 lambda red wire, and the BLUE_NODE represents the LOAD imposed by the 4×4 lambda blue box.

We redefine TOP_PULL_DOWN_UNIT as follows:

```
TOP_PULL_DOWN_UNIT:=
    [  LAYOUT:          {  -(2#2)   \BB    2#2  ;
                          -(2#1)   \RB    2#1       }
       T:  {    [ P:0#2    W:4    C:BLUE    S:SIGNAL2    E:BLUE_NODE  ]  ;
                [ P:0#2    W:4    C:GREEN   S:SIGNAL2         ]   }
       B:  {    [ P:0#-2   W:4    C:BLUE    S:SIGNAL2    E:BLUE_NODE  ]  ;
                [ P:0#-2   W:4    C:GREEN   S:  THE_GND_SIGNAL    ]    }
       L:  {    [ P:-2#0   W:2    C:RED     S:SIGNAL1    E:RED_NODE  ]  }
       R:  {    [ P:2#0    W:2    C:RED     S:SIGNAL1    E:RED_NODE  ]  }  ];
```

We see that the blue ports refer to the same BLUE_NODE, because the ports touch the same blue electrical island. Similarly, the red ports refer to the same RED_NODE. The green ports refer to no NODE because there is no green layout. [The green ports were included in the original definition so to inspire the \TOWER operator (Section 6.3.3) to route green to either end, maintaining thereby the possibility of the subsequent introduction of a green link to complete the transistor.]

We now construct another cell, ACTIVE_TOP_PULLDOWN_UNIT, which includes the green link built in:

```
BLUE_NODE:=  [  LOAD:  BLUE(4,4)  ]  ;
RED_NODE:=  [  LOAD:  RED(4,2)  \CONNECT    [  PULL_UP:  INFINITY
                                              TUB:      .01  \PFS    ]  ]  ;

GREEN_NODE:= [LOAD:  GREEN(3,2)  \CONNECT   [  PULL_UP:  INFINITY
                                              TUB:      .01  \PFS    ]
                     WAIT:  {  [  DELAY:  0  \NS    FROM:  RED_NODE  ]  }       ]  ;

ACTIVE_TOP_PULL_DOWN_UNIT:=
    [  LAYOUT:          {  -(2#2)  \BB   2#2  ;
                          -(2#1)  \RB   2#1  ;
                          -(1#2)  \GB   1#2       }
```

```
T:  {     [  P:0#2   W:4  C:BLUE   S:SIGNAL2  E:BLUE_NODE   ]  ;
          [  P:0#2   W:4  C:GREEN  S:SIGNAL2  E:GREEN_NODE  ]  }
B:  {     [  P:0#-2  W:4  C:BLUE   S:SIGNAL2  E:BLUE_NODE   ]  ;
          [  P:0#-2  W:4  C:GREEN  S:THE_GND_SIGNAL  ]                }
L:  {     [  P:-2#0  W:2  C:RED    S:SIGNAL1  E:RED_NODE    ]  }
R:  {     [  P:2#0   W:2  C:RED    S:SIGNAL1  E:RED_NODE    ]  }  ];
```

The blue ports still refer to the BLUE_NODE, as in the previous example; the blue island does not interact with any other island in these examples. The RED_NODE in this example feels an additional capacitance due to the red-green intersection.

The GREEN_NODE represents the LOAD felt by the green LINK in isolation and an additional capacitance introduced by the red-green intersection. We have chosen to represent the green island as having length 3, not 4. This reflects an assumption that this green pulldown transistor is turned off, rendering the bottom 1 lambda disconnected. We make this ''turned off'' assumption to reflect our desire to model pull-up times, not pull-down times. Section 1.3.6 discusses why pull-up times exceed pull-down times, and hence why pull-up times determine the electrical performance.

Note finally that the GREEN_NODE depends logically on the RED_NODE. This of course represents that the NOR gate's output (SIGNAL2) depends on the input (SIGNAL1).

We define PULL_UP_CELL as follows. Recall that our original definition occurs in a rotated orientation, so that VDD appears to be taken on the right:

```
VAR       OUT_NODE  =   NODE  ;
OUT_NODE:=  [  LOAD:    [  PULL_UP:  40  \KOHMS
                           TUB:      .01*4  \PFS  ]     ]  ;
PULL_UP_CELL:=
    [  LAYOUT:              (as before)
        L:  {     [  P:0#0   W:4  C:GREEN  S:SIGNAL1  E:OUT_NODE  ]  ;
                  [  P:0#0   W:4  C:BLUE   S:SIGNAL1  E:OUT_NODE  ]     }
        R:  {     [  P:11#0  W:  .125    C:GREEN  S:  THE_VDD_SIGNAL  ]  }  ]  ;

PULL_UP_CELL   ::=   \ROT_CCW  ;
```

The OUT_NODE represents the 40-kilohm resistance up to VDD felt by the ''bottom'' port on the upright PULL_UP_CELL. It also represents the capacitance contributed by the long pull-up transistor.

We have included no electrical information for power ports. Power ports by assumption are meant to be connected to VDD or GND for all time. Thus, power ports do not change voltage and hence do not affect speed of operation.

9.3.2   The CELL Abutment Process

We see that the NODEs from distinct cells become electrically connected when they appear on the inner edges of cells in the process of abutment. Figure 9.9 shows this process. Figure 9.8A and B illustrate more explicitly the connection between one pair of inner ports.

We augment the ABUT operator so to incorporate the electrical model simply by having ABUT apply a CONNECT operator between NODEs referenced in each corresponding pair of ports (Figure 9.9). That is, where ABUT has assured geometric (and hence electrical) connection between corresponding ports, we now have ABUT reflect this fact in the electrical model. We consider now what it means to connect two NODEs together.

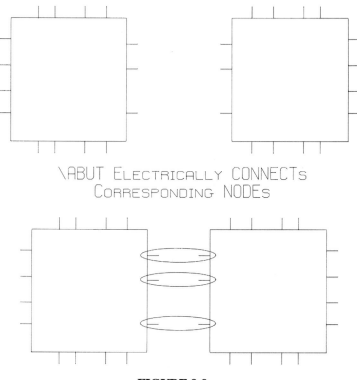

FIGURE 9.9

9.3.2.1 Connecting NODEs together. How does ABUT connect NODEs together? Perhaps ABUT specifies

   CONNECT(N1, N2) ;

for each pair of corresponding NODEs N1 and N2. However, if the NODE CONNECT operator were defined just like the LOAD CONNECT operator:

   node \CONNECT node   → node

then ABUT could not specify

   CONNECT(N1, N2);

but would instead have to specify something like

   N3 := N1 \CONNECT N2 ;

A NODE CONNECT operator introduced as

   node \CONNECT node   → node

by definition returns a value, a new NODE. In contrast, a NODE CONNECT operator introduced as

   CONNECT(node , node);

yields no new NODE, but instead affects one or the other or both of the given NODEs.
  If we include only the form

   node \CONNECT node   → node

then we must wonder what ABUT will do with the result node (N3). In contrast, the form

$$\text{CONNECT}(\quad node \quad , \quad node \quad);$$

yields no new NODE and hence removes any question of what to do with such a new node. However, this form of CONNECT must affect the given NODEs themselves if CONNECT is to have any effect.

We have thus far introduced operators which yield no values only in conjunction with SIGNALs, namely

$$\text{SET}(\quad signal \quad , \quad boolean \quad); \qquad \text{(for simulation), and}$$
$$\text{INDIRECT}(\quad signal \quad , \quad signal \quad); \qquad \text{(to render equivalence)}$$

All other operators introduced in this text have been specified to yield values. The few exceptions, for example,

$$\text{EXECUTE}(\quad equation \quad);$$

have implemented their effects through one of the first two basic operators just shown. In common to these two basic, non-value-returning operators is the use of the @-operator (Sections 3.2.4.3 and 7.1.2).

Let us for the moment define a value-returning version of CONNECT:

$$node \quad \backslash \text{CONNECT} \quad node \quad \rightarrow \quad node$$

so that we can understand the intended behavior for a fused NODE. We write:

```
DEFINE    CONNECT( A, B : NODE ) = NODE :
          [LOAD:    A.LOAD  \CONNECT   B.LOAD
           WAIT:    A.WAIT  $$ B.WAIT              ]            ENDDEFN
```

The two islands become one by fusing their two LOADs into one LOAD. This combined LOAD represents all the capacitances and resistances of the two LOADs taken together, now that they are electrically connected to form a single island. Thus, the "inertia" of the combined LOAD incorporates the inertia presented by the two LOADs independently. The combined LOAD has greater inertia than either one of the "lighter" LOADs.

The combined NODE depends logically on precisely the set of all islands upon which either of the given NODEs depends. That is, the combined NODE begins to stabilize only when each of the given NODEs could have begun to stabilize independently. Figure 9.10 illustrates this concatenation of DEPENDENCIES (the WAIT fields).

9.3.2.2 Objective treatment for NODEs and their fusion. Figure 9.11A again shows two inverters being fused. Figure 9.11B shows the new NODE created by the value-returning \CONNECT operator. This new NODE depends logically on what each of the two given NODEs have depended upon. (The second of the given NODEs in this example depended on nothing.)

Figure 9.11E shows a different story. Here, this new NODE has replaced each of the two given NODEs, in all conceivable ways. This is the result we would like; it matches our original intentions (Figure 9.8B).

Consider what happens physically when we fuse two islands (NODEs) together. The two given islands cease to exist; instead each now becomes one and the same, combined island. Neither of the two original islands continues to exist independently. In fact, there are no points of view that see either of the original islands. Island fusion is apparent uniformly from all points of view. Figure 9.12 illustrates this.

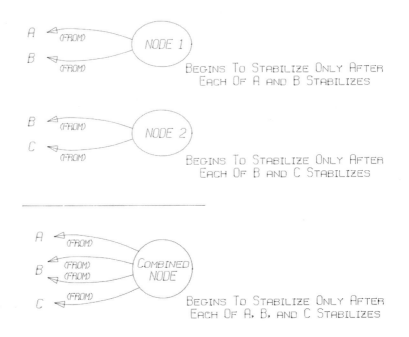

FUSION OF LOGICAL DEPENDENCIES

FIGURE 9.10

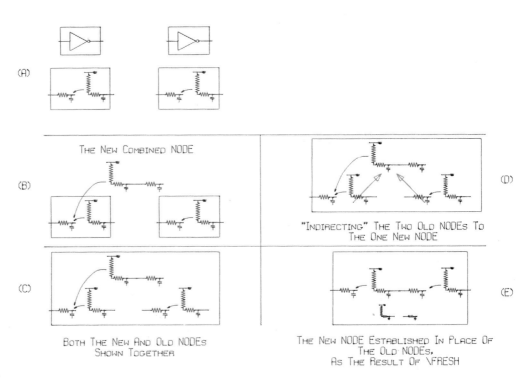

CONNECTING TWO NODES OBJECTIVELY

FIGURE 9.11

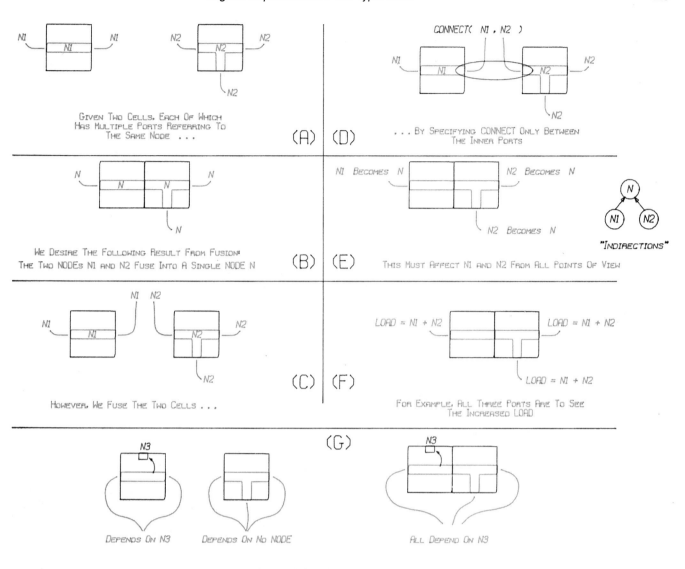

(A) GIVEN TWO CELLS, EACH OF WHICH HAS MULTIPLE PORTS REFERRING TO THE SAME NODE ...

(B) WE DESIRE THE FOLLOWING RESULT FROM FUSION: THE TWO NODES N1 AND N2 FUSE INTO A SINGLE NODE N

(C) HOWEVER, WE FUSE THE TWO CELLS ...

(D) ... BY SPECIFYING CONNECT ONLY BETWEEN THE INNER PORTS

CONNECT(N1 , N2)

(E) THIS MUST AFFECT N1 AND N2 FROM ALL POINTS OF VIEW

"INDIRECTIONS"

(F) FOR EXAMPLE, ALL THREE PORTS ARE TO SEE THE INCREASED LOAD

(G) DEPENDS ON N3   DEPENDS ON NO NODE   ALL DEPEND ON N3

ALSO, ALL THREE PORTS ARE TO SEE THE COMBINED DEPENDENCIES

CONSIDERATION FOR NODE FUSION: THE NEED FOR OBJECTIVE TREATMENT

FIGURE 9.12

We therefore imagine that the CONNECT operator,

CONNECT(node   ,   node   )   ;

computes the new combined NODE and then replaces each of the two given NODEs with this combined NODE. This replacement is meant to be apparent from all points of view, so that any references to either of the two given NODEs will now see only the new combined NODE. Such a replacement, or modification of existing data, is called an ''objective'' modification.

9.3.2.3   *The use of indirection to implement objective fusion.* Our only other encounter with objective modification concerned the type SIGNAL. We discovered then the desire to treat a SIGNAL as a place of storage, i.e., a place in which the logic simulator could store that signal's "present" boolean value. We introduced the operator

> SET(signal   ,   boolean   )

to store a given boolean into a given SIGNAL. This "store" operator was unusual because the effects of this operation were meant to become apparent from all points of view (i.e., so that all references to that SIGNAL could see the new boolean value).

We have stored with SIGNALs not only booleans, but also, in Section 7.1.1, we have stored with signals other, alias signals. We desired then to render two signals equivalent, so that two distinct signals would appear from all points of view to be one and the same signal. We introduced the operator

> INDIRECT(signal   ,   signal   )   ;

as the first step in rendering the two signals equivalent. This operator stores the second signal into the first signal's INDIRECT field. We then introduced a variety of \FRESH operators:

signal \FRESH	$\rightarrow$	signal
signal_expr \FRESH	$\rightarrow$	signal_expr
equation \FRESH	$\rightarrow$	equation
equations \FRESH	$\rightarrow$	equations
named_signals \FRESH	$\rightarrow$	named_signals
logic_cell \FRESH	$\rightarrow$	logic_cell

Each of these \FRESH operators produces a copy of its parameter which has the following property:

> All SIGNALs accessible throughout the given parameter are replaced by their aliases in the result.

We have a similar situation now with the type NODE. We wish that the effect of fusing two separate NODEs becomes apparent to all points of view, i.e., so that all references to either of the given NODEs now see one fused NODE instead.

For example, Figure 9.12 illustrates that a NODE may be referenced from more than one port. We see in this figure that the effects of NODE fusion, specified from the view of one pair of ports, is to become apparent to the other ports.

Figure 9.11A illustrates another source for multiple references to a NODE, via logical dependencies. The input NODE to the second inverter is referenced both from the left port of that inverter cell and also from the output NODE's dependencies (WAIT field). In this example again, the fusion of this NODE with another occurs from the point of view of the port, but the fusion is to become apparent also from the point of view of the logical dependence (Figure 9.11E). This renders an apparent chain of dependencies starting from the output NODE, through the fused middle NODE, to the input NODE of the first inverter.

We might define the objective NODE CONNECT operator as follows, using a NODE INDIRECT operator analogous to the INDIRECT operator for SIGNALs:

```
DEFINE    CONNECT( A , B : NODE ) :         BEGIN  VAR  FUSION  =  NODE ;
    FUSION:=    A \CONNECT B ;
    INDIRECT( A , FUSION ) ;
    INDIRECT( B , FUSION ) ;                END      ENDDEFN
```

This operator computes a new node, FUSION, which represents the fusion of the nodes A and B, via the value-returning node \CONNECT oeprator. Figure 9.11B shows this new node. This operator then INDIRECTs each of the nodes A and B to this new node (Figure 9.11D). Figure 9.11E shows the intended result; the new NODE appears to have replaced each of A and B.

The INDIRECT operator only implants the alias node (FUSION) as shown in Figure 9.11D; it does not itself render Figure 9.11E. As with the SIGNAL INDIRECT mechanism, we must apply a \FRESH operator in order to render a fresh copy with all NODEs now replaced by their aliases. Thus, a node \FRESH operator will transform Figure 9.11D into Figure 9.11E.

Section 7.1.2 discusses in more detail the following uniform procedure for implementing and incorporating indirections:

1	INDIRECT:	Specify all desired indirections.
2	FRESH:	Yield a fresh copy of the world with the aliases incorporated directly (i.e., without reference to indirected objects).
3	Cleanup:	Restore the original copy to its status prior to step 1.

We note one difference between SIGNAL fusion and NODE fusion. Fusion between SIGNALs has been specified simply by indirecting one signal to the other. In contrast, two NODEs are fused by indirecting each NODE to a newly created third NODE. That is, the domain of SIGNALs uses the operator INDIRECT directly to fuse two signals, whereas the domain of NODEs uses instead the operator CONNECT, which applies INDIRECT twice. NODEs involve two indirections to a third NODE because the alias is meant to be neither of the two given NODEs, but instead the larger NODE yielded by the value-returning \CONNECT operator.

We go on now to define for NODEs the INDIRECT operator and a variety of \FRESH operators, as we did previously for SIGNALs. We will finally return to redefine the objective CONNECT operator presented here, so to accommodate the possiblity that the two given nodes A and B might themselves refer to aliases of their own.

9.3.2.4 The NODE operator \OFFICIAL. We define the operator

$$\text{node} \quad \backslash \text{OFFICIAL} \qquad \rightarrow \qquad \text{node}$$

to yield the NODE officially represented by the given NODE. The result is usually just the given NODE itself. However, if the given NODE refers to another NODE via its INDIRECT field, therefore indicating an alias established previously, this function yields this intended alias.

We define \OFFICIAL by writing

```
DEFINE    OFFICIAL( N: NODE ) = NODE :
          IF DEFINED( N.INDIRECT ) THEN    N.INDIRECT \OFFICIAL
                                    ELSE    N                        FI
ENDDEFN
```

This definition is identical to that given in Section 7.1.1 to accommodate indirections in SIGNALs. We have chosen, however, to use the name \OFFICIAL instead of \FRESH because we will define \FRESH upon NODEs slightly differently.

9.3.2.5 *The NODE operators \EQ and INDIRECT.* We provide for the indirection from one NODE to another by writing

```
DEFINE     INDIRECT( FROM, TO: NODE ) :
           FROM:=  FROM \OFFICIAL  ;
           @(FROM).INDIRECT:=  TO  ;
           MODIFIED_NODES:=  FROM  <$  MODIFIED_NODES  ;      ENDDEFN

VAR    MODIFIED_NODES  =  NODES  ;
```

This definition matches that of the SIGNAL INDIRECT procedure (Section 7.1.2).

We also provide an operator that determines if two NODEs are already one and the same NODE:

```
          node  \EQ  node        →       boolean
```

We write

```
DEFINE    EQ( A,B  :  NODE )  =  BOOL:
          ( A \OFFICIAL )     ==     ( B \OFFICIAL )          ENDDEFN
```

\EQ compares the identities of the two NODEs (==) after each is rendered official. As with SIGNALs, we say that two NODEs are equal only when the reside at the same location in computer memory, i.e., only when it is assured that they are identical in all conceivable ways, so that modifications implanted objectively upon A are visible also from B, and vice versa.

9.3.2.6 *The objective CONNECT operator.* We define the objective CONNECT operator, the one to be used by the CELL abutment procedure, as follows:

```
DEFINE    CONNECT( A,B: NODE ):           BEGIN    VAR FUSION = NODE ;
          A:=  A \OFFICIAL;
          B:=  B \OFFICIAL;
          IF - ( A \EQ B )      THEN
              FUSION:=    A \CONNECT B  ;
              INDIRECT( A, FUSION );
              INDIRECT( B, FUSION );                          FI
END       ENDDEFN
```

This procedure connects two NODEs objectively by forming a new combined node, FUSION, and then by indirecting each of A and B to this new combined node (Figure 9.11D). This operator does nothing if A and B are already the same node.

Notice that this operator first renders each of A and B official, so to accommodate aliases established previously. For example, the given node A might itself have participated previously in a CONNECT operation with yet another NODE. Such a previous participation would render A indirected to another NODE.

More specifically, consider the following sequence which connects together three nodes, N1, N2, and N3:

```
          CONNECT( N1 , N2 ) ;
          CONNECT( N2 , N3 ) ;
```

The first CONNECT indirects each of N1 and N2 to a new node, say X. The second CONNECT affects not N2, but X instead, because CONNECT renders each of N2 and N3 official prior to using the INDIRECT operator. Figure 9.13C illustrates this effect. In fact, since the first CONNECT indirects both of N1 and N2 to X, we could specify the second CONNECT equivalently as

```
          CONNECT( N1 , N3 ) ;
```

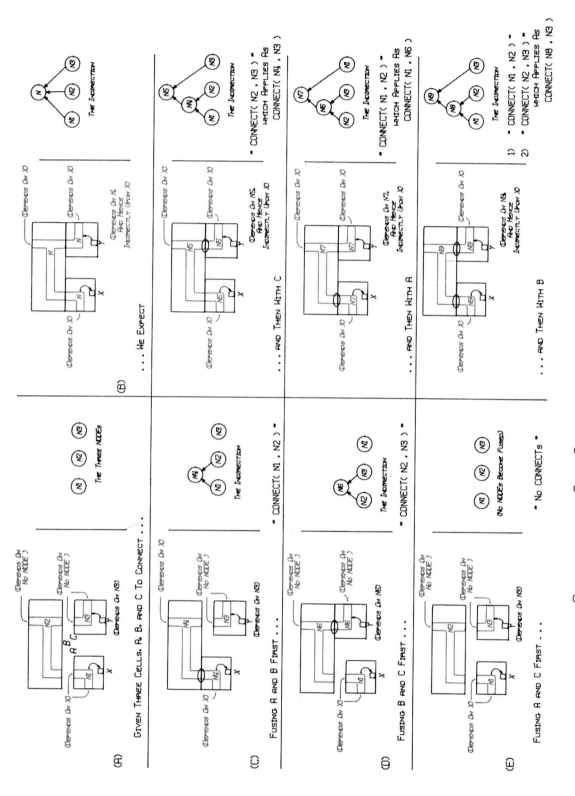

ASSOCIATIVE AND COMMUTATIVE LAW OF CONNECT

FIGURE 9.13

433

We are beginning to see a delightful freedom in how we may specify CONNECTions.

This CONNECT operator in fact obeys two simple and very useful mathematical laws. CONNECT is both commutative and associative. That is:

1 Commutativity: CONNECT(N1 , N2) ; and
CONNECT(N2 , N1) ;
each render identical situations, and

2 Associativity: The sequence

CONNECT(N1 , N2) ;
CONNECT(N2 , N3) ;
renders a situation identical to that rendered by
CONNECT(N2 , N3) ;
CONNECT(N1 , N2) ;

The commutative law indicates that the order of the two parameters to CONNECT is irrelevant. The associative law indicates that we may connect together three nodes without concern for which pair we CONNECT together first. Figure 9.13C, D, and E illustrate the three possible sequences by which three NODEs may be CONNECTed.

It is important to verify these two mathematical laws for CONNECT. Such knowledge relieves us of any concern about the order in which we CONNECT any set of NODEs. In turn, this relieves any concern for the order in which we ABUT sets of cells (Figure 9.13).

It will be fortunate that the electrical model imposes no requirement on the order of cell abutment simply because other, unrelated processes impose their own orders. For example, the translation from a LOGIC_CELL into a layout CELL abuts cells together in one particular order. In Figure 9.13, cell B might represent an interconnect cell produced by \PACK, designed to integrate the cells A and C. Of the three possible abutment orders shown in this figure, \PACK choses order (Figure 9.13E), fusing the interconnect cell after A and C have been fused via \UNION_DX.

There is another, perhaps more important reason to verify these mathematical laws for CONNECTion: The physics of connection is itself order independent. For example, we can plug three house extension cords together in series by any one of two orders. We can plug the first two cords together, and then plug in the third, or we can plug the second two cords together and then plug in the first. We can also exchange the first cord with the third cord, and so on. In each case, we expect the same result, one long extension cord. Similarly, the order in which we might connect strings of Christmas lights in series affects in no way the electrical behavior of the lights. We therefore require that our representation of physics (electrical behavior) shares these mathematical properties with that which it represents (physics).

Verifying the commutative and associative laws for CONNECT.

We verify the commutative law for CONNECT by noting that its definition remains unchanged if we substitute all appearances of A with B and vice versa. Such an exchange between A and B renders

```
B:=   B  \OFFICIAL  ;
A:=   A  \OFFICIAL  ;
IF   - (  B  \EQ  A  )     THEN
         FUSION:=  B  \CONNECT  A  ;
         INDIRECT(  B  ,  FUSION  )  ;
         INDIRECT(  A  ,  FUSION  )  ;              FI
```

The first two assignments appear in reverse order. However, each operates entirely independently of the other, and so their order is irrelevant. Similarly, the order of parameters to \EQ is reversed, but this order is irrelevant because \EQ is itself commutative. The value returning \CONNECT operator is also commutative, so we see no change yet. Finally, the two INDIRECT statements appear in reverse order. However, since A and B are distinct NODEs, guaranteed by the IF clause, neither INDIRECT affects the other.

We assumed in this argument that the value-returning \CONNECT operator is itself commutative. This fact can be verified by examining its definition, in Section 9.3.2.1. It forms its result by applying the operators

load \CONNECT load $\rightarrow$ load and

dependencies $\$\$$ dependencies $\rightarrow$ dependencies

to the two independent components of the type NODE. Each of these operators is commutative. (The LOAD \CONNECT operator is known to be commutative because it employs independently the operators \PARALLEL, \SERIES, and \PLUS, each of which is itself commutative. Also, the "$\$\$$" operator, which forms the concatenation of two strings, is commutative when applied to the type DEPENDENCIES because the meaning we have associated with this type is order independent; for example, all examinations of DEPENDENCIES are not affected by order.)

We verify the associate law for CONNECT in a similar manner. Figure 9.13C, D, and E each show that the three given NODEs, N1, N2, and N3, all reference the same new NODE via the implied indirect chain. That is,

no matter in which order we CONNECT   N1, N2, and N3, the three nodes

N1   \OFFICIAL

N2   \OFFICIAL

N3   \OFFICIAL

are one and the same NODE.

This equivalence is seen via the \OFFICIAL operator, which always climbs to the end of INDIRECT chains. We use the \OFFICIAL operator in all our functions (e.g., in CONNECT itself) so to acknowledge always such implied equivalences.

We have verified the associative law for the INDIRECT structure; that is, we know that N1, N2, and N3 always refer to one NODE, but we still need to verify that this common NODE represents the same behavior no matter which order is chosen. That is, it is conceivable for one order of CONNECTion to produce a common NODE which differs in behavior from the common NODE produced by another CONNECTion order.

The behavior of a NODE is defined by the value-returning \CONNECT operator. The behaviors of the common NODEs will be independent of CONNECTion order as long as this value-returning \CONNECT operator is itself associative. Fortunately, this \CONNECT operator is associative. Each of its internal operators, i.e.,

load \CONNECT load $\rightarrow$ load and

dependencies $\$\$$ dependencies $\rightarrow$ dependencies

is associative (because in part each of \SERIES, \PARALLEL, and \PLUS is associative).

Examples: Automatic modeling for NOR gates, NOR planes, PLAs, and interconnect.

Figure 9.14 shows how the electrical model for a NOR gate forms naturally from tiny cells, each of which includes its own electrical model. We assume here that the

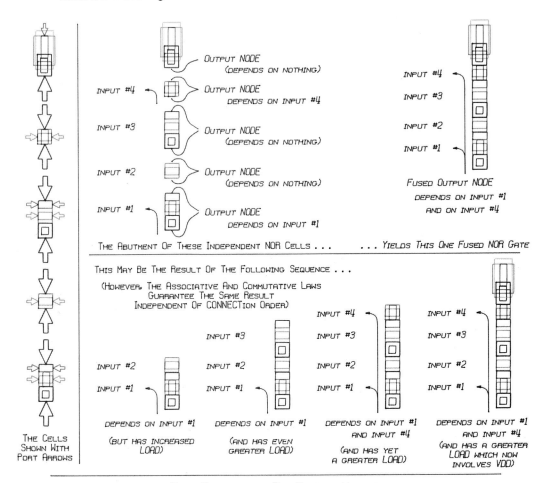

THE CELLS
SHOWN WITH
PORT ARROWS

OUTPUT NODE
(DEPENDS ON NOTHING)

INPUT #4 — OUTPUT NODE
DEPENDS ON INPUT #4

INPUT #3 — OUTPUT NODE
(DEPENDS ON NOTHING)

INPUT #2 — OUTPUT NODE
(DEPENDS ON NOTHING)

INPUT #1 — OUTPUT NODE
DEPENDS ON INPUT #1

THE ABUTMENT OF THESE INDEPENDENT NOR CELLS ...

INPUT #4
INPUT #3
INPUT #2
INPUT #1

FUSED OUTPUT NODE
DEPENDS ON INPUT #1
AND ON INPUT #4

... YIELDS THIS ONE FUSED NOR GATE

THIS MAY BE THE RESULT OF THE FOLLOWING SEQUENCE ...

(HOWEVER, THE ASSOCIATIVE AND COMMUTATIVE LAWS
GUARANTEE THE SAME RESULT
INDEPENDENT OF CONNECTION ORDER)

INPUT #3
INPUT #2
INPUT #1

DEPENDS ON INPUT #1
(BUT HAS INCREASED
LOAD)

INPUT #3
INPUT #2
INPUT #1

DEPENDS ON INPUT #1
(AND HAS EVEN
GREATER LOAD)

INPUT #4
INPUT #3
INPUT #2
INPUT #1

DEPENDS ON INPUT #1
AND INPUT #4
(AND HAS YET
A GREATER LOAD)

INPUT #4
INPUT #3
INPUT #2
INPUT #1

DEPENDS ON INPUT #1
AND INPUT #4
(AND HAS A GREATER
LOAD WHICH NOW
INVOLVES VDD)

THE ABUTMENT OF CELLS MAINTAINS
THE ACCUMULATION OF LOGICAL DEPENDENCIES

FIGURE 9.14

CELL abutment procedure CONNECTs corresponding NODEs between CELLs. Notice that the logical dependencies accumulate in the growing output NODE. This illustration views each NODE through the \OFFICIAL operator.

The associative and commutative laws assure this same result no matter in which order these tiny cells become fused.

Figure 9.15A shows the formation of a NOR plane from NOR gates, where corresponding input NODEs become CONNECTed (via the CELL abutment process). Figure 9.15B also shows CONNECTion with another NOR plane, in the formation of a PLA. Figure 9.15C shows the inclusion of input inverters. Again, the associative and commutative laws guarantee the same results no matter what we connect to what first; for example, we can introduce the inverters to the AND-plane either before or after introducing the OR plane.

Figure 9.15D shows the formation of a piece of interconnect, from the operator \FLY_AT. The electrical model can be incorporated into interconnect cells by treating each wire and feedthrough as a separate cell with electrical properties built in. \FLY_AT simply CONNECTs together the NODE associated with each piece.

For example, we can show this technique with the one-sided \FLY_AT operator, which we presented in complete detail in Section 6.2.5.2. We show its definition here

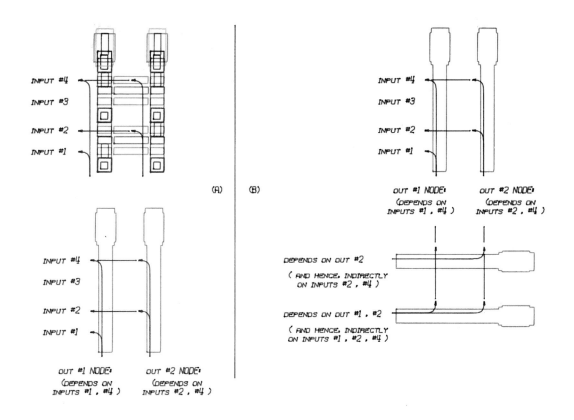

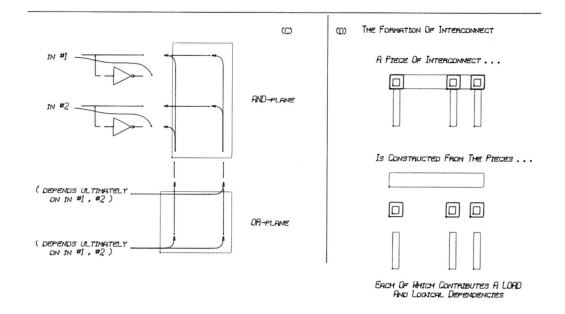

NODE CONNECTions Performed
By The CELL Abutment Operator
Grow A Complex And Accurate Overall Model

FIGURE 9.15

again, but we show all the original text in lowercase, so that the maintenance of the electrical model can be seen in uppercase:

```
define  fly_at( floor:  connections  y:  real  )  =  conn_status:
    begin    var  l,h  =  point;    rest  =  conn_status ;  p  =  port ;
             BLUE_NODE  =  NODE  ;
    if  defined(floor)  then
        do  [ low: l    high: h ]  :=    floor[1]  \mbb ;
            BLUE_NODE:= [LOAD:    BLUE( H.X - L.X + 4 , 4 ) ] ;
            rest:=  floor[2-]  \right_of h.x    \fly_at y ;
    give  [  layout:        l.x  #  y-2  \bb    h.x  #  y+2            \union
                            rest.layout                              \union
                {collect    {  if  p=red  then  rcb
                               ef  p=green  then  gcb
                               else  nil  fi            \at  p.x  #  y ;
                               p  \up_to  y         }
                for         p  $e  floor[1];    with  p.y < y ;
                            EACH_DO  CONNECT( P.E ,    [ LOAD:
                                        IF  P=RED  THEN  RED( Y-P.Y, 2 )
                                        ELSE  GREEN(Y-P.Y, 2) FI ] );
                            CONNECT( P.E , BLUE_NODE ) ; ; }
            do: ( floor[2-] \left_of h.x ) $$  rest.do   ]
    else    nil    fi                                        end    enddefn
```

This new, electrically complete rendition forms first the BLUE_NODE, which represents the behavior of the single horizontal blue wire (the first element in the LAYOUT field). This blue wire as yet relates logically to no other node.

The EACH_DO clause CONNECTs to the port below (P.E) the LOAD introduced by the red or green wire which extends the port "\UP_TO" the blue wire. This clause then CONNECTs this port to the BLUE_NODE. Thus, the EACH_DO clause ultimately CONNECTs together all ports interconnected by the blue wire. We can now deduce that these ports all reference the same NODE; all have been CONNECTed with the BLUE_NODE.

The associative and commutative laws have thus provided for this very natural expression of NODE interconnection. We specify each desired CONNECTion in any order, including the order in which we generate the interconnecting layout pieces.

As a result, all logical dependencies taken from each port are now felt by all ports. Thus, the interconnect performs electrically as imagined, (e.g., Figure 9.12).

9.3.2.7 *The FRESH operator for NODEs.* As with SIGNALs, we provide a \FRESH operator for NODEs, so to render fresh copies devoid of any indirections. We define this operator,

$$\text{node } \backslash \text{FRESH} \quad \rightarrow \quad \text{node}$$

as follows:

```
DEFINE   FRESH( N:NODE )  =  NODE :
         DO    N:=  N \OFFICIAL ;
               IF - N.BEEN_HERE_BEFORE  THEN
                    @(N).BEEN_HERE_BEFORE:=  TRUE ;
                    @(N).WAIT:=  N.WAIT \FRESH ;
                    MODIFIED_NODES:=  N <$ MODIFIED_NODES ;    FI
         GIVE  N                                      ENDDEFN
```

This \FRESH operator looks quite a bit different from the \FRESH operator defined for SIGNALs. The \FRESH for SIGNALs is, in fact, the same as the \OFFICIAL operator for NODEs.

This \FRESH operator for NODEs is different from that for SIGNALs because NODEs and SIGNALs differ in one fundamental way. NODEs reference other NODEs via the WAIT field. In contrast, SIGNALs reference no other SIGNALs.

The INDIRECT and EXPR fields of a SIGNAL do reference other SIGNALs, but these fields are not part of the inherent structure of a SIGNAL. These fields are used exclusively in the SIGNAL indirection mechanism. In contrast, the WAIT field of a NODE is inherent in the NODE structure. It exists independent of any indirection mechanism.

Any \FRESH operator is supposed to remove all indirections represented anywhere within the given structure, so to yield a fresh copy in which the intent of all indirections is now established naturally, without the use of INDIRECT fields. Thus, this \FRESH operator for NODEs applies a \FRESH operator to its own WAIT field, so to render fresh all nodes referenced from that field, i.e.,

$$@(N).WAIT \quad := \quad N.WAIT \quad \backslash FRESH \quad ;$$

We use the @-operator in this assignment so to implant the newly freshened WAIT field into the NODE itself. We have, and will always use, the @-operator to modify any fields in a NODE or a SIGNAL. Thus, the effect of freshening this WAIT field is apparent from all points of view. For example, this fact justifies the IF statement appearing in this operator; that is, if this node has been freshened previously, the WAIT field has been freshened previously (or is presently in the process of being freshened).

The \FRESH operator for the type DEPENDENCIES (e.g., the WAIT field of a NODE) is defined by

```
DEFINE    FRESH(  DS:  DEPENDENCIES  )  =  DEPENDENCIES:
   BEGIN          VAR  D  =  DEPENDENCE  ;
      {COLLECT    D     FOR  D  $E  DS  ;
                          EACH_DO    D.FROM  :=  D.FROM  \FRESH;  ;  }
   END                                                    ENDDEFN
```

This operator applies \FRESH to all accessible NODEs, that is, the FROM field in each DEPENDENCE.

Let us return to the NODE FRESH operator. The NODE \FRESH operator uses the BEEN_HERE_BEFORE field for the first time. This field indicates whether or not this NODE has been through \FRESH already. In case it has, \FRESH does nothing further. In all cases, however, note that \FRESH yields a NODE devoid of an INDIRECT field (an \OFFICIAL node).

The BEEN_HERE_BEFORE field is used not only to save computation. This nonduplication of work is essential because in the process of freshening the WAIT field, freshening a DEPENDENCE may in fact refer back to this very NODE. In other words, if a NODE depends logically on itself, then the freshening of its WAIT field will naturally attempt to refreshen this same NODE (from the FROM field of a DEPENDENCE), and hence establish an infinite loop via recursion.

Can a NODE depend logically on itself? Section 3.1.3 shows that such a cyclic dependence renders infinite propogations of unsteadiness, and hence represents an unreliable circuit. Our language of behavior, synchronous logic, forbids behaviors that have such cyclic dependencies. This language forbids \EQU (unclocked) equations that introduce cyclic dependencies, but it does allow "cyclic" dependencies in \NEXT equations. The "cyclic" dependencies introduced in \NEXT equations are not really cyclic; each "cycle" is, in fact, broken, by insulation in the time dimension. The unit memory provides this insulation.

However, our electrical model does not as yet provide for the existence of clocking units (i.e., unit memories). Thus, this model as yet provides no distinction between \NEXT and \EQU equations. Without a representation for clocks, our model will see cyclic dependencies (from \NEXT equations) without the knowledge that these cycles are broken by time.

We will incorporate clocks into this model shortly. At that time, the model will correctly break cyclic dependencies. (If we had introduced clocks already, we could avoid the possibility of infinite recursion right now. However, it is still simpler to accommodate "cycles" as we have, and to consider clocks separately.)

Finally, \FRESH places the NODE on the list MODIFIED_NODES when it modifies the BEEN_HERE_BEFORE field. This list refers to all NODEs that need to be cleaned up by the third phase. For example, the NODE INDIRECT operator has put onto this list all NODEs that have had their INDIRECT fields modified (i.e., defined). The SIGNAL INDIRECT operator maintains a similar list, called INDIRECTS in Section 7.1.2.

The cleanup process for NODEs is similar to that for SIGNALs. The cleanup process is defined by

```
DEFINE   END_NODE_INDIRECT:      BEGIN    VAR  N  =  NODE  ;
FOR  N  $E  MODIFIED_NODES;
        DO       @(N).INDIRECT   :=  NIL  ;
                 @(N).BEEN_HERE_BEFORE:=  FALSE  ;            END
MODIFIED_NODES:=  NIL  ;
END                                            ENDDEFN
```

This operator resets all fields set temporarily during the INDIRECT and FRESH phases. This renders the world with a clean slate so that a subsequent INDIRECT/FRESH sequence will have no stray INDIRECT intentions left over from this INDIRECT/FRESH sequence. The BEEN_HERE_BEFORE field, besides the INDIRECT field, is cleared so that the FRESH phase of a subsequent INDIRECT/FRESH sequence will not conclude prematurely that any given NODE is already fresh.

9.4 MODEL FOR CLOCKS

Figure 9.16A shows a clocking element. Figure 9.16B and C show that it is formed from two cells, a pass transistor followed immediately by an inverter. The role of each part is described in Section 3.1.5. Figure 3.7C shows that it takes two phases, phase1 and phase2, to implement a full unit memory. Section 4.2.3 discusses how a pair of clocking elements implements the two-phase clocking in a PLA.

We have already provided the electrical model for the inverter part. We now provide a model for the pass transistor. A pass transistor introduces a new concept into our model. A pass transistor makes or breaks a connection between the two halves of the green wire. We therefore see the existence of a "conditional" island. The two halves of the green wire may or may not form a single island. Thus, the LOAD introduced by the left half of the green wire may or may not include the LOAD introduced by the right half.

We will represent the LOADs on the two halves separately. When the halves become connected by a 1 on the red wire, we will still imagine for the purposes of this model that we have separate islands. Fortunately, the right half represents a very small LOAD because it is always connected directly to the small load on the inverter input. Thus, the variation introduced by the conditional connectedness renders physically only small variations on the left half LOAD.

There is a much more significant variation introduced by the conditional connectedness. Logical dependence and not merely island connectivity now becomes condition-

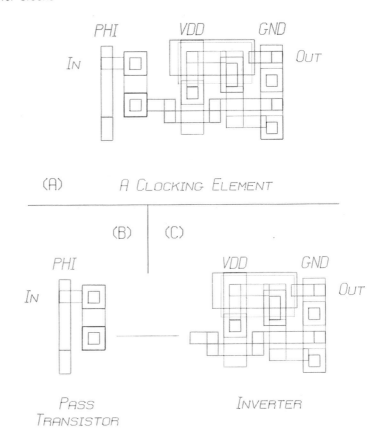

(A)   A CLOCKING ELEMENT

(B) | (C)

PASS
TRANSISTOR   INVERTER

FIGURE 9.16   *(See also color plate)*.

al. Figure 9.17A shows the pass transistor, with its three NODEs labeled IN, OUT, and PHI. OUT depends logically on IN when PHI carries a 1 (Figure 9.17B), but OUT depends not at all on IN when PHI carries a 0 (Figure 9.17C).

We have included in the DEPENDENCE type a field called THRU, of type SIGNAL, which now becomes useful. The THRU field of a DEPENDENCE represents a condition upon which the particular DEPENDENCE exists. Figure 9.17D shows how the OUT node depends logically on the IN node. This DEPENDENCE includes a THRU signal, PH1, which indicates that this dependence exists only when the signal PH1 carries a 1.

In practice, the PHI node of a clocking element will be connected only to the signal ph1 or the signal ph2. These two signals control the opening and closing of the two gates shown in Figure 3.7C. Clocking elements placed at PLA inputs take the ph2 signal and those placed at (some) outputs take the ph1 signal (Section 4.2.3).

Recall from the previous section where we accommodated cyclic logical dependencies. These arise due to feedback, even in \NEXT equations. Figure 9.18A shows a PLA that includes a feedback wire. We show the PLA output with the ph1 clock because feedback may occur only with \NEXT equations. Figure 9.18B shows the same PLA but with logical dependencies drawn in. We see here that the output depends on the AND term, which depends on the inputs, one of which depends on the output. Thus, the output participates in a cyclic dependency.

Figure 9.18C shows the same dependency graph, this time without the PLA. We still see the dependency cycle. However, two links in this cycle are conditional. One exists only when ph1 is on and the other exists only when ph2 is on. Figure 3.7C shows that ph1 and ph2 are never both on at the same time. Thus, this cycle really never exists; it is never completely connected at any one time.

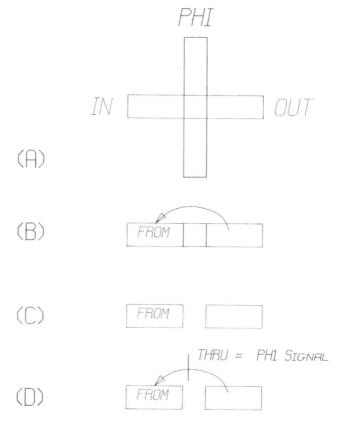

FIGURE 9.17   Conditional dependence. (*see also color plate*)

Nonetheless, our representation does contain cycles, as does Figure 9.18C, but we will acknowledge the conditional links when we interpret the results of this model to report the electrical performance of a chip.

9.4.1   Clocks Depend "Artificially" on Other Signals

Figure 9.19B shows that the OUT node of the pass transistor depends not only on the IN node, but also on the PHI node. This represents the fact that OUT can begin to stabilize only after both of IN and PHI each stabilize. Figure 9.19E shows the same for three pass transistors.

Figure 9.19C shows another dependence, PHI depending on IN. This is an artificial dependence. This dependence is physically nonexistent because PHI is not at all affected by IN. However, we can use this artificial dependence to represent the fact that PHI need not turn on before IN stabilizes. In fact, nothing will be gained by turning on PHI before IN stabilizes.

Why include this artificial dependence? One of the most important questions asked of a chip's performance is

"How fast can we clock this chip; that is, what is its maximum operating frequency?"

This boils down to four separable questions, shown in Figure 9.20:

1   How long must ph1 remain on?
2   How long must we wait after ph1 shuts off before we can turn on ph2?
3   How long must ph2 remain on?
4   How long must we wait after ph2 shuts off before we can turn on ph1?

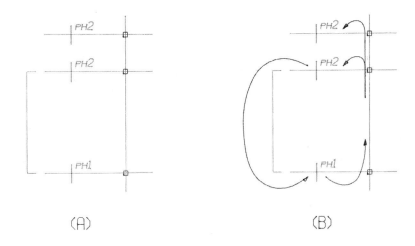

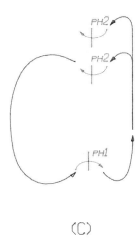

FIGURE 9.18   Logical dependencies in a PLA.

These may be restated more simply as requesting four numbers:

1   ph1-Width
2   ph1-to-ph2 Separation
3   ph2-Width
4   ph2-to-ph1 Separation

The sum of these four numbers yields the duration of each clock cycle, and hence the operating speed.

Figure 9.21 sketches how these four numbers can be derived. Consider part 1 in this figure. This represents the output of a ph1 clock feeding the input of another ph1 clock. The OUT node of the first clock depends on the ph1 node as described earlier; that is, OUT begins to stabilize only when ph1 turns on. Once OUT stabilizes, the nodes that depend logically on OUT begin to stabilize, (e.g., the IN node for the second clock can begin to stabilize). Once this second IN node stabilizes, this IN value can seep across to the final OUT node. Ph1 must remain on at least until this final OUT node stabilizes. Thus, the width of ph1 must be sufficiently great to accommodate the entire propagation delay from the output of any ph1 clock to the input of any other ph1 clock.

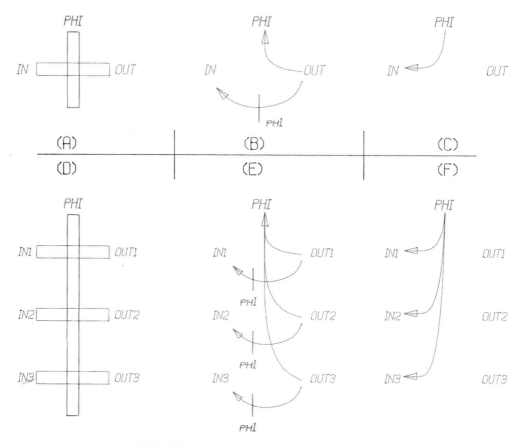

FIGURE 9.19 Clocks and signals are interdependent.

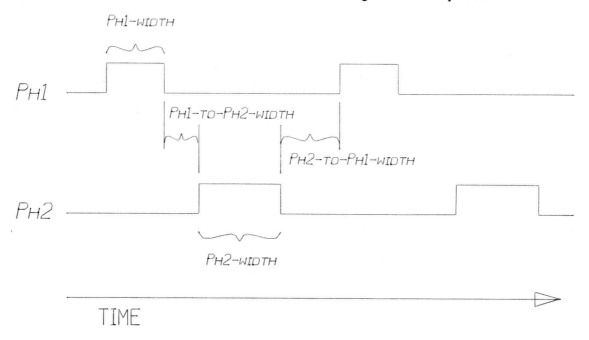

CLOCK PARAMETERS

FIGURE 9.20

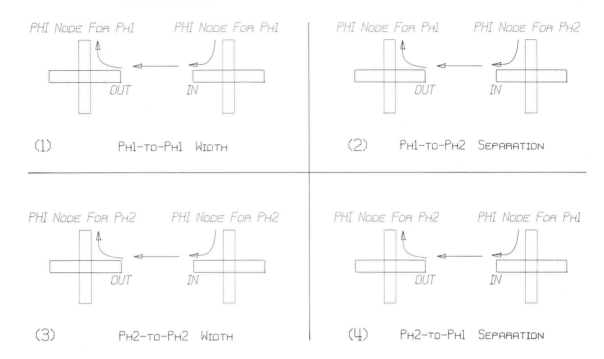

DETERMINING CLOCK PARAMETERS
(OPERATING FREQUENCY)

FIGURE 9.21

Part 2 of Figure 9.21 shows the output of a ph1 clock feeding the input of a ph2 clock. Suppose that we shut off the ph1 clock as soon as possible, to minimize the ph1 width. We assume therefore (pessimistically) that the OUT node stabilizes only just as ph1 turns off. Suppose also that we turn on the ph2 clock as late as possible, again, to minimize ph2's width. We will turn on ph2 therefore only when data arrive on its IN node. Thus, the time between ph1 shut off and ph2 turn on is the propagation delay between the first clock's OUT node and the second clock's IN node.

We will return to consider performance reporting in more detail. However, we can see now the primary motivation for including the artificial dependencies from PHI nodes. These serve to let the clocks know when data arrive at their front doors. These data most often themselves depend on clocks naturally, so the artificial dependencies effectively let clocks see other clocks and the delays apparent between clocks.

9.4.2 Clocks in a CELL

Let us include a new field in the CELL type to represent the artificial dependencies of clocks on other signals. This field provides the starting point for the timing analysis suggested earlier. This field in a CELL refers to the type defined by

```
TYPE    CLOCKS  =  {  CLOCK  }  ;
TYPE    CLOCK  =  [ PHI: SIGNAL    BODY: NODE    WAIT: DEPENDENCIES  ]  ;
```

A CLOCK is thus identified by its PHI field. This signal will always be either ph1 or ph2. The other fields state the following about that clock:

1   WAIT references all NODEs which are inputs to the clock (i.e., the "artificial" dependencies shown in Figure 9.19C and F).
2   BODY references the NODE used within the CELL to represent the red clock gate. In other words, any NODE dependent on the output of the clock references this NODE (e.g., the OUT dependence on the PHI node in Figure 9.19B and E).

We introduce CLOCKS into a CELL by redeclaring the type CELL as follows:

TYPE   CELL = [CLOCKS: CLOCKS   LAYOUT: LAYOUT
                                            T, R, B, L: PORTS
                                            TL, TR, BL, BR: SIGNALS] ;

The CLOCKS field serves to gather into one place all (artificial) dependencies of clocks on other NODEs. This is the field we will read when producing a report about the CELL's electrical performance.

Example: The pass transistor CELL for the clocking element.

Figure 9.22 shows the following clock transistor cell.

```
DEFINE     CLOCK_TRANSISTOR( IN, OUT, GATE: SIGNAL )  =  CELL:
   BEGIN    VAR NODE_IN, NODE_OUT, NODE_PHI = NODE ;
   NODE_IN:= [ LOAD:       [PULL_UP:        INFINITY
                            PASS:           0\OHMS
                            TUB:            0\PFS           ] ] ;
   NODE_PHI:=[ LOAD:       [PULL_UP:        INFINITY
                            PASS:           POLY_RESISTANCE \TIMES 6
                            TUB:            .001 * 5 +.01 \PFS    ] ] ;
   NODE_OUT:=[ LOAD:       [PULL_UP:        INFINITY
                            PASS:           10\OHMS
                            TUB:            2*12 *.001 + .01 \PFS  ]
               WAIT:       { [DELAY:0\NS  FROM: NODE_PHI] ;
                             [DELAY:0\NS  FROM: NODE_IN THRU: PHI ] } ];

   GIVE  [LAYOUT:   {   GCB \AT 0#7;    RCB;
                        -2.#2 \BB 2#5 ;
                        -6.#6 \GB -2.#8 ;
                        -(6#2) \RB -4.#10     }
          L:     { [ P: -6.#7   C: GREEN   S: IN   E: NODE_IN ] }
          T:     { [ P: -5.#10  C: RED     S: GATE E: NODE_PHI ] }
          B:     { [ P: -5.#-2. C: RED     S: GATE E: NODE_PHI ] }
          R:     { [ P: 2#0     C: RED     S: OUT E: NODE_OUT] }
          CLOCKS: { [ BODY: NODE_PHI   S: GATE
                      WAIT: { [DELAY: 0\NS FROM: NODE_IN] } ]    }      ]
   END      ENDDEFN
```

This function takes in the three signals desired at the three terminals. The resulting CELL has the dependencies shown in Figure 9.22B. Notice that the NODE_OUT depends on both NODE_IN and NODE_PHI. Although NODE_PHI itself shows no dependencies, the artificial dependence of NODE_PHI on NODE_IN is represented separately in the CLOCKS field.

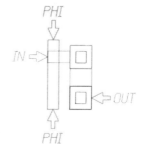

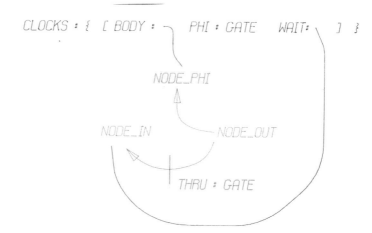

(A)   The CLOCK_TRANSISTOR Layout

(B)   The DEPENDENCIES

FIGURE 9.22

This is the only CELL we will ever specify which includes the notion of clocks. However, this cell will be integrated many times into a final chip, both as ph1 and ph2 clocking elements. The integration of the CLOCKS fields of various cells occurs during the abutment process, as described next. A final chip will itself be a CELL and it will have a CLOCKS field derived from all the clocking elements in the chip.

9.5 THE ABUTMENT PROCESS GROWS THE ELECTRICAL MODEL

In the four-sided cell mechanism, there is one process that ultimately fuses all pairs of cells. This operator is called ABUT. The one-sided mechanism could be rewritten easily so to combine all cells via ABUT. (The one-sided operators \UNION_DX and \PACK would offload some of their work onto ABUT.)

Recall that ABUT places two cells to the left and right of one another. ABUT fuses the two inner edges of cells by connecting corresponding pairs of ports.

We install the electrical model developed thus far into the entire fusion process merely by affecting the ABUT operator. Except for the definitions of leaf cells, no other modification to the existing programs is required.

ABUT accommodates the electrical model by doing the following:

1 Apply CONNECT between the NODEs in each corresponding pair of ports (along the two inner edges).

2 Produce in the CLOCKS field the concatenation of the two given cells' CLOCKS.

3 Detect and mark isolated NODEs.

4 Apply FRESH to the finished cell, to incorporate the effects of the CONNECT operator (step 1).

We describe each step separately in more detail.

9.5.1   Connecting Corresponding PORTs

ABUT places a bridge between each corresponding pair of ports (Section 8.3.1). ABUT maintains the electrical model for the resulting fused cell by performing the following:

```
FOR   P1   $E   LEFT.R;      &&      FOR   P2   $E   RIGHT.L;     &&
                                                 FOR   L   $E   BRIDGE_LOADS  ;
DO     CONNECT(   P1.E   ,   P2.E  )  ;
       CONNECT(   P1.E   ,   [ LOAD:  L  ]  )  ;                    END
```

This fuses the NODEs in each corresponding pair of PORTs. The first CONNECT performs this fusion (Figure 9.9).

The second CONNECT fuses in another tiny NODE which represents the tiny bridge ABUT places between the two ports. This NODE includes no logical dependencies, but it does introduce a small additional LOAD. These small LOADs presumably reside in the list BRIDGE_LOADS, which ABUT has constructed as it has chosen the layout for each bridge.

The order in which these CONNECTs appear is entirely irrelevant because the CONNECT operator is both commutative and associative.

9.5.2   Connecting the Clocks

ABUT produces in the CLOCKS field of the fused cell the following:

      LEFT.CLOCKS $$ RIGHT.CLOCKS

Thus, the fused cell represents all the artificial dependencies of both cells.

9.5.3   NODEs Isolated Due to Abutment

Of all the NODEs accessible through the ports on all eight sides of the two given cells, some may become inaccessible as the result of the cell fusion. Only six of the eight sides of the two cells remain accessible. NODEs referenced from ports residing along the two inner edges become inaccessible if no port on the six exposed sides also refers to that NODE. Figure 9.23A and C show two inverters about to be ABUTed. The second example shows the second inverter's input appearing also on a top port. In each case, ABUT first CONNECTs the two inner ports. Figure 9.23B shows that this fused NODE becomes inaccessible in the first example; it appears on no port of the result. In contrast, Figure 9.23D shows the fused NODE still accessible in the second example, via the top port.

ABUT determines the set of isolated NODEs after it CONNECTs the pairs of corresponding ports. This set is defined formally by

```
ISOLATED_NODES:=
        {COLLECT    P.E    FOR  P  $E  LEFT.R  ;
                            WITH
                NEVER    P.E  \EQ  P1.E    FOR  P1  $E
                                LEFT.L  $$  LEFT.T  $$  LEFT.B  $$
                                RIGHT.R  $$  RIGHT.T  $$  RIGHT.B  ;  ;  }  ;
```

ISOLATED_NODES thus consists of all NODEs resident in LEFT.R which appear on none of the six accessible sides.

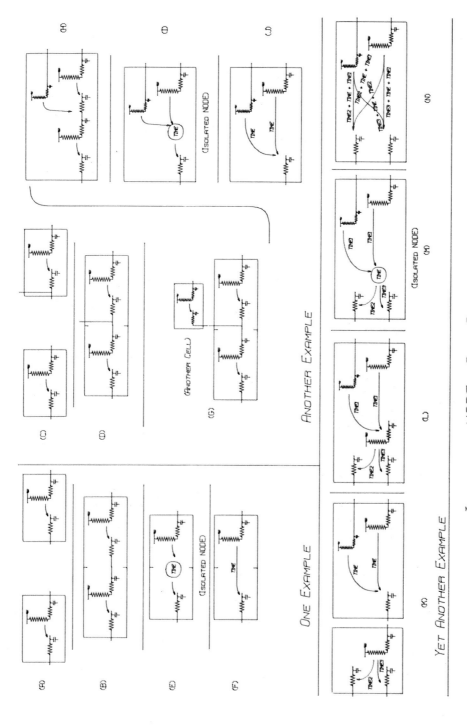

ISOLATED NODES AND SIMPLIFICATION

FIGURE 9.23

449

Each of the two inner edges, LEFT.R and RIGHT.L, now refer to precisely the same NODEs. These previously unrelated NODEs have been CONNECTed prior to this assignment into ISOLATED_NODES. Note also the possibility that a NODE in LEFT.R which resides on no other edge of LEFT may, in fact, remain accessible, via an accessible port on RIGHT. This occurs if the corresponding port in RIGHT.L refers to a NODE which appears also on another edge of RIGHT.

Isolated NODEs have a valuable property shared by no other NODEs: They are never again subject to CONNECTion with other nodes. Their absence from all ports guarantees eternal isolation from such external interactions. Thus, isolated NODEs contain invariant LOADs.

The invariant LOADs in isolated NODEs represent for the first time reliable delay times (Figure 9.23E). In contrast, LOADs in accessible NODEs are subject to grow as these accessible NODEs are subject to further CONNECTion (Figure 9.23G).

We may therefore forget the LOAD in an isolated NODE by replacing the LOAD by a delay time instead. Figure 9.23F shows how useful this reduction can be. The two logical dependencies shown in part E may now be represented equivalently as a single dependence which incorporates the time imposed by the LOAD in the DEPENDENCE's DELAY field.

In contrast, Figure 9.23G shows that our second example, with the top port, remains vulnerable to subsequent CONNECTion. Such a subsequent CONNECTion increases the LOAD of the middle NODE. However, Figure 9.23H shows that eventually, this middle NODE itself may become isolated. Again, this newly isolated NODE may be reduced to a single time (Figure 9.23I), rendering a simplification for the resulting cell (Figure 9.23J).

The potential simplification provided by isolated NODEs is so valuable that we will have ABUT mark each isolated NODE so that at least some other process can render the simplifications:

```
FOR  N   $E   ISOLATED_NODES  ;
   DO    N  :=  N  \OFFICIAL  ;
         @(N).ISOLATED  :=  TRUE  ;           END
```

We have now made use of all fields in a NODE. We summarize these fields, which together represent an electrical island:

1	LOAD: LOAD	the electrical inertia of the island
2	WAIT: DEPENDENCIES	all logical dependencies that can cause this island to change status
3	ISOLATED: BOOL	this island is forever isolated
4	BEEN_HERE_BEFORE: BOOL	for implementation of \FRESH so to avoid infinite recursion
5	INDIRECT: NODE	represents the official alias for the implementation of objective NODE fusion

We also summarize the fields of the DEPENDENCE type:

1	FROM: NODE	the node depended upon
2	DELAY· TIME	an extra delay to endure even after FROM stabilizes
3	THRU: SIGNAL	condition upon which this DEPENDENCE exists

9.5.4 Final Step in ABUT

Just before ABUT yields its fused cell, ABUT applies \FRESH to each NODE accessible in the cell. Suppose that the variable FUSION holds this final cell. ABUT performs the following:

$$
\begin{aligned}
\text{FUSION.T} &:= \text{FUSION.T} \quad \text{\textbackslash FRESH} ; \\
\text{FUSION.B} &:= \text{FUSION.B} \quad \text{\textbackslash FRESH} ; \\
\text{FUSION.R} &:= \text{FUSION.R} \quad \text{\textbackslash FRESH} ; \\
\text{FUSION.L} &:= \text{FUSION.L} \quad \text{\textbackslash FRESH} ; \\
\text{FUSION.CLOCKS} &:= \text{FUSION.CLOCKS} \quad \text{\textbackslash FRESH} ;
\end{aligned}
$$

This FRESHens all NODEs represented in FUSION. (The \FRESH operators used here, that is, \FRESH upon the type PORTS and upon the type CLOCKS, are defined by

```
DEFINE    FRESH( PS: PORTS ) = PORTS:            BEGIN VAR P = PORT ;
{COLLECT    P    FOR P $E PS ;
                 EACH_DO    P.E := P.E \FRESH ; ; }
END                                              ENDDEFN

DEFINE    FRESH( CS: CLOCKS ) = CLOCKS:          BEGIN VAR C = CLOCK ;
{COLLECT    C    FOR C $E CS ;
                 EACH_DO    C.BODY := C.BODY \FRESH ;
                            C.WAIT := C.WAIT \FRESH ; ; }
END                                              ENDDEFN    )
```

This \FRESH procedure in ABUT implements all the NODE fusions represented by all NODEs' INDIRECT fields. The result is now represented without the use of INDIRECT fields. Thus, this cell may participate in subsequent ABUTments, starting without preexisting INDIRECT fields.

9.6 RECURSIVE ELECTRICAL SIMPLIFICATION

We have seen at least in concept that isolated NODEs can drop out of our electrical model, being replaced instead by increased delay times in DEPENDENCIES (Figure 9.23E, F, I and J). We now formalize this simplification process. It occurs upon each ABUTment of two cells, so such simplification occurs incrementally with the growth of cells.

As a result of such simplification, we can actually determine an upper bound for the computer memory consumed in the representation of electrical behavior of any CELL, no matter how complex. In addition, we can report the electrical performance very easily from the simplified model.

The simplification considered here has no bearing on the accuracy of this model. In fact, this electrical model is completely accurate independent of this simplification, except for the abstraction made already in the LOAD representation. (This model does not account for pass transistors in general, however. It rests on the assumption that the pass transistors occur directly in front of inverters, as in clocking elements, so that the concept of a conditional LOAD may be avoided.)

The simplification removes all isolated NODEs that are otherwise represented implicitly in the cell. That is, although all accessible NODEs, NODEs in ports, are themselves not isolated, they often refer to isolated NODEs via the logical dependencies represented in their WAIT fields. Such isolated NODEs themselves often depend on other isolated nodes.

In fact, in the absence of simplification, a cell will always reference all NODEs (islands) apparent physically in the cell's layout. The unsimplified electrical model contains a NODE for each distinct island on the chip; that is, one NODE for each region that would provide unique information if probed.

However, the performance of a chip is determined by measuring only the chips pads, or equivalently, a cell's ports. The questions we can ask of a cell's performance are:

1 If we change the signal on a given input port, how long does it take before this change propagates to another given output port?

2 How fast can we clock the chip?

The first question refers only to the cell's ports. We will address the second question shortly, but it also refers to ports, namely the two ports for the ph1 and ph2 clocks.

A simplified electrical model devoid of isolated NODEs refers to at most as many NODEs as there are ports on the cell. (All other NODEs are by definition, isolated.) Each port's NODE may depend logically on other NODEs, but again in the absence of isolated NODEs, all logical dependencies refer only to NODEs in other ports. Thus, we obtain an upper bound on memory consumption of n-squared, where n is the number of ports on the cell. [Each port may at most depend on all the other n - 1 ports (e.g., Figure 9.23F, J and N).]

Because the simplified model represents logical dependencies only among ports, the answer to the first question stated above resides directly in the representation. For any given output port, we look at that port's NODE and find directly:

1 The set of input ports upon which it depends

2 The propagation time from each input port to this output port, (via the DELAY field in each DEPENDENCY emanating from the output port's node)

(Output ports that are the result of \NEXT equations will show delays dependent on the clock ports, therefore indicating how long after the clock stabilizes the output port stabilizes).

9.6.1 Simplification Occurs in \FRESH on DEPENDENCIES

We implement simplification by redefining the \FRESH operator

dependencies \FRESH   →   dependencies

Section 9.3.2.7 contains the original definition. The new definition will account for isolated NODEs, which have been marked (especially for this process) by ABUT.

We construct our new DEPENDENCIES \FRESH operator in several steps. First, we introduce a \FRESH operator which considers only one dependence:

dependence \FRESH   →   dependencies

This operator can transform a single dependence into several dependencies. Figure 9.24 shows how.

From the point of view of the given dependence, the isolated node appears merely as an additional delay imposed on each of the isolated node's own dependencies (Figure 9.24C). In other words, the given dependence can be seen to represent a dependence not on the isolated node, but instead on those nodes that affect the isolated node (Figure 9.24D).

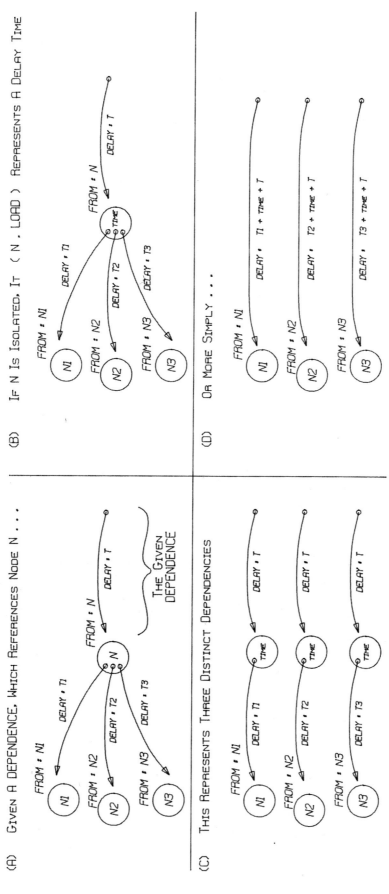

(A) Given A Dependence, Which References Node N . . .

(B) If N Is Isolated, It ⟨ N . LOAD ⟩ Represents A Delay Time

(C) This Represents Three Distinct Dependencies

(D) Or More Simply . . .

Removing An Isolated FROM Node From A DEPENDENCE

FIGURE 9.24

453

Each such extended dependence, upon N1 say, accommodates the following sequence of delays:

1   The isolated node, N, can begin to stabilize only after time=T1 elapses subsequent to the stabilization of N1.

2   The isolated node N then requires time=N.LOAD to stabilize itself.

3   After N stabilizes, the given dependence imposes its time=T.

The legitimacy of this reduction (i.e., the removal of the isolated node) relies heavily on the fact that this node is in fact isolated. Of all nodes, only isolated nodes remain unchanged forever. This invariance supports the assumption implicit in this reduction—that the removed node will never be subjected to a change in either

1   Its LOAD, or

2   The set of NODEs upon which it depends.

The definition of this \FRESH operator, which transforms a single dependence into potentially several dependencies, follows:

```
DEFINE    FRESH( D: DEPENDENCE ) = DEPENDENCIES:
    BEGIN    VAR    T, T1 = TIME ;   N, N1 = NODE ;    C, C1 = SIGNAL ;
        DO    [ DELAY: T    FROM: N    THRU: C ]    :=    D ;
              N:= N \FRESH ;
    GIVE    IF   - N.ISOLATED    THEN
                    { [ DELAY: T    FROM: N    THRU: C ] }
            ELSE
              { FOR [ DELAY:T1 FROM:N1 THRU:C1 ] $E N.WAIT;
                      WITH    C1 \CLOCK_COMPATABLE C ;
                  COLLECT    [ DELAY: T \SERIES T1 \SERIES N.LOAD
                              FROM:    N1
                              THRU:    C \CLOCK C1 ]           } FI
    END                              ENDDEFN
```

From the top, we see in the first two assignments that the FROM node, N, is FRESHened (as before, in Section 9.3.2.7). If the FROM node N is not isolated, the THEN clause in this \FRESH operator simply yields a list containing the one given dependence with N freshened. This result matches the result given by the original \FRESH operator defined for dependencies.

If N is isolated, the ELSE clause renders the situation shown in Figure 9.24D. It produces a set of dependencies corresponding to the set N.WAIT. The DELAY in each corresponding dependence includes the time contributed by the isolated node's LOAD and the time T present in the given dependence.

This process for the first time creates a dependence with nonzero DELAY, so to reflect the inertia contributed by the isolated node. Because many isolated nodes can be reduced to pure TIMEs, we accommodate in general nonzero times in the left and right dependencies (T1 and T).

Also for the first time, we see an examination of the THRU field of a DEPENDENCE. Recall that this field represents a condition upon which this dependence owes its very existence. This dependence exists only when the THRU signal, a clock, carries a 1.

Figure 9.25 shows one dependence pair with the THRU fields labeled. The resulting single dependence (Figure 9.25B) exists only when both of the given dependencies

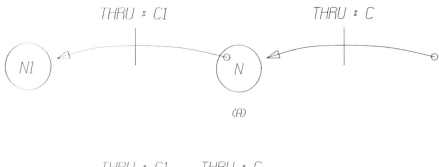

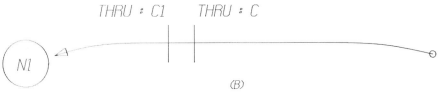

FIGURE 9.25 Clocks in dependence fusion.

exist. If the two given dependencies exist only at mutually exclusive times, we know unconditionally that the fused dependence never exists. This \FRESH operator thus omits fused dependencies, which can never exist, by means of the WITH clause.

The compatibility between two conditions (clocks) is defined by

```
DEFINE    CLOCK_COMPATABLE( C1,C2 : SIGNAL ) = BOOL:
          - DEFINED( C1 )    !
          - DEFINED( C2 )    !
          ( C1 \EQ C2 )                                    ENDDEFN
```

This function yields TRUE as long as one or the other dependence exists unconditionally, or if both exist at the same time. It yields FALSE when the two dependencies exist at mutually exclusive times (i.e., one is ph1 and the other is ph2). (In fact, this model can tolerate systems with more than two clocks, as long as each pair of clocks occur at mutually exclusive times.)

The \FRESH operator not only examines such conditions, it also defines the THRU field in each dependence it yields. The condition upon which a fused dependence exists is defined by

```
DEFINE    CLOCK( C1,C2: SIGNAL ) = SIGNAL:
          IF DEFINED( C1 )    THEN        C1
                              ELSE        C2      FI          ENDDEFN
```

This yields the following intersections of existence:

1	unconditional, unconditional	$\rightarrow$	unconditional	(ELSE)
2	ph1, unconditional	$\rightarrow$	ph1	(THEN)
	ph2, unconditional	$\rightarrow$	ph2	(THEN)
3	unconditional, ph1	$\rightarrow$	ph1	(ELSE)
	unconditional, ph2	$\rightarrow$	ph2	(ELSE)
4	ph1, ph1	$\rightarrow$	ph1	(THEN)
	ph2, ph2	$\rightarrow$	ph2	(THEN)

9.6.2 The Full Plural Dependencies \FRESH Operator and Compaction

We have provided the operator

dependence \FRESH   →   dependencies

We now define the plural-to-plural version, which replaces the original DEPENDEN-CIES \FRESH operator defined in Section 9.3.2.7:

```
DEFINE  FRESH(  DS:  DEPENDENCIES  )  =  DEPENDENCIES:
     BEGIN       VAR  D  =  DEPENDENCE  ;
          (  $$     D  \FRESH     FOR  D  $E  DS;  )     \COMPACT
     END                                              ENDDEFN
```

It forms the concatenation of all the dependencies generated by the singular-to-plural \FRESH operator presented in the preceding section.

The output from this plural \FRESH operator preserves the intentions represented in its input. That is, the singular \FRESH transforms each individual dependence into an equivalent set of dependencies. The concatenation of these equivalent representations for the individual dependences therefore yields a grand set of dependencies equivalent to the one given set of dependencies.

Figure 9.26A shows a given set of dependencies and Figure 9.26B shows the result of the concatenation. Figure 9.26C shows the set actually yielded by this plural \FRESH operator (i.e., the result of \COMPACT applied to the concatenation).

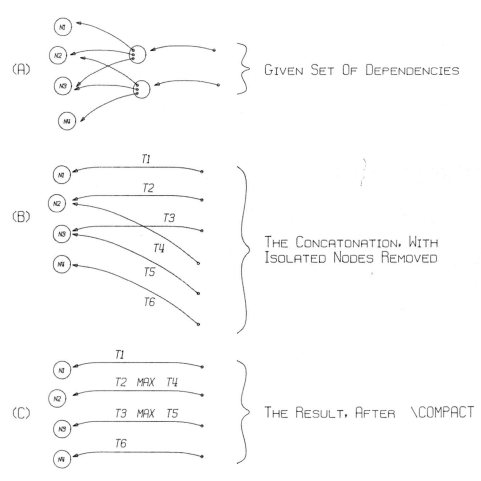

FIGURE 9.26 Parallel dependence fusion.

So far, we have seen only serial fusions of dependencies, in the singular \FRESH operator. In contrast, the \COMPACT operator, defined below, forms parallel fusions of dependencies. \COMPACT fuses dependencies which depend on the same NODE. More precisely, \COMPACT fuses dependencies which are entirely indistinguishable from one another.

The \COMPACT operator,

$$\text{dependencies} \quad \text{\COMPACT} \quad \rightarrow \quad \text{dependencies}$$

makes use of a \UNION operator defined for dependencies:

$$\text{dependencies} \quad \text{\UNION} \quad \text{dependence} \quad \rightarrow \quad \text{dependencies}$$

COMPACT is defined by

```
DEFINE  COMPACT(  DS:  DEPENDENCIES  )  =  DEPENDENCIES:
   BEGIN     VAR  RESULT  =  DEPENDENCIES  ;    D  =  DEPENDENCE  ;
      DO       RESULT:=  NIL  ;
               FOR  D  $E  DS;  DO
                                   RESULT:=  RESULT  \UNION  D  ;      END
         GIVE     RESULT
   END                                                    ENDDEFN
```

COMPACT thus forms its result by contributing each dependence, one at a time, to the list RESULT.

The \UNION operator performs the parallel fusion. It considers one new dependence, and merges it into the existing set if it is indistinguishable from some member in the set. If no dependence in the set matches the given dependence, \UNION augments the set to include the new dependence:

```
DEFINE  UNION(  DS:  DEPENDENCIES     NEW:  DEPENDENCE  )  =  DEPENDENCIES:
   BEGIN       VAR  D  =  DEPENDENCE  ;
      DO        DS:=  {COLLECT  D  FOR  D  $E  DS  ;
                  EACH_DO    IF  (  D.FROM  \EQ  NEW.FROM  )  &
                             (  D.THRU  \EQ  NEW.THRU  )
                         THEN
                             D.DELAY::=  \PARALLEL  NEW.DELAY;
                             NEW:=  NIL  ;      FI  ;    }  ;
      GIVE   NEW  <$  DS                END      ENDDEFN
```

\UNION sets the set of dependencies, DS, to a newly formed copy of itself, where each element, D, is compared against the NEW dependence. NEW and D are considered indistinguishable if they share the same FROM node and THRU signal. In case of a match, the variable D is modified to include the DELAY time of NEW in parallel with the DELAY time already in D. This modified dependence D takes the place of the original D in the set. Also, whenever such an incorporation of NEW takes place, this function sets NEW to NIL so that it will drop out of the GIVE expression

NEW <$ DS

9.6.3 One More Detail: A \COMPACT for CLOCKS

We also wish to modify the \FRESH operator for the type CLOCKS (Section 9.5.4) so to render CLOCKS compact just as we have now rendered DEPENDENCIES compact. Recall that the entire electrical model represented in a cell emanates from the cell's ports and also from its CLOCKS field.

We modify the CLOCKS \FRESH operator so that it applies a \COMPACT operator on its results, just as we have done in the plural-to-plural DEPENDENCIES \FRESH operator.

We provide a \COMPACT on CLOCKS similar to that for DEPENDENCIES, again employing a \UNION operator:

```
DEFINE    COMPACT( CS:  CLOCKS  )  =  CLOCKS:
   BEGIN    VAR  RESULT  =  CLOCKS ;  C  =  CLOCK  ;
      DO        RESULT:= NIL;
                FOR  C  $E  CS;  DO        RESULT:=  RESULT  \UNION  C; END
   GIVE     RESULT                                END      ENDDEFN
```

(This definition looks identical to the one for DEPENDENCIES, except that we have substituted "CLOCK" for "DEPENDENCE.") We now define the \UNION operator for CLOCKS.

Recall our intention that \UNION accept a new CLOCK into an existing set of CLOCKS by determining whether or not the new CLOCK is distinguishable from any member of the set. We say that two CLOCKs are indistinguishable when

1   They represent the same signal (ph1 or ph2)

2   They refer to the same node   (the BODY field)

The definition for \UNION follows:

```
DEFINE    UNION( CS:CLOCKS  NEW:CLOCK  )  =  CLOCKS:
   BEGIN VAR  C  =  CLOCK  ;
      DO      CS:=  {COLLECT  C  FOR  C  $E  CS;
                     EACH_DO  IF  (C.PHI  \EQ  NEW.PHI)  &
                                  (C.BODY  \EQ  NEW.BODY)
                              THEN    C.WAIT:=  C.WAIT  $$  NEW.WAIT
                                                          \COMPACT  ;
                                      NEW:=  NIL;    FI ; } ;
   GIVE    NEW  <$  CS                     END      ENDDEFN
```

This definition is identical to the \UNION operator for dependencies except in

1   How it measures "distinguishability"

2   How it combines two indistinguishable clocks.

The two \UNION operators both measure "distinguishability" by comparing both a signal and a node. Each operator combines indistinguishable elements by combining the other field, the field not used in the distinguishability test.

We see that the CLOCKS \UNION operator combines two indistinguishable clocks by concatenating their "artificial" dependencies, and applying the DEPENDENCIES \COMPACT operator on this combined set. (The DEPENDENCIES \UNION operator combined the DELAY field via \PARALLEL.)

9.6.4   Completeness of Simplification

We have provided a new \FRESH operator which transforms a given set of dependencies into an equivalent set of dependencies which references fewer isolated NODEs. We now show that it removes all isolated NODEs. This is not merely a matter of academic interest, this fact is assumed in the procedure which will interpret all these data in order to report performance.

We need to show, for example, that the node N1 in Figure 9.24 is itself not an isolated NODE, because N1 is referenced from the result. We know our singular dependency \FRESH operator removes the node N in this figure if N is isolated, but this operator does not even examine N1 to see if N1 is isolated. Can such second generation nodes remain referenced even if they are isolated?

9.6.4.1 First attempt at proving completeness. Let us introduce the term "clean" to denote the absence of isolated NODEs throughout all accessible DEPENDENCIES. Specifically, we introduce this term to denote a property about a NODE and also about a DEPENDENCE. As in many mathematical proofs, we choose the following definition so to represent our desired situation of completeness, although it may not be clear how our programs maintain such a situation:

1   A DEPENDENCE, D, is "clean" if the node D.FROM is not isolated, and if this node is itself "clean."

2   A NODE, N, is "clean" if each DEPENDENCE in N.WAIT is "clean."

Thus, the "cleanliness" of a NODE depends on the cleanliness of its DEPENDENCIES and the cleanliness of a DEPENDENCE depends on the cleanliness of the NODE it references.

We now wish to prove that the NODE in each port of a cell is "clean." Such certain knowledge would guarantee that no matter how one might climb from a port into and through the net of dependencies, all NODEs encountered on such a journey would be clean, hence not isolated.

We prove the cleanliness of each port NODE by proving both of the following:

1   The operator

dependence \FRESH → dependencies

yields clean dependencies.

2   The operator

node \FRESH → node

yields a clean node.

The second statement alone would guarantee that each port NODE, which is subject to \FRESH via ABUT, is clean.

One way to prove both of these statements at the same time is to imagine that one or the other (or both) is not always true. Imagine that our program is running smoothly, when all of a sudden one of these operators yields an unclean object. Let us concentrate on the first such failure.

Suppose that the DEPENDENCE \FRESH operator yields the very first unclean object. We concentrate on the very first occurrence so that we can assume that all other applications of either operator up to this time have produced clean objects. For example, we can assume, looking at the definition for this \FRESH operator, that the node N defined in the second assignment is clean. Here N is the result of an earlier application of the NODE \FRESH operator.

Since N is clean, we know by definition that each dependence in N.WAIT is clean, and again by definition, we know that the FROM node, N1, in each dependence is itself also clean.

The cleanliness of N1 is important to know because each dependence yielded by \FRESH refers to N1, via the COLLECT clause. Since we know that N1 is clean, we also know by definition that each dependence yielded by \FRESH is in fact clean. This does contradict our original assumption and hence we conclude that this \FRESH operator for dependencies is not the first operator to yield an unclean object.

It must be, then, that the NODE \FRESH operator yields the very first unclean object. Looking at the definition of this operator, we see that as long as

    N.BEEN_HERE_BEFORE

is false, the THEN clause assures that N.WAIT is clean, that is, N.WAIT is the result of the DEPENDENCIES \FRESH operator, which as we have shown does not yield the first unclean object.

Thus, the NODE \FRESH operator can yield an unclean NODE only if

    N.BEEN_HERE_BEFORE

is true. In this case, the THEN clause does not execute.

The only place in all our programs which sets the BEEN_HERE_BEFORE field is in this THEN clause. We conclude that because N.BEEN_HERE_BEFORE is true, the THEN clause has been executed with N at an earlier time.

To be very careful, we can really assume only that the THEN clause was entered and that at least the first of its two assignments,

    @(N).BEEN_HERE_BEFORE :=   TRUE ;
    @(N).WAIT :=   N.WAIT   \FRESH ;

was executed. Assuming that the second assignment also executed completely at this earlier time, we conclude as before that N.WAIT is clean. Thus, under this assumption, we again see that N itself is clean (by definition), and hence this encounter with the NODE \FRESH operator is not the first to yield an unclean object.

However, it is possible that the \FRESH operator appearing in the second assignment has not returned yet; that is, this DEPENDENCE \FRESH operator might itself be calling our present NODE \FRESH operator in its effort to produce a clean N.WAIT. Figure 9.27B shows such a possibility. Figure 9.27D shows this troublesome second encounter with N. This second encounter finds

1 N.BEEN_HERE_BEFORE   true, but
2 N.WAIT   has not yet been rendered clean
                                   (from the first encounter)

Thus, the second encounter with a NODE in a cycle produces the very first unclean object.

At this point we have failed to prove the cleanliness of all NODEs, and hence have not proven the complete absence of isolated NODEs. There is a good reason this proof can not be completed: Its statement is in fact not entirely true. Our algorithms in fact do not guarantee to remove all isolated NODEs.

We have gone through this analysis to emphasize how important it is to try to prove the correctness of programs. This effort has exposed a situation of potential failure. Figure 9.26F shows, in fact, a particular failure, where an isolated node remains:

In case N itself is isolated, the DEPENDENCIES \FRESH operator, which causes this second encounter, called from node M, will naturally bypass the isolated N, and hence refer to a node in N.WAIT. Unfortunately, this second encounter has not yet \FRESHened

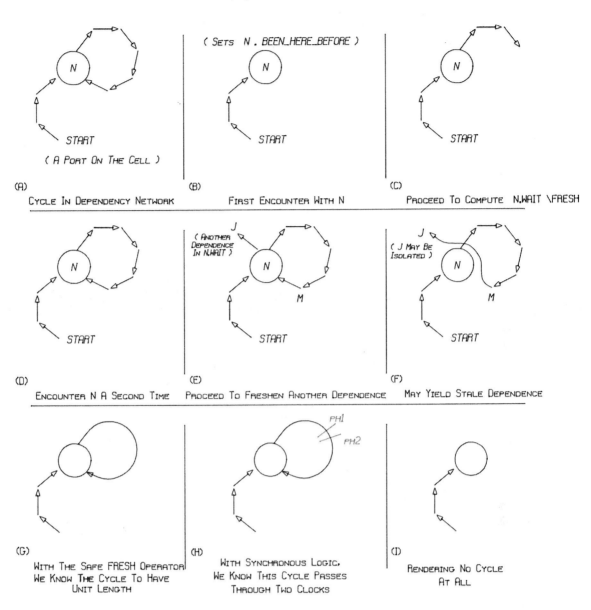

(Sets N . Been_Here_Before)

(A Port On The Cell)

(A) Cycle In Dependency Network

(B) First Encounter With N

(C) Proceed To Compute N.Wait \FRESH

(D) Encounter N A Second Time

(Another Dependence In N.Wait)

(E) Proceed To Freshen Another Dependence

(J May Be Isolated)

(F) May Yield Stale Dependence

(G) With The Safe FRESH Operator We Know The Cycle To Have Unit Length

(H) With Synchronous Logic, We Know This Cycle Passes Through Two Clocks

(I) Rendering No Cycle At All

QUESTION OF CYCLIC LOGICAL DEPENDENCIES

FIGURE 9.27

N.WAIT, and hence N.WAIT can indeed refer to an isolated node. This isolated node thus comes to reside in the FROM field of a dependence in the "freshened" M.WAIT. This renders M referencing an isolated node.

Now that we see a failure mode, as rare as it might occur, we can fix it quite simply. We note that any dependence yielded by the singular-to-plural \FRESH operator can indeed refer to an isolated node (when N is involved in a cycle). Let us therefore apply \FRESH once again to each of these resulting dependencies. We imagine that this second examination, which examines the FROM fields in the result, will sense the (rare) occurrence of an isolated node lingering in the allegedly clean result.

9.6.4.2 Modification to the \FRESH system, and a second, successful proof. We modify the singular-to-plural operator simply by applying \FRESH to the entire result in the ELSE clause. The following abbreviated redefinition shows this tiny modification in uppercase:

```
define    fresh(   d:   dependence   )   =   dependencies:
  begin    ...
      do       ....
      give    if  -  n.isolated   then      ...
              else    {   ...   }  \FRESH   fi              end     enddefn
```

The new call to \FRESH in the ELSE clause refers to the plural-to-plural \FRESH operator, due to context. However, the plural-to-plural \FRESH operator itself applies this singular-to-plural \FRESH operator upon each dependence individually. Thus, we can think of this new application of \FRESH merely as a recursive call back into this singular-to-plural \FRESH operator.

It is now easy to prove that each DEPENDENCE yielded by this new rendition has in its FROM field a valid, nonisolated NODE. First, we know as before that if the result comes from the THEN clause, its FROM node is not isolated (due clearly to the IF clause). On the other hand, if the result comes from the ELSE clause, what do we know?

The ELSE clause produces now merely the result of \FRESH itself. In other words, this singular-to-plural \FRESH operator yields either

1 A certified result from the THEN clause, or

2 Another result from this \FRESH operator.

Assuming that this program terminates, we see that all results come ultimately from the THEN clause. In conclusion, all dependencies yielded by \FRESH refer only to valid, nonisolated nodes.

This technique and proof may seem somewhat peculiar. Generally, one can always "throw more money at the problem," that is, introduce a recursive call on the results of any clause that is hard to prove. As we have seen in the proof, clauses that directly yield the results of recursive calls can never be held responsible for bad results.

There is, however, a problem with this technique. Whereas recursion removes the need to consider some clauses, it also increases the probability that the program will in fact not terminate; that is, the program may enter an infinite loop by means of recursion.

Before we prove that this program terminates, let us assume that it does terminate, and go on to prove that this entire system does render complete simplification.

ABUT replaces the NODE in each port of a cell by the result of \FRESH applied to that node. We know by definition that ports' nodes are valid, nonisolated nodes. We have seen that the NODE \FRESH operator applies the DEPENDENCIES \FRESH operator on the node's dependencies, its WAIT field. Our latest proof shows that this WAIT field comes to refer only to valid, nonisolated nodes. Therefore, we conclude completeness of simplification; each port node depends only on other port nodes. In other words, if we start at a port node and travel via dependencies, we will touch only other port nodes, and never encounter an isolated node.

Our first attempt to prove completeness failed because we relied on properties of the NODE \FRESH operator in our attempt to prove the DEPENDENCIES \FRESH operator. In contrast, we have now proven the new DEPENDENCIES \FRESH operator without even considering the NODE \FRESH operator. We used to rely on the expectation that the NODE \FRESH operator would itself render N1 nonisolated, or in other words, render N.WAIT fresh for us.

Now, instead of relying on the NODE \FRESH operator for this assurance, the new DEPENDENCIES \FRESH operator itself makes a recursive call so to render this assurance. For example, even if the NODE \FRESH operator returns from a "second encounter'' within a cycle, hence rendering a node whose WAIT field is not entirely fresh, this new \FRESH operator reapplies itself on the incompleted dependencies, guaranteeing a fresh result in either case.

We need now show only that the new \FRESH operator terminates. This proof is based on the fact that our circuits implement synchronous logic, or more specifically, that there are no race conditions. Any cycle in logical dependence passes through both clocks, ph1 and ph2.

Suppose we find that this new \FRESH operator calls itself infinitely many times. We then deduce that the ELSE clause is executed an infinite number of times. (The THEN clause does not call \FRESH.) We enter the ELSE clause infinitely many times only if

N.ISOLATED

is true infinitely many times. However, since our model represents at worst only a finite number of nodes, N obviously refers to some node more than once. (This finite set of nodes was created before the \FRESH process ever starts, and \FRESH itself creates no new nodes.)

In addition, each N is a node referenced in the WAIT field of the previously encountered N. That is, the N1 produced in the FROM field within the ELSE clause becomes the N in the next (recursive) call.

We conclude from both these facts that N appears in a cycle that includes only isolated nodes.

In fact, we can actually conclude that this cycle includes exactly one node. Each call to \FRESH, which we know finds N to be isolated (in the ELSE clause), produces dependencies that refer not to N, but only to those nodes on which N itself depends. These are the dependencies that are subjected to the next call to \FRESH. Thus, each call removes one node from this cycle, unless N depends directly on itself, in which case N1 and N are the same node. Hence the cycle is reduced to one node that depends on itself, as shown in Figure 9.27G, before the infinite recursion engages.

We show that such a cycle can not exist by noting first that any cyclic logical dependence must pass through both clocks (Figure 9.27H and 9.18C). Recall that synchronous logic admits cyclic dependencies only via \NEXT equations. A \NEXT equation introduces a unit memory in the path through which the output depends on the inputs. The unit memory introduces both clocks into this path.

The guaranteed appearance of both clocks in this cycle implies that this dependence does not exist. We see in the ELSE clause that the set of dependencies yielded for the recursive application of \FRESH includes only those dependencies which are clock compatible (due to the WITH clause). Thus, this one-node cycle could never have come to exist.

In summary, infinite recursion is avoided because as isolated nodes are removed, previously distinct dependencies merge into single, extended dependencies. Many of these extended dependencies now drop out of the picture for the first time because these extended dependencies find their existence conditioned upon both clocks. The individual, nonextended dependencies have lasted so long, with their conflicting clocks, only because until now each was not considered as a single, merged dependence.

9.6.5 Reporting the Electrical Performance of a Chip

We have invested a great deal of effort to maintain an electrical model for cells, both for leaf cells and for cells resulting from fusion. We have also maintained ''complete simplicity'' in the model so that only those nodes resident in ports remain in the electrical model. We now provide for the interpretation of this model, thus making this effort worthwhile.

There are two overall questions to be answered in the report of performance:

1   If we change the signal on a given input port, how long does it take before this change propagates to another given output port?
2   How fast can we clock the chip?

Let us answer the first question. Suppose that we are given two ports of the final cell, say IN and OUT. We find the propagation delay from IN to OUT via the following assignment. We first declare a variable D of type DEPENDENCE:

```
VAR    D   =   DEPENDENCE  ;
VAR        DELAY_FROM_IN_TO_OUT   =   TIME  ;

DELAY_FROM_IN_TO_OUT:=
         IF    FOR  D  $E  OUT.E.WAIT;  THERE_IS    D.FROM  \EQ  IN.E
         THEN    D.DELAY
         ELSE    0  \NS              FI                        ;
```

That is, if OUT's node (OUT.E) contains a dependency D (from the node's WAIT field) which depends on the node at port IN (IN.E), then the propagation delay from IN's node to OUT's node is the time D.DELAY. (If OUT does not depend on IN, there is no delay between these two ports.)

We may wish to add to this delay the time it takes OUT to stabilize once the derived delay elapses after IN's stablization. (Recall that a dependence's DELAY field represents only the time between the end of IN's stabilization and the start of OUT's stabilization.) We write

```
DELAY_FROM_IN_TO_OUT::=   +   OUT.E.LOAD  ;
```

That is, the time it takes OUT to stabilize, once all its logical dependencies stabilize, is the delay imposed by OUT's LOAD. (We introduced a coercion from the type LOAD to the type TIME in Section 9.2.2.)

The validity of this interpretation rests heavily on the fact that the model contains no isolated nodes. That is, if OUT really can be affected at all by IN, OUT depends directly on the port at IN, and not through some indirect chain of isolated nodes. (We do not consider OUT to depend on IN if OUT depends only on another port P, which itself depends on IN. Such a port P would have to act both as an input port, from OUT's point of view, and as an output port, to depend on IN.)

We are free to stop our search after finding one dependence because the existence of two or more dependencies between IN and OUT is impossible due to the parallel fusion of "indistinguishable" dependencies maintained by \COMPACT (within the plural \FRESH operator).

This derivation of propagation delay is valid even if IN represents a CLOCK. The delay in this case represents how long after the clock changes that OUT will stabilize.

The most important of the two questions posed earlier is that of operating frequency. How many clocking cycles can be crammed into 1 second? We have maintained in each cell a CLOCKS field which serves now to answer this question.

Given a pair of CLOCKs, say THIS and OTHER, we can derive three numbers. We will derive a total of six numbers by performing a procedure twice, once where

1   THIS = ph1 and OTHER = ph2,   and once where
2   THIS = ph2 and OTHER = ph1

The six numbers derived will be

1a   Diffusion time for ph1

1b   Width for ph1

1c   Separation from end of ph2 to start of ph1.

2a   Diffusion time for ph2

2b   Width for ph2

2c   Separation from end of ph1 to start of ph2

In other words, each set of three numbers represents the following, expressed in terms of two clocks THIS and OTHER:

(a)   Diffusion time for THIS (clock)

(b)   Width of THIS (clock)

(c)   Separation from end of OTHER to start of THIS

(The "diffusion time" for a clock represents the time it takes simply to charge all the wires in the chip which distribute that clock signal. The clock is neither on nor off during these twilight, diffusion times).

Given two clocks, THIS and OTHER, we define the three numbers as follows:

```
VAR    DIFFUSION_TIME,  WIDTH,  SEPARATION  =  TIME  ;

DIFFUSION_TIME:=   THIS.BODY.LOAD;

WIDTH:=     \PARALLEL    D.DELAY    FOR  D  $E  THIS.WAIT;
               WITH     THIS.BODY  \EQ  D.FROM ;
               WITH     THIS.PHI  \CLOCK_COMPATABLE    D.THRU ;   ;

SEPARATION:=  \PARALLEL    D.DELAY    FOR  D  $E  THIS.WAIT;
               WITH     OTHER.BODY  \EQ  D.FROM;
               WITH    -  DEFINED(  D.THRU  );              ;
```

The first assignment, to DIFFUSION_TIME, represents how long it takes to charge the node represented by the clock THIS.

The WIDTH of the clock THIS is computed by considering all its artificial dependencies, THIS.WAIT. As discussed in Section 9.4.1, we measure the required width for a clock by finding the longest delay between any electrical island that depends on the clock and any island that feeds the clock. The WAIT field of a CLOCK refers to all nodes that feed the clock.

Of all nodes that feed into the clock, we are interested only in those which themselves depend on this clock. The expression

```
\PARALLEL    D.DELAY    FOR  D  $E  THIS.WAIT;
```

represents the maximum over all delays that feed the clock, but the expression

```
\PARALLEL    D.DELAY    FOR  D  $E  THIS.WAIT;
                        WITH    D.FROM  \EQ  THIS.BODY  ;
```

represents the maximum over precisely those delays which themselves depend on this clock. The WITH clause is present to focus our consideration on those dependencies D that depend on the node represented by this clock (THIS.BODY).

Once again, the validity of this interpretation relies heavily on the completeness of simplification maintained in our overall electrical model. That is, we are assuming that

> if node A can be affected by node B in any way whatsoever,
> then A.WAIT contains a dependence whose FROM field refers directly
> to node B.

The guarantee of simplicity relieves the need to consider any intermediate nodes between A and B, through which a dependence may be propagated indirectly.

Finally, in the consideration of WIDTH, we include a second WITH clause, which serves further to remove dependencies from consideration. Of all dependencies that present a propagation delay from the output of this clock to the input of this clock, we wish to consider only those which actually exist during the reign of this clock. That is, since we are measuring delays imposed while the clock is turned on, we must consider only those delays that actually exist during this period. The second WITH clause allows for consideration only those delays that are compatible with this clock's being on.

For example, suppose that the clock THIS is ph1. The required width of ph1 is determined by propagations that occur during ph1. A propagation conditioned upon ph2 does not exist during ph1, because ph2 is off (at least) while ph1 is on. The second WITH clause is therefore present to remove from consideration such dependencies as are nonexistent during ph1.

Let us consider now the derived SEPARATION. The expression of computation mirrors closely the expression used to compute WIDTH. This time, however, of all dependencies that feed into the clock, we consider only those that depend on the OTHER clock. That is, the required separation between clocks is determined by propagations from the output of the OTHER clock to the input of THIS clock. The first WITH clause is therefore present to focus consideration on those delays whose FROM nodes are in fact the node represented by the OTHER clock.

We include a second WITH clause in the derivation for SEPARATION, as we did for the WIDTH derivation. This time, however, we are measuring delays imposed during a period between clocks, when both clocks are shut off. Therefore, we limit our consideration to only those dependencies that are conditioned on no clock. (Any dependence that exists only while one or the other clock is on is broken during the period between clocks.)

Our discussion so far has made reference to the two variables THIS and OTHER, each of which is of type CLOCK. Given a completed chip, represented as a cell, how do we find the clocks ph1 and ph2 so that we may define values for these two variables?

The completed layout cell presents us with a set of clocks in its CLOCKS field. How many elements are in this set, and which one(s) are ph1 and which one(s) are ph2? Our discussion so far has assumed implicitly that there is exactly one ph1 CLOCK and one ph2 CLOCK delivered with the cell. In fact, we have restricted most of the discussion to avoid ph1 and ph2, and instead refer only to THIS and OTHER.

We show now that a completed cell will always deliver exactly two clocks in its CLOCKS field. We consider only completed cells with pads, so that we may assume that all ph1 ports of all cells are connected up to a single "ph1 pad," and similarly for ph2. We also assume that a clock signal per se never goes through an amplifier (e.g., inverter) or is subject to blockage through pass transistors. These two assumptions together imply that in the completed chip, there is exactly one, far reaching electrical island for ph1, and likewise for ph2.

We are making a statement that need not apply during the cell's construction. That is, separate cells entering into fusion may have distinct clock nodes. However, the node CONNECT operator assures that as ports become connected, their previously distinct nodes become merged into single, shared nodes. Thus, cell completion represents for us the first time that we know all ph1 clock nodes have fused into one and the same node, and likewise for ph2.

Given that there is only one ph1 node and one ph2 node in the completed cell, we can see that there will exist exactly two elements in the cell's CLOCKS field. The CLOCKS \FRESH operator applies the CLOCKS \COMPACT operator, which renders the set of clocks so to contain distinct elements only when they represent distinct nodes. Knowing that there are only two clock nodes throughout the entire chip thus proves that the CLOCKS field contains only two elements.

In addition, we know that any dependence of one clock upon another is represented in the first clock's WAIT field by a dependence that refers to the other clock's single, chip-wide node. Again, this unique node identity is maintained by our consistent application of \FRESH upon all nodes in a chip, including the nodes referenced from all cells' CLOCKS' BODY and WAIT fields. Thus, we have in fact computed clock timing by considering implicitly only two nodes.

9.6.6   Some Results

Refer to Figures 8.31 through 8.34. These are all functional renditions of our light dimmer example, differing only in logic reorganization (Section 7.4.1). These layouts have been rendered automatically in the domain of four-sided cells (Section 8.8), and include the maintenance of this kind of electrical model. (These correspond to Figures 7.29, 7.35, 7.36, and 7.39, rendered directly with our one-sided compiler.) The following tabulates various parameters derived from these four chips:

		8.31	*8.32*	*8.33*	*8.34*
0)	CPU Minutes for Fusion	5	3	<2	<1
1a)	Ph1 Diffusion	610 ns	135 ns	67 ns	23 ns
1b)	Ph1 Width	0 ns	0 ns	0 ns	0 ns
1c)	Ph2-to-Ph1 Separation	13 ns	21 ns	21 ns	38 ns
2a)	Ph2 Diffusion	714 ns	180 ns	83 ns	14 ns
2b)	Ph2 Width	309 ns	185 ns	135 ns	205 ns
2c)	Ph1-to-Ph2 Separation	138 ns	27 ns	52 ns	80 ns
3)	Cycle Time	1784 ns	548 ns	358 ns	360 ns
4)	Cycle Time Less Diffusion	460 ns	233 ns	208 ns	323 ns
5)	Layout Area (1000 lambdas)	2512	1267	1176	1307
6)	Square Root of Area (lambda)	1585	1125	1084	1143

The diffusion times listed show to the greatest extent the pessimistic simplifications made in our formalization of the type LOAD. The ph1 clock wires, for example, constitute one large electrical island (LOAD). Even though these wires are connected in both parallel and serial formations, our LOAD model treats these wires as though they were all connected end to end serially.

In addition, even though such a long "wire" would have distributed capacitance and resistance, our model even more pessimistically assumes that all of the resistance appears between VDD and the entire capacitance. This renders a pessimism which grows faster than linearly compared with chip dimensions. We have therefore tabulated cycle times twice, once in the absence of diffusion delays.

The Ph1 width is consistently zero because ph1 need stay on only long enough to let charge flow from an OR-gate's output into an inverter which immediately follows the ph1 pass transistor. Zero is not a realistic clock width. However, a realistic ph1 width would be so small as to be insignificant in the overall picture.

Our model predicts exactly zero because, as discussed in Section 9.4, we pretend that the LOAD between the pass transistor and the inverter is nonexistent. This approximation has been made so as to avoid the notion of a "conditional" island.

The ph2-width represents propagation delay due to unclocked (\EQU) propagations through more than one PLA. That is, the input gate to a PLA, ph2, must remain on long enough so that an input can

1   Enter the PLA
2   Travel through the PLA to an unclocked (no ph1) exit
3   Travel through the interconnect from this PLA to the input of another PLA

Ph2 can turn off only after the signal stabilizes the second PLA's input. Generally, ph2 accommodates \EQU propagations for the longest unclocked journey through any sequence of PLAs.

Note, for example, that the ph2 width of the second chip is substantially greater than the ph2 width for the third chip. The second chip contains a counter, and two comparators, each of which is implemented by six PLAs, one for each bit. The carry chains in these cases are of length 5. In contrast, the third chip implements the same with only three PLAs, where each PLA implements 2 bits. The third chip therefore has a carry chain of length 2, hence has a shorter ph2 width. (The reduction in ph2 width is not as great as 5/2, because each of the three PLAs is now bigger.)

Although the first chip as compared to the second chip shows an even greater difference in ph2 width, this difference is due primarily to the gross difference in area. We have chosen to compare the second and third chips because they have nearly identical areas.

The ph2-to-ph1 separation represents propagation delays imposed within a single PLA [i.e., from input (ph2) to output (ph1)]. Note that the first chip has the smallest ph2-to-ph1 separation; it has the smallest PLAs. Scanning the table from left to right, we can see this number increasing, as does the size of individual PLAs in each chip.

Finally, the ph1-to-ph2 separation represents propagation delays imposed by interconnect, routing from PLA clocked outputs (ph1) to PLA inputs (ph2). This therefore reflects intertia imposed by interconnect, and this tends to grow with chip area.

In conclusion, we see an overall cycle time that reflects chip area. All four of these chips and their electrical performance parameters were derived from their logic_cell specifications (in text form) within a total of 25 minutes of CPU time.

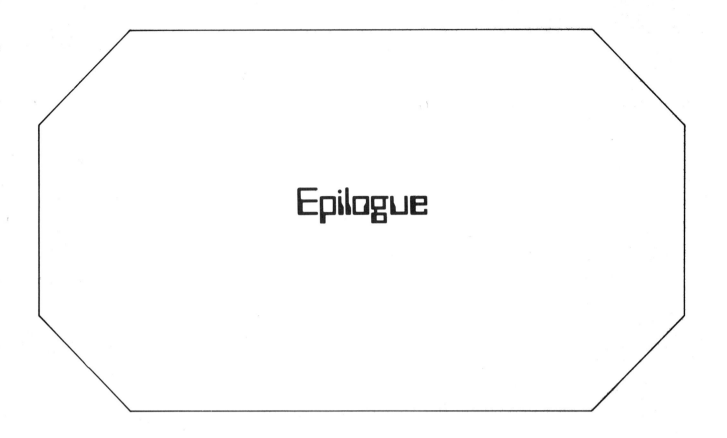

Epilogue

We live in an age of accelerated growth, both in the sheer amount of available information and in the ability to process that information. The need to process information quickly is accentuated today by the great potential of "better living through computing" and by the threat of self-destruction via nuclear warfare or pollution. Our top priority is to facilitate human communication, removing bottlenecks that make communication anything but easy, so that we can more fully concentrate on the contents of our communications. Methods of communication must be flexible so that we can adapt them to rapidly changing needs. Very large scale integration, or more likely ultra large scale integration may come to refer to integration of people, benignly tied together with a society-wide nervous system whose cells consist of home and centralized computing.

Since people's needs change rapidly, adaptability, or custom computing, is of primary importance. We cannot tolerate hindered growth due to large lead times, or proposed computing services not pursued because of uncertain expense or success. The design and construction of new and varied computing services must be rendered so inexpensive that truly novel ideas can beome implemented by very small groups of people, without having to take the time required to convince large numbers of perhaps less courageous people. Persisting in the belief that it is tough to design microchips, for example, delays our recognition that we have a much larger goal to meet, that is, to design entire systems usable by great numbers of people, adaptable to rapidly evolving needs.

Computing per se is not human; it is meant to work by itself even in the absence of people. For this reason, computer implementations consist of formal systems, like mathematical systems.

COMPILATION AND TRANSLATION

A language translation by definition has two sides, the source language and the target language.

An implementation therefore needs a source representation and necessarily writes a target representation. This creates conceptually two distinct phases, a read phase and a write phase.

These two phases interact in a particular way; the execution of the write phase does not affect the read phase. A translator does not affect the source expression he/she/it reads.

This insulation between the read and write phases provides for an invariant "objective" space in which to describe formally the translation process between the source and target languages. The existence of such a space is essential in order to provide automatic and reliable translation. This invariant space consists of the programming language (mathematical notation) and the conventions (axioms) of the source and target representations. This invariant space is sufficiently insulated from the source and target representations because, in fact, neither the source nor target representations depend in any way on this invariant space; no representation references the programming language per se, nor does any representation reference its conventions—conventions are obeyed implicitly by a representation.

We have seen automatic translations from textual languages to memory representations, from one memory representation to another (e.g., from LOGIC_CELL to layout CELL), and from memory representations to languages such as silicon layout, and to programs such as simulators.

We have defined complex translations such as these, each in terms of a sequence of elementary translations. Each element in the sequence was defined confidently in one invariant space residing between two distinct representations. The methods of translation were entirely independent of one another, except of course, that one element's target representation must be the next element's source representation. We have taken the liberty to freely introduce new intermediate representations so as to maximize our confidence by rendering smaller elements of translation.

The insulation provided by each element, between the source and target representations, appears also in microchip design methodologies. Clocking mechanisms in silicon insulate present (source) from future (target); clocking keeps the time dimension from collapsing by keeping units of time separated from one another. Similarly, the transistor keeps space from collapsing by providing electrical isolation between distinct electrical circuits.

Insulation like this, the division of a process into two distinct phases, provides for the existence of tools, items which are created in one environment and used in another environment. This is the basic element of compilation: the distinction between compile-time and run-time.

FURTHER APPLICATION

Many of the ideas presented here have been about compilation. These apply equally well to other technologies, present and future, such as Ultra Large Scale Integration, optical, biological, and three-dimensional computing, to mention but a few. Technologies that require human intent specified in terms of enormous, precise detail benefit by compilation. Such complex technologies provide enormous capability, but require adherence to a set of global design constraints. In fact, by having compilation methods available, we widen the choice of available technologies in the future, many of which will require such automatic translation services in order to exist at all.

Consider the challenge of providing interconnect in three dimensions. Routing between two 3-D cells, would we talk about scan-planes, or scan-lines within scan-planes? How about four-dimensional interconnect, interconnect that moves information not only in space, but in time as well? Whereas wires provide interconnection in space, memories provide interconnection in time, capturing information at one moment and presenting it at a later time; the time analogy of a wire is a one-bit register.

What solutions might our two-dimensional wire routers render if applied to problems in time, e.g., to static process scheduling? The scan-line algorithms that provide interconnection in two dimensions can be seen as providing interconnection in both time and a one-dimensional space. Think of the vertical dimension as time. Each vertical wire in the interconnect represents a one-bit register at a particular horizontal position in space. The low endpoint of the vertical wire represents the time when the register reads, and the top endpoint represents the time when the register is read and is hence freed to forget its contents.

A vertical channel that contains two or more vertical wires represents a register shared in time. The register services two or more distinct needs which do not overlap in time. Where the scan-line algorithms allocate extra vertical channels to avoid vertical overlap, that same algorithm viewed in time can be seen as allocating new registers so as to avoid conflicted use of existing registers.

The interconnection process is basically one of resource allocation, (e.g., the resource being communication lines on silicon). Vertical channels can represent not only wires in space or memories in time, but any process that consumes resources. We can think of a single computer as a single vertical channel.

Timesharing computers facilitate multiple users by swapping out one user before swapping in another user. Swap-out corresponds to the top endpoint of a vertical segment, the end of a user's residence on the vertical channel (CPU). The user being swapped-out then travels horizontally, away from the CPU, coming to rest on another vertical channel, the wait queue. Swap-in, the commencement of another user, corresponds to a horizontal journey landing at the vertical channel (CPU), the bottom endpoint of a higher segment, then turning so as to travel upward in the vertical channel (consuming the CPU resource), until such time as the journey leaves the vertical channel, upon the user's swap-out.

Timesharing's process scheduling differs however from wire routing in that process scheduling must behave differently as different groups of processes compete. In contrast, a chunk of interconnect finds itself in a constant environment; the cells it services are fixed for all time. It is this static nature of interconnect (and microchip designs in general) that allows their effective compilation. Of course, a microchip provides dynamic behavior, but its completed design per se is still static.

Any piece of a problem that can be factored out and rendered static, as opposed to dynamic, relieves the cost of the problem's overall solution. Static pieces are constant and hence require no ongoing cost to keep them solved. To obtain an effective factoring that maximizes the static component, we often need to consider the problem from many points of view, at least until some conception of the problem breaks down obviously into clear static and dynamic pieces. Today's ongoing osmosis of processing from software into hardware is one such example. Processes which use to require long sequences of instructions (time) come now to take large areas of silicon designed especially to perform the same function in a more immediate, less interpreted fashion. That is, more of the process is "built-in" to the silicon; this static part of the process is expected to require modification much less frequently than the remaining "soft" part. The fact that this static part never changes allows the silicon to implement this part as efficiently as possible, with never a nanosecond wasted in considering the existence of other possible functions.

Rendering new and improved solutions requires courage to view the overall problem outside of customary ways of thinking; to recognize the intrinsic bottle necks of the problem, not in terms of existing machine language instruction sets, but in terms of parallel or co-processes that can come to exist with VLSI. Very Large Scale Integration refers not only to integration on a single microchip, but to integration throughout the entire spectrum of computing media, hardware and software alike, so that for example software can consist mostly of instructions directed at the task at hand, as opposed to fighting or "getting around" the non-customized hardware.

As the computer sciences and technologies continue to evolve, one need will remain always to be satisfied: how to map human intent into the widening choice of computing media. As the relative attention paid to the microchip medium increases, it is no wonder that compilation comes now to serve microchip design.

Bibliography

Aho A. and **J. Ullman,** *Principles of Compiler Design*. New York: Addison-Wesley, 1977.

Ayres, R., "A Language Processor and a Sample Language," Caltech Computer Science Technical Report 2276, Ph.D. dissertation, 1978.

Ayres, R., "IC Specification Language," 16th Design Automation Conference Proceedings, San Diego, California, 1979.

Ayres, R., "Silicon Compilation—A Hierarchical Use of PLAs," 16th Design Automation Conference, San Diego, California, 1979.

Bell, C. G., J. C. Mudge, and **J. E. McNamara,** *Computer Engineering*. Bedford, Mass.: Digital Press, Digital Equipment Corp., 1978.

Bell, C. G., and **A. Newell,** *Computer Structures: Readings and Examples*. New York: McGraw-Hill, 1971.

Boole, G., *An Investigation of the Laws of Thought*. London: 1854. Reprinted by Dover Publications, 1953.

Brooks, F. P., Jr., *The Mythical Man-month, Essays on Software Engineering*, Reading, Mass.: Addison-Wesley, 1975.

Earley, J. "An Efficient Context-free Parsing Algorithm," Comm. ACM 1970, 13: 2, 94-102.

Feynman, R., R. Leighton, and **M. Sands,** *The Feynman Lectures on Physics*, vols. 1-3, Reading, Mass.: Addison-Wesley, 1963-1965.

Gries, D. *Compiler Construction for Digital Computers*. New York: Wiley, 1971.

Grove, A., *Physics and Technology of Semiconductor Devices*. New York: Wiley, 1967.

Ingalls, D. H.: "The Smalltalk-76 Programming System Design and Implementation," Fifth ACM Symp. Prin. Programming Lang., Jan 1978, pp. 9-16.

Johannsen, D., "Bristle Blocks: A Silicon Compiler," 16th Design Automation Conference, San Diego, California, 1979.

Johannsen, D., A Design Technique for VLSI Chips," Proceedings of the Caltech Conference on VLSI, Jan. 1979.

Johannsen, D., "Silicon Compilation," Caltech Computer Science Technical Report 4530, Ph.D. dissertation, 1981.

Mead, C. A., and **L. A. Conway,** *Introduction to VLSI Systems*. Reading, Mass.: Addison-Wesley, 1980.

Newman, W. and **R. Sproull,** *Principles of Interactive Graphics, 2nd edition*. New York: McGraw-Hill, 1979.

Oldham, W. G., "The Fabrication of Microelectronic Circuits," Scientific American, Sept. 1977.

Index

TYPE DEFINITION INDEX

FUNCTION DEFINITION INDEX